CALCULUS:
A MODELING
APPROACH

CALCULUS: A MODELING APPROACH

MARVIN L. BITTINGER
Indiana University-
Purdue University at Indianapolis

ADDISON-WESLEY
PUBLISHING COMPANY
Reading, Massachusetts
Menlo Park, California
London · Amsterdam
Don Mills, Ontario · Sydney

This book is in the
ADDISON-WESLEY SERIES IN MATHEMATICS

Lynn H. Loomis
Consulting Editor

Second printing, November 1976

Cover and title page photo:
Georg Gerster from Rapho/Photo Researchers, Inc.

ISBN 0-201-00851-3-H
ISBN 0-201-00852-1-P
CDEFGHIJKLM-HA-798

Preface

This book is a brief introduction to calculus as applied to business, the behavioral sciences, the social sciences, and biology. Most of the book can be covered in one term, but will adapt to a two-term course by complete coverage and/or slower pacing. Prerequisite for the text is one course in intermediate algebra.

The approach is "intuitive." While this word has many meanings and interpretations, its use here, for the most part, means "experienced based." That is, when a concept is being taught, the learning is based on the student's prior experience or new experience given before the concept is formalized. For example, in a maximum-minimum problem a function is usually derived which is to be maximized or minimized. Instead of forging ahead with the standard calculus solution, the student is asked to stop and compute some function values. This experience provides the student with more insight into the problem. Not only does the student discover that different dimensions yield different volumes, if volume is to be maximized, but the dimensions which yield the maximum volume might even be conjectured as a result of the calculations. Provision for use of the hand calculator also provides for an intuitive approach (see later comments).

Some other distinguishing features of the book are as follows:

1. Design and format. Each page has an outer margin which is used in several ways. (1) In the margin are sample, developmental, and exploratory exercises, placed with the text material so that the student can become actively involved in the development of the topic. These margin exercises have proved to be extremely beneficial. (2) For each section the objectives are stated in behavioral terms at the top of the page. These can be easily spotted by the student, and when the typical question arises "What material am I responsible for?" these objectives provide an answer. They may also help take the fear out of the word "Calculus."

2. The hand calculator. Exercises designed for use with a hand calculator are included throughout the text, *but not in such a way as to encumber the student who does not have a calculator.* That is, a hand calculator is helpful but not essential. Our experience has been that when we make the statement "The purchase of a hand calculator will ease your work, but is not essential," virtually all of the students obtain one. The hand calculator also allows for the solving of relevant problems which might otherwise not be attempted, such as those involving exponential functions (see Chapters 4, 6, and 7). The simplest calculator (add, subtract, multiply, divide) is sufficient, since tables of exponential and logarithmic functions are provided. Exceptions are a few exercises which require a square root key or a power key, but these can easily be omitted or done in class.

3. Applications. Relevant and factual applications are included throughout the text to maintain interest and motivation. Population growth is considered in the context of several mathematical models, not just exponential (see Chapters 4 and 7). When the exponential model is studied, other applications such as continuously compounded interest, and the demand for natural resources are also considered. The notions of total revenue, total cost, and total profit, together with their related derivatives (marginal functions) are threads which run through the text, providing continued reinforcement and unification. Below is a *sampling* of the applications.

Business and Economics:

Minimizing Inventory Costs, pp. 170–173
Doubling Time, pp. 221–222
Interest Compounded n Times Per Year, p. 7
Interest Compounded Continuously, p. 221
Total Cost, Revenue, and Profit, pp. 42–44, 121–123

Learning, p. 380
Industrial Psychology of Workers, p. 85

Sociology:

Life Expectancy, p. 407
Divorce Rate, pp. 94, 292
Marriage Rate, p. 94
When Was the Murder Committed?, pp. 235–237
Diffusion of Information, p. 372
The Gravity Model, p. 388
Murders and Robberies in the U.S., p. 269

General Interest:

Alcohol Absorption and the Risk of Having an Accident, pp. 225–226
Miles Per Gallon of a Compact Car Versus an Average Size Car, p. 155
The Effects of Ice on Scotch, p. 236
Operating Cost of an Automobile as a Function of Speed, pp. 63–65
Transportation Planning, p. 332

4. Tests and Exercises. Each chapter ends with a chapter test and there is a comprehensive final examination. All the answers to these tests are in the book. In the paperback version of the book there is an extra form of the tests at the end of the book. The answers to these tests are in the *Instructor's Manual.* Two additional alternate forms of the tests appear in the *Instructor's Manual.* Great care has been given to constructing exercises, most of which are based on the behavioral objectives. The first exercises in each set are quite easy, while later ones become progressively difficult. The exercises are also arranged in matching pairs; that is, any odd-numbered exercise is very much like the one that immediately follows. In effect, this makes each exercise set two exercise sets. The odd-numbered exercises have answers in the book, while the even-numbered exercises do not. This allows for various ways of assigning exercises. If the instructor wants students to have all the answers, the odd-numbered exercises are assigned. If the instructor does not want students to have the answers, the even-numbered exercises are assigned. If the instructor wants some of each, that option also exists. All margin exercises have answers in the text. It is recommended that students do all of these, stopping to do them when the text so indicates.

Some choice of topics may need to be made for a one-term course. To aid in making this choice, optional sections and chapters are marked by asterisk in the table of contents, and syllabi for various kinds of one-and two-term courses are provided in the *Instructor's Manual*. Chapter 1 is basically review, but has been written in such a way as to anticipate future work. Functions are developed carefully with special attention to notation necessary for calculating difference quotients. Other topics included are the compound interest formula and supply and demand functions. Many interesting and factual problems are considered as well as an introduction to mathematical modeling. Chapters 6 and 7 are completely optional, but due to the relevant applications, should be considered if time permits.

The Appendixes may be used for reference and review. Appendix A discusses semilogarithmic graphing; Appendix B explains the method of graphing inequalities and constraints in linear programming, and is followed by tables of powers and roots, logarithms and exponential functions, integration formulas, and areas under the normal curve. Appendix C, on multiple integration, and Appendix D, on trigonometric functions, are included for readers who may have special interest in these areas.

The author wishes to express his appreciation to many people who helped with the development of the book; to his own students for providing suggestions and criticisms so willingly during the extensive class testing; and to Judy Beecher of Indiana University-Purdue University at Indianapolis and Alan Weinheimer of Butler University for making suggestions which contributed to the continuity and clarity of the book. Lynn Loomis of Harvard University was extremely helpful in the course of his reviewing and in frequent brainstorming sessions with the author. Special thanks go to Professor Loomis for his permission to use some developments from his book *Calculus*, Addison-Wesley Publishing Co.; Reading, Mass., 1974. Special thanks go to my good friend and coauthor of other books, M. L. Keedy of Purdue University, for his exacting review of the final manuscript and his support and patience through the years of our writing and friendship. In addition, I wish to thank William L. Paschke, University of Kansas; and John G. Pierce, University of Southern California for their thorough reviewing. I am also grateful to the editorial and production staff at Addison-Wesley for their hard work and encouragement.

The text is available in a paperback and a hardback version. The paperback version differs by having an alternate form of chapter tests and final examination at the end.

Indianapolis, Indiana   M. L. B.
January 1976

Contents

---

* Indicates optional section or chapter in the sense that subsequent material is not dependent on this section or chapter.

U.S. Forest Service

1 ALGEBRA REVIEW, FUNCTIONS, AND MODELING

OBJECTIVES

You should be able to:

a) Rename an exponential expression without exponents.
b) Multiply exponential expressions by adding exponents.
c) Divide exponential expressions by subtracting exponents.
d) Raise a power to a power by multiplying exponents.
e) Multiply algebraic expressions.
f) Factor algebraic expressions.
g) Solve applied problems involving the comparison of a power like $(3.1)^2$ with 3^2.
h) Solve applied problems involving compound interest.

Rename without exponents.

1. 3^4 **2.** $(-3)^2$

3. $(1.02)^3$ **4.** $(\frac{1}{4})^2$

Rename without exponents.

5. $(5t)^0$ **6.** $(5t)^1$

7. k^0 **8.** m^1

9. $(\frac{1}{4})^1$ **10.** $(\frac{1}{4})^0$

1.1 EXPONENTS, MULTIPLYING, AND FACTORING

Exponential Notation

The set of integers is as follows:

$$\ldots, -3, -2, -1, 0, 1, 2, 3, \ldots$$

Let us review the meaning of an expression

$$a^n,$$

where n is an integer. The number a above is called the *base* and n is called the *exponent*. When n is larger than 1, then

$$a^n = \underbrace{a \cdot a \cdot a \cdots a}_{n \text{ factors}}.$$

In other words, a^n is the product of n factors, each of which is a.

Examples   Rename without exponents.

a) $4^3 = 4 \cdot 4 \cdot 4$, or 64
b) $(-2)^5 = (-2)(-2)(-2)(-2)(-2)$, or -32
c) $(1.08)^2 = 1.08 \times 1.08$, or 1.1664
d) $(\frac{1}{2})^3 = \frac{1}{2} \cdot \frac{1}{2} \cdot \frac{1}{2}$, or $\frac{1}{8}$

Do Exercises 1 through 4. (Exercises are in the margin.)

We define an exponent of 1 as follows:

$$a^1 = a, \quad \text{for any number } a.$$

That is, any number to the first power is that number itself. We define an exponent of 0 as follows:

$$a^0 = 1, \quad \text{for any nonzero number } a.$$

That is, any nonzero number to the 0 power is 1.

Examples   Rename without exponents.

a) $(-2x)^0 = 1$ b) $(-2x)^1 = -2x$ c) $(\frac{1}{2})^0 = 1$
d) $e^0 = 1$ e) $e^1 = e$ f) $(\frac{1}{2})^1 = \frac{1}{2}$

Do Exercises 5 through 10.

The meaning of a negative integer as an exponent is as follows:

$$a^{-n} = \frac{1}{a^n}, \quad \text{for any nonzero number } a.$$

That is, any nonzero number to the $-n$ power is the reciprocal of a^n.

Examples   Rename without negative exponents.

a) $2^{-5} = \dfrac{1}{2 \cdot 2 \cdot 2 \cdot 2 \cdot 2} = \dfrac{1}{32}$

b) $10^{-3} = \dfrac{1}{10 \cdot 10 \cdot 10} = \dfrac{1}{1000}$, or 0.001

c) $(\frac{1}{4})^{-2} = \dfrac{1}{(\frac{1}{4})^2} = \dfrac{1}{\frac{1}{4} \cdot \frac{1}{4}} = \dfrac{1}{\frac{1}{16}} = 1 \cdot \dfrac{16}{1} = 16$ d) $x^{-5} = \dfrac{1}{x^5}$

e) $e^{-k} = \dfrac{1}{e^k}$ f) $t^{-1} = \dfrac{1}{t^1} = \dfrac{1}{t}$

Do Exercises 11 through 17.

Properties of Exponents

Note the following:

$$b^5 \cdot b^{-3} = (b \cdot b \cdot b \cdot b \cdot b) \cdot \dfrac{1}{b \cdot b \cdot b}$$

$$= \dfrac{b \cdot b \cdot b \cdot b \cdot b}{b \cdot b \cdot b}$$

$$= \dfrac{b \cdot b \cdot b}{b \cdot b \cdot b} \cdot b \cdot b$$

$$= 1 \cdot b \cdot b$$

$$= b^2.$$

The result could have been obtained by adding the exponents. This is true in general.

> **For any number a, and any integers n and m,**
>
> $$a^n \cdot a^m = a^{n+m}.$$
>
> **(To multiply when the bases are the same, add the exponents.)**

Examples   Multiply.

a) $x^5 \cdot x^6 = x^{5+6} = x^{11}$ b) $x^{-5} \cdot x^6 = x^{-5+6} = x$

c) $2x^{-3} \cdot 5x^{-4} = 10x^{-3+(-4)} = 10x^{-7}$ d) $r^2 \cdot r = r^{2+1} = r^3$

Do Exercises 18 through 22.

Rename without negative exponents.

11. 2^{-4} **12.** 10^{-2}

13. $(\frac{1}{4})^{-3}$ **14.** t^{-7}

15. e^{-t} **16.** M^{-1}

17. $(x + 1)^{-2}$

Multiply.

18. $t^4 \cdot t^5$ **19.** $t^{-4} \cdot t$

20. $10e^{-4} \cdot 5e^{-9}$

21. $t^{-3} \cdot t^{-4} \cdot t$

22. $4b^5 \cdot 6b^{-2}$

Divide.

23. $\dfrac{x^6}{x^2}$ **24.** $\dfrac{x^2}{x^6}$

25. $\dfrac{e^t}{e^t}$ **26.** $\dfrac{e^2}{e^k}$

27. $\dfrac{e^5}{e^{-7}}$ **28.** $\dfrac{e^{-5}}{e^{-7}}$

Simplify.

29. $(x^{-4})^3$ **30.** $(e^2)^2$

31. $(e^x)^3$ **32.** $(t^4)^k$

33. $(5x^3y^5)^2$

Note the following:

$$b^5 \div b^2 = \frac{b^5}{b^2} = \frac{b \cdot b \cdot b \cdot b \cdot b}{b \cdot b} = \frac{b \cdot b}{b \cdot b} \cdot b \cdot b \cdot b = 1 \cdot b \cdot b \cdot b = b^3.$$

The result could have been obtained by subtracting the exponents. This is true in general.

For any nonzero number a and any integers n and m,

$$\frac{a^n}{a^m} = a^{n-m}.$$

(To divide when the bases are the same, subtract the exponents.)

Examples   Divide.

a) $\dfrac{a^3}{a^2} = a^{3-2} = a^1 = a$ b) $\dfrac{x^7}{x^7} = x^{7-7} = x^0 = 1$

c) $\dfrac{e^3}{e^{-4}} = e^{3-(-4)} = e^{3+4} = e^7$ d) $\dfrac{e^{-4}}{e^{-1}} = e^{-4-(-1)} = e^{-4+1} = e^{-3}$, or $\dfrac{1}{e^3}$

Do Exercises 23 through 28.

Note the following:

$$(b^2)^3 = b^2 \cdot b^2 \cdot b^2 = b^{2+2+2} = b^6.$$

The result could have been obtained by multiplying the exponents. This is true in general.

For any number a, and any integers n and m,

$$(a^n)^m = a^{nm}.$$

(To raise a power to a power, multiply the exponents.)

Examples   Simplify.

a) $(x^{-2})^3 = x^{-2 \cdot 3} = x^{-6}$ b) $(e^x)^2 = e^{2x}$

c) $(3x^3y^4)^2 = 3^2(x^3)^2(y^4)^2 = 9x^6y^8$ d) $(k^3)^t = k^{3t}$

Do Exercises 29 through 33.

Multiplication

The distributive laws are important in multiplying. The laws are as follows:

For any numbers a, b, and c,

$$a(b + c) = ab + ac \quad \text{and}$$
$$a(b - c) = ab - ac.$$

Examples Multiply.

a) $3(x - 5) = 3 \cdot x - 3 \cdot 5 = 3x - 15$

b) $P(1 + i) = P \cdot 1 + P \cdot i = P + Pi$

c) $(x - 5)(x + 3) = (x - 5)x + (x - 5)3 = x \cdot x - 5x + 3x - 5 \cdot 3$
$$= x^2 - 2x - 15$$

d) $(a + b)(a + b) = (a + b)a + (a + b)b = a \cdot a + ba + ab + b \cdot b$
$$= a^2 + 2ab + b^2$$

Do Exercises 34 through 38.

The following formulas, which are obtained using the distributive laws, are useful in multiplying.

$$(a + b)^2 = a^2 + 2ab + b^2 \qquad (1)$$
$$(a - b)^2 = a^2 - 2ab + b^2 \qquad (2)$$
$$(a - b)(a + b) = a^2 - b^2 \qquad (3)$$

Examples Multiply.

a) $(x + h)^2 = x^2 + 2xh + h^2$

b) $(2x - t)^2 = (2x)^2 - 2(2x)t + t^2 = 4x^2 - 4xt + t^2$

c) $(3c + d)(3c - d) = (3c)^2 - d^2 = 9c^2 - d^2$

Do Exercises 39 through 41.

Factoring

Factoring is the reverse of multiplication. That is, to factor an expression, we find an equivalent expression which is a product.

Examples Factor.

a) $P + Pi = P \cdot 1 + P \cdot i = P(1 + i)$ We used a distributive law.

b) $x^2 - 6xy + 9y^2 = (x - 3y)^2$

c) $x^2 - 5x - 14 = (x - 7)(x + 2)$ Here we looked for factors of -14 whose sum is -5.

d) $x^2 - 9t^2 = (x - 3t)(x + 3t)$ We used $(a - b)(a + b) = a^2 - b^2$.

e) $2xh + h^2 = h(2x + h)$

Do Exercises 42 through 46.

In later work we will consider expressions like

$$(x + h)^2 - x^2.$$

Multiply.

34. $2(x + 7)$ **35.** $P(1 - i)$

36. $(x - 4)(x + 7)$

37. $(a - b)(a - b)$

38. $(a - b)(a + b)$

Multiply.

39. $(x - h)^2$ **40.** $(3x + t)^2$

41. $(5t - m)(5t + m)$

Factor.

42. $P - Pi$

43. $x^2 + 10xy + 25y^2$

44. $x^2 + 7x + 10$

45. $25c^2 - d^2$

46. $3x^2h + 3xh^2 + h^3$

47. How close is $(5.1)^2$ to 5^2?

To simplify this, first note that

$$(x + h)^2 = x^2 + 2xh + h^2.$$

Subtracting x^2 on both sides of this equation, we get

$$(x + h)^2 - x^2 = 2xh + h^2.$$

Factoring out an h on the right side we get

$$(x + h)^2 - x^2 = h(2x + h). \tag{4}$$

Let us now use this result to compare two squares.

Example   How close is $(3.1)^2$ to 3^2?

Solution   Substituting $x = 3$ and $h = 0.1$ in equation (4) we get

$$(3.1)^2 - 3^2 = 0.1(2 \cdot 3 + 0.1) = 0.1(6.1) = 0.61.$$

So $(3.1)^2$ differs from 3^2 by 0.61.

Do Exercise 47.

Compound Interest

Suppose we invest P dollars at interest rate i, compounded annually. The amount A_1 in the account at the end of 1 year is given by

$$A_1 = P + Pi = P(1 + i) = Pr,$$

where, for convenience,

$$r = 1 + i.$$

Going into the second year we have Pr dollars, so by the end of the second year we would have the amount A_2 given by

$$A_2 = A_1 \cdot r = (Pr)r = Pr^2.$$

Going into the third year we have Pr^2 dollars, so by the end of the third year we would have the amount A_3 given by

$$A_3 = A_2 \cdot r = (Pr^2)r = Pr^3.$$

In general,

If an amount P is invested at interest rate i, compounded annually, in t years it will grow to the amount A given by

$$A = P(1 + i)^t.$$

Example 1   Suppose $1000 is invested at 8% compounded annually. How much is in the account at the end of 2 years?

Solution   We substitute into the equation $A = P(1 + i)^t$ and get

$$A = 1000(1 + 0.08)^2 = 1000(1.08)^2 = 1000(1.1664) = \$1166.40.$$

Do Exercise 48.

If interest is compounded quarterly, we can find a formula like the one above as follows:

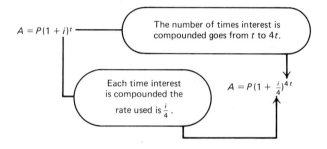

In general,

    If an amount P is invested at interest rate i, compounded n times a year, in t years it will grow to the amount A given by

$$A = P\left(1 + \frac{i}{n}\right)^{nt}.$$

Example 2   Suppose $1000 is invested at 8% compounded quarterly. How much is in the account at the end of 2 years?

Solution   We substitute into the equation $A = P\left(1 + \dfrac{i}{n}\right)^{nt}$ and get

$$A = 1000\left(1 + \frac{0.08}{4}\right)^{4 \times 2} = 1000(1 + 0.02)^8 = 1000(1.02)^8,$$

$$\approx 1000(1.17166) = \$1171.66.$$

Do Exercise 49.

48. Suppose $1000 is invested at 7% compounded annually. How much is in the account at the end of 2 years?

49. Suppose $1000 is invested at 8% compounded semiannually $(n = 2)$. How much is in the account at the end of 1 year?

EXERCISE SET 1.1

Rename without exponents.

1. 5^3 **2.** 7^2 **3.** $(-7)^2$ **4.** $(-5)^3$ **5.** $(1.01)^2$

6. $(1.01)^3$ **7.** $(\frac{1}{2})^2$ **8.** $(\frac{1}{4})^3$ **9.** $(6x)^0$ **10.** $(6x)^1$

11. t^1 **12.** t^0 **13.** $(\frac{1}{3})^0$ **14.** $(\frac{1}{3})^1$

Rename without negative exponents.

15. 3^{-2} **16.** 4^{-2} **17.** $(\frac{1}{2})^{-3}$ **18.** $(\frac{1}{2})^{-2}$ **19.** 10^{-1}

20. 10^{-4} **21.** e^{-b} **22.** t^{-k} **23.** b^{-1} **24.** h^{-1}

Multiply.

25. $x^2 \cdot x^3$ **26.** $t^3 \cdot t^4$ **27.** $x^{-7} \cdot x$ **28.** $x^5 \cdot x$ **29.** $5x^2 \cdot 7x^3$

30. $4t^3 \cdot 2t^4$ **31.** $x^{-4} \cdot x^7 \cdot x$ **32.** $x^{-3} \cdot x \cdot x^3$ **33.** $e^{-t} \cdot e^t$ **34.** $e^k \cdot e^{-k}$

Divide.

35. $\dfrac{x^5}{x^2}$ **36.** $\dfrac{x^7}{x^3}$ **37.** $\dfrac{x^2}{x^5}$ **38.** $\dfrac{x^3}{x^7}$ **39.** $\dfrac{e^k}{e^k}$

40. $\dfrac{t^k}{t^k}$ **41.** $\dfrac{e^t}{e^4}$ **42.** $\dfrac{e^k}{e^3}$ **43.** $\dfrac{t^6}{t^{-8}}$ **44.** $\dfrac{t^5}{t^{-7}}$

45. $\dfrac{t^{-9}}{t^{-11}}$ **46.** $\dfrac{t^{-11}}{t^{-7}}$

Simplify.

47. $(t^{-2})^3$ **48.** $(t^{-3})^4$ **49.** $(e^x)^4$ **50.** $(e^x)^5$ **51.** $(t^4)^x$

52. $(t^5)^p$ **53.** $(2x^2y^4)^3$ **54.** $(2x^2y^4)^5$

Multiply.

55. $5(x-7)$ **56.** $4(x-3)$ **57.** $x(1-t)$ **58.** $x(1+t)$

59. $(x-5)(x-2)$ **60.** $(x-4)(x-3)$ **61.** $(x+5)(x-2)$ **62.** $(x+4)(x-3)$

63. $(2x+5)(x-1)$ **64.** $(3x+4)(x-1)$ **65.** $(a-2)(a+2)$ **66.** $(3x-1)(3x+1)$

67. $(5x + 2)(5x - 2)$ **68.** $(t - 1)(t + 1)$ **69.** $(a - h)^2$ **70.** $(a + h)^2$

71. $(5x + t)^2$ **72.** $(7a - c)^2$

Factor.

73. $x - xt$ **74.** $x + xh$ **75.** $x^2 + 6xy + 9y^2$ **76.** $x^2 - 10xy + 25y^2$

77. $x^2 - 2x - 15$ **78.** $x^2 + 8x + 15$ **79.** $x^2 - x - 20$ **80.** $x^2 - 9x - 10$

81. $49x^2 - t^2$ **82.** $9x^2 - b^2$ **83.** $36t^2 - 16m^2$ **84.** $25y^2 - 9z^2$

Use

$$(x + h)^2 - x^2 = h(2x + h)$$

for Exercises 85 and 86.

85. a) How close is $(4.1)^2$ to 4^2?
    b) How close is $(4.01)^2$ to 4^2?
    c) How close is $(4.001)^2$ to 4^2?

86. a) How close is $(2.1)^2$ to 2^2?
    b) How close is $(2.01)^2$ to 2^2?
    c) How close is $(2.001)^2$ to 2^2?

Note the following:

$$(x + h)^3 = (x + h)(x + h)^2 = (x + h)(x^2 + 2xh + h^2)$$
$$= (x + h)x^2 + (x + h)2xh + (x + h)h^2$$
$$= x^3 + x^2h + 2x^2h + 2xh^2 + xh^2 + h^3$$
$$= x^3 + 3x^2h + 3xh^2 + h^3.$$

Thus

$$(x + h)^3 - x^3 = h(3x^2 + 3xh + h^2).$$

Use this for Exercises 87 and 88.

87. a) How close is $(2.1)^3$ to 2^3?
    b) How close is $(2.01)^3$ to 2^3?
    c) How close is $(2.001)^3$ to 2^3?

88. a) How close is $(4.1)^3$ to 4^3?
    b) How close is $(4.01)^3$ to 4^3?
    c) How close is $(4.001)^3$ to 4^3?

89. Suppose $1000 is invested at 8%. How much is in the account at the end of 1 year, if interest is compounded
 a) annually?
 b) semiannually?
 c) quarterly?
 d) daily (need calculator with a^b key)?

90. Suppose $1000 is invested at 10%. How much is in the account at the end of 1 year, if interest is compounded
 a) annually?
 b) semiannually?
 c) quarterly?
 d) daily (need calculator with a^b key)?

OBJECTIVES

You should be able to:

a) Solve equations like
   $-5x + 7 = 8x + 4$, and $2t^2 = 9 + t$.
b) Solve inequalities like
   $-5x + 7 < 8x + 4$.
c) Solve applied problems.
d) Write interval notation for a given graph or inequality.

---

50. Solve
   $-\frac{7}{8}x + 5 = \frac{1}{4}x - 2$.

1.2 EQUATIONS, INEQUALITIES, AND INTERVAL NOTATION

Equations

Basic to the solution of many equations are these two simple principles.

THE ADDITION PRINCIPLE. If an equation $a = b$ is true, then the equation $a + c = b + c$ is true for any number c.

THE MULTIPLICATION PRINCIPLE. If an equation $a = b$ is true, then the equation $ac = bc$ is true for any number c.

Example 1   Solve $-\frac{5}{6}x + 10 = \frac{1}{2}x + 2$.

Solution   We first multiply on both sides by 6 to clear of fractions.

$$6(-\tfrac{5}{6}x + 10) = 6(\tfrac{1}{2}x + 2) \qquad \text{(Multiplication Principle)}$$

$$6(-\tfrac{5}{6}x) + 6 \cdot 10 = 6(\tfrac{1}{2}x) + 6 \cdot 2 \qquad \text{(Distributive Law)}$$

$$-5x + 60 = 3x + 12 \qquad \text{(Simplifying)}$$

$$60 = 8x + 12 \qquad \text{(Addition Principle: we add } 5x \text{ to get the variable by itself on one side of the equation.)}$$

$$48 = 8x \qquad \text{(We add } -12.)$$

$$\tfrac{1}{8} \cdot 48 = \tfrac{1}{8} \cdot 8x \qquad \text{(We multiply by } \tfrac{1}{8}.)$$

$$6 = x$$

The number 6 checks when it is substituted into the original equation, thus it is the solution.

Do Exercise 50.

To solve applied problems we first translate to mathematical language, usually an equation. Then we solve the equation and check to see if the solution of the equation is a solution of the problem.

Example 2   After a 5% gain in weight an animal weighs 693 lbs. What was its original weight?

Solution   We first translate to an equation.

$$\underbrace{\text{(Original weight)}}_{w} + \underbrace{5\%(\text{Original weight})}_{+\ 5\% \quad \cdot \quad w} = 693$$
$$= 693$$

Now we solve the equation.

$$w + 5\%w = 693$$
$$1 \cdot w + 0.05w = 693$$
$$(1 + 0.05)w = 693$$
$$1.05w = 693$$
$$w = \frac{693}{1.05} = 660$$

Check: $660 + 5\% \times 660 = 660 + 0.05 \times 660 = 660 + 33 = 693$

Do Exercise 51.

A third principle for solving equations is the *principle of zero products*.

THE PRINCIPLE OF ZERO PRODUCTS. **For any numbers a and b, if $ab = 0$, then $a = 0$ or $b = 0$; and if $a = 0$ or $b = 0$, then $ab = 0$.**

To solve an equation using this principle, there *must* be a 0 on one side of the equation and a product on the other. The solutions are then obtained by setting each of the factors equal to 0 and solving the resulting equations.

Example 3 Solve $3x(x - 2)(5x + 4) = 0$.

Solution $3x(x - 2)(5x + 4) = 0$

$3x = 0$ or $x - 2 = 0$ or $5x + 4 = 0$ (Principle of zero products)

$\frac{1}{3} \cdot 3x = \frac{1}{3} \cdot 0$ or $x = 2$ or $5x = -4$ (Solve each separately.)

$x = 0$ or $x = 2$ or $x = -\frac{4}{5}$

The solutions are 0, 2, and $-\frac{4}{5}$.

Do Exercise 52.

Example 4 Solve $x^2 - x = 20$.

Solution $x^2 - x = 20$

$x^2 - x - 20 = 0$ (Adding -20)

$(x - 5)(x + 4) = 0$ (Factoring)

$x - 5 = 0$ or $x + 4 = 0$ (Principle of zero products)

$x = 5$ or $x = -4$

The solutions are 5 and -4.

Do Exercise 53.

51. An investment is made at 8%, compounded annually. It grows to $783 at the end of 1 year. How much was invested originally?

52. Solve $5x(x + 2)(2x - 3) = 0$.

53. Solve $x^2 + x = 12$.

54. Solve $x^3 = x$.

Example 5   Solve $4x^3 = x$.

Solution $4x^3 = x$

$$4x^3 - x = 0 \qquad \text{(Adding } -x\text{)}$$
$$x(4x^2 - 1) = 0$$
$$x(2x - 1)(2x + 1) = 0 \qquad \text{(Factoring)}$$

$x = 0$ or $2x - 1 = 0$ or $2x + 1 = 0$ (Principle of zero products)

$x = 0$ or $2x = 1$ or $2x = -1$

$x = 0$ or $x = \frac{1}{2}$ or $x = -\frac{1}{2}$

The solutions are 0, $\frac{1}{2}$, and $-\frac{1}{2}$.

Do Exercise 54.

Inequalities

Principles for solving inequalities are similar to those for solving equations. We can add the same number on both sides of an inequality. We can also multiply on both sides by the same nonzero number; but if that number is negative, we must reverse the inequality sign. Let us see why this is necessary. Consider the true inequality

$$5 < 9. \qquad (1)$$

Let us multiply both members by 2. We get another true inequality

$$10 < 18.$$

Let us multiply both members in (1) by -3.

$$-15 < -27$$

This time the inequality is false. However, if we reverse the inequality symbol (use $>$ instead of $<$), we will get a true inequality

$$-15 > -27.$$

The following is a reformulation of the inequality-solving principles.

> If the inequality $a < b$ is true, then
> i) $a + c < b + c$ is true, for any c,
> ii) $a \cdot c < b \cdot c$, for any *positive* c,
> iii) $a \cdot c > b \cdot c$, for any *negative* c.

Similar principles hold when $<$ is replaced by $\leqslant$, and $>$ is replaced by $\geqslant$.

Example 6   Solve $5x > 12 - 3x$.

Solution

$$5x > 12 - 3x$$
$$5x + 3x > 12 \qquad \text{(Adding } 3x)$$
$$8x > 12$$
$$\tfrac{1}{8} \cdot 8x > \tfrac{1}{8} \cdot 12 \qquad \text{(Multiplying by } \tfrac{1}{8})$$
$$x > \tfrac{3}{2}$$

Any number greater than $\frac{3}{2}$ is a solution.

Do Exercise 55.

Example 7   Solve $17 - 8x \geqslant 5x - 4$.

Solution

$$17 - 8x \geqslant 5x - 4$$
$$-8x \geqslant 5x - 21 \qquad \text{(Adding } -17)$$
$$-13x \geqslant -21 \qquad \text{(Adding } -5x)$$
$$-\tfrac{1}{13} \cdot -13x \leqslant -\tfrac{1}{13}(-21) \qquad \begin{array}{l}\text{(Multiplying by } -\tfrac{1}{13}, \text{ and}\\ \textit{reversing} \text{ the inequality sign)}\end{array}$$
$$x \leqslant \tfrac{21}{13}$$

Any number less than or equal to $\frac{21}{13}$ is a solution.

Do Exercise 56.

Example 8   Raggs, Ltd., a clothing firm, determines that its total revenue, in dollars, from the sale of x suits is

$$2x + 50.$$

Determine the number of suits the firm must sell so that its total revenue will be more than $70,000.

Solution   We translate to an inequality and solve

$$2x + 50 > 70{,}000$$
$$2x > 69{,}950 \qquad \text{(Adding } -50)$$
$$x > 34{,}975. \qquad \text{(Multiplying by } \tfrac{1}{2})$$

Thus the company's total revenue will exceed $70,000 when it sells more than 34,975 suits.

Do Exercise 57.

55. Solve $3x < 11 - 2x$.

56. Solve $16 - 7x \leqslant 10x - 4$.

57. In Example 8, determine the number of suits the firm must sell so that its total revenue will be more than $40,000.

Daniel S. Brody from Stock, Boston

58. Write interval notation for each graph.

a)
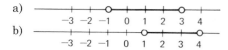
    −3 −2 −1 0 1 2 3 4

b)
    −3 −2 −1 0 1 2 3 4

59. Write interval notation for
a) the set of all numbers x such that $-1 < x < 4$;
b) the set of all numbers x such that $-\frac{1}{4} < x < \frac{1}{4}$.

Interval Notation

The set of real numbers corresponds to the set of points on a line.

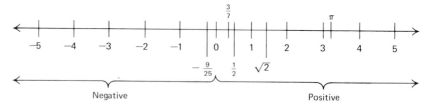

For real numbers a and b such that $a < b$ (a is to the left of b on a number line), we define the *open interval* (a, b) to be the set of numbers between, but not including, a and b. That is,

    (a, b) = the set of all numbers x such that $a < x < b$.

```
        ○───────────────────────○
        a                       b
```

The graph of (a, b) is shown above. The open circles and the parentheses indicate that a and b are *not* included. The numbers a and b are called *endpoints*.

Do Exercises 58 and 59.

The *closed interval* $[a, b]$ is the set of numbers between and including a and b. That is,

    $[a, b]$ = the set of all numbers x such that $a \leqslant x \leqslant b$.

```
        ●───────────────────────●
        a                       b
```

The graph of $[a, b]$ is shown above. The solid circles and the brackets indicate that a and b are included.

There are two kinds of *half-open intervals* defined as follows:

    $(a, b]$ = the set of all numbers x such that $a < x \leqslant b$.

```
        ○───────────────────────●
        a                       b
```

The open circle and the parentheses indicate that a is not included. The solid circle and the bracket indicate that b is included. Also,

    $[a, b)$ = the set of all numbers x such that $a \leqslant x < b$.

```
        ●───────────────────────○
        a                       b
```

The solid circle and the bracket indicate that a is included. The open circle and the parenthesis indicate that b is not included.

Do Exercises 60 and 61.

Some intervals are of unlimited extent in one or both directions. In such cases we use the infinity symbol ∞. For example,

$$[a, \infty) = \text{the set of all numbers } x \text{ such that } x \geqslant a.$$

Note that ∞ is not a number.

$$(a, \infty) = \text{the set of all numbers } x \text{ such that } x > a.$$

$$(-\infty, b] = \text{the set of all numbers } x \text{ such that } x \leqslant b.$$

$$(-\infty, b) = \text{the set of all numbers } x \text{ such that } x < b.$$

We can name the entire set of real numbers using $(-\infty, \infty)$.

Do Exercises 62 and 63.

Any point in an interval which is not an endpoint is an *interior* point.

Note that all of the points in an open interval are interior points.

60. Write interval notation for each graph.

a)
```
   ●———+———+———+———+———●
  -1   0   1   2   3   4
```

b)
```
   ○———+———+———+———+———●
  -1   0   1   2   3   4
```

c)
```
   ●———+———+———+———+———○
  -1   0   1   2   3   4
```

d)
```
   ○———+———+———+———+———○
  -1   0   1   2   3   4
```

61. Write interval notation for
a) the set of all numbers x such that $-\sqrt{2} < x < \sqrt{2}$;

b) the set of all numbers x such that $0 \leqslant x < 1$;

c) the set of all numbers x such that $-6.7 < x \leqslant -4.2$;

d) the set of all numbers x such that $3 \leqslant x \leqslant 7\frac{1}{2}$.

62. Write interval notation for each graph.

a)
```
  ←————————————●
               5
```

b)
```
  ———————○————————→
         4
```

c)
```
  ←————————○————→
           4.8
```

d)
```
  ←————————————●
               5
```

63. Write interval notation for
a) the set of all numbers x such that $x \geqslant 8$;

b) the set of all numbers x such that $x < -7$;

c) the set of all numbers x such that $x > 10$;

d) the set of all numbers x such that $x \leqslant -0.78$.

EXERCISE SET 1.2

Solve.

1. $-7x + 10 = 5x - 11$

2. $-8x + 9 = 4x - 70$

3. $5x - 17 - 2x = 6x - 1 - x$

4. $5x - 2 + 3x = 2x + 6 - 4x$

5. $x + 0.8x = 216$

6. $x + 0.5x = 210$

7. $x + 0.08x = 216$

8. $x + 0.05x = 210$

Applied Problems

9. After a 6% gain in weight an animal weighs 508.8 lb. What was its original weight?

10. After a 7% gain in weight an animal weighs 363.8 lb. What was its original weight?

11. An investment is made at 9%, compounded annually. It grows to $708.50 at the end of 1 year. How much was invested originally?

12. An investment is made at 7%, compounded annually. It grows to $856 at the end of 1 year. How much was invested originally?

13. After a 2% increase, the population of a city is 826,200. What was the former population?

14. After a 3% increase, the population of a city is 741,600. What was the former population?

Solve.

15. $2x(x + 3)(5x - 4) = 0$

16. $7x(x - 2)(2x + 3) = 0$

17. $x^2 + 1 = 2x + 1$

18. $2t^2 = 9 + t^2$

19. $t^2 - 2t = t$

20. $6x - x^2 = x$

21. $6x - x^2 = -x$

22. $2x - x^2 = -x$

23. $9x^3 = x$

24. $16x^3 = x$

25. $(x - 3)^2 = x^2 + 2x + 1$

26. $(x - 5)^2 = x^2 + x + 3$

Solve.

27. $3 - x \leqslant 4x + 7$

28. $x + 6 \leqslant 5x - 6$

29. $5x - 5 + x > 2 - 6x - 8$

30. $3x - 3 + 3x > 1 - 7x - 9$

31. $-7x < 4$

32. $-5x \geqslant 6$

Applied Problems

33. A firm determines that the total revenue, in dollars, from the sale of x units of a product is

$$3x + 1000.$$

Determine the number of units that must be sold so that its total revenue will be more than $22,000.

34. A firm determines that the total revenue, in dollars, from the sale of x units of a product is

$$5x + 1000.$$

Determine the number of units that must be sold so that its total revenue will be more than $22,000.

35. To get a B in a course a student's average must be greater than or equal to 80% (at least 80%) and less than 90%. On the first three tests she scores 78%, 90%, and 92%. Determine the scores on the 4th test that will yield a B.

36. To get a C in a course a student's average must be greater than or equal to 70% and less than 80%. On the first three tests she scores 65%, 83%, and 82%. Determine the scores on the 4th test that will yield a C.

Write interval notation for each graph.

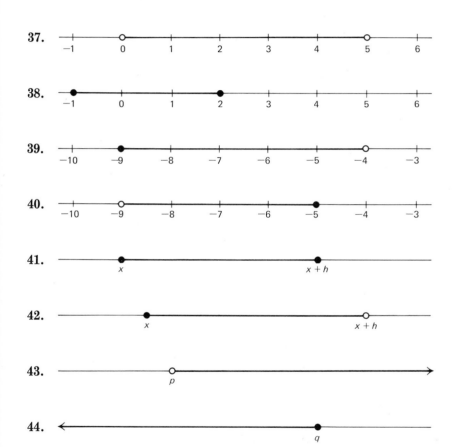

41.

x $x + h$

42.

x $x + h$

43.

p

44.

q

Write interval notation for:

45. The set of all numbers x such that $-3 \leqslant x \leqslant 3$.

46. The set of all numbers x such that $-4 < x < 4$.

47. The set of all numbers x such that $-14 \leqslant x < -11$.

48. The set of all numbers x such that $6 < x \leqslant 20$.

49. The set of all numbers x such that $x \leqslant -4$.

50. The set of all numbers x such that $x > -5$.

OBJECTIVES

You should be able to:

a) Given a function and several inputs, find the outputs.
b) Graph a given function.
c) Decide if a graph is that of a function.
d) Given the graph of a function, tell where it is increasing, decreasing, or neither.

David A. Krathwohl from Stock, Boston

64. Graph these ordered pairs: (2, 0), (0, 2), (−1, 3), (4, 3), and (−2, −3).

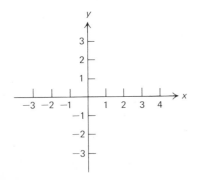

1.3 GRAPHS AND FUNCTIONS

Graphs

Each point in the plane corresponds to an ordered pair of numbers. Note that the pair (2, 5) is different from the pair (5, 2). This is why we call (2, 5) an *ordered pair*. The first member 2 is called the *first coordinate* and the second member 5 is called the *second coordinate*. Together these are called the *coordinates of a point*. The vertical line is called the *y-axis* and the horizontal line is called the *x-axis*.

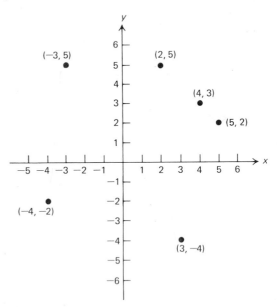

Do Exercise 64.

Graphs of Equations

A *solution* of an equation in two variables is an ordered pair of numbers. For example, (−1, 2) is a solution of the equation $3x^2 + y = 5$, because the numbers −1 and 2 make it true:

$$3x^2 + y = 5$$

$3(-1)^2 + 2$	5
$3 + 2$	
5	

Note that -1 is to be substituted for x and 2 is to be substituted for y. Generally, make substitutions for the variables in alphabetical order.

Do Exercise 65.

A *graph* of an equation is a geometric representation of all of its solutions. It could be a line, curve (or curves), or some other configuration. To draw a graph we plot enough points to see a pattern.

Example 1.   Graph $y = 2x + 1$.

x	0	-1	-2	1	2
y	1	-1	-3	3	5

← We choose these numbers at random (since y is expressed in terms of x).
← We find these numbers by substituting in the equation.

For example, when $x = -2$, $y = 2(-2) + 1 = -3$. This yields the pair $(-2, -3)$. We plot all the pairs from the table and, in this case, draw a line to complete the graph.

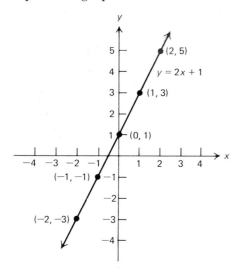

Do Exercise 66.

Example 2.   Graph $y = x^2 - 1$.

x	0	1	2	-1	-2
y	-1	0	3	0	3

← We choose these numbers at random (since y is expressed in terms of x).
← We find these numbers by substituting in the equation.

65. Decide whether each pair is a solution of

$$x^2 - 2y = 6.$$

a) $(-2, -1)$ b) $(3, 0)$

$(-2)^2 - 2(-1)$

$4 - (-2)2$

$4 + 2 = 6$ True

$3^2 - 2(0) = 9 \cdot 2 = 17 \neq 6$

66. Graph $y = -2x + 1$.

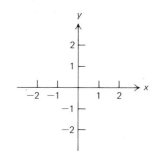

67. Graph $y = x^2 - 3$.

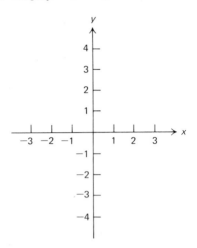

Graph

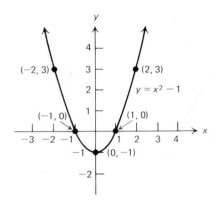

Do Exercise 67.

68. Graph $x = y^2 + 1$.

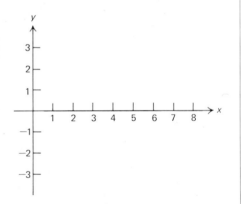

Example 3   Graph $x = y^2$.

x	0	1	4	1	4
y	0	1	2	-1	-2

We find these numbers by substituting in the equation.

This time we choose these numbers at random since x is expressed in terms of y.

We plot these points, keeping in mind that x is still the first coordinate and y the second.

Graph

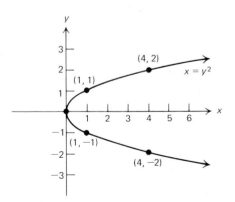

Do Exercise 68.

Functions

A *function* is a special kind of relation between two or more variables. Such relations are of fundamental importance in calculus. We shall describe them in several ways.

A Function as an Input-Output Relation

DESCRIPTION 1.   A *function* is a relation which assigns to each "input" number a unique "output" number. The set of all input numbers is called the *domain*. The set of all output numbers is called the *range*.

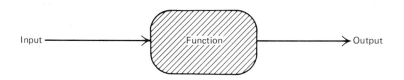

Example 1   Squaring numbers is a function. We can take any number as an input. We square that number to find the output, x^2.

Inputs	Outputs
-3	9
1	1
k	k^2
$\sqrt{a}$	a
$1 + t$	$(1 + t)^2$, or $1 + 2t + t^2$

The domain of this function is the set of all real numbers, because any real number can be squared.

Do Exercise 69.

It is customary to use letters such as f and g to represent functions. Suppose f is a function and x is a number in its domain. For the input x, we can name the output as

$$f(x), \text{ read "}f \text{ of } x\text{," or "the value of } f \text{ at } x\text{."}$$

If f is the squaring function, then $f(3)$ is the output for the input 3. Thus $f(3) = 3^2 = 9$.

69. The operation of "taking the reciprocal" is a function. That is, the operation of going from x to $\dfrac{1}{x}$ is a function defined for all numbers except 0. Thus the domain is the set of all nonzero real numbers.

Complete this table.

Inputs	Outputs
5	
$-\frac{2}{3}$	
$\frac{1}{4}$	
$\frac{1}{a}$	
k	
$1 + t$	

70. The reciprocal function is given by

$$f(x) = \frac{1}{x}.$$

Find $f(5)$, $f(-2)$, $f(\frac{1}{4})$, $f\left(\dfrac{1}{a}\right)$, $f(k)$, $f(1 + t)$, and $f(x + h)$.

Example 2   The squaring function is given by

$$f(x) = x^2.$$

Find $f(-3)$, $f(1)$, $f(k)$, $f(\sqrt{k})$, $f(1 + t)$, and $f(x + h)$.

Solution

$$f(-3) = (-3)^2 = 9, \qquad f(1) = 1^2 = 1,$$
$$f(k) = k^2, \qquad\qquad f(\sqrt{k}) = (\sqrt{k})^2 = k,$$
$$f(1 + t) = (1 + t)^2 = 1 + 2t + t^2,$$
$$f(x + h) = (x + h)^2 = x^2 + 2xh + h^2$$

To find $f(x + h)$, remember what the function does—it squares the input. Thus $f(x + h) = (x + h)^2 = x^2 + 2xh + h^2$. This amounts to replacing x on both sides of $f(x) = x^2$, by $x + h$.

Do Exercise 70.

Example 3   A function f subtracts the square of an input from the input. A description of f is given by

$$f(x) = x - x^2.$$

Find $f(4)$ and $f(x + h)$.

Solution   We replace the x's on both sides by the inputs. Thus

$$f(4) = 4 - 4^2 = 4 - 16 = -12,$$
$$f(x + h) = (x + h) - (x + h)^2 = x + h - (x^2 + 2xh + h^2)$$
$$= x + h - x^2 - 2xh - h^2.$$

Do Exercise 71.

71. A function t is given by

$$t(x) = x + x^2.$$

Find $t(5)$, $t(-5)$, and $t(x + h)$.

Taking square roots is *not* a function. This is because an input can have more than one output. For example, the input 4 has two outputs 2 and -2.

Example 4   Taking principal square roots (nonnegative roots) is a function. Let g be this function. Then g can be described as

$$g(x) = \sqrt{x}.$$

(Recall from algebra that the symbol "$\sqrt{a}$" represents the nonnegative square root of a). The domain of this function is the set of nonnegative real numbers. Find $g(0)$, $g(2)$, $g(a)$, $g(16)$, and $g(t + h)$.

Solution

$$g(0) = \sqrt{0} = 0, \qquad g(2) = \sqrt{2},$$
$$g(a) = \sqrt{a}, \qquad g(16) = \sqrt{16} = 4,$$
$$g(t + h) = \sqrt{t + h}$$

Do Exercise 72.

A Function as a Mapping

Another description of functions is a "mapping" of one set to another.

DESCRIPTION 2. A *function* **is a mapping which associates with each number** x **in one set (called the domain) a unique number** y **in another set.**

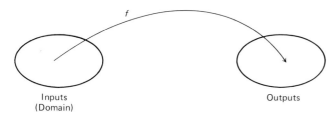

For example, the squaring function maps members of the set of real numbers to members of the set of nonnegative numbers.

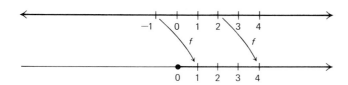

The statement

$$y = f(x)$$

means that the number x is mapped to the number y by the function f. Functions are often implicit in certain equations. For example, consider

$$xy = 2.$$

For any nonzero x there is a unique number y satisfying the equation. This yields a function which is given explicitly by

$$y = f(x) = \frac{2}{x}.$$

72. Subtracting 3 from a number and then taking the reciprocal is a function f given by

$$f(x) = \frac{1}{x - 3}.$$

a) What is the domain of this function? Explain.

b) Find $f(5)$, $f(4)$, and $f(2.5)$.

The number of people at the beach is a function of the temperature.

Ellis Herwig from Stock, Boston

On the other hand, consider the equation

$$x = y^2.$$

A number x would be related to two values of y, namely $\sqrt{x}$ and $-\sqrt{x}$. Thus, this equation is not an implicit description of a function which maps inputs x to outputs y.

Graphs of Functions

Consider again the squaring function. The input 3 is associated with the output 9. The input-output pair $(3, 9)$ is one point on the *graph* of this function.

> A *graph* of a function f consists of a geometric representation of all of its input-output pairs $(x, f(x))$. In cases where the function is given by an equation, the graph of a function is the graph of the equation $y = f(x)$.

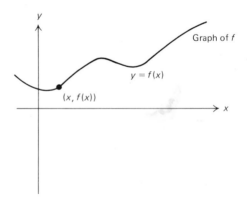

It is customary to locate input values (the domain) on the horizontal axis and output values on the vertical axis.

Example 5   Graph $f(x) = 2x + 1$.

Solution

x	0	-1	-2	1	2	←—We choose these inputs at random.
$f(x)$	1	-1	-3	3	5	←—We compute these outputs.

Next we plot the input-output pairs from the table and, in this case, draw a line to complete the graph.

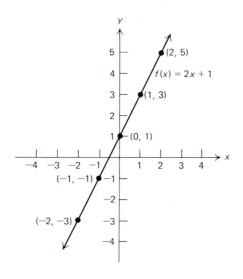

73. Graph $f(x) = -2x + 1$.

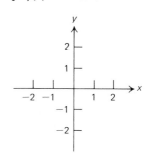

Example 6   Graph $f(x) = x^2 - 1$.

Solution

x	0	1	2	-1	-2
$f(x)$	-1	0	3	0	3

←—We choose these inputs at random.
←—We compute these outputs.

Next we plot the input-output pairs from the table and, in this case, draw a curve to complete the graph.

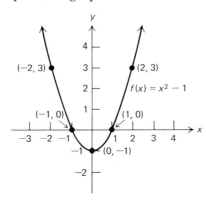

74. Graph $g(x) = x^2 - 3$.

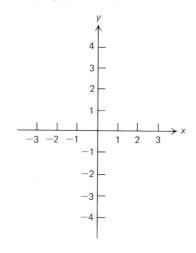

Do Exercises 73 and 74.

The following figure illustrates how the idea of a mapping is connected with the graph of a function.

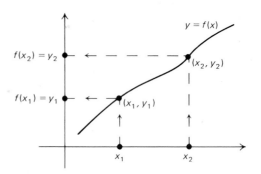

Let us now determine how we can look at a graph and decide whether it is a graph of a function. We already know that

$$x = y^2$$

does not yield a function which maps a number x to a unique number y. Look at its graph.

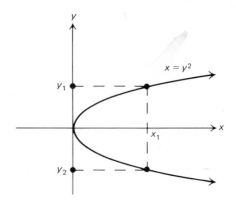

Note that there is a point x_1 which has two outputs. Equivalently, we have a vertical line which meets the graph more than once.

VERTICAL LINE TEST. A graph is that of a function provided no vertical line meets the graph more than once.

Examples   Which of the following are graphs of functions?

a)

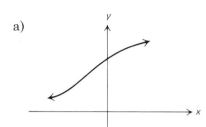

b)

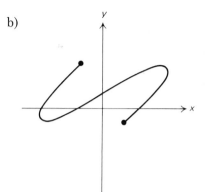

c)

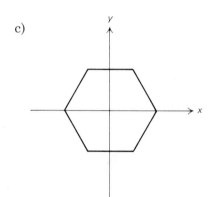

d)

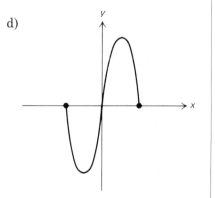

Solution

a) A function. No vertical line meets the graph more than once.
b) Not a function. A vertical line (in fact many) meets the graph more than once.
c) Not a function.
d) A function.

Do Exercise 75.

Increasing and Decreasing Functions

If the graph of a function rises from left to right, it is said to be *increasing*. If the graph drops from left to right, it is said to be *decreasing*.

75. Which of the following are graphs of functions?

a)

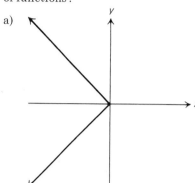

b)

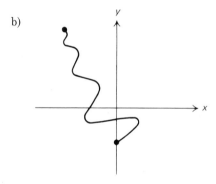

c)

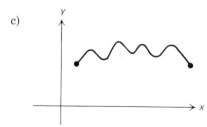

d)

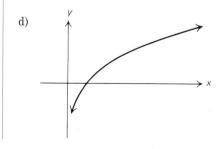

76. Which are (a) increasing? (b) decreasing? (c) neither?

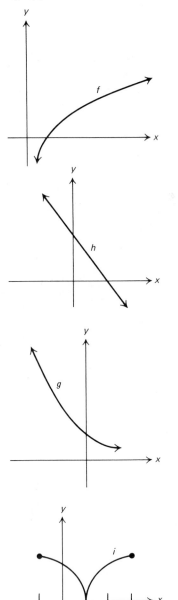

77. For the function i of Margin Exercise 76, on what interval is the function (a) increasing? (b) decreasing?

Examples

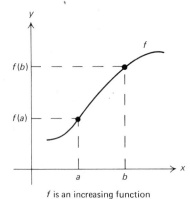

f is an increasing function

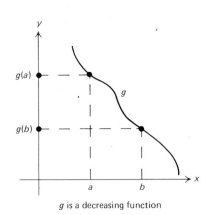

g is a decreasing function

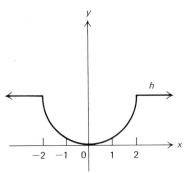

h is neither increasing nor decreasing

Note that while the function h is neither increasing nor decreasing it is decreasing on the interval $[-2, 0]$ and increasing on the interval $[0, 2]$.

Do Exercises 76 and 77.

Some Final Remarks

Almost all of the functions in this text can be described by equations. Some functions, however, cannot. We sometimes use the terminology *y is a function of x*. This means that x is an input and y is an output. We sometimes refer to x as the *independent* variable when it represents inputs, and y as the *dependent* variable when it represents outputs. We may refer to an equation like

$$y = x^2$$

as a function without naming it with a letter f. We may simply refer to x^2 (alone) as a function.

The height attained is a function of the force applied by the hammer.

David Krasnor from Photo Researchers, Inc.

EXERCISE SET 1.3

1. A function f is given by

$$f(x) = 2x + 3.$$

This function takes a number x, multiplies it by 2 and adds 3.

a) Complete this table.

Inputs	Outputs
4.1	11.2
4.01	11.02
4.001	11.002
4	11

b) Find $f(5)$, $f(-1)$, $f(k)$, $f(1 + t)$, and $f(x + h)$.

3. A function g is given by

$$g(x) = x^2 - 3.$$

This function takes a number x, squares it, and subtracts 3.

Find $g(-1)$, $g(0)$, $g(1)$, $g(5)$, $g(u)$, $g(a + h)$, and $g(1 - h)$.

2. A function f is given by

$$f(x) = 3x - 1.$$

This function takes a number x, multiplies it by 3 and subtracts 1.

a) Complete this table.

Inputs	Outputs
5.1	
5.01	
5.001	
5	

b) Find $f(4)$, $f(-2)$, $f(k)$, $f(1 + t)$, and $f(x + h)$.

4. A function g is given by

$$g(x) = x^2 + 4.$$

This function takes a number x, squares it, and adds 4.

Find $g(-3)$, $g(0)$, $g(-1)$, $g(7)$, $g(v)$, $g(a + h)$, and $g(1 - t)$.

5. A function f is given by

$$f(x) = (x - 3)^2.$$

This function takes a number x, subtracts 3 from it, and squares the result.

a) Find $f(4)$, $f(-2)$, $f(0)$, $f(a)$, $f(t + 1)$, $f(t + 3)$, and $f(x + h)$.

b) Note that f could also be given by

$$f(x) = x^2 - 6x + 9.$$

Explain what this does to an input number x.

6. A function f is given by

$$f(x) = (x + 4)^2.$$

This function takes a number x, adds 4 to it, and squares the result.

a) Find $f(3)$, $f(-6)$, $f(0)$, $f(k)$, $f(t - 1)$, $f(t - 4)$, and $f(x + h)$.

b) Note that f could also be given by

$$f(x) = x^2 + 8x + 16.$$

Explain what this does to an input number x.

Graph the following functions.

7. $f(x) = 2x + 3$ **8.** $f(x) = 3x - 1$ **9.** $g(x) = -4x$ **10.** $g(x) = -2x$

11. $f(x) = x^2 - 1$ **12.** $f(x) = x^2 + 4$ **13.** $g(x) = x^3$ **14.** $g(x) = \frac{1}{2}x^3$

Which of the following are graphs of functions?

15.

16.
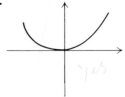

17.
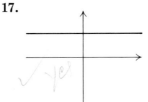

18.

19.
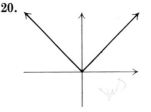

20.

21.

22.
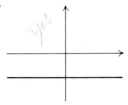

23. a) Graph $x = y^2 - 1$.
    b) Is this a function?

25. For $f(x) = x^2 - 3x$, find $f(x + h)$.

24. a) Graph $x = y^2 - 3$.
    b) Is this a function?

26. For $f(x) = x^2 + 4x$, find $f(x + h)$.

27. Raggs, Ltd., a clothing firm, determines that its total revenue (money coming in) from the sale of x suits is given by the function

$$R(x) = 2x + 50,$$

where $R(x)$ is the revenue, in dollars, from the sale of x suits. Find $R(10)$ and $R(100)$.

28. The amount of money in a savings account at 8% compounded annually depends on the initial investment x and is given by the function

$$A(x) = x + 8\%x,$$

where $A(x)$ = amount in the account at the end of one year. Find $A(100)$ and $A(1000)$.

Decide whether increasing, decreasing, or neither.

29.

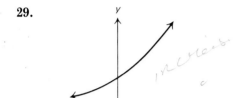

30.

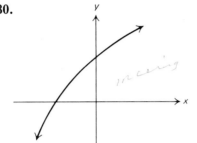

31.

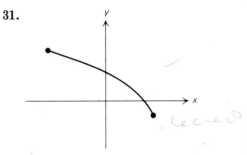

32.

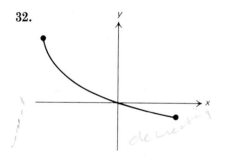

33.

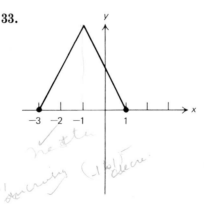

34.

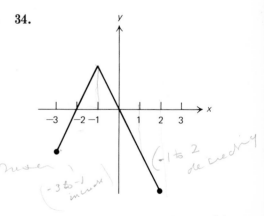

35. In reference to Exercise 33, on what interval is the function increasing? decreasing?

36. In reference to Exercise 34, on what interval is the function increasing? decreasing?

1.4 STRAIGHT LINES AND LINEAR FUNCTIONS

Horizontal and Vertical Lines

Let us consider graphs of equations $y = b$ and $x = a$.

OBJECTIVES

You should be able to:

a) Graph equations of the type $y = b$ and $x = a$.
b) Graph linear functions.
c) Find an equation of a line given its slope and one point on the line.
d) Find the slope of the line containing a given pair of points.
e) Find an equation of the line containing a given pair of points.
f) Given a linear function, tell whether it is increasing, decreasing, or neither, without graphing.

78. a) Graph $y = 3$.
    b) Decide if it is a function.

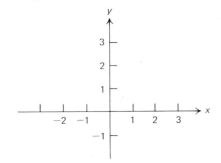

Example 1
a) Graph $y = 4$.
b) Decide if the relation is a function.

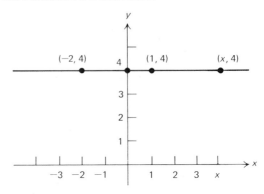

Solution
a) The graph consists of all ordered pairs whose second coordinate is 4. To see how a pair such as $(-2, 4)$ could be a solution we can consider the above equation in the form

$$0x + y = 4.$$

Then $(-2, 4)$ is a solution because

$$0(-2) + 4 = 4 \text{ is true.}$$

b) The vertical line test holds. Thus, this is a function.

Do Exercise 78.

Example 2
a) Graph $x = -3$.
b) Decide if it is a function.

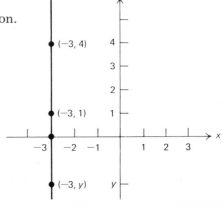

Solution

a) The graph consists of all ordered pairs whose first coordinate is -3.

b) This is *not* a function. It fails the vertical line test. The line itself meets the graph more than once. In fact, infinitely many times.

Do Exercise 79.

In general,

> **The graph of $y = b$, a horizontal line, is that of a function.**
> **The graph of $x = a$, a vertical line, is not that of a function.**

The Equation $y = mx$

Consider the following table of numbers and look for a pattern.

x	1	-1	$-\frac{1}{2}$	2	-2	3	-7	5
y	3	-3	$-\frac{3}{2}$	6	-6	9	-21	15

Notice that the ratio of the bottom number to the top one is 3. That is,

$$\frac{y}{x} = 3, \qquad \text{or} \qquad y = 3x.$$

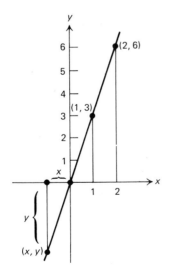

Ordered pairs from the table can be used to graph the equation

$$y = 3x.$$

79. a) Graph $x = 1$.

   b) Decide if it is a function.

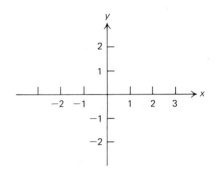

80. a) Graph $y = -2x$.

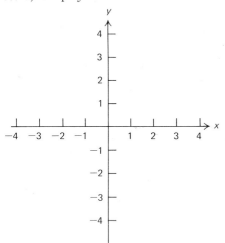

b) Is this a function?

c) What is the slope?

The graph is shown on the preceding page. Note that this is a function.

The function f given by

$$y = mx, \quad \text{or} \quad f(x) = mx,$$

is the straight line through the origin $(0,0)$ and the point $(1,m)$. The constant m is called the *slope* of the line.

Do Exercise 80.

Various graphs of $y = mx$ for positive m are shown below. Note that such graphs rise from left to right. A line with large positive slope rises faster than a line with smaller positive slope.

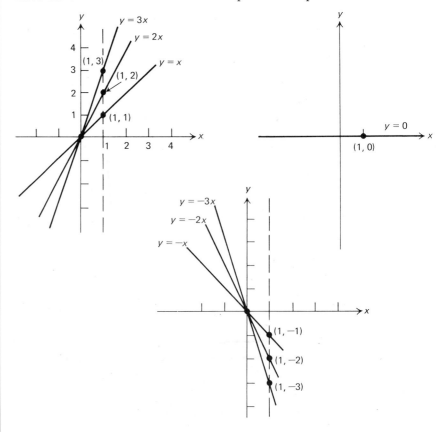

When $m = 0$, $y = 0x$, or $y = 0$. The middle graph is a graph of $y = 0$. Note that this is the x-axis and is a horizontal line. Graphs of $y = mx$ for negative m are shown to the right. Note that such graphs fall from left to right. A line with small negative slope is steeper than a line with larger negative slope.

Do Exercise 81.

Direct Variation

There are many applications involving equations like $y = mx$, where m is some positive number. In such situations we say we have *direct variation*, and m (the slope) is called the *variation constant*, or *constant of proportionality*. Usually only positive values of x and y are considered.

> The variable y *varies directly* as x if there is some positive constant m such that $y = mx$. We also say that y is *directly proportional* to x.

Example   The number N of inches which human hair will grow is directly proportional to the time t in months. Hair will grow 6 inches in 12 months.
a) Find an equation of variation.
b) How many months does it take for hair to grow 10 inches?

Solution
a) $N = mt$, so $6 = m(12)$ and $\frac{1}{2} = m$. Thus $N = \frac{1}{2}t$.
b) To find how many months it takes for hair to grow 10 inches we solve
$$10 = \tfrac{1}{2}t$$
and get
$$20 = t.$$

Thus it takes 20 months for hair to grow 10 inches.

Ira Kirschenbaum from Stock, Boston

81. Consider these lines.

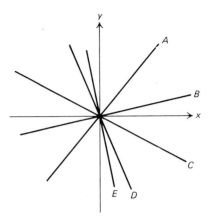

a) Which line has the largest positive slope?
b) Which line has the smallest positive slope?
c) Which line has the largest negative slope?
d) Which line has the smallest negative slope?
e) Which line has the largest slope?
f) Which line has the smallest slope?

82. *Newspaper recycling.* The number T of trees saved by recycling is directly proportional to the height h of a stack of recyclable newspaper.

a) It is known that a stack of newspaper 36 in. high will save 1 tree. Find an equation of variation expressing T as a function of h.

b) How many trees are saved by a stack of paper 162 in. (13.5 ft) high?

Anna Kaufman Moon from Stock, Boston

83. a) Using the same axes, graph

$$y = 3x$$

and

$$y = 3x + 1.$$

b) How can the graph of $y = 3x + 1$ be obtained from the graph of $y = 3x$?

Do Exercise 82.

The Equation $y = mx + b$

Compare the graphs of the equations

$$y = 3x$$

and

$$y = 3x - 2.$$

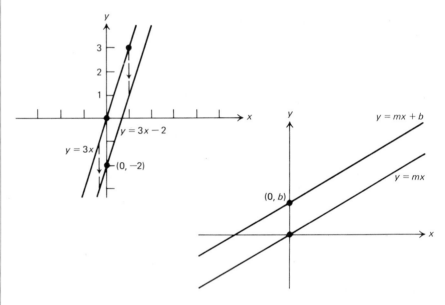

Note that $y = 3x - 2$ is a shift downward 2 units of the graph of $y = 3x$ and $y = 3x - 2$ has y-intercept $(0, -2)$. Note also that $y = 3x - 2$ is a graph of a function.

Do Exercise 83.

A *linear function* is given by

$$y = mx + b,$$

or

$$f(x) = mx + b,$$

and has a graph which is the straight line parallel to $y = mx$ with y-intercept $(0, b)$. The constant m is called the *slope*.

When $m = 0$, $y = 0x + b = b$, and we have what is known as a *constant function*. The graph of such a function is a horizontal line.

The Slope-Intercept Equation

Any nonvertical line l is uniquely determined by its slope m and its y-intercept $(0, b)$. In other words, the slope describes the "slant" of the line and the y-intercept is the point where it crosses the y-axis. Accordingly,

$y = mx + b$ is called the *slope-intercept* equation of a line.

Example 1   Find the slope and y-intercept of $2x - 4y - 7 = 0$.

Solution   We solve for y: $-4y = -2x + 7$

$$y = \tfrac{1}{2}x - \tfrac{7}{4}$$

Slope: $\tfrac{1}{2}$ y-intercept: $(0, -\tfrac{7}{4})$

Do Exercise 84.

The Point-Slope Equation

Suppose we know the slope of a line and some point of the line other than the y-intercept. We can still find an equation of the line.

Example 2   Find an equation of the line with slope 3, and containing the point $(-1, -5)$.

Solution   From the slope intercept equation we have

$$y = 3x + b,$$

so we must determine b. Since $(-1, -5)$ is on the line, it follows that

$$-5 = 3(-1) + b,$$
$$\text{so } -2 = b, \quad \text{and} \quad y = 3x - 2.$$

Do Exercise 85.

If a point (x_1, y_1) is on the line

$$y = mx + b, \tag{1}$$

it must follow that

$$y_1 = mx_1 + b. \tag{2}$$

84. Find the slope and y-intercept of $2x + 3y - 6 = 0$.

85. Find an equation of the line with slope -4 containing the point $(2, -7)$.

86. Find an equation of the line with slope -4 containing the point $(2, -7)$.

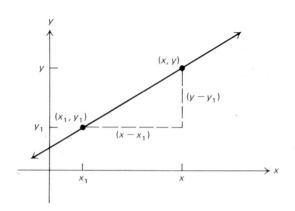

Subtracting equation (2) from (1) gets rid of the b's and we have

$$y - y_1 = (mx + b) - (mx_1 + b)$$
$$= mx + b - mx_1 - b$$
$$= mx - mx_1 = m(x - x_1).$$

Now

$y - y_1 = m(x - x_1)$ **is called the *point-slope* equation**

of a line L. This allows us to write an equation of a line given its slope and the coordinates of *any* point on it.

Example 3   Find an equation of the line with slope 3, and containing the point $(-1, -5)$.

Solution   Substituting in

$$y - y_1 = m(x - x_1),$$

we get

$$y - (-5) = 3[x - (-1)].$$

Simplifying and solving for y we get the slope-intercept equation as found in Example 2.

$$y + 5 = 3(x + 1)$$
$$y = 3x + 3 - 5$$
$$y = 3x - 2$$

Do Exercise 86.

We now determine a way to compute the slope of a line when we know the coordinates of two of its points. Suppose (x_1, y_1) and (x_2, y_2) are

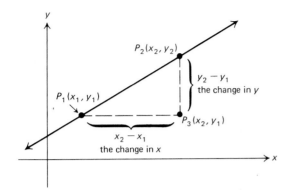

the coordinates of two different points P_1 and P_2 on a line which is not parallel to an axis. Consider a right triangle as shown, with legs parallel to the axes. The point P_3 with coordinates (x_2, y_1) is the third vertex of the triangle. As we move from P_1 to P_2, y changes from y_1 to y_2. The change in y is $y_2 - y_1$. Similarly, the change in x is $x_2 - x_1$. The ratio of these changes is the slope. To see this, consider the point-slope equation

$$y - y_1 = m(x - x_1).$$

Since (x_2, y_2) is on the line, it must follow that

$$y_2 - y_1 = m(x_2 - x_1).$$

Since the line is not vertical, the two x coordinates must be different, so $x_2 - x_1$ is nonzero and we can divide by it to get

$$m = \frac{y_2 - y_1}{x_2 - x_1} = \frac{\textbf{change in } y}{\textbf{change in } x} = \begin{array}{l}\textbf{slope of line containing points}\\ (x_1, y_1) \textbf{ and } (x_2, y_2).\end{array}$$

Example 4   Find the slope of the line containing the points $(-2, 6)$ and $(-4, 9)$.

Solution

$$m = \frac{y_2 - y_1}{x_2 - x_1} = \frac{6 - 9}{-2 - (-4)} = \frac{-3}{2} = -\frac{3}{2}$$

Note that it does not matter which point is taken first, as long as we subtract coordinates in the same order. In this example we can also find m as follows:

$$m = \frac{9 - 6}{-4 - (-2)} = \frac{3}{-2} = -\frac{3}{2}.$$

Find the slope of the line containing each pair of points.

87. (1, 3), (2, 5)

88. (−6, 4), (2, 5)

89. (4, 7), (6, −10)

90. (3, 5), (−1, 5)

Find the slope, if it exists, of the line containing each pair of points.

91. (4, −7), (−2, −7)

92. (4, −7), (4, −9)

Do Exercises 87 through 90.

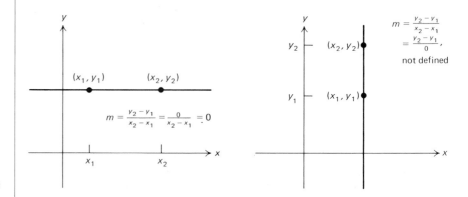

If a line is horizontal the change in y for any two points is 0. Thus a horizontal line has slope 0. If a line is vertical, the change in x for any two points is 0. Thus the slope is not defined because we cannot divide by 0. A vertical line has no slope. Thus "0 slope" and "no slope" are two very distinct concepts.

Do Exercises 91 and 92.

Increasing and Decreasing Linear Functions

We do not need to graph a linear function $f(x) = mx + b$ to determine whether it is increasing, decreasing, or neither. We merely look at the slope m. If $m > 0$, the function is increasing. If $m < 0$, the function is decreasing. If $m = 0$, the function is constant, so is neither increasing nor decreasing.

Example 5   Determine whether increasing, decreasing, or neither:

$$g(x) = -2x + 3, \qquad f(x) = \tfrac{2}{3}x + 2, \qquad h(x) = 4.$$

Solution   The graphs are provided for illustration and should not be needed when doing the exercises.

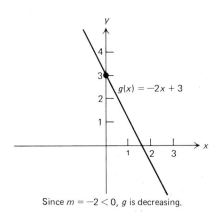

Since $m = -2 < 0$, g is decreasing.

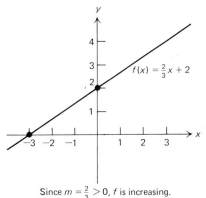

Since $m = \frac{2}{3} > 0$, f is increasing.

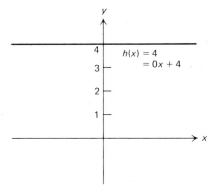

Since $m = 0$, h is neither increasing nor decreasing.

93. Without graphing, decide whether each function is increasing, decreasing, or neither.

a) $f(x) = -\frac{1}{4}x - 9$

b) $g(x) = x - 9$

c) $h(x) = -9$

Do Exercise 93.

Applications of Linear Functions

Many applications are modeled by linear functions.

Example 6　Raggs, Ltd., a clothing firm, has *fixed costs* of $10,000 per year. These are costs such as rent, maintenance, and so on, which must be paid no matter how much the company produces. To produce x units of a certain kind of suit it costs $20 per unit in addition to the fixed costs. That is, the *variable costs* are $20x$ dollars. These are costs which are directly related to production, such as material, wages, fuel, and so on. Then the *total cost C(x)* of producing x suits in a year is given by a function C:

$$C(x) = \text{(variable costs)} + \text{(fixed costs)} = 20x + 10{,}000$$

a) Graph the variable cost, fixed cost, and total cost functions.
b) What is the total cost of producing 100 suits? 400 suits?
c) How much more does it cost to produce 400 suits than 100 suits?

Solution
a) The variable cost and fixed cost functions are shown at the left. The total cost function is shown at the right. From a practical standpoint, the domains of these functions are nonnegative integers 0, 1, 2, 3, and so on. This is because it does not make sense to make a negative number of suits or a fractional number of suits. Nevertheless, it is common practice to draw the graphs as if the domains were the entire set of nonnegative real numbers.

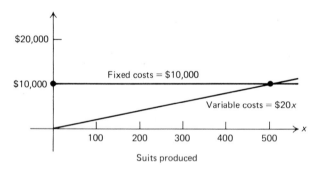

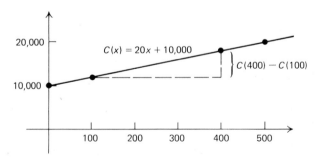

b) The total cost of producing 100 suits is

$$C(100) = 20 \cdot 100 + 10{,}000 = \$12{,}000.$$

The total cost of producing 400 suits is

$$C(400) = 20 \cdot 400 + 10{,}000 = \$18{,}000.$$

c) The extra cost of producing 400 suits over 100 suits is given by

$$C(400) - C(100) = \$18,000 - \$12,000 = \$6000.$$

Do Exercise 94.

94. Rework Example 6, where variable costs = $30x$, fixed costs = \$15,000, and total costs = $C(x) = 30x + 15,000$.

Example 7 In reference to Example 6, Raggs, Ltd. determines that its total revenue (money coming in) from the sale of x suits is \$80 per suit. That is, total revenue $R(x)$ is given by the function

$$R(x) = 80x.$$

a) Graph $R(x)$ and $C(x)$ using the same axes.
b) Total profit $P(x)$ is given by a function P:

$$P(x) = (\text{total revenue}) - (\text{total costs}) = R(x) - C(x).$$

Determine $P(x)$ and draw its graph using the same axes.
c) The company will *break even* at that value of x for which $P(x) = 0$ (that is, no profit and no loss). This is where $R(x) = C(x)$. Find the break-even value of x.

Solution
a) The graphs of $R(x) = 80x$ and $C(x) = 20x + 10,000$ are shown here.

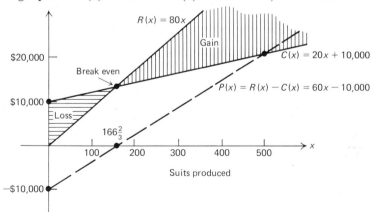

b) $P(x) = R(x) - C(x) = 80x - (20x + 10,000) = 60x - 10,000$. The graph of $P(x)$ is shown.
c) To find the break-even value we solve $R(x) = C(x)$.

$$80x = 20x + 10,000$$
$$60x = 10,000$$
$$x = 166\tfrac{2}{3}$$

95. Rework Example 7, where

$$C(x) = 30x + 15,000$$

and

$$R(x) = 90x.$$

How do we interpret the fractional answer, since it is not possible to produce $\frac{2}{3}$ of a suit? One would simply round to 167. Estimates of break-even points are usually sufficient since companies want to operate well above break-even points where profit is maximized.

Do Exercise 95.

EXERCISE SET 1.4

Graph.

1. $y = -4$ **2.** $y = -3.5$ **3.** $x = 4.5$ **4.** $x = 10$

Graph. Find the slope and y-intercept.

5. $y = -3x$ **6.** $y = -0.5x$ **7.** $y = 0.5x$ **8.** $y = 3x$

9. $y = -2x + 3$ **10.** $y = -x + 4$ **11.** $y = -x - 2$ **12.** $y = -3x + 2$

Find the slope and y-intercept.

13. $2x + y - 2 = 0$ **14.** $2x - y + 3 = 0$ **15.** $2x + 2y + 5 = 0$ **16.** $3x - 3y + 6 = 0$

Find an equation of the line:

17. with $m = -5$, containing $(1, -5)$.   **18.** with $m = 7$, containing $(1, 7)$.

19. with $m = -2$, containing $(2, 3)$.   **20.** with $m = -3$ containing $(5, -2)$.

21. with y-intercept $(0, -6)$ and slope $\frac{1}{2}$.   **22.** with y-intercept $(0, 7)$ and slope $\frac{4}{3}$.

23. with slope 0, containing $(2, 3)$.   **24.** with slope 0, containing $(4, 8)$.

Find the slope of the line containing each pair of points.

25. $(-4, -2), (-2, 1)$ **26.** $(-2, 1), (6, 3)$ **27.** $(2, -4), (4, -3)$.

28. $(-5, 8), (5, -3)$ **29.** $(3, -7), (3, -9)$ **30.** $(-4, 2), (-4, 10)$

31. $(2, 3), (-1, 3)$ **32.** $(-6, \frac{1}{2}), (-7, \frac{1}{2})$ **33.** $(x, 3x), (x + h, 3(x + h))$

34. $(x, 4x), (x + h, 4(x + h))$ **35.** $(x, 2x + 3), (x + h, 2(x + h) + 3)$

36. $(x, 3x - 1), (x + h, 3(x + h) - 1)$

THE TWO-POINT EQUATION   An equation of the nonvertical line containing the points (x_1, y_1) and (x_2, y_2) is given by

$$y - y_1 = \frac{y_2 - y_1}{x_2 - x_1}(x - x_1). \quad \textit{Two-point equation}$$

This can be proved by replacing m in the point-slope equation $y - y_1 = m(x - x_1)$ by $\frac{y_2 - y_1}{x_2 - x_1}$.

37.–48. Find an equation of the line containing each pair of points in Exercises 25–36.

Without graphing, decide whether increasing, decreasing, or neither.

49. $f(x) = 43$ **50.** $f(x) = -27$ **51.** $f(x) = -4x + 3$ **52.** $f(x) = -3x - 7$

53. $f(x) = 0.2x + 170$ **54.** $f(x) = 0.1x + 50{,}000$

Applied Problems

55. The R-factor of home insulation is directly proportional to its thickness T.

a) Find an equation of variation where $R = 12.51$ when $T = 3$ in.

b) What is the R-factor for insulation which is 6 inches thick?

56. Impulses in nerve fibers travel at a speed of 293 ft/sec. The distance D traveled in t sec is given by $D = 293t$. How long would it take an impulse to travel from the brain to the toes of a person who is 6 ft tall?

Anna Kaufman Moon from Stock, Boston

57. *Brain weight.* The weight B of a human's brain is directly proportional to its body weight W.

a) It is known that a person who weighs 200 lb has a brain which weighs 5 lb. Find an equation of variation expressing B as a function of W.
b) Express the variation constant as a percent and interpret the resulting equation.
c) What is the weight of the brain of a person who weighs 120 lb?

59. A person makes an investment of P dollars at 8%. After 1 year it grows to an amount A.

a) Show that A is directly proportional to P.
b) Find A when $P =$ \$100.
c) Find P when $A =$ \$259.20.

61. *Stopping distance on glare ice.* The stopping distance (at some fixed speed) of regular tires is given by a linear function of the air temperature F:

$$D(F) = 2F + 115,$$

where $D(F) =$ stopping distance, in feet, when the air temperature is F, in degrees Fahrenheit.

a) Find $D(0°)$, $D(-20°)$, $D(10°)$, and $D(32°)$.
b) Graph $D(F)$.
c) Explain why the domain should be restricted to the interval $[-57.5°, 32°]$.

63. *Spread of an organism.* A certain kind of organism is released over an area of 2 sq. mi. It grows and spreads over more area. The area covered by the organism after time t is given by a linear function

$$A(t) = 1.1t + 2,$$

where $A(t) =$ area covered, in square miles, after time t, in years.

a) Find $A(0)$, $A(1)$, $A(4)$, and $A(10)$.
b) Graph $A(t)$.
c) Why should the domain be restricted to the interval $[0, \infty)$?

58. *Muscle weight.* The weight M of the muscles in a human is directly proportional to its body weight W.

a) It is known that a person who weighs 200 lb has 80 lb of muscles. Find an equation of variation expressing M as a function of W.
b) Express the variation constant as a percent and interpret the resulting equation.
c) What is the muscle weight of a person who weighs 120 lb?

60. The population of a town is P. After a growth of 2% its new population is N.

a) Assuming that N is directly proportional to P, find an equation of variation.
b) Find N when $P = 200{,}000$.
c) Find P when $N = 367{,}200$.

62. *Percentage of the population in college.* The percentage of the population in college is given by a linear function

$$P(t) = 1.25t + 15,$$

where $P(t) =$ percentage in college the tth year after 1940. Thus $P(0)$ is the percentage in college in 1940, $P(30)$ is the percentage in college in 1970, and so on.

a) Find $P(0)$, $P(1)$, $P(30)$, and $P(40)$.
b) What percentage of the population will be in college in 1980?
c) Graph $P(t)$.

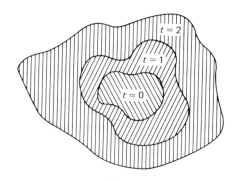

64. A ski manufacturer is planning a new line of skis. For the first year, the fixed costs for setting up the new production line are $22,500. Variable costs for producing each pair of skis are estimated to be $40. The sales department projects that 3000 pairs can be sold during the first year at a price of $85 per pair.

a) Formulate a function $C(x)$ for the total cost of producing x pairs of skis.

b) Formulate a function $R(x)$ for the total revenue from the sale of x pairs of skis.

c) Formulate a function $P(x)$ for the total profit from the production and sale of x pairs of skis.

d) What profit or loss will the company realize if expected sales of 3000 pairs occur?

e) How many pairs must the company sell to break even?

66. A saleswoman is offered alternative salary plans:

Plan A: She receives a base salary of $600 per month plus a commission of 4% of the gross sales for the month.

Plan B: She receives a base salary of $700 per month plus a commission of 6% of the gross sales for the month in excess of $10,000.

65. Boxowitz, Inc., a computer firm, is planning to sell a new minicalculator. For the first year, the fixed costs for setting up the new production line are $100,000. Variable costs for producing each calculator are estimated to be $20. The sales department projects that 150,000 calculators can be sold during the first year at a price of $45 each.

a) Formulate a function $C(x)$ for the total cost of producing x calculators.

b) Formulate a function $R(x)$ for the total revenue from the sale of x calculators.

c) Formulate a function $P(x)$ for the total profit from the production and sale of x calculators.

d) What profit or loss will the firm realize if expected sales of 150,000 calculators occur?

e) How many calculators must the firm sell to break even?

a) For each plan formulate a function which expresses the saleswoman's monthly earnings as a function of gross sales x.

b) For what gross sales values is Plan B preferable to the saleswoman?

1.5 OTHER TYPES OF FUNCTIONS

Quadratic Functions

A *quadratic function* f is given by

$$f(x) = ax^2 + bx + c, \text{ where } a \neq 0.$$

We have already considered some such functions, for example $f(x) = x^2$ and $g(x) = x^2 - 1$. Graphs of quadratic functions are always cup-shaped, like those in Example 1. They all have a line of symmetry like the dashed lines.

OBJECTIVES

You should be able to:

a) Graph a given function.

b) Convert from radical notation to fractional exponents, and from fractional exponents to radical notation.

c) Determine the domain of a rational function.

d) Given a demand and supply function, find the equilibrium point.

96. Using the same axes, graph $y = x^2$ and $y = -x^2$. [*Note*: $-x^2$ means $-1 \cdot x^2$.]

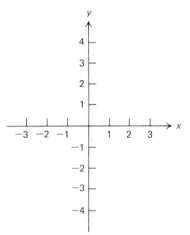

97. a) Using the same axes, graph $y = x^2$ and $y = (x - 6)^2$.

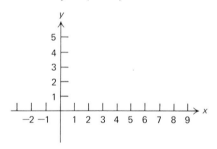

b) How could the graph of $y = (x - 6)^2$ be obtained from the graph of $y = x^2$?

Example 1   Graph $y = x^2 - 2x - 3$ and $y = -2x^2 + 4x + 1$.

Solutions $y = x^2 - 2x - 3$ $y = -2x^2 + 4x + 1$

x	0	1	2	3	4	-1	-2
y	-3	-4	-3	0	5	0	5

x	0	1	2	3	-1
y	1	3	1	-5	-5

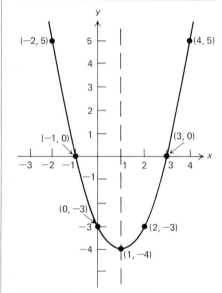

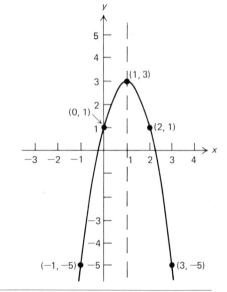

If the coefficient a is positive, the graph opens upward. If a is negative, the graph opens downward.

Do Exercises 96 and 97.

Polynomial Functions

Linear and quadratic functions are part of a general class of polynomial functions.

A *polynomial function f* is given by
$$f(x) = a_n x^n + a_{n-1}x^{n-1} + \cdots + a_2 x^2 + a_1 x^1 + a_0,$$
where n is a nonnegative integer.

The following are some examples:

$f(x) = -5$ (a constant function)
$f(x) = 4x + 3$ (a linear function)
$f(x) = -x^2 + 2x + 3$ (a quadratic function)
$f(x) = 2x^3 - 4x^2 + x + 1$ (a cubic function)

In general, graphing polynomial functions other than linear and quadratic is difficult. Some *power* functions

$$y = ax^n,$$

are relatively easy to graph.

Example 2 Using the same set of axes, graph $y = x^2$ and $y = x^3$.

Solution

x	-2	-1	$-\frac{1}{2}$	0	$\frac{1}{2}$	1	2
x^2	4	1	$\frac{1}{4}$	0	$\frac{1}{4}$	1	4
x^3	-8	-1	$-\frac{1}{8}$	0	$\frac{1}{8}$	1	8

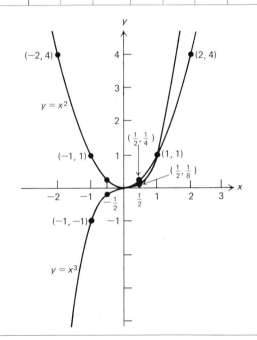

Do Exercise 98.

Rational Functions

Functions given by the ratio of two polynomials are called *rational*.

The following are examples of rational functions.

$$f(x) = \frac{x^2 - 9}{x - 3}, \qquad g(x) = \frac{x^2 - 16}{x + 4}, \qquad h(x) = \frac{x - 3}{x^2 - x - 2}$$

The domain of a rational function is restricted to those input values which do not result in division by 0. Thus for f the domain consists

98. Using the same set of axes, graph $y = x^2$ and $y = x^4$.

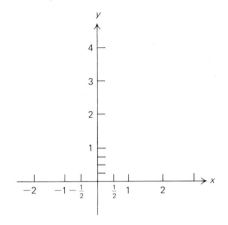

99. Determine the domain of each function.

a) $g(x) = \dfrac{x^2 - 16}{x + 4}$

b) $t(x) = \dfrac{x + 7}{x^2 + 4x - 5}$

c) $k(x) = \dfrac{1}{x - 5}$

of all real numbers except 3. To determine the domain of h, we set the denominator equal to 0 and solve.

$$x^2 - x - 2 = 0$$
$$(x + 1)(x - 2) = 0$$
$$x = -1 \quad \text{or} \quad x = 2$$

Thus -1 and 2 are not in the domain. The domain consists of all real numbers except -1 and 2.

Do Exercise 99.

One important class of rational functions is given by $y = \dfrac{k}{x}$.

Example 3   Graph $y = \dfrac{1}{x}$.

Solution

x	-3	-2	-1	$-\frac{1}{2}$	$-\frac{1}{4}$	$\frac{1}{4}$	$\frac{1}{2}$	1	2	3
y	$-\frac{1}{3}$	$-\frac{1}{2}$	-1	-2	-4	4	2	1	$\frac{1}{2}$	$\frac{1}{3}$

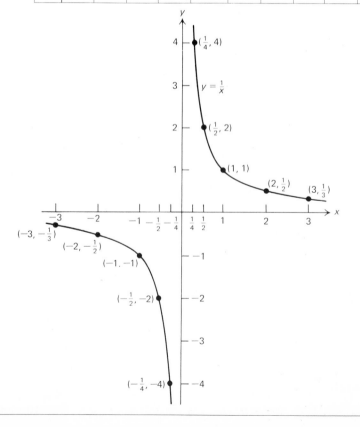

Note that 0 is not in the domain of this function since it would yield a 0 denominator. This function is decreasing over the intervals $(-\infty, 0)$ and $(0, \infty)$. It is an example of inverse variation. That is,

y varies inversely as x if there is some positive number k such that $y = \dfrac{k}{x}$. *We also say that y is inversely proportional to x.*

Do Exercise 100.

Absolute Value Functions

The following is an example of an absolute value function and its graph. The absolute value of a number is its distance from 0.

Example 4   Graph $y = |x|$.

Solution

x	-3	-2	-1	0	1	2	3
y	3	2	1	0	1	2	3

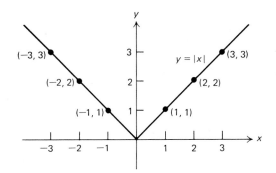

Do Exercise 101.

Square Root Functions

The following is an example of a square root function and its graph.

Example 5   Graph $y = -\sqrt{x}$.

Solution   The domain of this function is just the nonnegative

100. Graph $y = \dfrac{-1}{x}$.

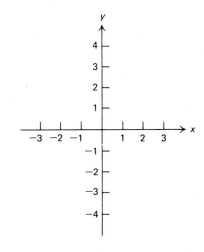

101. Graph $y = |x - 1|$. To find an output, take an input, subtract 1 from it, and then take the absolute value.

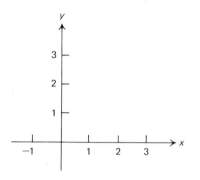

numbers—the interval $[0, \infty)$. Table 1 at the back of the book contains approximate values of square roots of certain numbers.

x	0	1	2	3	4	5	10
$-\sqrt{x}$	0	-1	-1.4	-1.7	-2	-2.2	-3.1

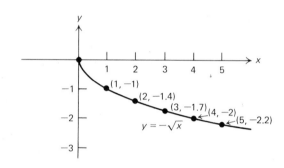

102. Graph $y = \sqrt{x}$.

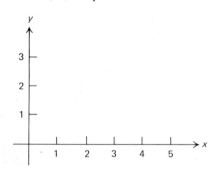

Do Exercise 102.

Power Functions with Fractional Exponents

We are motivated to define fractional exponents so that the same laws of Section 1.1 still hold. For example, if the laws of exponents are to hold, we would have

$$a^{1/2} \cdot a^{1/2} = a^{1/2 + 1/2} = a^1 = a.$$

Thus we are led to define $a^{1/2}$ to be $\sqrt{a}$. Similarly, we are led to define $a^{1/3}$ to be the cube root of a, $\sqrt[3]{a}$. In general,

$$a^{1/n} = \sqrt[n]{a}.$$

Again, if the laws of exponents are to hold, we would have

$$\sqrt[n]{a^m} = (a^m)^{1/n} = (a^{1/n})^m = a^{m/n}.$$

An expression $a^{-m/n}$ is defined by

$$a^{-m/n} = \frac{1}{a^{m/n}} = \frac{1}{\sqrt[n]{a^m}}.$$

Examples   Convert to fractional exponents.

a) $\sqrt[3]{x^2} = x^{2/3}$ b) $\sqrt[4]{y} = y^{1/4}$

c) $\dfrac{1}{\sqrt[3]{b^5}} = \dfrac{1}{b^{5/3}} = b^{-5/3}$ d) $\dfrac{1}{\sqrt{x}} = \dfrac{1}{x^{1/2}} = x^{-1/2}$

e) $\sqrt{x^8} = x^{8/2}$, or x^4

Do Exercise 103.

Examples   Convert to radical notation.

a) $x^{1/3} = \sqrt[3]{x}$ b) $t^{6/7} = \sqrt[7]{t^6}$

c) $x^{-2/3} = \dfrac{1}{x^{2/3}} = \dfrac{1}{\sqrt[3]{x^2}}$ d) $e^{-1/4} = \dfrac{1}{e^{1/4}} = \dfrac{1}{\sqrt[4]{e}}$

Do Exercise 104.

Thus earlier when we graphed $y = \sqrt{x}$, we were also graphing $y = x^{1/2}$, or $y = x^{0.5}$. The power functions

$$y = ax^k, \quad k \text{ fractional},$$

do arise in application. For example, the *home range* of an animal is defined to be the region to which it confines its movements. It has

103. Convert to fractional exponents.

a) $\sqrt[4]{t^3}$ b) $\sqrt[5]{y}$

c) $\dfrac{1}{\sqrt[5]{x^2}}$ d) $\dfrac{1}{\sqrt[3]{t}}$

e) $\sqrt{x^6}$ f) $\sqrt{x^7}$

104. Convert to radical notation.

a) $y^{1/7}$ b) $x^{3/2}$

c) $t^{-3/2}$ d) $b^{-1/2}$

Charlie Ott from the National Audubon Society

been hypothesized in statistical studies* that the area H of that region can be approximated using the body weight W of an animal by the function

$$H = W^{1.41}.$$

W	0	10	20	30	40	50
H	0	25	68	120	181	248

Note that

$$H = W^{1.41} = W^{141/100} = \sqrt[100]{W^{141}}.$$

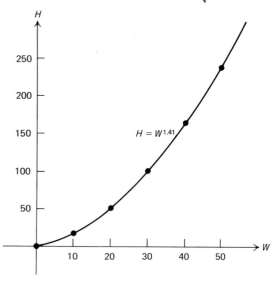

The graph is shown here. It would be hard to find function values unless we used logarithms or an appropriate hand calculator; we are simply illustrating that such functions do have application. Note that this is an increasing function. As body weight increases, the area over which the animal moves increases.

Supply and Demand Functions

Supply and demand in economics are modeled by increasing and decreasing functions. While specific scientific formulas for these concepts are not usually known, the notions of increasing and decreasing yield understanding of the ideas.

---

* See J. M. Emlen, *Ecology: An Evolutionary Approach*, Reading, Mass.: Addison-Wesley, 1973, p. 200.

DEMAND FUNCTIONS.   Look at the following table.

Demand Schedule	
Quantity x (number of 5-lb bags) in millions	Price p (per bag)
4	$5
5	4
7	3
10	2
15	1

The table shows the relationship between the price p per bag of sugar and the quantity x of 5-lb bags which the consumer will buy at that price. Note that as price per bag increases, the quantity demanded by the consumer decreases; and as price per bag decreases, the quantity demanded by the consumer increases. Thus it is natural to think of x as a function of p. In our later work it will be more convenient to think of p as a function of x. Thus, for a *demand* function D, $D(x)$ is the price per unit of an item when x units are demanded by the consumer. The following figure is the graph of a demand function for sugar (using the preceding table).

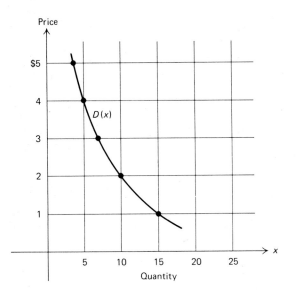

SUPPLY FUNCTIONS.   Look at the following table.

Supply Schedule

Quantity x (number of 5-lb bags) in millions	Price p (per bag)
24	$5
20	4
15	3
10	2
0	1

The table shows the relationship between the price per bag p of sugar and the quantity x of 5-lb bags which the seller is willing to supply at that price. Note that as the price per bag increases, the more the seller is willing to supply; and as the price per bag decreases, the less the seller is willing to supply. Again, it is natural to think of x as a function of p, but for our later work it is more convenient to think of p as a function of x. Thus, for a *supply* function S, $S(x)$ is the price per unit of an item at which the seller is willing to supply x units of a product to the consumer. The following figure is the graph of a supply function for sugar (using the preceding table).

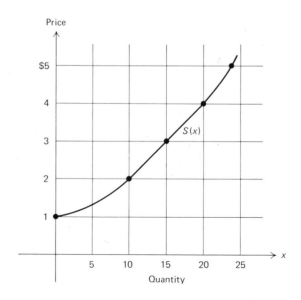

Let us now look at these curves together. Note that as supply increases demand decreases, and as supply decreases demand increases. The point of intersection of the two curves (x_E, p_E) is called the *equilibrium point*. The equilibrium price p_E (in this case $2 per bag) is where the amount x_E (in this case 10 million bags) which the seller willingly supplies is the same as the amount which the consumer willingly demands. The situation is analogous to a buyer and seller haggling over the sale of an item. The equilibrium, or selling, price is what they finally agree on.

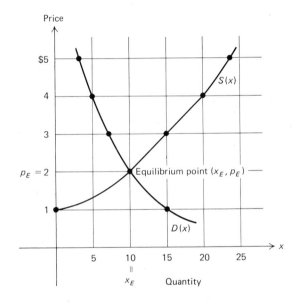

Example 1   Find the equilibrium point for the demand and supply functions

$$D(x) = (x - 6)^2 \quad \text{and} \quad S(x) = x^2 + x + 10.$$

Solution   To find the equilibrium point we set $D(x) = S(x)$ and solve.

$$(x - 6)^2 = x^2 + x + 10$$
$$x^2 - 12x + 36 = x^2 + x + 10$$
$$-12x + 36 = x + 10$$
$$-13x = -26$$
$$x = \frac{-26}{-13}$$
$$x = 2$$

105. Given

$$D(x) = (x - 5)^2$$

and

$$S(x) = x^2 + x + 3,$$

find the equilibrium point.

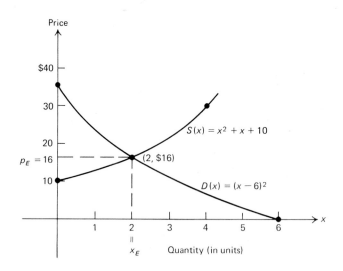

Thus $x_E = 2$(units). To find p_E we substitute x_E into either $D(x)$ or $S(x)$. We use $D(x)$. Then

$$p_E = D(x_E) = D(2) = (2 - 6)^2 = (-4)^2 = \$16.$$

Thus the equilibrium price is \$16 per unit and the equilibrium point is (2, \$16).

Do Exercise 105.

EXERCISE SET 1.5

Using the same set of axes, graph each pair of equations.

1. $y = \frac{1}{2}x^2$, $y = -\frac{1}{2}x^2$

2. $y = \frac{1}{4}x^2$, $y = -\frac{1}{4}x^2$

3. $y = x^2$, $y = (x - 1)^2$

4. $y = x^2$, $y = (x - 3)^2$

5. $y = x^2$, $y = (x + 1)^2$

6. $y = x^2$, $y = (x + 3)^2$

7. $y = |x|$, $y = |x + 3|$

8. $y = |x|$, $y = |x + 1|$

9. $y = x^3$, $y = x^3 + 1$

10. $y = x^3$, $y = x^3 - 1$

11. $y = \sqrt{x}$, $y = \sqrt{x + 1}$

12. $y = \sqrt{x}$, $y = \sqrt{x - 2}$

Graph.

13. $y = x^2 - 4x + 3$

14. $y = x^2 - 6x + 5$

15. $y = -x^2 + 2x - 1$

16. $y = -x^2 - x + 6$ **17.** $y = \dfrac{2}{x}$ **18.** $y = \dfrac{3}{x}$

19. $y = \dfrac{-2}{x}$ **20.** $y = \dfrac{-3}{x}$ **21.** $y = \dfrac{1}{x^2}$

22. $y = \dfrac{1}{x-1}$ **23.** $y = \sqrt[3]{x}$ [*Hint:* Use Table 1 at the end of the book.]   **24.** $y = \dfrac{1}{|x|}$

Convert to fractional exponents.

25. $\sqrt{x^3}$ **26.** $\sqrt{x^5}$ **27.** $\sqrt[5]{a^3}$ **28.** $\sqrt[4]{b^2}$ **29.** $\sqrt[7]{t}$

30. $\sqrt[8]{c}$ **31.** $\dfrac{1}{\sqrt[3]{t^4}}$ **32.** $\dfrac{1}{\sqrt[5]{b^6}}$ **33.** $\dfrac{1}{\sqrt{t}}$ **34.** $\dfrac{1}{\sqrt{m}}$

35. $\dfrac{1}{\sqrt{x^2+7}}$ **36.** $\sqrt{x^3+4}$

Convert to radical notation.

37. $x^{1/5}$ **38.** $t^{1/7}$ **39.** $y^{2/3}$ **40.** $t^{2/5}$ **41.** $t^{-2/5}$

42. $y^{-2/3}$ **43.** $b^{-1/3}$ **44.** $b^{-1/5}$ **45.** $e^{-17/6}$ **46.** $m^{-19/6}$

47. $(x^2-3)^{-1/2}$ **48.** $(y^2+7)^{-1/4}$

Determine the domain of each function.

49. $f(x) = \dfrac{x^2-25}{x-5}$ **50.** $f(x) = \dfrac{x^2-4}{x+2}$ **51.** $f(x) = \dfrac{x^3}{x^2-5x+6}$

52. $f(x) = \dfrac{x^4+7}{x^2+6x+5}$

Find the equilibrium point for the following demand and supply functions.

53. $D(x) = -2x+8,\ S(x) = x+2$ **54.** $D(x) = -\frac{5}{6}x+10,\ S(x) = \frac{1}{2}x+2$

55. $D(x) = (x-3)^2,\ S(x) = x^2+2x+1$ **56.** $D(x) = (x-4)^2,\ S(x) = x^2+2x+6$

57. $D(x) = (x-4)^2,\ S(x) = x^2$ **58.** $D(x) = (x-6)^2,\ S(x) = x^2$

59. (A hand calculator problem—need an a^b key.) The *territory area* of an animal is defined to be its defended region, or exclusive region. For example, a lion has a certain region over which it is ruler. It has been hypothesized in statistical studies* that the area T of that region is approximated using body weight W by the power function

$$T = W^{1.31}.$$

W	0	10	20	30	40	50	100	150
T	0	20						

Complete the table of approximate function values and graph the function.

1.6 MATHEMATICAL MODELING

OBJECTIVES

You should be able to use curve fitting to find a model for a set of data. Then use the model to make predictions.

What is a Mathematical Model?

When the essential parts of a problem situation are described in mathematical language, we say that we have a *mathematical model*. For example, the arithmetic of the natural numbers constitutes a mathematical model for situations in which counting is the essential ingredient. Situations in which calculus can be brought to bear often require the use of equations and functions, and typically there is concern with the way a change in one variable affects a change in another.

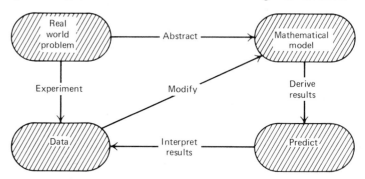

Mathematical models are abstracted from real world situations. Procedures within the mathematical model then give results which hopefully allow one to predict what will happen in that real-world situation. To the extent that these predictions are inaccurate or the results of experimentation do not conform to the model, the model is in need of modification. This is shown in the diagram.

---

* Ibid, p. 54.

The diagram seems to indicate that mathematical modeling is an ongoing, possibly ever-changing, process. This is often the case. For example, finding a mathematical model that will enable accurate prediction of population growth is not a simple problem. Apparently any model which one might devise will have to be altered, as further information is acquired.

On p. 55 we saw an example of devising a mathematical model utilizing supply and demand functions. In general, the idea is to find a function which fits observations and theoretical reasoning (including common sense) as well as possible. Later we will see how calculus can be used to develop and analyze models. For now we will consider one type of modeling procedure called *curve fitting*.

Curve Fitting

The following four functions fit many situations.

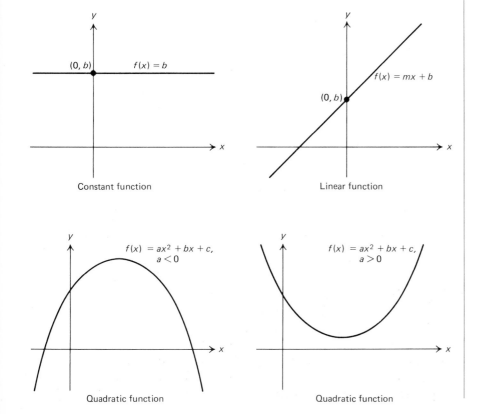

Constant function

Linear function

Quadratic function

Quadratic function

The following is a procedure that sometimes works for finding mathematical models.

CURVE FITTING.   Given a set of data,
 1. **Graph the data.**
 2. **Look at the data and determine whether a known function seems to fit.**
 3. **Find a function which fits the data by using data points to derive the constants.**

Example 1   For the given set of data, find a model, then use the model to predict the sales of the company in the 5th year.

Year (t)	Sales (S) in dollars
1	$10,000
2	21,000
3	27,000
4	37,000

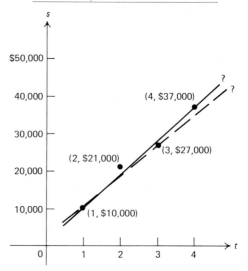

Solution
a) The graph is shown at the right. It looks like a linear function fits this data fairly well,

$$S = mt + b. \tag{1}$$

To derive the constants (or parameters) m and b, we pick two data points. This is a subjective matter, but, of course, you should not pick a point which deviates greatly from the general pattern. We pick the points (1, $10,000) and (4, $37,000). Since the points are to be solutions of (1) it follows that

$$37,000 = m \cdot 4 + b, \quad \text{or} \quad 37,000 = 4m + b; \tag{2}$$
$$10,000 = m \cdot 1 + b, \quad \text{or} \quad 10,000 = m + b. \tag{3}$$

This is a system of equations. We subtract (3) from (2) to get rid of b:

$$27,000 = 3m.$$

Then

$$\frac{27,000}{3} = m,$$

and

$$9,000 = m.$$

Then equation (3) becomes

$$10,000 = 9000 + b,$$

so

$$1000 = b.$$

Substituting these values of m and b in equation (1) we get the function (model) given by

$$S = 9000t + 1000. \tag{4}$$

b) Sales in the 5th year are found by letting $t = 5$.

$$S = 9000 \cdot 5 + 1000 = \$46,000.$$

Do Exercise 106.

The following problem is based on factual data.

Example 2 For the given set of data, find a model, then use the model to determine the cost per mile to drive at 55 mph, 70 mph. How much more does it cost to drive a car at 70 mph than at 55 mph?

Speed x of car (mph)	Operating cost C, in cents, per mile
15	15¢
20	12
25	10.5
45	12

106. Rework Example 1, only this time use the data points (1, $10,000) and (3, $27,000). How does the answer to (b) compare to (b) in Example 1?

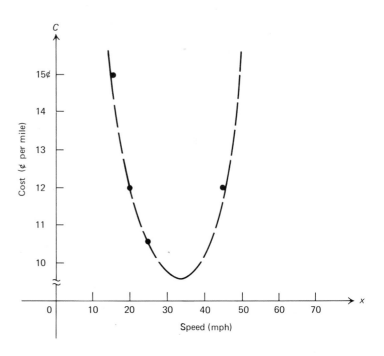

Solution

a) The graph is shown here. It looks as if a quadratic function might fit,

$$C = ax^2 + bx + c. \tag{1}$$

To derive the constants (or parameters) a, b, and c, we pick three data points $(15, 15)$, $(20, 12)$, and $(45, 12)$. Since these three points are to be solutions of (1), it follows that

$$15 = a \cdot 15^2 + b \cdot 15 + c, \quad \text{or} \quad 15 = 225a + 15b + c; \tag{2}$$
$$12 = a \cdot 20^2 + b \cdot 20 + c, \quad \text{or} \quad 12 = 400a + 20b + c; \tag{3}$$
$$12 = a \cdot 45^2 + b \cdot 45 + c, \quad \text{or} \quad 12 = 2025a + 45b + c. \tag{4}$$

This is a system of three equations in three unknowns. We subtract (3) from (4) to get rid of c:

$$0 = 1625a + 25b. \tag{5}$$

We subtract (3) from (2) which also gets rid of c;

$$3 = -175a - 5b. \tag{6}$$

Now we solve the system (5) and (6) which has just two unknowns. We multiply equation (6) by 5 and add.

$$0 = 1625a + 25b$$
$$15 = -875a - 25b$$

$$15 = 750a$$

Thus

$$a = \frac{15}{750} = 0.02.$$

Then substituting 0.02 for a in equation (5) we solve for b.

$$0 = 1625(0.02) + 25b$$
$$0 = 32.5 + 25b$$
$$-32.5 = 25b$$
$$\frac{-32.5}{25} = b$$
$$-1.3 = b$$

Then substituting 0.02 for a and -1.3 for b in equation (3) we solve for c.

$$12 = 400(0.02) + 20(-1.3) + c$$
$$12 = 8 - 26 + c$$
$$30 = c$$

Substituting these values of a, b, and c in equation (1) we get the function (model) given by

$$C = 0.02x^2 - 1.3x + 30. \tag{7}$$

b) The cost per mile at 55 mph is given by

$$C = 0.02(55^2) - 1.3(55) + 30 = 19\text{¢}.$$

The cost per mile at 70 mph is given by

$$C = 0.02(70^2) - 1.3(70) + 30 = 37\text{¢}.$$

Thus it costs 18¢ per mile more to drive at 70 mph than at 55 mph.

Do Exercise 107.

---

107. (A hand calculator would be helpful.)

Age x of driver in years	Number A of daytime accidents committed by driver of age x
20	420
40	150
60	210
70	400

a) For the given set of data, graph the data, and find a quadratic function which fits the data using the data points (20, 420), (40, 150), and (70, 400). First give exact fractional values for a, b, and c. Then give decimal values rounded to the nearest thousandth.

b) How many daytime accidents are committed by a driver of age 16?

EXERCISE SET 1.6

For each set of data,

 a) graph the data;

 b) look at the data and determine whether one of the six functions listed in the text of this section seems to fit.
A hand calculator would be helpful for Exercises 3 and 4.

1. Raggs, Ltd. keeps track of its total costs of producing x items of a certain suit. The data is shown below.

Number of suits x	Total cost C of producing x suits
0	$10,000
1	10,030
2	10,059
3	10,094

 c) Use the data points (1, $10,030) and (3, $10,094) to find a linear function which fits the data.

 d) Predict the total cost of producing 4 suits, 10 suits.

 e) Use the data points (0, $10,000) and (2, $10,059) to find a linear function which fits the data.

 f) Use the model of (e) to predict the total cost of producing 4 suits, 10 suits.

2. Pizza, Unltd. keeps track of its total costs of producing x pizzas. The data is shown below.

Number of pizzas x	Total cost C of producing x pizzas
0	$1000
1	1001
2	1001.80
3	1002.50

 c) Use the data points (1, $1001) and (3, $1002.50) to find a linear function which fits the data.

 d) Predict the total cost of producing 4 pizzas, 100 pizzas.

 e) Use the data points (0, $1000) and (2, $1001.80) to find a linear function which fits the data.

 f) Use the model of (e) to predict the total cost of producing 4 pizzas, 100 pizzas.

The problems in Exercises 3 and 4 are based on factual data.

3.

Travel speed x in mph	Number D of vehicles involved in an accident in daytime (for every 100 million miles of travel)
20	10,000
30	1,000
40	200
50	150
60	95
70	90
80	190

 c) Use the data points (30, 1000), (50, 150), and (70, 90) to find a quadratic function which fits the data.

4.

Travel speed x in mph	Number N of vehicles involved in an accident in nighttime (for every 100 million miles of travel)
20	10,000
30	2,000
40	400
50	250
60	250
70	350
80	1,500

 c) Use the data points (20, 10,000), (50, 250), and (80, 1500) to find a quadratic function which fits the data.

d) Use the model to find the number of vehicles involved in an accident at 60 mph. Check this with the data.

5.

Time t (in years)	Total sales S
1	$100,310
2	100,290
3	100,305
4	100,280

c) Use the data points (1, $100,310) and (2, $100,290) to find a linear function which fits the data.

d) This data approximates a constant function. What procedure, apart from that of (c), could you use to find the constant?

d) Use the model to find the number of vehicles involved in an accident at 80 mph. Check this with the data.

CHAPTER 1 TEST

---

1. Rename without a negative exponent. e^{-k}

2. Divide. $\dfrac{e^{-5}}{e^8}$

3. Multiply. $(x + h)^2$

4. Factor. $25x^2 - t^2$

5. A woman makes an investment at 8% compounded annually. It grows to $993.60 at the end of 1 year. How much did she originally invest?

6. Solve. $-3x < 12$

7. A function is given by $f(x) = x^2 - 4$. Find

    a) $f(-3)$.   b) $f(x + h)$.

8. What is the slope and y-intercept of $y = -3x + 2$?

9. Find an equation of the line with slope $\frac{1}{4}$, containing the point $(8, -5)$.

10. Find the slope of the line containing the points $(-2, 3)$ and $(-4, -9)$.

11. The weight F of fluids in a human is directly proportional to its body weight W. It is known that a person who weighs 180 lb has 120 lb of fluids. Find an equation of variation expressing F as a function of W.

12. A record company has fixed costs of $10,000 of producing a record master. Thereafter, the variable costs are $.50 per record, for duplicating a record from the master. The revenue from each record is expected to be $1.30.

  a) Formulate a function $C(x)$ for the total cost of producing x records.

  b) Formulate a function $R(x)$ for the total revenue from the sale of x records.

  c) Formulate a function $P(x)$ for the total profit from the production and sale of x records.

  d) How many records must the company sell to break even?

13. Decide whether this function is increasing, decreasing, or neither.

$$f(x) = -0.2x + 7$$

14. Find the equilibrium point for the demand and supply functions

$$D(x) = (x - 7)^2 \text{ and } S(x) = x^2 + x + 4.$$

15. Graph. $y = \dfrac{4}{x}$

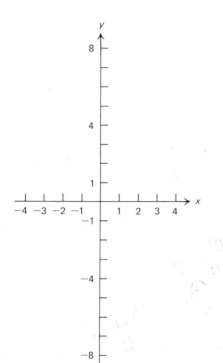

16. Convert to fractional exponents. $\dfrac{1}{\sqrt{t}}$

17. Convert to radical notation. $t^{-3/5}$

18. Determine the domain of

$$f(x) = \frac{x^2 + 20}{(x - 2)(x + 7)}.$$

19. Find a linear function which fits the data points (1, 3) and (2, 7).

20. Find a quadratic function which fits the data points (1, 5), (2, 9), and (3, 4).

21. Write interval notation for this graph.

Jonathan Rawle from Stock, Boston

2 DIFFERENTIATION

OBJECTIVES

You should be able to:

a) Decide if a graph is of a continuous function.
b) Decide if a function is continuous at a given point a.
c) Find
$$\lim_{x \to a} f(x),$$
if such a limit exists, by considering input-output tables.
d) Find a limit like
$$\lim_{h \to 0}(3x^2 + 3xh + h^2).$$

Pro Pix from Monkmeyer

2.1 CONTINUITY AND LIMITS

In this section we give a relatively short, intuitive (meaning "based on experience") treatment of two important notions: continuity and limits.

Continuity

The output x^3 varies "continuously" with the input x, in the sense that a small change in the input x produces a small change in the output x^3. Moreover, the change in output x^3 can be kept as small as we want by sufficiently restricting the input x. To get a feel for this let us make some calculations.

Example   Consider $f(x) = x^3$. Use the expression
$$(x + h)^3 - x^3 = h(3x^2 + 3xh + h^2),$$
which we developed in Exercise Set 1.1, to answer the following.
a) How close is $(4.1)^3$ to 4^3?
b) How close is $(4.01)^3$ to 4^3?
c) Does f appear to be "continuous" at 4?

Solution
a) Letting $x = 4$ and $h = 0.1$ in the above expression, we get
$$(4.1)^3 - 4^3 = 0.1[3 \cdot 4^2 + 3 \cdot 4 \cdot 0.1 + (0.1)^2] = 0.1(48 + 1.2 + 0.01)$$
$$= 0.1(49.21)$$
$$= 4.921.$$

b) Letting $x = 4$ and $h = 0.01$ in the above expression, we get
$$(4.01)^3 - 4^3 = 0.01[3 \cdot 4^2 + 3 \cdot 4 \cdot 0.01 + (0.01)^2]$$
$$= 0.01(48 + 0.12 + 0.0001)$$
$$= 0.01(48.1201)$$
$$= 0.481201.$$

c) Note that as h gets smaller, the difference $(4 + h)^3 - 4^3$ gets smaller. A reason why this happens is that the difference contains h as a factor. Thus f appears to be "continuous" at 4.

Do Exercise 1.

DEFINITION 1.   A function f is *continuous at a point x* if x is in the domain of f, that is, f(x) exists; and a small change in x produces a small change in f(x). Moreover, the change in f(x) can be kept as small as we wish by sufficiently restricting the change in x.

DEFINITION 2.   A function f is *continuous on an interval I*, or over an interval I, if f is continuous at each x in I.

The following functions are continuous (over the whole real line).

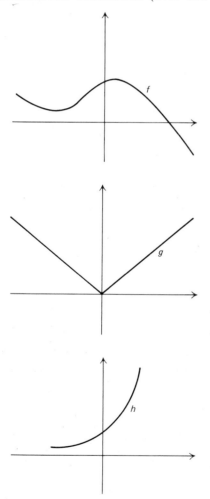

Note that there are no "breaks" in the graphs. The following functions are *not* continuous (over the whole real line).

1. Consider $f(x) = x^2$. Use the expression
$$(x + h)^2 - x^2 = h(2x + h),$$
which we developed in Chapter 1 to answer the following.

a) How close is $(3.1)^2$ to 3^2?

b) How close is $(3.01)^2$ to 3^2?

c) How close is $(3.001)^2$ to 3^2?

d) Does f appear to be "continuous" at 3?

2. Which functions are continuous?

a)

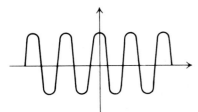

b)

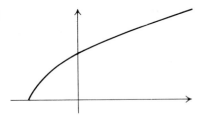

c)

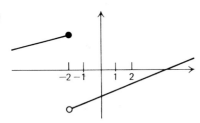

d)

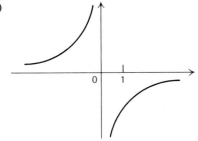

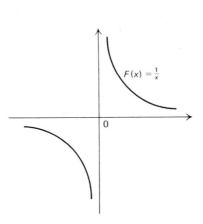

$F(x) = \frac{1}{x}$

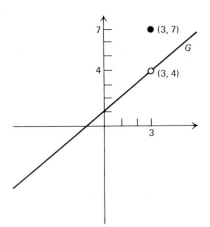

(3, 7)

G

(3, 4)

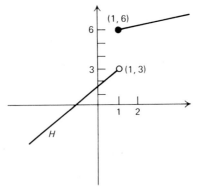

(1, 6)

(1, 3)

H

3. a) For the function in Margin Exercise 2(c), decide if the function is continuous at -2, at 1.

b) For the function in Margin Exercise 2(d), decide if the function is continuous at 1, at 0.

For G and H the open circle indicates that the circled point is not part of the graph. Let us discuss why each function fails to be continuous.

F: The function F fails to be continuous over the whole real line because it is not continuous at 0. This is because 0 is not in its domain.

G: The function G is not continuous over the whole real line because it is not continuous at 3. The output is 7 for the input 3, but a small change in input which is close to 3 has an output close to 4.

H: The function H is not continuous over the whole real line because it is not continuous at 1. The output is 6 for the input 1, but a small change in input which is close to 1, but to the left, has an output which is close to 3.

Do Exercises 2 and 3.

Almost every function we encounter in calculus is continuous. The following continuity principles, which we will take as assumptions, allow us to build up continuous functions.

I. Any constant function is continuous (such a function never varies).

II. For any positive integer n, x^n and $\sqrt[n]{x}$ are continuous.

III. If $f(x)$ and $g(x)$ are continuous, then so are $f(x) + g(x)$, $f(x) - g(x)$, and $f(x) \cdot g(x)$.

IV. If $f(x)$ is continuous, so is $\dfrac{1}{f(x)}$, as long as the inputs x are not such that the outputs $f(x) = 0$.

Let us convince ourselves that $x^2 - 3x + 2$ is continuous. Now x^2 is continuous by II. The constant function 3 is continuous by I, the function x is continuous by II, so the product $3x$ is continuous by III. Thus $x^2 - 3x$ is continuous by III, and since the constant 2 is continuous, we can apply III again to show that $x^2 - 3x + 2$ is continuous. In similar fashion, any polynomial like

$$f(x) = x^4 - 5x^3 + x^2 - 7$$

is continuous. A rational function is a quotient of two polynomials

$$r(x) = \frac{f(x)}{q(x)}.$$

Thus by IV, a rational function is continuous as long as the inputs x are not such that $q(x) = 0$.

Do Exercise 4.

Limits

The notion of *limit* is basic to a study of calculus. We will introduce the notion with an example. Consider the function f given by

$$f(x) = 2x + 3.$$

4. Give an argument to show that the following function is continuous

$$\frac{\sqrt[3]{x} - 7x^2}{x - 2}$$

as long as $x \neq 2$.

5. Consider

$$f(x) = 3x - 1.$$

a) Complete each table. (A hand calculator would be helpful, though not essential.)

Inputs x	Outputs $3x - 1$
7	
6.9	
6.4	
6.1	
6.01	
6.001	

Inputs x	Outputs $3x - 1$
5	
5.7	
5.8	
5.9	
5.99	
5.999	

b) Complete.

$$3x - 1 \rightarrow \boxed{} \text{ as } x \rightarrow 6$$

c) Complete.

$$\lim_{x \to 6}(3x - 1) = \boxed{}$$

Suppose we select input numbers x closer and closer to the number 4, and look at the output numbers $2x + 3$. Study the following tables.

A Inputs x	Outputs $2x + 3$
5	13
4.8	12.6
4.3	11.6
4.1	11.2
4.01	11.02
4.001	11.002

B Inputs x	Outputs $2x + 3$
2	7
3.6	10.2
3.8	10.6
3.9	10.8
3.99	10.98
3.999	10.998

In Table A, the input numbers approach 4 from above. In Table B, the input numbers approach 4 from below. In both cases the outputs approach 11. Thus we say

$2x + 3$ *approaches* 11, *as* x *approaches* 4.

An arrow $\rightarrow$ is often used for the word "approaches." Thus the above can be written

$$2x + 3 \rightarrow 11 \quad \text{as} \quad x \rightarrow 4.$$

The number 11 is said to be the *limit* as x approaches 4. We can abbreviate this statement as follows:

$$\lim_{x \to 4}(2x + 3) = 11.$$

This is read "the limit, as x approaches 4, of $2x + 3$ is 11."

Do Exercise 5.

A natural question here is, why didn't we just substitute 4 into $2x + 3$ to find the limit? Part of the answer to this question is that the limit at a point a does not depend upon the value of the function at a, $f(a)$. That is, we should be able to compute the limit without substitution, though this may not always be the way we find it. To complete the answer to the question, we can substitute to find a limit when the function is continuous at a. If the function is not continuous at a, we would have to use input-output tables or some other procedure to evaluate the limit. As an example of a function for which direct substitution will not work, consider

$$f(x) = \frac{x^2 - 1}{x - 1}.$$

Let us try to determine

$$\lim_{x \to 1} \frac{x^2 - 1}{x - 1}.$$

Note that we cannot substitute 1 into the formula, since it would result in division by 0. Nevertheless we can investigate the behavior of the function near 1 as shown in the following input-output tables.

Inputs x	Outputs $\dfrac{x^2 - 1}{x - 1}$
2	3
1.6	2.6
1.2	2.2
1.1	2.1
1.01	2.01
1.001	2.001

Inputs x	Outputs $\dfrac{x^2 - 1}{x - 1}$
0	1
0.7	1.7
0.8	1.8
0.9	1.9
0.99	1.99
0.999	1.999

Note that as the inputs x approach 1 from either above or below the outputs approach 2. Thus

$$\lim_{x \to 1} \frac{x^2 - 1}{x - 1} = 2.$$

Do Exercise 6.

You may have noticed a pattern in the input-output tables which we can reveal as follows. Whenever $x \neq 1$, as is the case for any of the inputs which are approaching 1, then

$$\frac{x^2 - 1}{x - 1} = \frac{(x - 1)(x + 1)}{x - 1} = x + 1, \qquad x \neq 1.$$

Thus the outputs can be found by adding 1 to the inputs. Accordingly, the limit as $x \to 1$ could have been found by substituting directly into $x + 1$.

Some limits are not quite so obvious. Consider

$$\lim_{x \to 1} \frac{2 - \sqrt{x + 3}}{x - 1}.$$

6. Consider

$$f(x) = \frac{x^2 - 9}{x - 3}.$$

a) Complete each table. (A hand calculator would again be helpful, though not essential.)

Inputs x	Outputs $\dfrac{x^2 - 9}{x - 3}$
4	
3.6	
3.2	
3.1	
3.01	
3.001	

Inputs x	Outputs $\dfrac{x^2 - 9}{x - 3}$
1	
2	
2.4	
2.9	
2.99	
2.999	

b) Find

$$\lim_{x \to 3} \frac{x^2 - 9}{x - 3}.$$

7. (A hand calculator problem—you need a $\sqrt{a}$ key.)

Complete this input-output table.

Inputs x	Outputs $\dfrac{2 - \sqrt{x + 3}}{x - 1}$
0	
0.5	
0.9	
0.99	
0.999	

Look at this input-output table.

Inputs x	Outputs $\dfrac{2 - \sqrt{x + 3}}{x - 1}$
2	-0.236
1.8	-0.239
1.1	-0.248
1.01	-0.2498
1.001	-0.249984

Do Exercise 7.

The limit is -0.25, or $-\frac{1}{4}$.

That it is necessary to check limits from above and below is seen in the following example. Consider

$$f(x) = \frac{|x|}{x}.$$

Let us try to determine

$$\lim_{x \to 0} \frac{|x|}{x}.$$

Look at the input-output tables.

x	$\dfrac{|x|}{x}$
2	$\dfrac{|2|}{2}$, or $\dfrac{2}{2}$, or 1
1	1
0.1	1
0.01	1
0.001	1

x	$\dfrac{|x|}{x}$
-2	$\dfrac{|-2|}{-2}$, or $\dfrac{2}{-2}$, or -1
-1	-1
-0.1	-1
-0.01	-1
-0.001	-1

Note that as x approaches 0 from above, $\dfrac{|x|}{x}$ approaches 1, but as x approaches 0 from below, $\dfrac{|x|}{x}$ approaches -1. Thus

$$\lim_{x \to 0} \frac{|x|}{x} \text{ does not exist.}$$

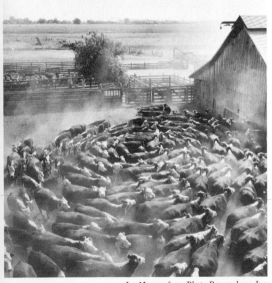

Let us consider another limit that does not exist. Consider

$$f(x) = \frac{1}{x-1}.$$

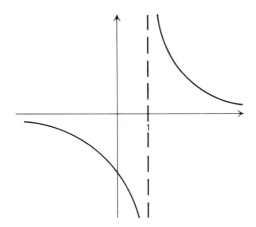

Let us try to determine

$$\lim_{x \to 1} \frac{1}{x-1}.$$

Note, again, that we cannot substitute 1, since it would result in division by 0; that is, the function is not continuous at 1. Let us investigate the behavior of the function as x approaches 1.

Inputs x	Outputs $\frac{1}{x-1}$	Inputs x	Outputs $\frac{1}{x-1}$
2	1	0	-1
1.6	1.667	0.7	-3.333
1.2	5.0	0.8	-5
1.1	10	0.9	-10
1.01	100	0.99	-100
1.001	1000	0.999	-1000

As x approaches 1 from above, the outputs get larger and larger.

These numbers do not approach any real number, though it might be said that "the limit from above is ∞ (infinity)." As x approaches 1 from below, the outputs get smaller and smaller.

8. Consider

$$f(x) = \frac{1}{x - 3}.$$

a) Complete each table. (A hand calculator would be helpful.)

Inputs x	Outputs $\dfrac{1}{x-3}$
4	
3.6	
3.2	
3.1	
3.01	
3.001	

Inputs x	Outputs $\dfrac{1}{x-3}$
1	
2	
2.4	
2.9	
2.99	
2.999	

b) Find

$$\lim_{x \to 3} \frac{1}{x - 3},$$

if it exists.

9. Consider

$$f(x) = \frac{1}{x - 3}.$$

These numbers do not approach any real number, though it might be said that "the limit from below is $-\infty$ (negative infinity)." Thus

$$\lim_{x \to 1} \frac{1}{x - 1} \text{ does not exist.}$$

Do Exercise 8.

For any number $a \neq 1$, the limit

$$\lim_{x \to a} \frac{1}{x - 1} \text{ does exist.}$$

For example, let us try to determine

$$\lim_{x \to -5} \frac{1}{x - 1}.$$

Again we use input-output tables to investigate the behavior of the function as x approaches -5.

Inputs x	Outputs $\dfrac{1}{x-1}$	Inputs x	Outputs $\dfrac{1}{x-1}$
-6	-0.1429	-4	-0.2
-5.4	-0.1563	-4.3	-0.1887
-5.3	-0.1587	-4.8	-0.1724
-5.1	-0.1639	-4.9	-0.1695
-5.01	-0.1664	-4.99	-0.1669
-5.001	-0.1666	-4.999	-0.1667

The limit can be expressed by the infinite repeating decimal

$$-0.166666 \ldots.$$

Since $\dfrac{1}{x - 1}$ is continuous at -5, we could have found this limit by substitution. That is,

$$\lim_{x \to -5} \frac{1}{x - 1} = \frac{1}{-5 - 1} = \frac{1}{-6} = -0.166666 \ldots.$$

Do Exercise 9.

In the next section we will encounter expressions with two variables x and h, and we will be interested in limits where x is fixed and $h \to 0$.

Example   Find $\lim\limits_{h \to 0}(3x^2 + 3xh + h^2)$.

Solution   We set up an input-output table with values of h approaching 0 from above. The reader should set up a table for values of h approaching 0 from below.

h	$3x^2 + 3xh + h^2$	
1	$3x^2 + 3x \cdot 1 + 1^2$, or	$3x^2 + 3x + 1$
0.8	$3x^2 + 3x(0.8) + (0.8)^2$, or	$3x^2 + 2.4x + 0.64$
0.5	$3x^2 + 3x(0.5) + (0.5)^2$, or	$3x^2 + 1.5x + 0.25$
0.1	$3x^2 + 3x(0.1) + (0.1)^2$, or	$3x^2 + 0.3x + 0.01$
0.01	$3x^2 + 3x(0.01) + (0.01)^2$, or	$3x^2 + 0.03x + 0.0001$
0.001	$3x^2 + 3x(0.001) + (0.001)^2$, or	$3x^2 + 0.003x + 0.0000001$

From the pattern in the table it appears that

$$\lim_{h \to 0}(3x^2 + 3xh + h^2) = 3x^2.$$

Do Exercise 10.

Limits at Infinity

Sometimes we need to determine limits when the inputs get larger and larger. For example, consider

$$f(x) = 3 - \frac{1}{x}.$$

Look at this input-output table.

Inputs x	Outputs $3 - \dfrac{1}{x}$
1	2
10	2.9
50	2.98
100	2.99
2000	2.9995

a) Complete each table. (A hand calculator would be helpful.)

Inputs x	Outputs $\dfrac{1}{x-3}$
0	
−0.6	
−0.8	
−0.9	
−0.99	
−0.999	

Inputs x	Outputs $\dfrac{1}{x-3}$
−2	
−1.5	
−1.4	
−1.1	
−1.01	
−1.001	

b) Find

$$\lim_{x \to -1} \frac{1}{x-3},$$

if it exists.

10. a) Complete the table.

h	$2x + h$
1	
0.7	
0.4	
0.1	
0.01	
0.001	

b) Find

$$\lim_{h \to 0}(2x + h).$$

11. Consider
$$f(x) = \frac{2x + 5}{x}.$$

a) Complete this table. (A hand calculator would be helpful.)

Inputs x	Outputs $\dfrac{2x + 5}{x}$
4	
20	
80	
200	
1000	
10,000	

b) Find
$$\lim_{x \to \infty} \left(\frac{2x + 5}{x} \right).$$

Note that as the inputs get larger and larger, the outputs get closer to 3. We say "the limit as x goes to infinity of $3 - \dfrac{1}{x}$ is 3." We can abbreviate this

$$\lim_{x \to \infty} \left(3 - \frac{1}{x} \right) = 3.$$

Do Exercise 11.

EXERCISE SET 2.1

Which functions are continuous?

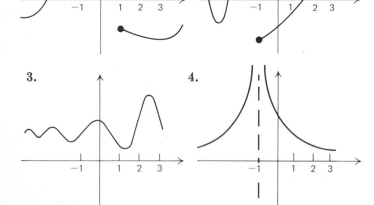

1.

2.

3.

4.

5–8. For each of Exercises 1–4, decide
a) if the function is continuous at -1.
b) if the function is continuous at 1.

9. a) Complete.

Inputs x	Outputs $x^2 - 3$
2	
1.5	
1.2	
1.1	
1.01	
1.001	

b) Find
$$\lim_{x \to 1}(x^2 - 3).$$

10. a) Complete.

Inputs x	Outputs $x^2 + 4$
2	
1.4	
1.2	
1.1	
1.01	
1.001	

b) Find
$$\lim_{x \to 1}(x^2 + 4).$$

Make up your own input-output tables and find the following limits, if they exist. (A hand calculator will be helpful.)

11. $\lim\limits_{x \to -5} \dfrac{x^2 - 25}{x + 5}$

12. $\lim\limits_{x \to -4} \dfrac{x^2 - 16}{x + 4}$

13. $\lim\limits_{x \to 0} \dfrac{1}{x}$

14. $\lim\limits_{x \to 0} \dfrac{3}{x}$

15. $\lim\limits_{x \to -2} \dfrac{3}{x}$

16. $\lim\limits_{x \to -4} \dfrac{1}{x}$

17. $\lim\limits_{x \to 2} \dfrac{x^3 - 8}{x - 2}$

18. $\lim\limits_{x \to 1} \dfrac{x^3 - 1}{x - 1}$

19. $\lim\limits_{x \to 1} \dfrac{x^2 - 1}{x^3 - 1}$

20. $\lim\limits_{x \to 1} \dfrac{x^3 - 1}{x^2 - 1}$

21. (Need $\sqrt{a}$ key.) $\lim\limits_{x \to 1} \dfrac{1 - \sqrt{x}}{1 - x}$

22. (Need $\sqrt{a}$ key.) $\lim\limits_{x \to 4} \dfrac{2 - \sqrt{x}}{4 - x}$

23. a) Complete.

h	$\dfrac{-1}{x(x + h)}$
1	
0.9	
0.6	
0.1	
0.01	
0.001	

b) Find
$$\lim_{h \to 0} \dfrac{-1}{x(x + h)}.$$

24. a) Complete.

h	$2x + h + 1$
1	
0.4	
0.3	
0.1	
0.01	
0.001	

b) Find
$$\lim_{h \to 0}(2x + h + 1).$$

25. a) Complete.   b) Find

x	$\dfrac{2x-4}{5x}$
8	
60	
100	
400	
6000	
20,000	

$$\lim_{x\to\infty}\left(\frac{2x-4}{5x}\right).$$

26. a) Complete.   b) Find

x	$\dfrac{3x+1}{4x}$
10	
80	
200	
500	
8000	
40,000	

$$\lim_{x\to\infty}\left(\frac{3x+1}{4x}\right).$$

Make up your own input-output tables and find the following limits.

27. $\lim\limits_{x\to\infty}\dfrac{1}{x}$

28. $\lim\limits_{x\to\infty}\dfrac{2}{x}$

29. $\lim\limits_{x\to\infty}\left(2+\dfrac{1}{x}\right)$

30. $\lim\limits_{x\to\infty}\left(5-\dfrac{1}{x}\right)$

31. A new conveyor system costs $10,000. In any year it depreciates 8% of its value at the beginning of that year.

a) What is the annual depreciation in each of the first five years?

b) What is the total depreciation at the end of 10 years?

c) What is the limit of the sum of the annual depreciation costs?

32. A new car costs $6000. In any year it depreciates 30% of its value at the beginning of that year.

a) What is the annual depreciation in each of the first five years?

b) What is the total depreciation at the end of 10 years?

c) What is the limit of the sum of the annual depreciation costs?

2.2 AVERAGE RATES OF CHANGE

The graph below shows the total production of suits by Raggs, Ltd. during one morning of work. Industrial psychologists have found curves like this typical of the production of factory workers.

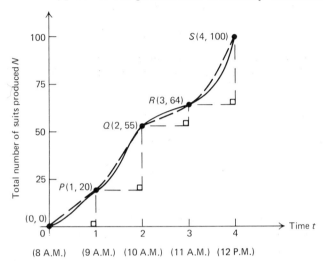

Example 1 What is the number of suits produced from 9 A.M. to 10 A.M.?

Solution At 10 A.M., 55 suits had been produced. At 9 A.M., 20 suits had been produced. In the hour from 9 A.M. to 10 A.M. the number of suits produced was

$$55 \text{ suits} - 20 \text{ suits}, \text{ or } 35 \text{ suits}.$$

Note that this is the slope of the line from P to Q.

Example 2 What was the average number of suits produced per hour from 9 A.M. to 11 A.M.?

Solution $\dfrac{64 \text{ suits} - 20 \text{ suits}}{11 \text{ A.M.} - 9 \text{ A.M.}} = \dfrac{44 \text{ suits}}{2 \text{ hr}} = 22 \, \dfrac{\text{suits}}{\text{hr}}$ (suits per hour)

This is the slope of the line from P to R. It is not shown in the graph.

Do Exercise 12.

OBJECTIVES

You should be able to

a) Compute an average rate of one variable with respect to another.

b) Find a simplified difference quotient.

12. In reference to the graph of suits produced,

a) Find the number of suits produced per hour from

8 A.M. to 9 A.M.,
9 A.M. to 10 A.M.,
10 A.M. to 11 A.M.,
11 A.M. to 12 P.M.

b) Which interval in (a) had the highest number?

c) Why do you think this happened?

d) Which interval in (a) had the lowest number?

e) Why do you think this happened?

f) What was the average number of suits produced per hour from 8 A.M. to 12 P.M.?

Let us consider a function $y = f(x)$ and two inputs x_1 and x_2. The *change in inputs*, or the *change in x*, is

$$x_2 - x_1.$$

The *change in outputs*, or the *change in y*, is

$$y_2 - y_1.$$

The *average rate of change of y with respect to x*, as x changes from x_1 to x_2, is the ratio of the change in outputs to the change in inputs.

$$\frac{y_2 - y_1}{x_2 - x_1}.$$

If we look at a graph of the function, we see that

$$\frac{y_2 - y_1}{x_2 - x_1} = \frac{f(x_2) - f(x_1)}{x_2 - x_1}$$

and that this is the slope of the line from $P(x_1, y_1)$ to $Q(x_2, y_2)$. The line $\overleftrightarrow{PQ}$ is called a *secant* line.

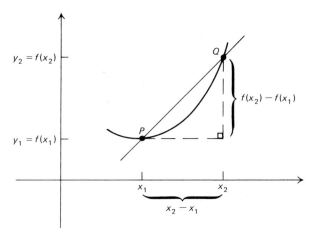

Example 3   For $y = f(x) = x^2$, find the average rates of change as

a) x changes from 1 to 3,

b) x changes from 1 to 2,

c) x changes from 2 to 3.

Solution The following graph is not necessary to the computations, but gives us a look at the secant lines whose slopes are being computed.

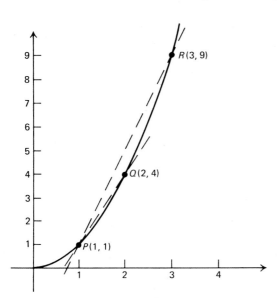

a) When $x_1 = 1$, $y_1 = f(x_1) = f(1) = 1^2 = 1$, and
   when $x_2 = 3$, $y_2 = f(x_2) = f(3) = 3^2 = 9$.
   The average rate of change is

$$\frac{y_2 - y_1}{x_2 - x_1} = \frac{f(x_2) - f(x_1)}{x_2 - x_1} = \frac{9 - 1}{3 - 1} = \frac{8}{2} = 4.$$

b) When $x_1 = 1$, $y_1 = f(x_1) = f(1) = 1^2 = 1$, and
   when $x_2 = 2$, $y_2 = f(x_2) = f(2) = 2^2 = 4$.
   The average rate of change is

$$\frac{4 - 1}{2 - 1} = \frac{3}{1} = 3.$$

c) When $x_1 = 2$, $y_1 = f(x_1) = f(2) = 2^2 = 4$, and
   when $x_2 = 3$, $y_2 = f(x_2) = f(3) = 3^2 = 9$.
   The average rate of change is

$$\frac{9 - 4}{3 - 2} = \frac{5}{1} = 5.$$

Do Exercises 13 and 14.

13. For
$$f(x) = x^3$$

find the average rates of change and sketch the secant lines as

a) x changes from 1 to 4,

b) x changes from 1 to 2,

c) x changes from 2 to 4,

d) x changes from -1 to -4.

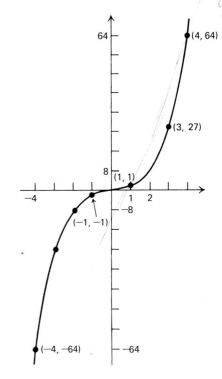

14. For
$$f(x) = \tfrac{1}{2}x + 1$$
find the average rates of change and sketch the secant lines as

a) x changes from 2 to 4,

b) x changes from 2 to 3,

c) x changes from -1 to 4.

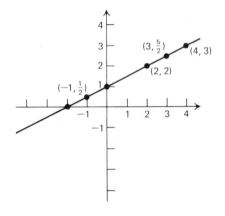

For a linear function average rates of change are the same, for any choice of x_1 and x_2, being equal to the slope m of the line. As seen in Example 3 and in Margin Exercise 13, a function which is not linear has average rates of change which vary with the choice of x_1 and x_2.

Difference Quotients

Let us now simplify our notation a bit, by doing away with subscripts. Instead of x_1, we will simply write x.

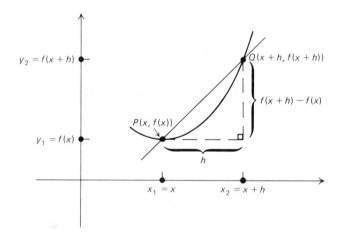

To get from x_1, or x, to x_2 we move a distance h. Thus $x_2 = x + h$. Then the average rate of change, which is also called a *difference quotient*, is given by

$$\frac{y_2 - y_1}{x_2 - x_1} = \frac{f(x_2) - f(x_1)}{x_2 - x_1} = \frac{f(x + h) - f(x)}{(x + h) - x} = \frac{f(x + h) - f(x)}{h}.$$

We shall be using the expression on the right.

> **The average rate of change of y with respect to x is also called the *difference quotient*. It is given by**
> $$\frac{f(x + h) - f(x)}{h}.$$
>
> **The difference quotient is equal to the slope of the line from $P(x, f(x))$ to $Q(x + h, f(x + h))$.**

Example 4   For $f(x) = x^2$, find the difference quotient when

a) $x = 5$ and $h = 3$,

b) $x = 5$ and $h = 0.1$.

Solutions

a) We substitute $x = 5$ and $h = 3$ into the formula,

$$\frac{f(x+h) - f(x)}{h} = \frac{f(5+3) - f(5)}{3} = \frac{f(8) - f(5)}{3}.$$

Now $f(8) = 8^2 = 64$, and $f(5) = 5^2 = 25$, and we have

$$\frac{f(8) - f(5)}{3} = \frac{64 - 25}{3} = \frac{39}{3} = 13.$$

b) We substitute $x = 5$ and $h = 0.1$ into the formula,

$$\frac{f(x+h) - f(x)}{h} = \frac{f(5+0.1) - f(5)}{0.1} = \frac{f(5.1) - f(5)}{0.1}.$$

Now $f(5.1) = (5.1)^2 = 26.01$ and $f(5) = 25$, and we have

$$\frac{f(5.1) - f(5)}{0.1} = \frac{26.01 - 25}{0.1} = \frac{1.01}{0.1} = 10.1.$$

Do Exercise 15.

For the function in Example 4, let us find a general form of the difference quotient. This will allow more efficient computations.

Example 5   For $f(x) = x^2$, find a simplified form of the difference quotient. Then find the value of the difference quotient when $x = 5$ and $h = 0.1$.

Solution

$$f(x) = x^2$$

so

$$f(x+h) = (x+h)^2 = x^2 + 2xh + h^2.$$

Then

$$f(x+h) - f(x) = (x^2 + 2xh + h^2) - x^2 = 2xh + h^2.$$

So

$$\frac{f(x+h) - f(x)}{h} = \frac{2xh + h^2}{h} = \frac{h(2x+h)}{h} = 2x + h.$$

15. For

$$f(x) = 4x^2,$$

complete the following table to find the difference quotients.

x	h	$x+h$	$f(x)$	$f(x+h)$	$f(x+h) - f(x)$	$\dfrac{f(x+h) - f(x)}{h}$
3	2					
3	1					
3	0.1					
3	0.01					
3	0.001					

16. For
$$f(x) = 4x^2$$
find a simplified form of the difference quotient by completing steps (a) to (c). Then complete the table in (d) using the simplified form.

a) Find $f(x + h)$.

b) Find $f(x + h) - f(x)$.

c) Find $\dfrac{f(x + h) - f(x)}{h}$, and simplify, if possible.

d)

x	h	$\dfrac{f(x + h) - f(x)}{h}$
6	-3	
6	-2	
6	-1	
6	-0.1	
6	-0.01	
6	-0.001	

17. a) For
$$f(x) = 4x^3$$
find a simplified difference quotient.
b) Complete.

x	h	$\dfrac{f(x + h) - f(x)}{h}$
-2	1	
-2	0.1	
-2	0.01	
-2	0.001	

It is important to note that a difference quotient is defined *only* when $h \neq 0$. The simplification above is valid only for nonzero values *of h*. When $x = 5$ and $h = 0.1$,
$$\frac{f(x + h) - f(x)}{h} = 2x + h = 2 \cdot 5 + 0.1 = 10 + 0.1 = 10.1.$$

Do Exercise 16.

Example 6 For $f(x) = x^3$ find a simplified form of the difference quotient.

Solution Now $f(x) = x^3$, so
$$f(x + h) = (x + h)^3 = x^3 + 3x^2h + 3xh^2 + h^3.$$
This is shown on p. 9. Then
$$f(x + h) - f(x) = (x^3 + 3x^2h + 3xh^2 + h^3) - x^3$$
$$= 3x^2h + 3xh^2 + h^3.$$
So
$$\frac{f(x + h) - f(x)}{h} = \frac{3x^2h + 3xh^2 + h^3}{h} = \frac{h(3x^2 + 3xh + h^2)}{h}$$
$$= 3x^2 + 3xh + h^2.$$
Again, this is true *only* for $h \neq 0$.

Do Exercise 17.

Example 7 For $f(x) = \dfrac{3}{x}$ find a simplified form of the difference quotient.

Solution Now $f(x) = \dfrac{3}{x}$, so $f(x + h) = \dfrac{3}{x + h}$. Then
$$f(x + h) - f(x) = \frac{3}{x + h} - \frac{3}{x}$$
$$= \frac{3}{x + h} \cdot \frac{x}{x} - \frac{3}{x} \cdot \frac{x + h}{x + h} \quad \text{(Here we are multiplying by 1 to get a common denominator.)}$$
$$= \frac{3x - 3(x + h)}{x(x + h)}$$
$$= \frac{3x - 3x - 3h}{x(x + h)} = \frac{-3h}{x(x + h)}.$$

So

$$\frac{f(x+h)-f(x)}{h} = \frac{\dfrac{-3h}{x(x+h)}}{h} = \frac{-3h}{x(x+h)} \cdot \frac{1}{h} = \frac{-3}{x(x+h)}.$$

This is true only for $h \neq 0$.

Do Exercise 18.

Instantaneous Rate of Change

You may have noticed in the margin exercises that values of h in the tables were approaching 0. We did this intentionally. Let us see why.

A car travels 100 miles in 2 hours. Its *average* speed (or velocity) is $\dfrac{100 \text{ mi}}{2 \text{ hr}}$, or $50 \dfrac{\text{mi}}{\text{hr}}$. This is the *average rate of change* of distance with respect to time. At various times during the trip the speedometer did not read 50, however. Thus we say that 50 is the *average*. A snapshot of the speedometer taken at any instant would indicate *instantaneous* speed, or rate of change.

Average rates of change are given by difference quotients. If distance s is a function of time t, then average velocity is given by

$$\text{Average velocity} = \frac{s(t+h)-s(t)}{h}.$$

Instantaneous rates of change are found by letting $h \to 0$. Thus

$$\text{Instantaneous velocity} = \lim_{h \to 0} \frac{s(t+h)-s(t)}{h}.$$

We shall return to this notion in Section 2.6.

18. a) For

$$f(x) = \frac{1}{x}$$

find a simplified difference quotient.

b) Complete.

x	h	$\dfrac{f(x+h)-f(x)}{h}$
2	3	
2	1	
2	0.1	
2	0.01	
2	0.001	

EXERCISE SET 2.2

1. *Utility.* *Utility* is a type of function which arises in economics. When a consumer receives x units of a certain product, he gets a certain amount of pleasure, or utility U, from them. To the right is a typical graph of a utility function.

a) Find the average rate of change of U as x changes from 0 to 1, 1 to 2, 2 to 3, 3 to 4.

b) Why do you think the average rates of change are decreasing?

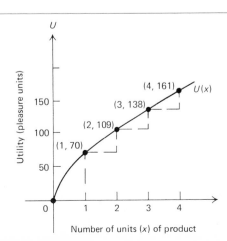

2. *Advertising.* The graph at the right shows a typical response to advertising. After an amount a is spent on advertising, the company sells $N(a)$ units of a product.

a) Find the average rate of change of N, as a changes from 0 to 1, 1 to 2, 2 to 3, 3 to 4.

b) Why do you think the average rates of change are decreasing?

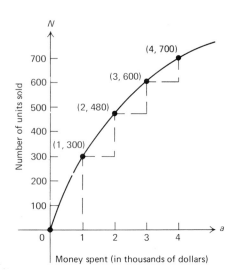

Money spent (in thousands of dollars)

3. *Memory.* The total number of words $M(t)$ which a person can memorize in time t, in minutes, is shown in the graph at the right.

a) Find the average rate of change of M as t changes from 0 to 8, 8 to 16, 16 to 24, 24 to 32, 32 to 36.

b) Why do the average rates of change become 0 after 24 minutes?

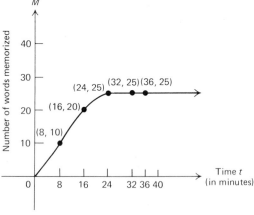

4. *Temperature during an illness.* The temperature T (°F) of a patient during an illness is given by the graph at the right, where t = time, in days.

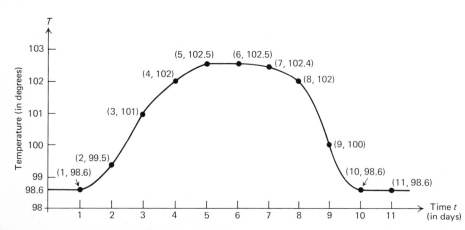

a) Find the average rate of change of T as t changes from 1 to 10. Using this rate of change, would you know that the person was sick?

b) Find the average rate of change of T with respect to t, as t changes from 1 to 2, 2 to 3, 3 to 4, 4 to 5, 5 to 6, 6 to 7, 7 to 8, 8 to 9, 9 to 10, 10 to 11.

c) When do you think the temperature began to rise?

d) When do you think the temperature reached its peak?

e) When do you think the temperature began to subside?

f) When was the temperature back to normal?

5. *Population growth.* The two graphs at the right describe the number of people in each of two countries A and B at time t, in years.

a) Find the average rate of change of each population (number of people in the population) with respect to time t, as t changes from 0 to 4. This is often called an *average growth rate.*

b) If the calculation in (a) were the only one made, would we detect the fact that the populations were growing differently?

c) Find the average rates of change of each population as t changes from 0 to 1, 1 to 2, 2 to 3, and 3 to 4.

d) For which population does the statement "the population grew 125 million each year" convey the least information about what really took place?

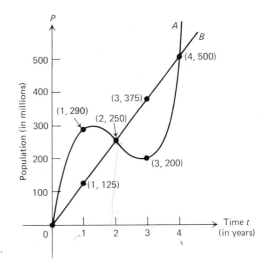

6. *Cost.* A firm determines that the total cost C of producing x units of a certain product is given by

$$C(x) = -0.05x^2 + 50x,$$

where $C(x)$ is in dollars.

a) Find $C(301)$.

b) Find $C(300)$.

c) Find $C(301) - C(300)$.

d) Find $\dfrac{C(301) - C(300)}{301 - 300}$.

7. *Revenue.* A firm determines that the total revenue (money coming in) from the sale of x units of a certain product is given by

$$R(x) = -0.01x^2 + 1000,$$

where $R(x)$ is in dollars.

a) Find $R(301)$.

b) Find $R(300)$.

c) Find $R(301) - R(300)$.

d) Find $\dfrac{R(301) - R(300)}{301 - 300}$.

8. *Average velocity.* A car is at a distance s (in miles) from its starting point in t hours, given by

$$s(t) = 10t^2.$$

a) Find $s(2)$ and $s(5)$.

b) Find $s(5) - s(2)$. What does this represent?

c) Find the average rate of change of distance with respect to time as t changes from $t_1 = 2$ to $t_2 = 5$. This is known as *average velocity*, or *speed*.

10. *Divorce rate.* It is known that in 1960 there were 400,000 divorces. In 1967 there were 550,000 divorces. Find the average rate of change of the number of divorces with respect to time. This is called an *average divorce rate*.

9. *Average velocity.* An object is dropped from a certain height. It is known that it will fall a distance s (in feet) in t seconds, given by

$$s(t) = 16t^2.$$

a) How far will the object fall in 3 seconds?

b) How far will the object fall in the next 2 seconds?

c) What is the average rate of change of distance with respect to time during this time? This is *average velocity*, or *speed*.

11. *Marriage rate.* It is known that in 1960 there were 1,450,000 marriages. In 1967 there were 1,850,000 marriages. Find the average rate of change of the number of marriages with respect to time. This is called an *average marriage rate*.

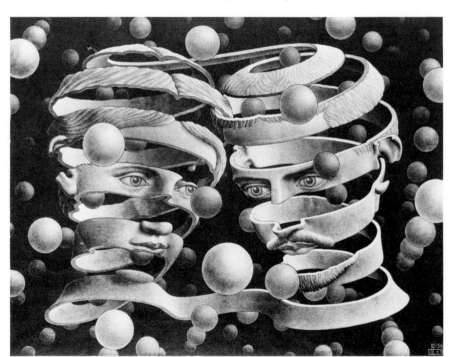

Bond of Union, Escher.

M. C. Escher from Haags Gemeentemuseum

12. At the beginning of a trip the odometer on a car reads 30,680 and it has a full tank of gas. At the end of the trip the odometer reads 30,970. It takes 20 gallons of gas to fill the tank again. What is the average rate of consumption (rate of change of the number of miles with respect to the number of gallons)?

13. In Exercise 12, what is the average rate of change of the number of gallons with respect to the number of miles?

For each function,
 a) find a simplified difference quotient,
 b) complete the table.

x	h	$\dfrac{f(x + h) - f(x)}{h}$
4	2	
4	1	
4	0.1	
4	0.01	

14. $f(x) = 5x^2$

15. $f(x) = 7x^2$

16. $f(x) = -5x^2$

17. $f(x) = -7x^2$

18. $f(x) = 5x^3$

19. $f(x) = 7x^3$

20. $f(x) = \dfrac{4}{x}$

21. $f(x) = \dfrac{5}{x}$

22. $f(x) = 2x + 3$

23. $f(x) = -2x + 5$

24. $f(x) = x^2 + x$

25. $f(x) = x^2 - x$

26. $f(x) = mx + b$

2.3 TANGENT LINES AND GRAPHICAL DIFFERENTIATION

Tangent Lines

A line tangent to a circle is a line which touches the circle exactly once.

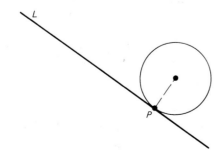

OBJECTIVES

You should be able to:

a) Given the graph of a function, sketch the graph of its derivative $y = m(x)$.
b) Sketch the graph of certain functions, then sketch their derivatives and discover a formula for the derivative.

Consider the following curve. Line L touches the curve at point P but meets the curve at other places. It will be considered a tangent line, but "touching at one point" cannot be its definition.

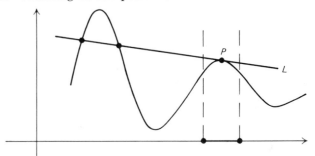

Note in the preceding figure that over a suitably small interval containing P line L does touch the curve exactly once. This is still not a suitable definition of tangent line because it allows a line like M in the following figure to be a tangent, which we will not accept.

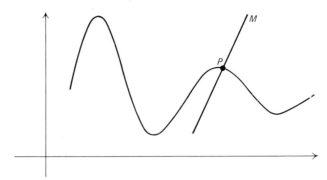

Later we will give a definition of a tangent line, but for now we will rely on our intuition (experience). In the figure L_1 and L_2 are not tangents. All the others are tangent lines.

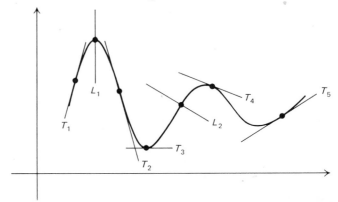

Do Exercise 19.

Why Do We Study Tangent Lines?

The reason for this will become evident in Chapter 3. To see briefly, look at the following graph of a total profit function.

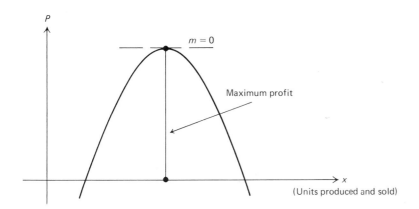

Note that the largest (or maximum) value of the function occurs where the graph has a horizontal tangent; that is, the tangent line has slope 0.

Graphical Differentiation

Given a function f, we can define another function m, by finding the slope of f, as follows.

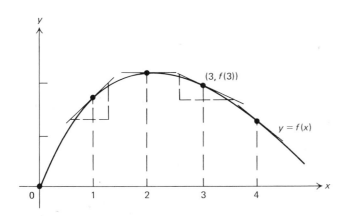

19. Which appear to be tangent lines?

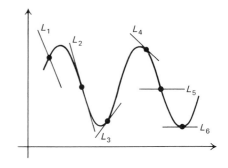

The roadway forms a tangent to the arch of the bridge.

Peter Southwick from Stock, Boston

At each point on the graph there is a unique tangent line, and that line has a slope m. Given x, we can determine m, so m is a function of x. This new function we derive this way is called the *derivative* of the given f. Any process for finding this derivative is called *differentiation*.

We can determine the slope of a curve approximately by holding a ruler tangent to the curve at various positions. In this example, for values of x between 0 and 2 the slopes of tangent lines are positive, but decreasing. This will happen whenever a graph is turning in the downward direction. At 2 the slope (the derivative) is 0. From there on the derivative is negative, and is decreasing, since the graph is still turning downward. We can make a rough graph of m by estimating slopes at several points. Let us use 1 and 3. We sketch a small right triangle with the tangent line as hypotenuse. Then we use the ratio of lengths of the legs of the triangles, and the knowledge of whether the slope is positive, negative, or 0, to make our estimate. Thus at 1, the slope $m(1)$ is about 1; and at 3 the slope $m(3)$ is about $-\frac{1}{2}$. Using all the previous information, we make the following rough sketch of $y = m(x)$.

A function

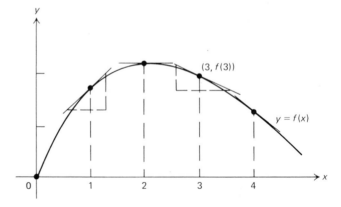

Its derivative

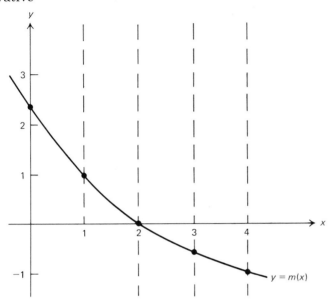

20. Sketch an approximate graph of the derivative $y = m(x)$. This is not an exact process.

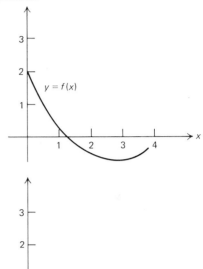

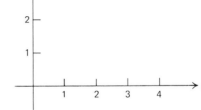

Do Exercise 20.

This procedure is called *graphical differentiation.* The procedure can be refined if we use graph paper.

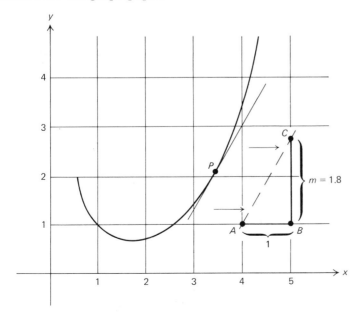

21. Below is a graph of $y = x^2$.

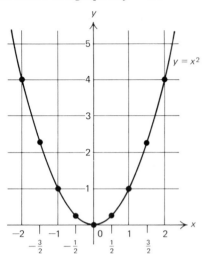

To find the slope of a tangent line at point P, we place a ruler at P and then move it parallel to itself until it goes through an intersection on the graph paper, as at A above. Then draw a segment of length 1 to the right to point B. From B draw a vertical segment which meets the dashed line at C. Since $\overline{AB}$ is of length 1, the length of $\overline{BC}$ is the slope ($m = 1.8$) and it is positive because the tangent line slants upward to the right. If the tangent line slants downward to the right, the slope will be negative.

Do Exercise 21.

a) Find the value of the derivative at each point listed in the table. Again, these are estimates.

x	$m(x)$
-2	
$-\frac{3}{2}$	
-1	
$-\frac{1}{2}$	
0	
$\frac{1}{2}$	
1	
$\frac{3}{2}$	
2	

b) Sketch a graph of $y = m(x)$, the derivative.

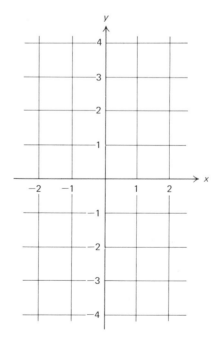

c) Try to discover a formula for $m(x)$, the derivative. This would be such that when we substitute an x value the result would be the slope of the tangent line to $y = x^2$ at x.

EXERCISE SET 2.3

Sketch an approximate graph of the derivative $y = m(x)$.

1.
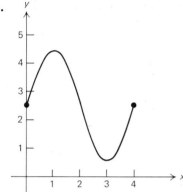

2.
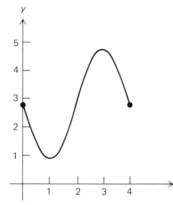

3.
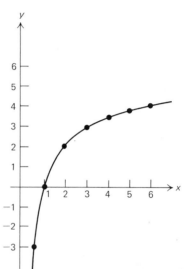

4.
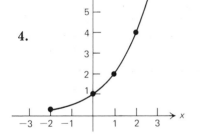

5.
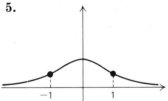

6.
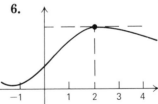

For each function in Exercises 7–18,
  a) sketch a graph on graph paper with a large grid;
  b) use graphical differentiation to sketch an approximate graph of the derivative $y = m(x)$;
  c) try to discover a formula for the derivative $m(x)$.

7. $y = \frac{1}{2}x^2$ **8.** $y = -\frac{1}{2}x^2$ **9.** $y = x^2 - 2$ **10.** $y = x^2 - 1$

11. $y = x^2 + x$ **12.** $y = x^2 - x$ **13.** $y = 3x + 1$ **14.** $y = 2x - 3$

15. $y = -4$ (constant function)   **16.** $y = 5$ (constant function)

17. $y = x^3$ **18.** $y = x^3 + 1$

OBJECTIVES

Given a formula for a function, find a formula for its derivative. Then find various values of the derivative.

2.4 DIFFERENTIATION USING LIMITS

Defining a tangent line as being a line that touches a curve only once makes sense when the curve is a circle, but for other curves it does not make sense. We shall define *tangent* line in such a way that it is sensible in general, using the notion of limit.

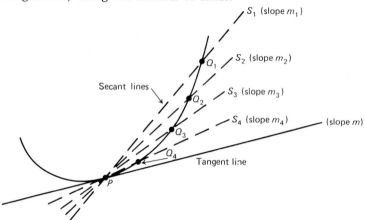

In this figure, we obtain the line tangent to the curve at point P by considering secant lines through P and neighboring points Q_1, Q_2, and so on. As the points Q approach P, the secant lines approach the tangent line. Each secant has a slope. The slopes of the secant lines approach the slope of the tangent line. In fact, we *define* the *tangent line* to be the line which contains the point P and has slope m, where m is the limit of the slopes of the secant lines as the points Q approach P.

How might we calculate the limit m?

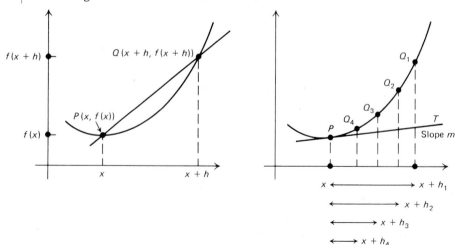

Suppose P has coordinates $(x, f(x))$. Then the first coordinate of Q is x plus some number h, or $x + h$. The coordinates of Q are $(x + h, f(x + h))$. Now from Section 2.2 we know that the slope of the secant line $\overleftrightarrow{PQ}$ is given by the difference quotient

$$\frac{f(x + h) - f(x)}{h}.$$

Now, as we see in the figure on the right above, as the points Q approach P, $x + h$ approaches x. That is, h approaches 0. Thus

The slope of the tangent line $= m = \lim\limits_{h \to 0} \dfrac{f(x + h) - f(x)}{h}.$

The formal definition of the *derivative of a function f* can now be given. We will designate the derivative at x, $f'(x)$, rather than $m(x)$.

DEFINITION. For a function $y = f(x)$, its derivative at x is defined as follows:

$$f'(x) = \lim_{h \to 0} \frac{f(x + h) - f(x)}{h}.$$

This is the basic definition of *differential calculus*.

Let us now calculate some formulas for derivatives. That is, given a formula for a function f, we will be trying to find a formula for f'.

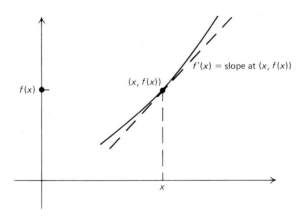

There are three steps in calculating a derivative.

a) **Write down the difference quotient** $\dfrac{f(x + h) - f(x)}{h}.$

b) **Simplify the difference quotient.**

c) **Find the limit as** $h \to 0$.

"Nothing in this world is so powerful as an idea whose time has come."

VICTOR HUGO

A formula for the derivative of a linear function

$$f(x) = mx + b$$

is

$$f'(x) = m.$$

Let us verify it using the definition.

Example 1   For $f(x) = mx + b$, find $f'(x)$.

Solution

a) $\dfrac{f(x + h) - f(x)}{h} = \dfrac{[m(x + h) + b] - (mx + b)}{h}$

b) $\dfrac{f(x + h) - f(x)}{h} = \dfrac{mx + mh + b - mx - b}{h}$

$$= \frac{mh}{h}$$

$$= m$$

c) $\lim\limits_{h \to 0} \dfrac{f(x + h) - f(x)}{h} = \lim\limits_{h \to 0} m = m,$ since m does not involve h.

Thus $f'(x) = m$.

In Margin Exercise 21 you may have conjectured that the function

$$f(x) = x^2$$

has derivative

$$f'(x) = 2x.$$

This would mean that the tangent line at $x = 4$ has slope $f'(4) = 8$. Let us verify this particular case and then the general formula.

Example 2   For $f(x) = x^2$, find $f'(4)$.

Solution

a) $\dfrac{f(4 + h) - f(4)}{h} = \dfrac{(4 + h)^2 - 4^2}{h}$

b) $\dfrac{f(4 + h) - f(4)}{h} = \dfrac{16 + 8h + h^2 - 16}{h}$

$$= \frac{8h + h^2}{h}$$

$$= \frac{h(8 + h)}{h}$$

$$= 8 + h$$

c) $\lim_{h\to 0}\dfrac{f(4+h)-f(4)}{h}=\lim_{h\to 0}(8+h)=8.$ Thus $f'(4)=8.$

Do Exercise 22.

22. For $f(x)=x^2$, find $f'(5)$ using the definition of a derivative.

Example 3   For $f(x)=x^2$, find (the general formula) $f'(x)$.

Solution

a) $\dfrac{f(x+h)-f(x)}{h}=\dfrac{(x+h)^2-x^2}{h}$

b) In Example 5 of Section 2.2, p. 89, we showed how this difference quotient can be simplified as follows:

$$\frac{f(x+h)-f(x)}{h}=2x+h.$$

c) We want to find

$$\lim_{h\to 0}\frac{f(x+h)-f(x)}{h}=\lim_{h\to 0}(2x+h).$$

h	$2x+h$
1	$2x+1$
0.1	$2x+0.1$
0.01	$2x+0.01$
0.001	$2x+0.001$

23. For $f(x)=4x^2$, find $f'(x)$. Then find $f'(5)$ and interpret the meaning.

As $h\to 0$, we see that $2x+h\to 2x$. Thus

$$\lim_{h\to 0}(2x+h)=2x,$$

and we have

$$f'(x)=2x.$$

This tells us, for example, that at $x=-3$, the curve has a tangent line whose slope is

$$f'(-3)=2(-3),\quad\text{or }-6.$$

We may say, simply, that the "curve has slope -6."

Do Exercise 23.

24. For $f(x) = 4x^3$, find $f'(x)$. Then find $f'(-5)$ and $f'(0)$.

Example 4 For $f(x) = x^3$, find $f'(x)$. Then find $f'(-1)$ and $f'(10)$.

Solution

a) $\dfrac{f(x + h) - f(x)}{h} = \dfrac{(x + h)^3 - x^3}{h}$

b) In Example 6 of Section 2.2, p. 90, we showed how this difference quotient can be simplified as follows:

$$\frac{f(x + h) - f(x)}{h} = 3x^2 + 3xh + h^2.$$

c) $\displaystyle\lim_{h \to 0} \dfrac{f(x + h) - f(x)}{h} = \lim_{h \to 0}(3x^2 + 3xh + h^2) = 3x^2$

An input-output table for this is shown on p. 81 of Section 2.1. Thus for $f(x) = x^3$, we have $f'(x) = 3x^2$. Then

$$f'(-1) = 3(-1)^2 = 3, \quad \text{and} \quad f'(10) = 3(10)^2 = 300.$$

Do Exercise 24.

Example 5 For $f(x) = \dfrac{3}{x}$, find $f'(x)$. Then find $f'(1)$ and $f'(2)$.

Solution

a) $\dfrac{f(x + h) - f(x)}{h} = \dfrac{\dfrac{3}{x + h} - \dfrac{3}{x}}{h}$

b) In Example 7 of Section 2.2, p. 90, we showed that this difference quotient can be simplified as follows:

$$\frac{f(x + h) - f(x)}{h} = \frac{-3}{x(x + h)}.$$

c) We want to find

$$\lim_{h \to 0} \frac{f(x + h) - f(x)}{h} = \lim_{h \to 0} \frac{-3}{x(x + h)}.$$

As $h \to 0$, $x + h \to x$, so we have

$$f'(x) = \lim_{h \to 0} \frac{-3}{x(x + h)} = \frac{-3}{x^2}.$$

Then

$$f'(1) = \frac{-3}{1^2} = -3, \quad \text{and} \quad f'(2) = \frac{-3}{2^2} = -\frac{3}{4}.$$

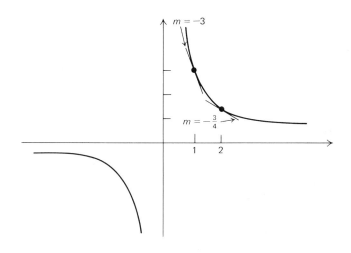

 25. For $f(x) = \dfrac{1}{x}$, find $f'(x)$. Then find $f'(-10)$ and $f'(-2)$.

Note that $f'(0)$ does not exist because $f(0)$ does not exist. We say that "f is not differentiable at 0."

Do Exercise 25.

It can happen that a function f is defined at a point but its derivative f' is not. The function f given by

$$f(x) = |x|$$

is an example. Note that

$$f(0) = |0| = 0,$$

so the function is defined at 0.

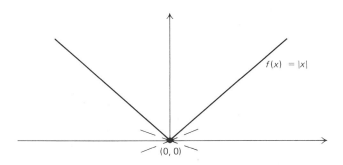

Suppose we tried to draw a tangent line at $(0, 0)$. A function like this with a corner (not smooth) would seem to have many tangents at $(0, 0)$,

26. List the points at which the function is not differentiable.

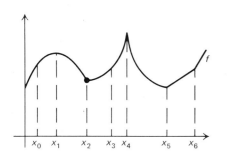

and hence many slopes. The derivative at such a point would not be unique. Let us try to calculate the derivative at 0. Now

$$f'(x) = \lim_{h \to 0} \frac{|x + h| - |x|}{h}.$$

Thus at $x = 0$, we have

$$f'(0) = \lim_{h \to 0} \frac{|0 + h| - |0|}{h}$$

$$= \lim_{h \to 0} \frac{|h|}{h}.$$

h	$\dfrac{|h|}{h}$
2	$\dfrac{|2|}{2}$, or $\dfrac{2}{2}$, or 1
1	1
0.1	1
0.01	1
0.001	1

Look at the input-output tables. Note that as h approaches 0 from above, $\dfrac{|h|}{h}$ approaches 1, but as h approaches 0 from below, $\dfrac{|h|}{h}$ approaches -1. Thus

$$\lim_{h \to 0} \frac{|h|}{h} \text{ does not exist,}$$

so

$$f'(0) \text{ does not exist.}$$

h	$\dfrac{|h|}{h}$
-2	$\dfrac{|-2|}{-2}$, or $\dfrac{2}{-2}$, or -1
-1	-1
-0.1	-1
-0.01	-1
-0.001	-1

If a function has a "sharp point" or "corner," it will not have a derivative at that point.

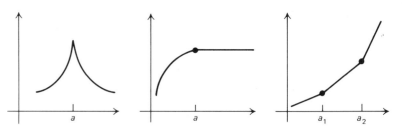

Do Exercise 26.

A function may also fail to be differentiable at a point by having a vertical tangent, as shown below.

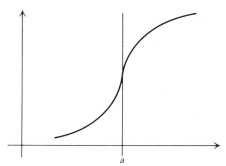

Recall that vertical lines have no slope, and hence there is no derivative at such a point.

Each of the preceding examples, including $f(x) = |x|$, is continuous at each point in an interval I but not differentiable at each point in I. That is, continuity does not imply differentiability. On the other hand, *if* we know that a function is differentiable at each point in an interval I, *then* it is continuous over I. The function $f(x) = x^2$ is an example. Thus when we know a function is differentiable over an interval, it is *smooth* in the sense that there are no "sharp points," "corners," or "breaks" in the graph.

EXERCISE SET 2.4

For each function, find $f'(x)$. Then find $f'(-2)$, $f'(-1)$, $f'(0)$, $f'(1)$, and $f'(2)$, if they exist.

1. $f(x) = 5x^2$ **2.** $f(x) = 7x^2$ **3.** $f(x) = -5x^2$ **4.** $f(x) = -7x^2$

5. $f(x) = 5x^3$ **6.** $f(x) = 7x^3$ **7.** $f(x) = 2x + 3$ **8.** $f(x) = -2x + 5$

9. $f(x) = -4x$ **10.** $f(x) = \frac{1}{2}x$ **11.** $f(x) = x^2 + x$ **12.** $f(x) = x^2 - x$

13. $f(x) = \dfrac{4}{x}$ **14.** $f(x) = \dfrac{5}{x}$ **15.** $f(x) = mx$ **16.** $f(x) = ax^2 + bx + c$

17. List the points at which the function is not differentiable.

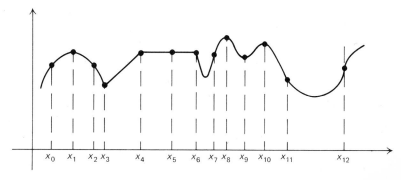

OBJECTIVES

You should be able to:

a) Differentiate using the Power Rule, the Sum-difference Rule, or the rule for differentiating a constant or a constant times a function.
b) Find the points on the graph of a function where the tangent line has a given slope.

27. Find $\dfrac{d}{dx} x^3$, using the results of previous work.

2.5 DIFFERENTIATION TECHNIQUES: POWER RULE, SUM-DIFFERENCE RULE

Leibniz's Notation

When y is a function of x, we will also designate the derivative, $f'(x)$, as follows

$$\frac{dy}{dx},$$

which is read "the derivative of y with respect to x." This notation was invented by the German mathematician Leibniz. It does *not* mean dy divided by dx! (That is, we cannot interpret $\dfrac{dy}{dx}$ as a quotient until meanings are given to dy and dx, which we will not do here.) For example, if $y = x^2$, then

$$\frac{dy}{dx} = 2x.$$

We may also write

$$\frac{d}{dx} f(x)$$

to denote the derivative of f with respect to x. For example,

$$\frac{d}{dx} x^2 = 2x.$$

Do Exercise 27.

The value of $\dfrac{dy}{dx}$ when $x = 5$ can be denoted by

$$\left. \frac{dy}{dx} \right|_{x=5}.$$

Thus for $\dfrac{dy}{dx} = 2x$,

$$\left. \frac{dy}{dx} \right|_{x=5} = 2 \cdot 5, \text{ or } 10.$$

In general, for $y = f(x)$,

$$\left. \frac{dy}{dx} \right|_{x=a} = f'(a).$$

Do Exercise 28.

The Power Rule

In the remainder of this section we will develop rules and techniques for efficient differentiating.

This table contains functions and derivatives which we have found in previous work. Look for a pattern.

Function	Derivative
x^2	$2x^1$
x^3	$3x^2$
x^{-1}, or $\dfrac{1}{x}$	$-1 \cdot x^{-2}$, or $-\dfrac{1}{x^2}$

Perhaps you have discovered the following.

POWER RULE.   **For any real number a,**

$$\frac{d}{dx}\, x^a = a \cdot x^{a-1}.$$

Note that this rule holds no matter what the exponent. That is, to differentiate x^a, write down the exponent a, followed by x with an exponent 1 less than a.

① x^a
$a \cdot x^{a-1}$ ②

① Bring down the exponent as a factor.

② Subtract 1 from the exponent.

Example 1 $\dfrac{d}{dx}\, x^5 = 5x^4$

Example 2 $\dfrac{d}{dx}\, x = 1 \cdot x^{1-1} = 1 \cdot x^0 = 1$

Example 3 $\dfrac{d}{dx}\, x^{-4} = -4 \cdot x^{-4-1} = -4x^{-5}$, or $-4 \cdot \dfrac{1}{x^5}$, or $-\dfrac{4}{x^5}$

The Power Rule allows us to differentiate $\sqrt{x}$.

Example 4 $\dfrac{d}{dx}\, \sqrt{x} = \dfrac{d}{dx}\, x^{1/2} = \dfrac{1}{2} \cdot x^{(1/2)-1} = \dfrac{1}{2} x^{-1/2}$, or $\dfrac{1}{2} \cdot \dfrac{1}{x^{1/2}}$, or

$\dfrac{1}{2} \cdot \dfrac{1}{\sqrt{x}}$, or $\dfrac{1}{2\sqrt{x}}$

28. For $\dfrac{dy}{dx} = 3x^2$, find

$$\left.\frac{dy}{dx}\right|_{x=4}.$$

The German mathematician and philosopher Gottfried Wilhelm von Leibniz (1646–1716) and the English mathematician, philosopher, and physicist Sir Isaac Newton (1642–1727) are both credited with the invention of the calculus, though each made the invention independent of the other. Newton used the dot notation $\dot{y}$ for $\dfrac{dy}{dt}$, where y is a function of time, and this notation is still used, though it is not as prevalent as Leibniz's notation.

Find $\dfrac{dy}{dx}$ (differentiate).

29. $y = x^6$

30. $y = x^{-7}$

31. $y = \sqrt[3]{x}$

32. $y = x^{-1/4}$

33. Find $f'(x)$.

$$f(x) = 67$$

34. Find $g'(x)$.

$$g(x) = -14$$

Example 5 $\dfrac{d}{dx}\, x^{-2/3} = -\dfrac{2}{3} x^{-2/3-1} = -\dfrac{2}{3} x^{-5/3}$, or $-\dfrac{2}{3}\, \dfrac{1}{x^{5/3}}$, or

$$-\dfrac{2}{\sqrt[3]{x^5}}$$

Do Exercises 29 through 32.

The Derivative of a Constant Times a Function

Look at the graph of the constant function $f(x) = c$. What is the slope at each point P on the graph? It follows that:

   the derivative of a constant function is 0.

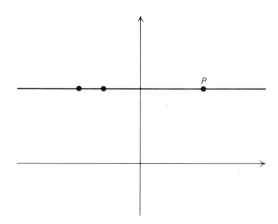

Examples $\dfrac{d}{dx}\, 3 = 0,$ $\dfrac{d}{dx}\left(-\dfrac{1}{4}\right) = 0$

Do Exercises 33 and 34.

Now let us consider differentiating functions like

$$f(x) = 5x^2 \quad \text{and} \quad g(x) = -7x^4.$$

Note that we already know how to differentiate x^2 and x^4. Let us again look for a pattern in the results of Section 2.4.

Function	Derivative
$5x^2$	$10x$
$-4x$	-4
$-7x^2$	$-14x$
$5x^3$	$15x^2$

Perhaps you have discovered the following.

> The derivative of a constant times a function is the constant times the derivative of the function. Using derivative notation this can be written

$$\frac{d}{dx}[c \cdot f(x)] = c \cdot f'(x).$$

Combining this with the Power Rule allows us to find many derivatives.

Example 1 $\dfrac{d}{dx} 5x^4 = 5 \dfrac{d}{dx} x^4 = 5 \cdot 4 \cdot x^{4-1} = 20x^3$

Example 2 $\dfrac{d}{dx} - 9x = -9 \dfrac{d}{dx} x = -9 \cdot 1 = -9$

With practice you will be able to differentiate many such functions in one step.

Example 3 $\dfrac{d}{dx} \dfrac{-4}{x^2} = \dfrac{d}{dx} - 4x^{-2} = -4 \cdot \dfrac{d}{dx} x^{-2} = -4(-2)x^{-2-1} =$

$8x^{-3}$, or $\dfrac{8}{x^3}$

Example 4 $\dfrac{d}{dx} - x^{0.7} = -1 \cdot \dfrac{d}{dx} x^{0.7} = -1 \cdot 0.7 \cdot x^{0.7-1} = -0.7x^{-0.3}$

Do Exercises 35 through 38.

The Derivative of a Sum or Difference

In Exercise 11 of Exercise Set 2.4 you found that for

$$f(x) = x^2 + x$$

the derivative is

$$f'(x) = 2x + 1.$$

Find $\dfrac{dy}{dx}$.

35. $y = 5x^{20}$

36. $y = -\dfrac{3}{x}$

37. $y = -8\sqrt{x}$

38. $y = 0.16x^{6.25}$

Find $\dfrac{dy}{dx}$ (differentiate).

39. $y = -\frac{1}{4}x - 9$

40. $y = 7x^4 + 6x^2$

41. $y = 15x^2 + \dfrac{4}{x} + \sqrt{x}$

Note that the derivative of x^2 is $2x$, and the derivative of x is 1; and the sum of these derivatives is $f'(x)$. This illustrates the following:

SUM-DIFFERENCE RULE

a) The derivative of a sum is the sum of the derivatives:

$$\text{if } t(x) = f(x) + g(x), \quad \text{then } t'(x) = f'(x) + g'(x).$$

b) The derivative of a difference is the difference of the derivatives:

$$\text{if } t(x) = f(x) - g(x), \quad \text{then } t'(x) = f'(x) - g'(x).$$

Any function which is a sum or difference of several terms can be differentiated term by term.

Example 1 $\dfrac{d}{dx}(3x + 7) = \dfrac{d}{dx}(3x) + \dfrac{d}{dx}(7)$

$$= 3\,\dfrac{d}{dx}\,x + 0$$

$$= 3 \cdot 1, \text{ or } 3$$

Example 2 $\dfrac{d}{dx}(5x^3 - 3x^2) = \dfrac{d}{dx}(5x^3) - \dfrac{d}{dx}(3x^2)$

$$= 5\,\dfrac{d}{dx}\,x^3 - 3\,\dfrac{d}{dx}\,x^2$$

$$= 5 \cdot 3x^2 - 3 \cdot 2x$$

$$= 15x^2 - 6x$$

Example 3 $\dfrac{d}{dx}\left(24x - \sqrt{x} + \dfrac{2}{x}\right) = \dfrac{d}{dx}(24x) - \dfrac{d}{dx}(\sqrt{x}) + \dfrac{d}{dx}\left(\dfrac{2}{x}\right)$

$$= 24 \cdot \dfrac{d}{dx}\,x - \dfrac{d}{dx}\,x^{1/2} + 2 \cdot \dfrac{d}{dx}\,x^{-1}$$

$$= 24 \cdot 1 - \dfrac{1}{2}\,x^{(1/2)-1} + 2(-1)x^{-1-1}$$

$$= 24 - \dfrac{1}{2}\,x^{-1/2} - 2x^{-2}$$

$$= 24 - \dfrac{1}{2\sqrt{x}} - \dfrac{2}{x^2}$$

Do Exercises 39 through 41.

A word of caution! The derivative of

$$f(x) + c,$$

a function plus a constant, is just the derivative of the function

$$f'(x).$$

The derivative of

$$c \cdot f(x),$$

a function times a constant, is the constant times the derivative

$$c \cdot f'(x).$$

That is, for a product the constant is retained, but for a sum it is not.

It is important to be able to determine points at which the tangent line to a curve has a certain slope; that is, points at which the derivative attains a certain value.

Example 1   Find the points on the graph of $y = x^3 + x^2$ at which the tangent line is horizontal.

Solution   A horizontal tangent has slope 0. Thus we seek the values of x for which $\dfrac{dy}{dx} = 0$. That is, we want to find x such that

$$3x^2 + 2x = 0.$$

We factor and solve.

$$x(3x + 2) = 0$$

$$x = 0 \quad \text{or} \quad 3x + 2 = 0$$

$$x = 0 \quad \text{or} \quad 3x = -2$$

$$x = 0 \quad \text{or} \quad x = -\tfrac{2}{3}$$

We are to find points *on the graph*, so we have to determine the second coordinates from the original equation $y = x^3 + x^2$.

For $x = 0$, $\quad y = 0^3 + 0^2 = 0$.

For $x = -\tfrac{2}{3}$, $\quad y = (-\tfrac{2}{3})^3 + (-\tfrac{2}{3})^2 = -\tfrac{8}{27} + \tfrac{4}{9} = -\tfrac{8}{27} + \tfrac{12}{27} = \tfrac{4}{27}$.

Thus the points we are seeking are $(0, 0)$ and $(-\tfrac{2}{3}, \tfrac{4}{27})$.

Do Exercise 42.

Example 2   Find the points on the graph of $y = x^3 + x^2$ at which the tangent line has slope 5.

42. Find the points on the graph of $y = x^3 + 3x^2 - 9x$ at which the tangent line is horizontal.

43. Find the points on the graph of $y = x^3$ at which the tangent line has slope 12.

Solution   We want to find values of x for which $\dfrac{dy}{dx} = 5$. That is, we want to find x such that

$$3x^2 + 2x = 5.$$

To solve, we add -5 and factor.

$$3x^2 + 2x - 5 = 0$$

$$(3x + 5)(x - 1) = 0$$

$$3x + 5 = 0 \quad \text{or} \quad x - 1 = 0$$

$$3x = -5 \quad \text{or} \qquad x = 1$$

$$x = -\tfrac{5}{3} \quad \text{or} \qquad x = 1$$

We determine the second coordinates from the original equation.

For $x = -\tfrac{5}{3}$, $y = (-\tfrac{5}{3})^3 + (-\tfrac{5}{3})^2 = -\tfrac{125}{27} + \tfrac{25}{9} = -\tfrac{125}{27} + \tfrac{75}{27} = -\tfrac{50}{27}$.
For $x = 1$, $y = 1^3 + 1^2 = 2.$

Thus the points we are seeking are $(-\tfrac{5}{3}, -\tfrac{50}{27})$ and $(1, 2)$.

We illustrate the results of Examples 1 and 2 in the graph below.

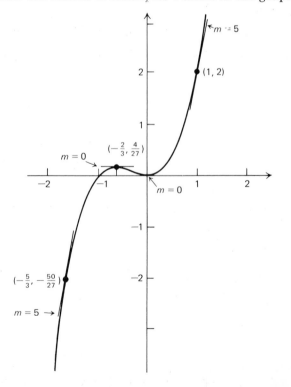

Do Exercise 43.

EXERCISE SET 2.5

Find $\dfrac{dy}{dx}$.

1. $y = x^7$ **2.** $y = x^8$ **3.** $y = 15$ **4.** $y = 78$

5. $y = 4x^{150}$ **6.** $y = 7x^{200}$ **7.** $y = x^3 + 3x^2$ **8.** $y = x^4 - 7x$

9. $y = 8\sqrt{x}$ **10.** $y = 4\sqrt{x}$ **11.** $y = x^{0.07}$ **12.** $y = x^{0.78}$

13. $y = \frac{14}{9}x$ **14.** $y = \frac{16}{9}x$ **15.** $y = x^{-3}$ **16.** $y = x^{-4}$

17. $y = 3x^2 - 8x + 7$ **18.** $y = 4x^2 - 7x + 5$ **19.** $y = \sqrt[4]{x} - \dfrac{1}{x}$ **20.** $y = \sqrt[5]{x} - \dfrac{2}{x}$

Find $f'(x)$.

21. $f(x) = 0.64x^{2.5}$ **22.** $f(x) = 0.32x^{12.5}$ **23.** $f(x) = \dfrac{5}{x} - x$

24. $f(x) = \dfrac{4}{x} - x$ **25.** $f(x) = 4x - 7$ **26.** $f(x) = 7x + 11$

27. $f(x) = 4x + 9$ **28.** $f(x) = 7x - 14$ **29.** $f(x) = \dfrac{x^4}{4}$

30. $f(x) = \dfrac{x^3}{3}$ **31.** $f(x) = -0.01x^2 - 0.5x + 70$ **32.** $f(x) = -0.01x^2 + 0.4x + 50$

33. $f(x) = ax^2 + bx + c$ **34.** $f(x) = mx + b$

For each function, find the points on the graph at which the tangent line is horizontal.

35. $y = x^2$ **36.** $y = -x^2$ **37.** $y = -x^3$

38. $y = x^3$ **39.** $y = 3x^2 - 5x + 4$ **40.** $y = 5x^2 - 3x + 8$

41. $y = -0.01x^2 - 0.5x + 70$ **42.** $y = -0.01x^2 + 0.4x + 50$ **43.** $y = 2x + 4$

44. $y = -2x + 5$ **45.** $y = 4$ **46.** $y = -3$

47. $y = -x^3 + x^2 + 5x - 1$ **48.** $y = -\frac{1}{3}x^3 + 6x^2 - 11x - 50$

For each function, find the points on the graph at which the tangent line has slope 1.

49. $y = 20x - x^2$ **50.** $y = 6x - x^2$ **51.** $y = -0.025x^2 + 4x$ **52.** $y = -0.01x^2 + 2x$

OBJECTIVES

You should be able to:

a) Given a distance function $s(t)$, find a formula for the velocity $v(t)$ and the acceleration $a(t)$, and evaluate $s(t)$, $v(t)$, and $a(t)$ for given values of t.

b) Given y as a function of x, find the rate of change of y with respect to x, and evaluate this rate of change for values of x.

2.6 RATES OF CHANGE

Recall the example of the car traveling 100 miles in 2 hours. Its average speed (or velocity) is $\dfrac{100 \text{ mi}}{2 \text{ hr}}$, or $50 \dfrac{\text{mi}}{\text{hr}}$. This is the average rate of change of distance with respect to time. At various times during the trip the speedometer did not read 50. A snapshot of the speedometer at any instant would indicate the *instantaneous* speed, or rate of change.

Average rates of change are given by difference quotients. If distance, s, is a function of time, t, then average velocity is given by

$$\text{Average velocity} = \frac{s(t + h) - s(t)}{h}.$$

Instantaneous rates of change are given by derivatives. Thus

$$\text{Instantaneous velocity} = \lim_{h \to 0} \frac{s(t + h) - s(t)}{h}.$$

An instantaneous velocity.

Robert V. Fuschetto from Photo Researchers, Inc.

Example 1   An object travels in such a way that distance s (in miles) from the starting point is a function of time t (in hours) as follows:

$$s(t) = 10t^2.$$

a) Find the average velocity between the times $t = 2$ and $t = 5$.

b) Find the (instantaneous) velocity when $t = 4$.

Solution

a) From $t = 2$ to $t = 5$, $h = 3$, so

$$\frac{s(t + h) - s(t)}{h} = \frac{s(2 + 3) - s(2)}{3} = \frac{s(5) - s(2)}{3} = \frac{10 \cdot 5^2 - 10 \cdot 2^2}{3}$$

$$= \frac{250 - 40}{3} = \frac{210}{3} = 70 \frac{\text{mi}}{\text{hr}}$$

b) Instantaneous velocity

$$= \lim_{h \to 0} \frac{s(4 + h) - s(4)}{h} = \lim_{h \to 0} \frac{10(4 + h)^2 - 10 \cdot 4^2}{h}$$

$$= \lim_{h \to 0} \frac{10(16 + 8h + h^2) - 160}{h} = \lim_{h \to 0} \frac{160 + 80h + 10h^2 - 160}{h}$$

$$= \lim_{h \to 0} \frac{80h + 10h^2}{h} = \lim_{h \to 0} \frac{h(80 + 10h)}{h} = \lim_{h \to 0}(80 + 10h) = 80 \frac{\text{mi}}{\text{hr}}$$

Do Exercise 44.

We usually use the letter v for velocity. Then

$$v(t) = \lim_{h \to 0} \frac{s(t + h) - s(t)}{h} = s'(t).$$

The rate of change of velocity is called *acceleration*. We usually use the letter a for acceleration,

$$\text{Acceleration} = a(t) = v'(t).$$

Example 2   For $s(t) = 10t^2$, find $v(t)$ and $a(t)$.

Solution $v(t) = s'(t) = 20t,$

$$a(t) = v'(t) = 20.$$

44. For the function in Example 1,

a) find the average velocity between the times $t = 1$ and $t = 6$.

b) find the (instantaneous) velocity when $t = 5$.

45. An object is dropped from a certain height. It will fall downward a distance of s feet in t seconds as given by

$$s(t) = 16t^2.$$

a) Find the velocity $v(t)$.

b) Find its velocity 2 sec after it has been dropped.

c) Find its velocity 10 sec after it has been dropped.

46. In reference to Margin Exercise 45, find $a(t)$. In what units should it be expressed?

47. The volume V of a cubical carton with a side of length s, in feet, is given by

$$V = s^3.$$

a) Find the rate of change of the volume V with respect to the length s of a side.

b) Find the rate of change of volume when $s = 10$ ft.

For an automobile we may give the velocity in *miles per hour*, and the acceleration, which is the change in velocity per unit time, in (*miles per hour*) *per hour*. We abbreviate this mi/hr². Thus in Example 2, the acceleration is a constant, 20 mi/hr².

Do Exercises 45 and 46.

In general, derivatives give instantaneous rates of change.

RATE OF CHANGE. **If y is a function of x, then the (instantaneous) *rate of change of y with respect to x* is given by the derivative**

$$\frac{dy}{dx}, \text{ or } f'(x).$$

Example 3   The spherical volume V of a cancer tumor is given by

$$V = \tfrac{4}{3}\pi r^3,$$

where r is the radius of the tumor, in centimeters. Find

a) the rate of change of the volume with respect to the radius,

b) the rate of change of volume at $r = 1.2$ cm.

Solution

a) $\dfrac{dV}{dr} = V'(r) = \dfrac{4}{3} \cdot 3 \cdot \pi r^2 = 4\pi r^2.$

b) $V'(1.2) = 4\pi(1.2)^2 = 5.76\pi \approx 18\,\dfrac{\text{cm}^3}{\text{cm}} = 18 \text{ cm}^2.$

Do Exercise 47.

Example 4   The initial population in a bacteria colony is 10,000. After t hours the colony grows to a number $P(t)$ given by

$$P(t) = 10,000(1 + 0.86t + t^2)$$

a) Find the rate of change of the population P with respect to time t. This is also known as the *growth rate*.

b) Find the number of bacteria present after 5 hours. Also find the growth rate when $t = 5$.

Solution

a) Note $P(t) = 10,000 + 8600t + 10,000t^2$. Then
$$P'(t) = 8600 + 20,000t.$$

b) The number of bacteria present when $t = 5$ hr is given by

$$P(5) = 10{,}000 + 8600 \cdot 5 + 10{,}000 \cdot 5^2 = 303{,}000.$$

The growth rate when $t = 5$ is given by

$$P'(5) = 8600 + 20{,}000 \cdot 5 = 108{,}600 \; \frac{\text{bacteria}}{\text{hr}}.$$

Thus at $t = 5$, there are 303,000 bacteria present, and the colony is growing at the rate of 108,600 bacteria per hour.

Do Exercise 48.

Example 5 Suppose $D(t)$ is the number of divorces occurring at time t. Then $D'(t)$ is the number of divorces occurring at a particular instant. It is the *rate of divorce*, or *divorce rate*. Later, we will give a formula for this function.

Rates of Change in Economics

The word *marginal** signifies a rate of change, or derivative, in economics. Recall that

$C(x) =$ the total cost of producing x units of a product (during some time period).

Then

$C'(x) =$ the marginal cost

     $=$ the rate of change of the total cost with respect to the number of units x produced

     $=$ the cost per unit, apart from fixed costs, at that stage in the production process where the x'th unit is being produced.

Let us think about these interpretations. The total cost of producing 5 units of a product is $C(5)$. The rate of change $C'(5)$ is the cost per unit at that stage in the production process. That this cost per unit does not include fixed costs is seen in this example.

$$C(x) = \underbrace{(x^2 + 4x)}_{\text{Variable costs}} + \underbrace{\$10{,}000}_{\text{Fixed costs (constant)}}$$

---

* The word "marginal" comes from the Marginalist School of Economic Thought which originated in Austria for the purpose of applying mathematics and statistics to the study of economics.

48. The initial population of a bacteria colony is 10,000. After t hours the colony grows to a number $P(t)$ given by

$$P(t) = 10{,}000(1 + 0.97t + t^2).$$

a) Find the growth rate of the population.

b) Find the number of bacteria present (the population) when $t = 5$ hr. Find the growth rate when $t = 5$ hr.

c) Find the number of bacteria present when $t = 6$ hr. Find the growth rate when $t = 6$.

Then
$$C'(x) = 2x + 4.$$

This is because the derivative of a constant is 0. This verifies an economic principle which says that the fixed costs of a company have no effect on marginal cost.

Following are some other marginal functions. Recall that

$R(x) = $ the total revenue from the sale of x units.

Then

$R'(x) = $ the marginal revenue

$= $ the rate of change of the total revenue with respect to the number x of units sold

$= $ the revenue per unit at that stage in the sales process where the x'th unit is being sold.

Also

$P(x) = $ the total profit from the product on and sale of x units of a product,

$= R(x) - C(x).$

Then

$P'(x) = $ the marginal profit

$= $ the rate of change of the total profit with respect to the number of units x produced and sold

$= $ the profit per unit at that stage of production and sales where the x'th unit is produced and sold,

$= R'(x) - C'(x).$

Example 6   Given
$$R(x) = 50x,$$
$$C(x) = 2x^3 - 12x^2 + 40x + 10,$$
find

a) $P(x)$

b) $R(2), C(2), P(2)$

c) $R'(x), C'(x), P'(x)$

d) $R'(2), C'(2), P'(2)$

Solution

a) $P(x) = R(x) - C(x) = 50x - (2x^3 - 12x^2 + 40x + 10)$
$$= -2x^3 + 12x^2 + 10x - 10$$

b) $R(2) = 50 \cdot 2 = \$100$ (the total revenue from the sale of the first 2 units)

   $C(2) = 2 \cdot 2^3 - 12 \cdot 2^2 + 40 \cdot 2 + 10 = \$58$ (the total cost of producing the first 2 units)

   $P(2) = R(2) - C(2) = \$100 - \$58 = \$42$ (the total profit from the production and sale of the first 2 units)

c) $R'(x) = 50,$ $C'(x) = 6x^2 - 24x + 40,$

   $P'(x) = R'(x) - C'(x) = 50 - (6x^2 - 24x + 40) = -6x^2 + 24x + 10$

d) $R'(2) = \$50$ per unit

   $C'(2) = 6 \cdot 2^2 - 24 \cdot 2 + 40 = \$16$ per unit

   $P'(2) = \$50 - \$16 = \$34$ per unit

Note that marginal revenue is constant. No matter how much is produced and sold, the revenue per unit stays the same. This may not always be the case. Also note that $C'(2)$, or $16 per unit, is not the average cost per unit which is given by

$$\frac{\text{Total cost of producing 2 units}}{2 \text{ units}} = \frac{\$58}{2} = \$29 \text{ per unit.}$$

In general,

$$A(x) = \textbf{average cost of producing } x \textbf{ units} = \frac{C(x)}{x}.$$

Do Exercise 49.

Let us look at a typical marginal cost function, C', and its associated total cost function C.

49. Given

$$R(x) = 50x - 0.5x^2,$$
$$C(x) = 10x + 3,$$

find

a) $P(x)$

b) $R(40), C(40), P(40)$

c) $R'(x), C'(x), P'(x)$

d) $R'(40), C'(40), P'(40)$

e) Is the marginal revenue constant?

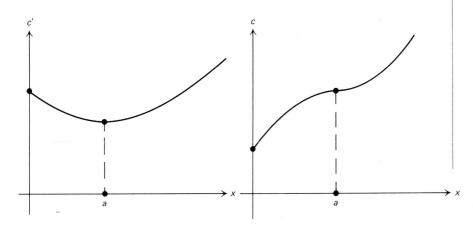

Marginal cost normally decreases as more units are produced until it reaches some minimum value at a, and then it increases. This is probably due to something like having to pay overtime or buying more machinery. Since $C'(x)$ represents slope of $C(x)$ and is positive and decreasing up to a, the graph turns downward as x goes from 0 to a. Then past a it turns upward.

EXERCISE SET 2.6

1. Given

$$s(t) = t^3 + t,$$

where s is measured in feet, and t in seconds, find

a) $v(t)$,

b) $a(t)$,

c) the velocity and acceleration when $t = 4$ sec.

2. Given

$$s(t) = t^2 + 3t,$$

where s is measured in feet, and t in seconds, find

a) $v(t)$,

b) $a(t)$,

c) the velocity and acceleration when $t = 10$ sec.

3. Given

$$s(t) = 3t + 10,$$

where s is measured in miles, and t in hours, find

a) $v(t)$,

b) $a(t)$,

c) the velocity and acceleration when $t = 2$ hr. When the distance function is given by a linear function, we have what is called *uniform motion*.

4. *Stopping distance on glare ice.* The stopping distance (at some fixed speed) of regular tires is given by a linear function of the air temperature F:

$$D(F) = 2F + 115,$$

where $D(F)$ = stopping distance, in feet, when the air temperature is F, in degrees Fahrenheit. Find the rate of change of the stopping distance D with respect to the air temperature F.

5. *Percentage of the population in college.* The percentage of the population in college is given by a linear function

$$P(t) = 1.25t + 15,$$

where $P(t)$ = percentage in college the t'th year after 1940. Find the rate of change of the percentage P with respect to time t.

6. The circular area A, in square centimeters, of a healing wound is given by

$$A = \pi r^2,$$

where r is the radius, in centimeters. Find the rate of change of the area with respect to the radius.

7. The circumference C, in centimeters, of a healing wound is given by

$$C = 2\pi r,$$

where r is the radius, in centimeters. Find the rate of change of the circumference with respect to the radius.

8. The population of a city grows from an initial size of 100,000 to an amount P given by

$$P = 100,000 + 2000t^2,$$

where t is measured in years.

a) Find the growth rate.

b) Find the number of people in the city after 10 years (at $t = 10$ yr).

c) Find the growth rate at $t = 10$ yr.

10. *Advertising.* A firm estimates that it will sell N units of a product after spending a dollars on advertising, where

$$N(a) = -a^2 + 300a + 6,$$

and a is measured in thousands of dollars.

a) What is the rate of change of the number of units sold with respect to the amount spent on advertising?

b) How many units will be sold after spending $10 thousand dollars on advertising?

c) What is the rate of change at $a = 10$?

9. The temperature T of a person during an illness is given by

$$T(t) = -0.1t^2 + 1.2t + 98.6,$$

where T is the temperature (°F) at time t, measured in days.

a) Find the rate of change of the temperature with respect to time.

b) Find the temperature at $t = 1.5$ days.

c) Find the rate of change at $t = 1.5$ days.

11. *Blood pressure.* For a certain dosage of x cc (cubic centimeters) of a drug, there is a resultant blood pressure B given by

$$B(x) = 0.05x^2 - 0.3x^3.$$

Find the rate of change of the blood pressure with respect to the dosage.

Ian Cleghorn from Photo Researchers, Inc.

12. *Home range.* The *home range H* of an animal is defined to be the region to which it confines its movements. The area of that region is related to its body weight by

$$H = W^{1.41} \text{ (see p. 53)}.$$

Find $\dfrac{dH}{dW}$.

14. Given

$$R(x) = 50x - 0.5x^2,$$
$$C(x) = 4x + 10,$$

find

a) $P(x)$,

b) $R(20)$, $C(20)$, $P(20)$,

c) $R'(x)$, $C'(x)$, $P'(x)$,

d) $R'(20)$, $C'(20)$, $P'(20)$.

13. *Territory area.* The *territory area T* of an animal is defined to be its defended, or exclusive, region. The area T of that region is related to its body weight by

$$T = W^{1.31} \text{ (see p. 60)}$$

Find $\dfrac{dT}{dW}$.

15. Given

$$R(x) = 5x,$$
$$C(x) = 0.001x^2 + 1.2x + 60,$$

find

a) $P(x)$,

b) $R(100)$, $C(100)$, $P(100)$,

c) $R'(x)$, $C'(x)$, $P'(x)$,

d) $R'(100)$, $C'(100)$, $P'(100)$.

OBJECTIVES

You should be able to differentiate using the Product and Quotient Rules.

2.7 DIFFERENTIATION TECHNIQUES: PRODUCT AND QUOTIENT RULES

The derivative of a sum is the sum of the derivatives, but the derivative of a product is *not* the product of the derivatives. To see this, consider x^2 and x^5. The product is x^7, and the derivative of this product is $7x^6$. The individual derivatives are $2x$ and $5x^4$, and the product of these derivatives is $10x^5$, which is not $7x^6$.

The following is the rule for finding the derivative of a product.

PRODUCT RULE. If $p(x) = f(x) \cdot g(x)$, then,

$$p'(x) = f(x) \cdot g'(x) + f'(x) \cdot g(x).$$

The derivative of a product is the first factor times the derivative of the second factor, plus the derivative of the first factor times the second factor.

Let us check this for $x^2 \cdot x^5$. There are four steps.

1. Write down the first factor.

2. Multiply it by the derivative of the second factor.

3. Write the derivative of the first factor.

4. Multiply it by the second factor.

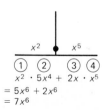

Example 1

$$\frac{d}{dx}(x^4 - 2x^3 - 7)(3x^2 - 5x)$$

$$= (x^4 - 2x^3 - 7)(6x - 5) + (4x^3 - 6x^2)(3x^2 - 5x)$$

Note that we could have multiplied the polynomials and then differentiated, avoiding the Product Rule, but this would have been more work.

Do Exercises 50 and 51.

The derivative of a quotient is not the quotient of the derivatives. To see why, consider x^5 and x^2. The quotient $\frac{x^5}{x^2}$ is x^3, and the derivative of this quotient is $3x^2$. The individual derivatives are $5x^4$ and $2x$, and the quotient of these derivatives $\frac{5x^4}{2x}$ is $\frac{5}{2}x^3$, which is not $3x^2$. The rule for differentiating quotients is as follows:

QUOTIENT RULE. If $q(x) = \dfrac{f(x)}{g(x)}$, then

$$q'(x) = \frac{g(x) \cdot f'(x) - g'(x) \cdot f(x)}{[g(x)]^2}.$$

The derivative of a quotient is the denominator times the derivative of the numerator, minus the derivative of the denominator times the derivative of the numerator, all divided by the square of the denominator.

Another way to remember this is shown below. It starts with squaring the denominator. The denominator is also used as the first factor of the first term above.

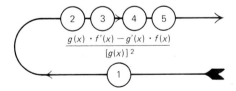

1. Square the denominator.
2. Write down the denominator.
3. Multiply the denominator by the derivative of the numerator.
4. Write the derivative of the denominator.
5. Multiply it by the numerator.

Use the Product Rule to find $f'(x)$.

50. $f(x) = 3x^8 \cdot x^{10}$

51. $f(x) = (9x^3 + 4x^2 + 10)(-7x^2 + x^4)$

52. For $f(x) = \dfrac{x^9}{x^5}$, find $f'(x)$ using the Quotient Rule.

Example 2 For $q(x) = \dfrac{x^5}{x^3}$, find $q'(x)$.

Solution $q'(x) = \dfrac{x^3 \cdot 5x^4 - 3x^2 \cdot x^5}{[x^3]^2} = \dfrac{5x^7 - 3x^7}{x^6} = \dfrac{2x^7}{x^6} = 2x$

Do Exercise 52.

Example 3 Differentiate $\dfrac{1 + x^2}{x^3}$.

Solution

$$\frac{d}{dx}\left(\frac{1 + x^2}{x^3}\right) = \frac{x^3 \cdot 2x - 3x^2(1 + x^2)}{(x^3)^2} = \frac{2x^4 - 3x^2 - 3x^4}{x^6} = \frac{-x^4 - 3x^2}{x^6}$$

$$= \frac{-1 \cdot x^2 \cdot x^2 - 3x^2}{x^6} = \frac{x^2(-x^2 - 3)}{x^6} = \frac{-x^2 - 3}{x^4}$$

Differentiate.

53. $\dfrac{1 - x^2}{x^5}$

Example 4 Differentiate $\dfrac{x^2 - 3x}{x - 1}$.

Solution

$$\frac{d}{dx}\left(\frac{x^2 - 3x}{x - 1}\right) = \frac{(x - 1)(2x - 3) - 1(x^2 - 3x)}{(x - 1)^2}$$

$$= \frac{2x^2 + 5x + 3 - x^2 + 3x}{(x - 1)^2}$$

$$= \frac{x^2 - 2x + 3}{(x - 1)^2}$$

It is not necessary to multiply out $(x - 1)^2$.

54. $\dfrac{x^2 - 1}{x^3 + 1}$

Do Exercises 53 and 54.

An Application

We discussed earlier that it is more typical for a total revenue function to vary depending on the number x of units sold. Let us see what can determine this. Recall the consumer's demand function $p = D(x)$, discussed on p. 55. It is the price p a seller must charge in order to sell exactly x units of a product. This is typically a decreasing function.

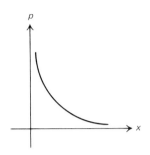

The total revenue from the sale of x units is then given by

$R(x) =$ (number of units sold) $\cdot$ (price charged to sell the units),

or

$R(x) = x \cdot p = xD(x).$

A typical graph of a revenue function is shown below.

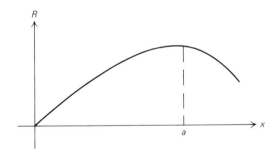

To sell more units, $D(x)$ decreases. Because we have a product $x \cdot D(x)$, the revenue typically rises for a while as x increases, but tapers off as $D(x)$ gets smaller and smaller.

Using the Product Rule, one can obtain an expression for the marginal revenue $R'(x)$ in terms of x and $D'(x)$ as follows:

$R(x) = xD(x),$

so

$R'(x) = 1 \cdot D(x) + x \cdot D'(x) = D(x) + xD'(x).$

You need not memorize this. One can merely repeat the Product Rule where necessary.

Do Exercise 55.

55. A company determines that the demand function for a certain product is given by

$$p = D(x) = 200 - x.$$

a) Find an expression for total revenue $R(x)$.

b) Find the marginal revenue $R'(x)$.

EXERCISE SET 2.7

Differentiate.

1. $x^3 \cdot x^8$; two ways

2. $x^4 \cdot x^9$; two ways

3. $\dfrac{-1}{x}$; two ways

4. $\dfrac{1}{x}$; two ways

5. $\dfrac{x^8}{x^5}$; two ways

6. $\dfrac{x^9}{x^5}$; two ways

7. $(8x^5 - 3x^2 + 20)(8x^4 - 3\sqrt{x})$

8. $(7x^6 + 4x^3 - 50)(9x^{10} - 7\sqrt{x})$

9. $x(300 - x)$

10. $x(400 - x)$

11. $\dfrac{x}{300 - x}$

12. $\dfrac{x}{400 - x}$

13. $\dfrac{3x - 1}{2x + 5}$

14. $\dfrac{2x + 3}{x - 5}$

15. $\dfrac{x^2 + 1}{x^3 - 1}$

16. $\dfrac{x^3 - 1}{x^2 + 1}$

17. $\dfrac{x}{1 - x}$

18. $\dfrac{x}{3 - x}$

19. $\dfrac{x - 1}{x + 1}$

20. $\dfrac{x + 2}{x - 2}$

21. $\dfrac{1}{x - 3}$

22. $\dfrac{1}{x + 2}$

23. $\dfrac{3x^2 + 2x}{x^2 + 1}$

24. $\dfrac{3x^2 - 5x}{x^2 - 1}$

25. $\dfrac{3x^2 - 5x}{x^8}$

26. $\dfrac{3x^2 + 2x}{x^5}$

In each of Exercises 27–30, a demand function $p = D(x)$ is given. Find

a) total revenue $R(x)$,
b) marginal revenue $R'(x)$.

27. $D(x) = 400 - x$

28. $D(x) = 500 - x$

29. $D(x) = \dfrac{4000}{x} + 3$

30. $D(x) = \dfrac{3000}{x} + 5$

31. In Section 2.6, we defined the average cost of producing x units of a product in terms of the total cost $C(x)$ by

$$A(x) = \frac{C(x)}{x}.$$

Use the Quotient Rule to find a general expression for *marginal average cost* $A'(x)$.

32. In this section we determined that

$$R(x) = xD(x).$$

Then $D(x) = \dfrac{R(x)}{x}$ = average revenue from the sale of x units. Use the Quotient Rule to find a general expression for *marginal average revenue* $D'(x)$.

2.8 FURTHER DIFFERENTIATION TECHNIQUES

We know how to differentiate the function

$$f(x) = x^5.$$

The derivative $f'(x)$ is $5x^4$.

How might we differentiate the function $y = (1 + x^3)^5$. Here we have something (the quantity $1 + x^3$) to the fifth power. For the moment, let us write $\boxed{}$ instead of $1 + x^3$. Then, since $\boxed{}$ is raised to the fifth power and f is the function which does this, we have

$$f(\boxed{}) = \boxed{}^5.$$

We differentiate this the way we differentiate x^5, and then we multiply the result by the derivative of $\boxed{}$. In other words,

$$\frac{d}{dx}\boxed{}^5 = 5\boxed{}^4 \cdot \frac{d}{dx}\boxed{}.$$

Once this is done, we can write $1 + x^3$ for $\boxed{}$ and complete the details. We have

$$\frac{d}{dx}(1 + x^3)^5 = 5(1 + x^3)^4 \cdot \frac{d}{dx}(1 + x^3)$$

$$= 5(1 + x^3)^4 \cdot 3x^2, \text{ or } 15x^2(1 + x^3)^4.$$

We are using the following new rule.

THE EXTENDED POWER RULE. Suppose $\boxed{}$ is some function of x. Then

$$\frac{d}{dx}\boxed{}^a = a\boxed{}^{a-1} \cdot \frac{d}{dx}\boxed{}.$$

More formally,

$$\frac{d}{dx}[g(x)]^a = a[g(x)]^{a-1} \cdot \frac{d}{dx}g(x).$$

Let us differentiate $(1 + x^3)^5$ again. There are four steps to carry out.

$\boxed{}^5$ 1. Mentally block out the "inside" function $1 + x^3$.

$5\boxed{}^4$ 2. Differentiate the "outside" function $\boxed{}^5$.

$5(1 + x^3)^4$ 3. Write in the "inside" function.

$5(1 + x^3)^4 \cdot 3x^2$ 4. Multiply by the derivative of the "inside"

$= 15x^2(1 + x^3)^4$ function.

Step 4 is most commonly omitted. Try not to forget it!

OBJECTIVES

You should be able to differentiate using the Extended Power Rule.

Differentiate.

56. $(1 + x^2)^{10}$

57. $(1 - x^2)^{1/2}$

58. Differentiate.
$$(1 + x^2)^2 - (1 + x^2)^3$$

59. Differentiate.
$$(x - 4)^5(6 - x)^3$$

Example 1 $\dfrac{d}{dx}(1 + x^3)^{1/2} = \tfrac{1}{2}(1 + x^3)^{1/2 - 1} \cdot 3x^2 = \tfrac{1}{2}(1 + x^3)^{-1/2} \cdot 3x^2$

$$= \frac{3x^2}{2\sqrt{1 + x^3}}$$

Do Exercises 56 and 57.

Example 2 Differentiate $(1 - x^2)^3 - (1 - x^2)^2$.

Solution Here we combine the Difference Rule and the Extended Power Rule.

$$\frac{d}{dx}[(1 - x^2)^3 - (1 - x^2)^2]$$

$= 3(1 - x^2)^2(-2x) - 2(1 - x^2)(-2x)$ (We differentiate each term using the Extended Power Rule.)

$= -6x(1 - x^2)^2 + 4x(1 - x^2)$

$= x(1 - x^2)[-6(1 - x^2) + 4]$ (Here we factor out $x(1 - x^2)$.)

$= x(1 - x^2)[-6 + 6x^2 + 4]$

$= x(1 - x^2)(6x^2 - 2)$

$= 2x(1 - x^2)(3x^2 - 1)$

Do Exercise 58.

Example 3 Differentiate $(x - 5)^4(7 - x)^{10}$.

Solution Here we combine the Product Rule and the Extended Power Rule.

$$\frac{d}{dx}(x - 5)^4(7 - x)^{10}$$

$= (x - 5)^4 \, 10(7 - x)^9(-1) + 4(x - 5)^3(7 - x)^{10}$

$= -10(x - 5)^4(7 - x)^9 + 4(x - 5)^3(7 - x)^{10}$

$= (x - 5)^3(7 - x)^9[-10(x - 5) + 4(7 - x)]$ (We factored out $(x - 5)^3(7 - x)^9$.)

$= (x - 5)^3(7 - x)^9[-10x + 50 + 28 - 4x]$

$= (x - 5)^3(7 - x)^9(78 - 14x)$

$= 2(x - 5)^3(7 - x)^9(39 - 7x)$

Do Exercise 59.

Example 4 Differentiate $\left(\dfrac{x+3}{x-1}\right)^{1/4}$.

Solution We have to use the Quotient Rule to differentiate the inside function $\dfrac{x+3}{x-1}$.

$$\frac{d}{dx}\left(\frac{x+3}{x-1}\right)^{1/4} = \frac{1}{4}\left(\frac{x+3}{x-1}\right)^{1/4-1}\left[\frac{(x-1)1 - 1(x+3)}{(x-1)^2}\right]$$

$$= \frac{1}{4}\left(\frac{x+3}{x-1}\right)^{-3/4}\left[\frac{x-1-x-3}{(x-1)^2}\right]$$

$$= \frac{1}{4}\left(\frac{x+3}{x-1}\right)^{-3/4}\cdot\frac{-4}{(x-1)^2}$$

$$= \left(\frac{x+3}{x-1}\right)^{-3/4}\cdot\frac{-1}{(x-1)^2}$$

Do Exercise 60.

The Chain Rule

The Extended Power Rule is a special case of a more general rule called the *Chain Rule*. It is as follows:

THE CHAIN RULE. Suppose ⬚ is some function of x. Then

$$\frac{d}{dx}f(\boxed{}) = f'(\boxed{})\cdot\frac{d}{dx}\boxed{}.$$

More formally,

$$\frac{d}{dx}f(g(x)) = f'(g(x))\cdot\frac{d}{dx}g(x).$$

Note how the Extended Power Rule is a special case.

$$\frac{d}{dx}\boxed{}^a = a\boxed{}^{a-1}\cdot\frac{d}{dx}\boxed{}.$$

60. Differentiate.

$$\left(\frac{x+5}{x-4}\right)^{1/3}$$

EXERCISE SET 2.8

Differentiate.

1. $(1-x)^{55}$ **2.** $(1-x)^{100}$ **3.** $\sqrt{1+x}$ **4.** $\sqrt{1-x}$ **5.** $\sqrt{3x^2-4}$

6. $\sqrt{4x^2+1}$ **7.** $(3x^2-6)^{-40}$ **8.** $(4x^2+1)^{-50}$ **9.** $x\sqrt{2x+3}$ **10.** $x\sqrt{4x-7}$

11. $x^2\sqrt{x-1}$

12. $x^3\sqrt{x+1}$

13. $\dfrac{1}{(x+8)^3}$

14. $\dfrac{1}{(x+5)^2}$

15. $(1+x^3)^3 - (1+x^3)^4$

16. $(1+x^3)^5 - (1+x^3)^4$

17. $x^2 + (200 - x)^2$

18. $x^2 + (100 - x)^2$

19. $(x+6)^{10}(x-5)^4$

20. $(x-4)^8(x+3)^9$

21. $(x-4)^8(3-x)^4$

22. $(x+6)^{10}(5-x)^9$

23. $-4x(2x-3)^3$

24. $-5x(3x+5)^6$

25. $\left(\dfrac{x-1}{x+1}\right)^{1/2}$

26. $\left(\dfrac{x+3}{x-2}\right)^{1/2}$

27. Consider

$$f(x) = \frac{x^2}{(1+x)^5}.$$

a) Find $f'(x)$ using the Quotient Rule and the Extended Power Rule.

b) Note that $f(x) = x^2(1+x)^{-5}$. Find $f'(x)$ using the Product Rule and the Extended Power Rule.

c) Compare answers to (a) and (b).

28. Consider

$$g(x) = (x^3 + 5x)^2.$$

a) Find $g'(x)$ using the Extended Power Rule.

b) Note that $g(x) = x^6 + 10x^4 + 25x^2$. Find $g'(x)$.

c) Compare answers to (a) and (b).

29. A total cost function is given by

$$C(x) = 1000\sqrt{x+2}.$$

Find the marginal cost $C'(x)$.

30. A total revenue function is given by

$$R(x) = 2000\sqrt{x^2+3}.$$

Find the marginal revenue $R'(x)$.

CHAPTER 2 TEST

Which functions are continuous?

1.

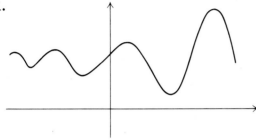

2.

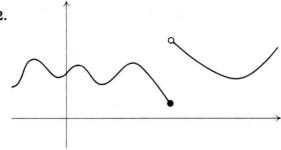

3. a) Complete.

Inputs x	Outputs $\dfrac{x^3 - 8}{x - 2}$
3	
2.5	
2.1	
2.01	
2.001	

b) Find

$$\lim_{x \to 2} \frac{x^3 - 8}{x - 2}.$$

4. Find a simplified difference quotient for

$$f(x) = 3x^2 + 1.$$

5. a) Complete.

x	$\dfrac{4x - 3}{x}$
5	
80	
200	
10,000	

b) Find

$$\lim_{x \to \infty} \left(\frac{4x - 3}{x} \right).$$

6. Find the points on the graph of $y = x^3 - 3x^2$ at which the tangent is horizontal.

Find $\dfrac{dy}{dx}$.

7. $y = x^{84}$ **8.** $y = 10\sqrt{x}$ **9.** $y = \dfrac{-10}{x}$

10. $y = x^{5/4}$ **11.** $y = -0.5x^2 + 0.61x + 90$

Differentiate.

12. $\frac{1}{3}x^3 - x^2 + 2x + 4$ **13.** $\dfrac{2x - 5}{x^4}$

14. $\dfrac{x}{5 - x}$ **15.** $(x + 3)^4(7 - x)^5$

16. $(x^5 - 4x^3 + x)^{-5}$ **17.** $x\sqrt{x^2 + 5}$

18. Given $R(x) = 50x$ and $C(x) = 0.001x^2 + 1.2x + 60$, find

a) $P(x)$.
b) $R(10)$, $C(10)$, $P(10)$.
c) $R'(x)$, $C'(x)$, $P'(x)$.
d) $R'(10)$, $C'(10)$, $P'(10)$.

19. In a certain memory experiment a person is able to memorize M words after t minutes, where

$$M = -0.001t^3 + 0.1t^2.$$

a) Find the rate of change of the number of words memorized with respect to time.
b) How many words are memorized the first 10 minutes (at $t = 10$)?
c) What is the memory rate at $t = 10$ minutes?

3 DIFFERENTIATION AND APPLICATIONS

OBJECTIVES

You should be able to find a higher order derivative.

1. Find the first six derivatives.

$$f(x) = 2x^6 - x^5 + 10.$$

2. For
$$y = x^7 - x^3,$$
find

a) $\dfrac{dy}{dx}$,

b) $\dfrac{d^2y}{dx^2}$,

c) $\dfrac{d^3y}{dx^3}$,

d) $\dfrac{d^4y}{dx^4}$.

3.1 HIGHER DERIVATIVES

Consider the function given by

$$f(x) = x^5 - 3x^4 + x.$$

Its derivative f' is given by

$$f'(x) = 5x^4 - 12x^3 + 1.$$

This function f' can be differentiated. We use the notation f'' for the derivative $(f')'$. We call f'' the *second derivative* of f. It is given by

$$f''(x) = 20x^3 - 36x^2.$$

Continuing in this manner, we have

$$f'''(x) = 60x^2 - 72x, \qquad \text{(the third derivative of } f)$$
$$f''''(x) = 120x - 72, \qquad \text{(the fourth derivative of } f)$$
$$f'''''(x) = 120. \qquad \text{(the fifth derivative of } f)$$

When notation, like $f'''''(x)$, gets lengthy we can abbreviate it using a numeral in parentheses. Thus

$$f^{(4)}(x) = 120x - 72, \qquad f^{(5)}(x) = 120, \qquad \text{and} \qquad f^{(6)}(x) = 0.$$

Do Exercise 1.

Leibniz's notation for the second derivative of a function given by $y = f(x)$ is

$$\frac{d^2y}{dx^2} \qquad \text{or} \qquad \frac{d}{dx}\left(\frac{dy}{dx}\right),$$

read "the second derivative of y with respect to x." The 2's in this notation are *not* exponents. If $y = x^5 - 3x^4 + x$, then

$$\frac{d^2y}{dx^2} = 20x^3 - 36x^2.$$

Leibniz's notation for the third derivative is $\dfrac{d^3y}{dx^3}$, for the fourth derivative $\dfrac{d^4y}{dx^4}$, and so on:

$$\frac{d^3y}{dx^3} = 60x^2 - 72x, \qquad \frac{d^4y}{dx^4} = 120x - 72, \qquad \frac{d^5y}{dx^5} = 120.$$

Do Exercise 2.

Example   For $y = \dfrac{1}{x}$, find $\dfrac{d^2y}{dx^2}$.

Solution $y = x^{-1}$, so

$$\frac{dy}{dx} = -1 \cdot x^{-1-1} = -x^{-2}, \quad \text{or} \quad -\frac{1}{x^2}.$$

Then

$$\frac{d^2y}{dx^2} = (-2)(-1)x^{-2-1} = 2x^{-3}, \quad \text{or} \quad \frac{2}{x^3}.$$

3. For $y = \dfrac{2}{x}$, find $\dfrac{d^2y}{dx^2}$.

Do Exercise 3.

Acceleration can be thought of as a second derivative. As an object moves, its distance from a fixed point after time t is some function of the time, say $s(t)$. Then

$$v(t) = s'(t) = \text{velocity at time } t,$$

and

$$a(t) = v'(t) = s''(t) = \text{acceleration at time } t.$$

Whenever a quantity is a function of time, the first derivative gives the rate of change with respect to time and the second derivative gives the acceleration. For example, if $y = P(t)$ gives the number of people in a population at time t, then $P'(t)$ gives how fast the size of the population is changing and $P''(t)$ gives the acceleration in the size of the population.

4. For $s(t) = 3t + t^4$, find the acceleration $a(t)$.

Do Exercise 4.

EXERCISE SET 3.1

Find $\dfrac{d^2y}{dx^2}$.

1. $y = 3x + 5$ **2.** $y = -4x + 7$ **3.** $y = -\dfrac{1}{x}$ **4.** $y = -\dfrac{3}{x}$ **5.** $y = x^{1/4}$

6. $y = \sqrt{x}$ **7.** $y = x^4 + \dfrac{4}{x}$ **8.** $y = x^3 - \dfrac{3}{x}$ **9.** $y = x^{-3}$ **10.** $y = x^{-4}$

11. $y = x^n$ **12.** $y = x^{-n}$ **13.** $y = x^4 - x^2$ **14.** $y = x^4 + x^3$ **15.** $y = \sqrt{x-1}$

16. $y = \sqrt{x+1}$ **17.** $y = ax^2 + bx + c$ **18.** $y = mx + b$

19. For $y = x^4$, find $\dfrac{d^4y}{dx^4}$.   **20.** For $y = x^5$, find $\dfrac{d^4y}{dx^4}$.   **21.** For $y = x^6 - x^3 + 2x$, find $\dfrac{d^5y}{dx^5}$.

22. For $y = x^7 - 8x^2 + 2$, find $\dfrac{d^6y}{dx^6}$.

23. For $y = x^n$, find $\dfrac{d^6y}{dx^6}$.

24. For $y = x^k$, find $\dfrac{d^5y}{dx^5}$.

25. If s is a distance given by $s(t) = t^3 + t^2 + 2t$, find the acceleration.

26. If s is a distance given by $s(t) = t^4 + t^2 + 3t$, find the acceleration.

27. A population grows from an initial size of 100,000 to an amount $P(t)$ given by

$$P(t) = 100,000(1 + 0.6t + t^2).$$

What is the acceleration in the size of the population?

28. A population grows from an initial size of 100,000 to an amount $P(t)$ given by

$$P(t) = 100,000(1 + 0.4t + t^2).$$

What is the acceleration in the size of the population?

OBJECTIVES

You should be able to find maximum and minimum values of functions.

5. Consider the following graph.

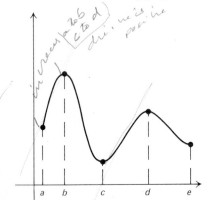

a) Over what intervals is the function increasing?
b) Over what intervals is the derivative positive? To determine this, locate a straightedge at points on the graph and decide whether slopes of tangent lines are positive.
c) Over what intervals is the function decreasing?
d) Over what intervals is the derivative negative?

Look for a pattern.

3.2 THE SHAPE OF A GRAPH, FINDING MAXIMUM AND MINIMUM VALUES

First and second derivatives give us information about the shape of a graph which may be relevant in finding maximum and minimum values of functions. Throughout this section we will assume the functions are continuous.

Increasing and Decreasing Functions

We have seen how the slope of a linear function determines whether it is increasing or decreasing (or neither). For a general function, the derivative yields similar information. Let us investigate how this happens in the margin exercise.

Do Exercise 5.

Perhaps you discovered the following:

If $f'(x) > 0$, for all x in an interval I, then f is increasing over I.

If $f'(x) < 0$, for all x in an interval I, then f is decreasing over I.

Concavity: Increasing and Decreasing Derivatives

Here are two functions. The graph on the left is turning upward and the other is turning downward. Let's see if we can relate this to their derivatives.

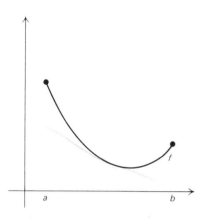

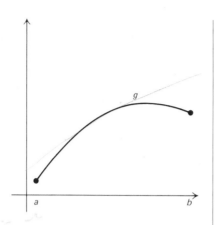

6. Consider the following graph.

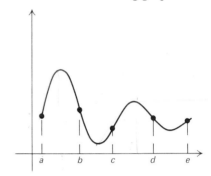

a) Over what intervals is the *derivative* increasing?

b) Over what intervals is the *derivative* decreasing?

Consider the graph of *f*. Take a ruler, or straightedge, and move along the curve from left to right. What happens to the slopes of the tangent lines? Do the same for the graph of *g*. Look for a pattern.

Do Exercise 6.

Perhaps you discovered the following:

> **A graph is turning upward over an interval *I* if *f′* is increasing over *I*. That is, $f''(x) > 0$ for all *x* in *I*. Such a graph is said to be *concave up over I*.**

> **A graph is turning downward over an interval *I* if *f′* is decreasing over *I*. That is, $f''(x) < 0$ for all *x* in *I*. Such a graph is said to be *concave down over I*.**

The following is a helpful memory device.

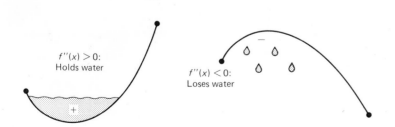

$f''(x) > 0$:
Holds water

$f''(x) < 0$:
Loses water

7. Consider the following graph.

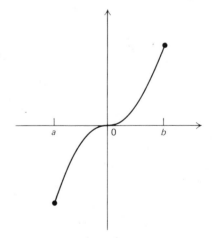

a) Over what intervals is the graph concave up?

b) Over what intervals is the graph concave down?

Do Exercise 7.

8. Which are points of inflection?

A *point of inflection*, or an *inflection point*, is a point across which the direction of concavity changes. For example, point P is an inflection point of the graph on the left. Points P, Q, R, and S are inflection points of the graph on the right. In Margin Exercise 7, the point $(0, 0)$ is an inflection point.

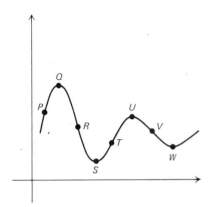

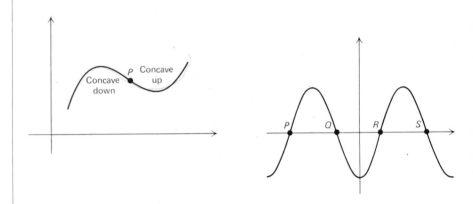

Do Exercise 8.

Just knowing the values of f' and f'' at some specific point x_0 can yield a lot of information about the shape of the graph over some (possibly small) interval containing x_0 as an interior point (assuming f'' exists and is continuous over the interval).

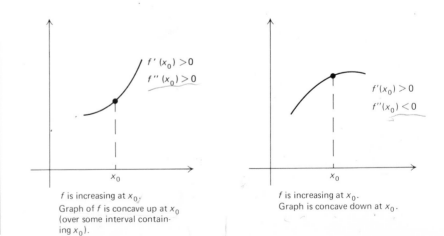

$f'(x_0) > 0$
$f''(x_0) > 0$

f is increasing at x_0.
Graph of f is concave up at x_0 (over some interval containing x_0).

$f'(x_0) > 0$
$f''(x_0) < 0$

f is increasing at x_0.
Graph is concave down at x_0.

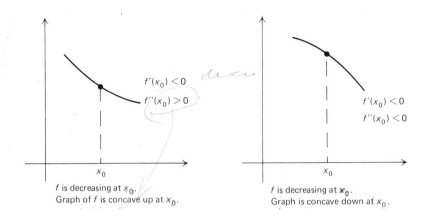

$f'(x_0) < 0$

$f''(x_0) > 0$

x_0

f is decreasing at x_0.
Graph of f is concave up at x_0.

$f'(x_0) < 0$

$f''(x_0) < 0$

x_0

f is decreasing at x_0.
Graph is concave down at x_0.

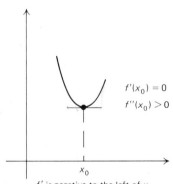
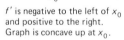

$f'(x_0) = 0$

$f''(x_0) > 0$

x_0

f' is negative to the left of x_0
and positive to the right.
Graph is concave up at x_0.

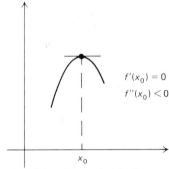

$f'(x_0) = 0$

$f''(x_0) < 0$

x_0

f' is positive to the left of x_0
and negative to the right.
Graph is concave down at x_0.

Example   Determine the shape of the graph of $f(x) = x^3 - x^2$ at $x = -1$.

Solution   For $f(x) = x^3 - x^2$,

$$f'(x) = 3x^2 - 2x \quad \text{and} \quad f''(x) = 6x - 2.$$

Then

$$f'(-1) = 3(-1)^2 - 2(-1) \quad \text{and} \quad f''(-1) = 6(-1) - 2$$
$$= 3 + 2 \qquad\qquad\qquad\qquad = -6 - 2$$
$$= 5 \qquad\qquad\qquad\qquad\qquad = -8.$$

9. Determine the shape of the graph of

$$f(x) = x^4 - 4x,$$

at

a) $x = 3$,

Thus the function is increasing at $x = -1$, since $f'(-1) > 0$; and concave down since $f''(-1) < 0$. This is shown at the right, where $f(-1) = (-1)^3 - (-1)^2 = -2$.

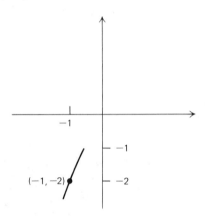

b) $x = 1$.

Do Exercise 9.

Let us take a more global look at two functions from the standpoint of the concepts we have considered. For example, consider

$$f(x) = x^2.$$

Now

$$f'(x) = 2x.$$

Note that $f'(0) = 0$. The graph has a horizontal tangent at 0. Also, when $x < 0$, $x^2 > 0$, so $3x^2 > 0$ and $f'(x) > 0$. Thus the function is decreasing on the interval $(-\infty, 0)$. When $x > 0$, $2x > 0$, so $f'(x) > 0$. This tells us that the function is increasing on the interval $(0, \infty)$. Check these facts on the graph.

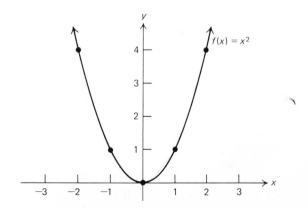

Let us look at the second derivative

$$f''(x) = 2.$$

The second derivative is positive for all values of x, since it is the constant 2; thus the graph is concave up over the entire real line. Check this on the graph.

As another example, consider

$$f(x) = x^3.$$

Now

$$f'(x) = 3x^2.$$

Note that $f'(0) = 0$. The graph has a horizontal tangent at 0. Also, when $x < 0$, $x^2 > 0$, so $3x^2 > 0$ and $f'(x) > 0$. Thus the function is increasing over the interval $(-\infty, 0)$. When $x > 0$, $x^2 > 0$, so $3x^2 > 0$ and $f'(x) > 0$. Thus the function is increasing over the interval $(0, \infty)$. In fact it is increasing over the entire real line. Check this on the graph.

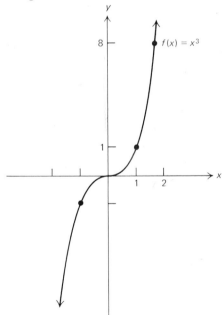

Let us look at the second derivative,

$$f''(x) = 6x.$$

When $x < 0$, $6x < 0$, so $f''(x) < 0$. Thus the graph is concave down over the interval $(-\infty, 0)$. When $x > 0$, $6x > 0$, so $f''(x) > 0$. Thus the graph is concave up over the interval $(0, \infty)$. Check this on the graph, noting also that the graph has an inflection point $(0, 0)$.

10. Consider this graph.

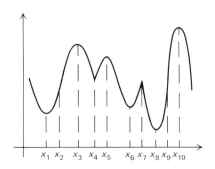

a) At which points are there horizontal tangents?

b) At which points does the derivative not exist?

c) Which are critical points?

11. Try to draw a graph of a continuous function from P to Q which increases on part, or parts, of $[a, b]$, and decreases on part, or parts, of $[a, b]$.

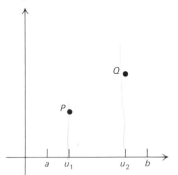

Does the function you drew have any critical points between u_1 and u_2?

Critical Points

A *critical point* of a function is an interior point c of its domain at which the function has a horizontal tangent, or at which the derivative does not exist. That is, c is a critical point if

$$f'(c) = 0 \quad \text{or} \quad f'(c) \text{ does not exist.}$$

Consider the following graph.

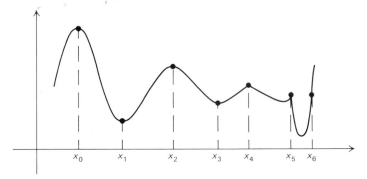

The points x_0, x_1, x_2, and x_3 are all critical points because the derivative is 0 at each of these points. The points x_4, x_5, and x_6 are all critical points because the derivative does not exist at these points.

Do Exercise 10.

The Shape of a Graph between Critical Points and Endpoints

Suppose we have a continuous function defined over an interval $[a, b]$.

Do Exercises 11 and 12.

Consider the following graph.

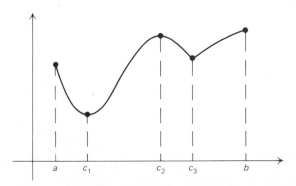

We have three critical points c_1, c_2, and c_3. These, together with the endpoints, will be referred to as *key* points. That is, the key points are

$$a, b, c_1, c_2, c_3.$$

Note in the above graph that between any two key points the function is either increasing, or decreasing.

This graph and the experience with Margin Exercises 11 and 12 lead us to the following principle.

SHAPE PRINCIPLE. **Suppose f is a continuous function over an interval $[a, b]$. Then between any two key points (a, b, plus critical points $c_1, c_2, c_3, \ldots, c_n$) the function is increasing, or it is decreasing.**

Finding Maximum and Minimum Values

What are the maximum and minimum values?   *Owen Franken from Stock, Boston*

12. Now try to draw a graph of a continuous function from P to Q which increases on part, or parts, of $[a, b]$, and decreases on part, or parts, of $[a, b]$, but in such a way that no critical points occur between u_1 and u_2.

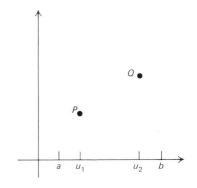

13. In each graph find where maximum and minimum values occur.

a)

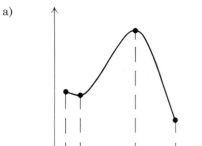

b)

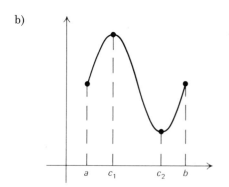

Consider the function f whose graph over the interval $[a, b]$ is as follows. The function value $f(c_1)$ is called a *minimum* value of the function, and $f(b)$ is called a *maximum* value of the function.

> A function f on an interval $[a, b]$ has a *maximum* at x_0 if
>
> $$f(x_0) \geq f(x) \text{ for all } x \text{ in } [a, b].$$
>
> A function f on an interval $[a, b]$ has a *minimum* at x_0 if
>
> $$f(x_0) \leq f(x) \text{ for all } x \text{ in } [a, b].$$

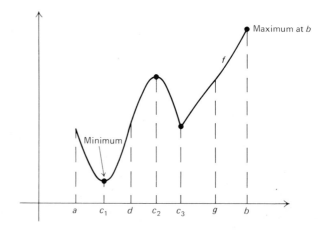

Do Exercise 13.

Look again at the preceding graph, but just consider the smaller interval $[d, g]$. Over that interval $f(c_2)$ is a maximum and $f(c_3)$ is a minimum. In relation to the larger interval $[a, b]$, we sometimes call $f(c_2)$ a relative maximum and $f(c_3)$ a relative minimum, because there is a smaller interval, namely $[d, g]$, over which they are indeed maximum and minimum values. We shall restrict our attention to finding *absolute*, or overall, *maximum* and *minimum* values.

Two results follow from Margin Exercise 13. The first is:

> A continuous function f defined on a closed interval $[a, b]$ must have a maximum and minimum value at points in $[a, b]$.

The second is a modification of the Shape Principle.

MAXIMUM-MINIMUM PRINCIPLE 1. Suppose f is a continuous function over an interval $[a, b]$, with critical points $c_1, c_2, \ldots, c_n$. The key points are $a, b, c_1, c_2, \ldots, c_n$. **Consider function values of the key points:**

$$f(a), f(b), f(c_1), f(c_2), \ldots, f(c_n).$$

The largest of these is the *maximum* of f on the interval $[a, b]$.

The smallest of these is the *minimum* of f on the interval $[a, b]$.

This follows from the Shape Principle because between two key points the function is either increasing or decreasing. Thus whatever the maximum and minimum values are they occur among function values of the key points.

Example 1   Find the maximum and minimum values of $f(x) = 3x^2 - x^3$ on the interval $[-\frac{1}{2}, 5]$.

Solution

a) First find $f'(x)$.
$$f'(x) = 6x - 3x^2$$

b) Determine the critical points. The derivative exists for all real numbers. Thus, the only candidates for critical points are those x's such that $f'(x) = 0$. Setting $f'(x)$ equal to 0 and solving, we get

$$f'(x) = 6x - 3x^2 = 0,$$
$$3x(2 - x) = 0,$$

$$\begin{aligned} 3x &= 0 &\text{or} &\quad 2 - x = 0 \\ x &= 0 &\text{or} &\quad -x = -2 \\ x &= 0 &\text{or} &\quad x = 2. \end{aligned}$$

The critical points are 0 and 2. The key points are $-\frac{1}{2}$, 5, 0, and 2.

c) We compute the *function* values at the key points.

$$\begin{aligned} f(-\tfrac{1}{2}) &= 3(-\tfrac{1}{2})^2 - (-\tfrac{1}{2})^3 = 3 \cdot \tfrac{1}{4} + \tfrac{1}{8} &&= \tfrac{7}{8} \\ f(5) &= 3 \cdot 5^2 - 5^3 = 3 \cdot 25 - 125 = 75 - 125 = -50 &&\quad\text{Minimum} \\ f(0) &= 3 \cdot 0^2 - 0^3 = 0 - 0 &&= 0 \\ f(2) &= 3 \cdot 2^2 - 2^3 = 3 \cdot 4 - 8 &&= 4 \qquad\text{Maximum} \end{aligned}$$

Thus

Maximum $= 4$ at $x = 2$,   and   Minimum $= -50$ at $x = 5$.

Do Exercise 14.

Example 2   Find the maximum and minimum values of $f(x) = 3x^2 - x^3$ on the interval $[7, 10]$.

14. Find the maximum and minimum values of
$$f(x) = x^3 - x^2 - x + 2$$
on the interval $[-1, 2]$.

15. Find the maximum and minimum values of

$$f(x) = x^3 - x^2 - x + 2$$

on the interval [5, 6].

Solution   As in Example 1 the derivative is 0 at 0 and 2. But neither 0 nor 2 is in the interval [7, 10], so there are no critical points in this interval. Thus the maximum and minimum values occur at the endpoints.

$$f(7) = 3 \cdot 7^2 - 7^3 = 3 \cdot 49 - 343 \qquad\qquad = -196 \quad \text{Maximum}$$
$$f(10) = 3 \cdot 10^2 - 10^3 = 3 \cdot 100 - 1000 = 300 - 1000 = -700 \quad \text{Minimum}$$

Note that a maximum can be a negative number.

Do Exercise 15.

When there is only *one* critical point c_0 in I, it can work out that we do not need to check the endpoint values. Consider these cases.

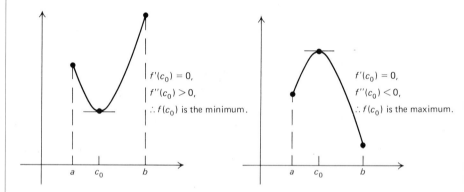

$f'(c_0) = 0,$
$f''(c_0) > 0,$
$\therefore f(c_0)$ is the minimum.

$f'(c_0) = 0,$
$f''(c_0) < 0,$
$\therefore f(c_0)$ is the maximum.

When $f'(c_0) = 0$ and $f''(c_0) > 0$, $f'(x)$ changes from negative to positive as x goes from the left of c_0 to the right. That is, the function f is decreasing to the left of c_0 and increasing to the right of c_0. It follows that $f(c_0)$ is the minimum value of f on I. Similarly, if $f'(c_0) = 0$ and $f''(c_0) < 0$, $f'(x)$ changes from positive to negative as x goes from the left of c_0 to the right. That is, the function f is increasing to the left of c_0 and decreasing to the right of c_0. It follows that $f(c_0)$ is the maximum value of f on I. The above turns out to hold no matter what the interval I, whether it is open, closed, or extends to infinity.

MAXIMUM-MINIMUM PRINCIPLE 2.   Suppose f is a function such that $f'(x)$ exists for every x in an interval I, and that there is *exactly one* (critical) point c_0, interior to I, for which $f'(c_0) = 0$. Then

$$f(c_0) \text{ is the maximum value on } I \text{ if } f''(c_0) < 0,$$

or

$$f(c_0) \text{ is the minimum value on } I \text{ if } f''(c_0) > 0.$$

If $f''(c_0) = 0$, we would have to use Maximum-Minimum Principle 1, or we would have to know more about the behavior of the function on the given interval.

Example 3 Find the maximum and minimum values of $f(x) = 4x - x^2$.

Solution When no interval is specified, we consider the entire domain of the function. In this case the domain is the set of all real numbers.

a) Find $f'(x)$.

$$f'(x) = 4 - 2x$$

b) Determine the critical points. The derivative exists for all real numbers. Thus we merely solve $f'(x) = 0$.

$$4 - 2x = 0$$
$$-2x = -4$$
$$x = 2.$$

Since there is only one critical point, we can use the second derivative

$$f''(x) = -2.$$

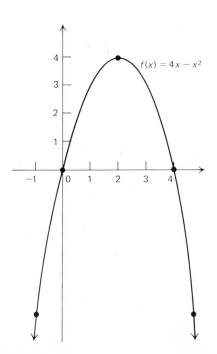

$f(x) = 4x - x^2$

16. Find the maximum and minimum values of

$$f(x) = x^2 - 4x.$$

Now the second derivative is constant, so $f''(2) = -2$, and since this is negative, we have the

$$\text{Maximum} = f(2) = 4 \cdot 2 - 2^2 = 8 - 4 = 4 \quad \text{at} \quad x = 2.$$

The function has no minimum as the graph indicates.

Do Exercise 16.

Example 4   Find the maximum and minimum values of $f(x) = 4x - x^2$ on the interval [0, 4].

Solution   By the reasoning in Example 3 we know that the maximum value is $f(2)$, or 4. We know this here also, without checking the endpoints. This time we have to check for the minimum:

$$f(0) = 4 \cdot 0 - 0^2 = 0, \quad \text{and} \quad f(4) = 4 \cdot 4 - 4^2 = 0.$$

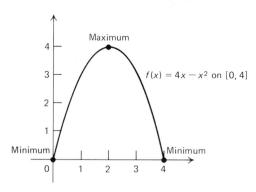

17. Find the maximum and minimum values of

$$f(x) = x^2 - 4x$$

on the interval [0, 4].

Thus the minimum is 0. It occurs twice at $x = 0$ and $x = 4$. Thus, the

$$\text{Maximum} = 4 \quad \text{at} \quad x = 2,$$

and the

$$\text{Minimum} = 0 \quad \text{at} \quad x = 0 \quad \text{and} \quad x = 4.$$

Do Exercise 17.

Example 5   Find the maximum and minimum values of $f(x) = x^3$.

Solution

a) Find $f'(x)$.

$$f'(x) = 3x^2.$$

b) Find the critical points.

$$3x^2 = 0$$
$$x^2 = 0$$
$$x = 0.$$

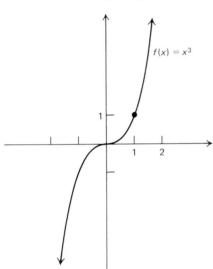

Since there is only one critical point we can use the second derivative

$$f''(x) = 6x.$$

Now $f''(0) = 6 \cdot 0 = 0$, so Maximum-Minimum Principle 2 fails.

We cannot use Maximum-Minimum Principle 1 because there are no endpoints. But note that $f'(x) = 3x^2$ is never negative. Thus it is increasing everywhere but at $x = 0$, so there is no maximum or minimum.

Do Exercise 18.

Example 6 Find the maximum and minimum values of $f(x) = 5x + \dfrac{500}{x}$ on the interval $(0, \infty)$.

Solution   a) Find $f'(x)$. We first express $f(x)$ as

$$f(x) = 5x + 500x^{-1}.$$

Then

$$f'(x) = 5 - 500x^{-2} = 5 - \frac{500}{x^2}.$$

18. a) Find the maximum and minimum values of

$$f(x) = x^3$$

on the interval $[-2, 2]$. [*Hint:* This function must have maximum and minimum values because it is restricted to a closed interval.] What are the only numbers at which these can occur?

b) Find the maximum and minimum values of

$$f(x) = x^3 - 4.$$

19. Find the maximum and minimum values of

$$f(x) = 10x + \frac{4000}{x}$$

on $(0, \infty)$.

b) Now $f'(x)$ exists for all values of x in $(0, \infty)$. Thus the only critical points are those for which $f'(x) = 0$.

$$5 - \frac{500}{x^2} = 0$$

$$5 = \frac{500}{x^2}$$

$$5x^2 = 500 \qquad \text{(Multiplying by } x^2, \text{ since } x \neq 0\text{)}$$

$$x^2 = 100$$

$$x = \pm 10$$

The only critical point in $(0, \infty)$ is 10. Thus we can use the second derivative

$$f''(x) = 1000x^{-3} = \frac{1000}{x^3}$$

to determine if we have a maximum or minimum. Now $f''(x)$ is positive for all values of x in $(0, \infty)$, so $f''(10) > 0$, and the

$$\text{Minimum} = f(10) = 5 \cdot 10 + \frac{500}{10} = 100 \qquad \text{at} \qquad x = 10.$$

The function has no maximum value.

In general,

> Suppose a function has only one critical point c in an interval which does not have endpoints, or does not contain its endpoints, such as $(-\infty, \infty)$, $(0, \infty)$, or (a, b). Then, if the function has a maximum, it will have no minimum; and if it has a minimum, it will have no maximum.

See Example 3 and Example 6.

Do Exercise 19.

EXERCISE SET 3.2

The graphs at the right show the gasoline mileage obtained when traveling at a constant speed, for an average size car and a compact car.

1. Consider the graph for the average size car over the interval [20, 80].

a) Estimate the speed at which the maximum gasoline mileage is obtained. ✓

b) Estimate the speed at which the minimum gasoline mileage is obtained. —

c) What is the mileage obtained at 70 mph?

d) What is the mileage obtained at 55 mph?

e) What percent increase in mileage is there by traveling at 55 mph rather than at 70 mph?

2. Answer the same questions in Exercise 1 for the compact car.

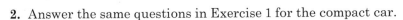

For the following functions, find the maximum and minimum values, if they exist, over the indicated interval. When no interval is specified, consider the set of all real numbers.

3. $f(x) = 5 + x - x^2$; [0, 2]

4. $f(x) = 4 + x - x^2$; [0, 2]

5. $f(x) = x^3 - x^2 - x + 2$; [0, 2]

6. $f(x) = x^3 + \frac{1}{2}x^2 - 2x + 5$; [0, 1]

7. $f(x) = x^3 - x^2 - x + 2$; [-1, 0]

8. $f(x) = x^3 + \frac{1}{2}x^2 - 2x + 5$; [-2, 0]

9. $f(x) = 3x - 2$; [-1, 1]

10. $f(x) = 2x + 4$; [-1, 1]

11. $f(x) = 3x - 2$

12. $f(x) = 2x + 4$

13. $f(x) = x(70 - x)$

14. $f(x) = x(50 - x)$

15. $f(x) = 2x^2 - 40x + 400$

16. $f(x) = 2x^2 - 20x + 100$

17. $f(x) = x - \frac{4}{3}x^3$; $(0, \infty)$

18. $f(x) = 16x - \frac{4}{3}x^3$; $(0, \infty)$

19. $f(x) = 17x - x^2$

20. $f(x) = 27x - x^2$

21. $f(x) = 40x - 0.5x^2 - 3$

22. $f(x) = 46x - 0.5x^2 - 10$

23. $f(x) = -0.001x^2 + 4.8x - 60$

24. $f(x) = -0.01x^2 + 1.4x - 30$

25. $f(x) = -\frac{1}{3}x^3 + 6x^2 - 11x - 50$; $(0, 3)$

26. $f(x) = -x^3 + x^2 + 5x - 1$; $(0, \infty)$

27. $f(x) = 15x^2 - \frac{1}{2}x^3$; [0, 30]

28. $f(x) = 4x^2 - \frac{1}{2}x^3$; [0, 8]

29. $f(x) = 2x + \dfrac{72}{x}$; $(0, \infty)$

30. $f(x) = x + \dfrac{3600}{x}$; $(0, \infty)$

31. $f(x) = x^2 + \dfrac{432}{x}$; $(0, \infty)$

32. $f(x) = x^2 + \dfrac{250}{x}$; $(0, \infty)$

33. $f(x) = 2x^4 - x$; $[-1, 1]$

34. $f(x) = 2x^4 + x$; $[-1, 1]$

35. $f(x) = x\sqrt{x + 3}$; $[-3, 3]$

36. $f(x) = \sqrt{x}$; $[0, 4]$

37. $f(x) = x^{2/3}$; $[-1, 1]$

38. $f(x) = x^{2/5}$; $[-1, 1]$

39. See Exercise 10 in Exercise Set 2.6. What is the maximum number of units sold? What must be spent on advertising to sell that number of units?

40. See Exercise 9 in Exercise Set 2.6. What is the maximum temperature during the illness and on what day does it occur?

41. See Exercise 4 in Exercise Set 2.6.

a) What is the maximum distance it takes to stop on glare ice? At what air temperature does this occur?

b) What is the minimum distance it takes to stop on glare ice? At what air temperature does this occur?

42. See Exercise 5 in Exercise Set 2.6. Consider that function over the interval $[0, 40]$; that is, the years 1940 to 1980.

a) What is the maximum percentage in college and in what year does it occur?

b) What is the minimum percentage in college and in what year does it occur?

43. In Exercise Set 1.6, Exercise 3 we determined that at a travel speed (constant velocity) x there are y accidents in daytime for every 100 million miles of travel, where y is given by

$$y = x^2 - 122.5x + 3775.$$

At what travel speed do the fewest accidents occur?

44. In Section 1.6, Example 2, we determined that at travel speed (constant velocity) x, the cost y, in cents per mile, of operating a car is given by

$$y = 0.02x^2 - 1.3x + 30.$$

At what travel speed is the cost of operating a car a minimum?

OBJECTIVES

You should be able to solve maximum-minimum problems.

3.3 MAXIMUM-MINIMUM PROBLEMS

One very important application of the differential calculus is the solving of maximum-minimum problems; that is, finding the maximum or minimum value of some varying quantity Q and where that maximum or minimum occurs.

Example 1   A hobby store has 20 ft of fencing to fence off a rectangular electric train area in one corner of its display room. What dimensions of the rectangle will maximize the area? What is the maximum area?

Exploratory Solution   Intuitively, one might think that it does not matter what dimensions one uses; they will all yield the same area. To show that this is not true, as well as to conjecture a possible solution, consider the exploratory exercises in Margin Exercise 20.

Owen Franken from Stock, Boston

But, before doing those exercises let us express the area in terms of one variable. If we let x = the length of one side, and y = the length of the other, then since the sum of the lengths must be 20 ft,

$$x + y = 20,$$

and

$$y = 20 - x.$$

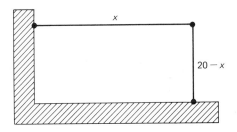

Then the area is given by

$$A = xy$$
$$A = x(20 - x) = 20x - x^2.$$

Do Exercise 20.

20. *Exploratory exercises.*

a) Complete this table.

x	y $20 - x$	A $x(20 - x)$
0		
4		
6.5		
8		
10		
12		
13.2		
20		

b) Make a graph of x versus A, that is, of points (x, A) from the table, and connect them with a smooth curve.

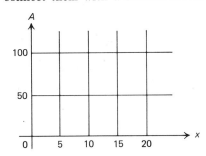

c) Does it matter what dimensions we use?

d) Make a conjecture about what the maximum might be and where it would occur.

21. A rancher has 50 ft of fencing to fence off a rectangular animal pen in the corner of a barn. What dimensions of the rectangle will yield the maximum area? What is the maximum area?

Calculus Solution   We are trying to find the maximum value of

$$A = 20x - x^2 \text{ on the interval } (0, 20).$$

We consider the interval $(0, 20)$ because x is the length of one side and cannot be negative. Since there is only 20 ft of fencing, x cannot be greater than 20. Also, x cannot be 20 because the length of y would be 0.

a) We first find $A'(x)$, where $A(x) = 20x - x^2$.

$$A'(x) = 20 - 2x.$$

b) This derivative exists for all values of x in $(0, 20)$. Thus the only critical points are where

$$A'(x) = 20 - 2x = 0,$$
$$-2x = -20,$$
$$x = 10.$$

Since there is only one critical point in the interval, we can use the second derivative to determine if we have a maximum. Note that

$$A''(x) = -2, \quad \text{which is a constant.}$$

Thus $A''(10)$ is negative, so $A(10)$ is a maximum. Now

$$A(10) = 10(20 - 10) = 10 \cdot 10 = 100.$$

Thus the maximum area of 100 sq. ft is obtained using 10 ft for the length of one side, and $20 - 10$ ft, or 10 ft, for the other. Note that while you may have conjectured this in Margin Exercise 20, the tools of calculus allowed us to prove it.

Do Exercise 21.

Example 2   A stereo manufacturer determines that in order to sell x units of a new stereo its price per unit must be

$$p = D(x) = 1000 - x.$$

It also determines that the total cost of producing x units is given by

$$C(x) = 3000 + 20x.$$

a) Find the total revenue $R(x)$.

b) Find the total profit $P(x)$.

c) How many units must the company produce and sell to maximize profit?

d) What is the maximum profit?

e) What price per unit must be charged to make this maximum profit?

Solution

a) $R(x)$ = Total revenue = (number of units) · (price per unit)

$$= \quad\quad x \quad\quad\quad\quad p$$
$$= x(1000 - x) = 1000x - x^2.$$

b) $\underline{P(x)} = R(x) - C(x) = (1000x - x^2) - (3000 + 20x)$
$$= -x^2 + 980x - 3000.$$

c) To find the maximum value of $P(x)$ we first find $P'(x)$.

$$P'(x) = -2x + 980.$$

This is defined for all real numbers (actually we are only interested in numbers x in $[0, \infty)$, since we cannot produce a negative number of stereos). Thus we solve

$$P'(x) = -2x + 980 = 0$$
$$-2x = -980$$
$$x = 490.$$

Since there is only one critical point, we can try to use the second derivative to determine if we have a maximum. Note that

$$P''(x) = -2, \text{ a constant.}$$

Thus $P''(490)$ is negative, so $P(490)$ is a maximum.

d) The maximum profit is given by

$$P(490) = -(490)^2 + 980 \cdot 490 - 3000 = \$237{,}100.$$

Thus the stereo manufacturer makes a maximum profit of \$237,100 by producing and selling 490 stereos.

e) The price per unit to make the maximum profit is $p = 1000 - 490 = \$510.$

Do Exercise 22.

Let us take a general look at the total profit function and its related functions.

In the first graph we have the total cost and total revenue functions. We can estimate what the maximum profit might be by looking for the widest gap between $R(x)$ and $C(x)$. Points B_0 and B_2 are "break even" points.

22. A company determines that in order to sell x units of a certain product its price per unit must be

$$p = D(x) = 200 - x.$$

It also determines that its total cost of producing x units is given by

$$C(x) = 5000 + 8x.$$

a) Find the total revenue $R(x)$.

b) Find the total profit $P(x)$.

c) How many units must the company produce and sell in order to maximize profit?

d) What is the maximum profit?

e) What price per unit must be charged to make this maximum profit?

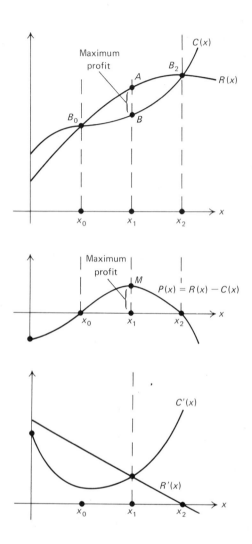

In the second graph we have the total profit function. Note that when production is too low ($<x_0$) there is a loss because of high fixed or initial costs and low revenue. When production is too high ($>x_2$), there is also a loss due to high marginal costs and low marginal revenues, as seen in the third graph.

The business operates at a profit everywhere between x_0 and x_2. Note that maximum profit occurs at a critical point x_1 of $P(x)$. Assuming $P'(x)$ to exist for all x in some interval, usually $[0, \infty)$, this critical point occurs at some number x such that

$$P'(x) = 0.$$

Since $P(x) = R(x) - C(x)$, it follows that

$$P'(x) = R'(x) - C'(x).$$

Thus the maximum profit occurs at some number x such that

$$R'(x) - C'(x) = 0,$$

or

$$R'(x) = C'(x).$$

In summary,

> **Maximum profit is achieved when marginal revenue equals marginal cost:**
>
> $$R'(x) = C'(x).$$

Here is a general strategy for solving maximum-minimum problems. While it may not guarantee success, it should certainly enhance one's chances.

1. **Read the problem carefully. If relevant, draw a picture.**
2. **Label the picture with appropriate variables and constants, noting what varies and what stays fixed.**
3. **Translate the problem to an equation, involving a quantity Q to be maximized or minimized.**
4. **Try to express Q as a function of *one* variable. Use the procedures developed in Section 3.2 to determine maximum or minimum values and where they occur.**

Example 3 From a thin piece of cardboard 8 in. by 8 in., square corners are cut out so that the sides can be folded up to make a box. What dimensions will yield a box of maximum volume? What is the maximum volume?

Exploratory Solution One might again think that it does not matter what the dimensions are, but our experience with Example 1 might lead us to think otherwise. We make a drawing as shown below.

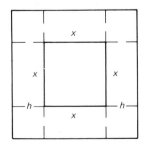 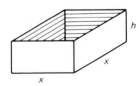

23. *Exploratory exercises.*

a) Complete this table.

x	h $\frac{1}{2}(8-x)$	V $x \cdot x \cdot \frac{1}{2}(8-x)$
0		
1		
2		
3		
4		
4.6		
5		
6		
6.8		
7		
8		

b) Make a graph of x versus V.

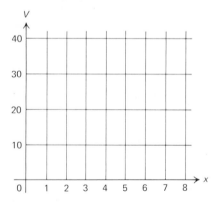

c) Make a conjecture about what the maximum might be and where it would occur.

When squares of length h on a side are cut out of the corners we are left with a square base of length x. The volume of the resulting box is

$$V = lwh = x \cdot x \cdot h.$$

We want to express V in terms of one variable. Note that the overall length of a side of the cardboard is 8 in. We see from the drawing that

$$h + x + h = 8,$$
or
$$x + 2h = 8.$$

Solving for h we get

$$2h = 8 - x$$
$$h = \tfrac{1}{2}(8 - x) = \tfrac{1}{2} \cdot 8 - \tfrac{1}{2}x = 4 - \tfrac{1}{2}x.$$

Thus

$$V = x \cdot x \cdot (4 - \tfrac{1}{2}x) = x^2(4 - \tfrac{1}{2}x) = 4x^2 - \tfrac{1}{2}x^3.$$

In Margin Exercise 23 you will compute some values of V.

Do Exercise 23.

Calculus Solution   You probably noted in Margin Exercise 23 that it was a bit more difficult, than in Example 1, to conjecture where the maximum occurs. At the least it seems reasonable that it occurs for some x between 5 and 6. Let us find out for certain using calculus. We are trying to find the maximum value of

$$V(x) = 4x^2 - \tfrac{1}{2}x^3 \text{ on the interval } (0, 8).$$

We first find $V'(x)$.

$$V'(x) = 8x - \tfrac{3}{2}x^2$$

Now $V'(x)$ exists for all x in the interval $(0, 8)$ so we set it equal to 0 to find the critical values.

$$V'(x) = 8x - \tfrac{3}{2}x^2 = 0,$$
$$x(8 - \tfrac{3}{2}x) = 0,$$

$$x = 0 \quad \text{or} \quad 8 - \tfrac{3}{2}x = 0$$
$$x = 0 \quad \text{or} \quad -\tfrac{3}{2}x = -8$$
$$x = 0 \quad \text{or} \quad x = -\tfrac{2}{3}(-8) = \tfrac{16}{3}.$$

The only critical point in $(0, 8)$ is $\frac{16}{3}$. Thus we can use second derivative

$$V''(x) = 8 - 3x$$

to determine if we have a maximum. Since

$$V''(\tfrac{16}{3}) = 8 - 3 \cdot \tfrac{16}{3} = -8,$$

$V''(\frac{16}{3})$ is negative, so $V(\frac{16}{3})$ is a maximum, and

$$V(\tfrac{16}{3}) = 4 \cdot (\tfrac{16}{3})^2 - \tfrac{1}{2}(\tfrac{16}{3})^3 = \tfrac{1024}{27} = 37\tfrac{25}{27}.$$

The maximum volume is $37\frac{25}{37}$ cu. in. The dimensions which yield this maximum volume are $x = \frac{16}{3} = 5\frac{1}{3}$ in., by $x = 5\frac{1}{3}$ in., by $h = 4 - \frac{1}{2}(\frac{16}{3}) = 1\frac{1}{3}$ in. It would surely have been difficult to guess this from Margin Exercise 23.

Do Exercise 24.

In the following problem an open top container of fixed volume is to be constructed. We want to determine the dimensions which will allow it to be built with the least amount of material. Such a problem could be important from an ecological standpoint.

Example 4   A container firm is designing an open-top rectangular box with a square base which will hold 108 cubic centimeters (cc). What dimensions yield the minimum surface area? What is the minimum surface area?

Solution   The surface area of the box is

$$S = x^2 + 4xy.$$

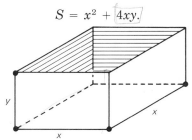

The volume must be 108 cc, and is given by

$$V = x^2 y = 108.$$

To express S in terms of one variable, we solve $x^2 y = 108$ for y:

$$y = \frac{108}{x^2}.$$

24. Repeat Example 3, but for a piece of cardboard which is 10 in. by 10 in.

25. Repeat Example 4, but for a fixed volume of 500 cc.

Then

$$S = x^2 + 4x \left(\frac{108}{x^2} \right) = x^2 + \frac{432}{x}.$$

Now S is defined only for positive numbers, and the problem dictates that the length x be positive, so we are minimizing S on the interval $(0, \infty)$. We first find $\frac{dS}{dx}$.

$$\frac{dS}{dx} = 2x - \frac{432}{x^2}.$$

Since $\frac{dS}{dx}$ exists for all x in $(0, \infty)$, the only critical points are where $\frac{dS}{dx} = 0$. Thus, we solve the following equation:

$$2x - \frac{432}{x^2} = 0$$

$$x^2 \left(2x - \frac{432}{x^2} \right) = x^2 \cdot 0 \qquad \text{(We multiply by x^2 to clear of fractions.)}$$

$$2x^3 - 432 = 0$$

$$2x^3 = 432$$

$$x^3 = 216$$

$$x = 6.$$

This is the only critical point so we can use the second derivative to determine if we have a minimum.

$$\frac{d^2S}{dx^2} = 2 + \frac{864}{x^3}$$

Note that this is positive for all positive values of x. Thus we have a minimum at $x = 6$. When $x = 6$, it follows that $y = 3$:

$$y = \frac{108}{6^2} = \frac{108}{36} = 3.$$

Thus the surface area is minimized when $x = 6$ cm (centimeters) and $y = 3$ cm. The minimum surface area is

$$S = 6^2 + 4 \cdot 6 \cdot 3 = 108 \text{ sq. cm.}$$

This, by coincidence, is the same number as the fixed volume.

Do Exercise 25.

Example 5 *Determining a ticket price.* Fight promoters ride a thin line between profit and loss, especially in determining the price to charge for admission to closed circuit television showings in local theaters. By keeping records, a theater determines that if the admission price is $20, it averages 1000 people in attendance. But, for every increase of $1, it loses 100 customers from the average. Every customer spends an average of $0.80 on concessions. What admission price should the theater charge to maximize total revenue?

Solution Let x = the amount by which the price of $20 should be increased (if x is negative the price would be decreased). We first express total revenue R as a function of x. Note that

$R(x)$ = (Revenue from tickets) + (Revenue from concessions)

$\quad$ = (Number of people) · (Ticket price) + $0.80(Number of people)

$\quad$ = $(1000 - 100x)(20 + x) + 0.80(1000 - 100x)$

$\quad$ = $20{,}000 - 2000x + 1000x - 100x^2 + 800 - 80x$

$R(x) = -100x^2 - 1080x + 20{,}800$

We are trying to find the maximum value of R over the set of all real numbers. To find x such that $R(x)$ is a maximum we first find $R'(x)$.

$$R'(x) = -200x - 1080$$

This derivative exists for all real numbers x; thus the only critical points are where $R'(x) = 0$, so we solve that equation.

$$-200x - 1080 = 0$$
$$-200x = 1080$$
$$x = -5.4 = -\$5.40$$

Since this is the only critical point, we can use the second derivative,

$$R''(x) = -200,$$

to determine if we have a maximum. Since $R''(-5.4)$ is negative, $R(-5.4)$ is a maximum. Thus to maximize revenue the theater should charge

$$\$20 + (-\$5.40) \quad \text{or } \$14.60 \text{ per ticket.}$$

That is, it will get more people into the theater, $1000 - 100(-5.4)$, or 1540, by decreasing its price, and this will result in maximum revenue.

Do Exercise 26.

26. Transit companies also ride a thin line between profit and loss. A company determines that at a fare of 30¢ it will average 10,000 fares a day. For every increase of 10¢, it loses 2000 customers. What fare should be charged to maximize revenue?

[*Hint*: Let x = the number of 10¢ fare increases (if x is negative the fare would be decreased). Then the new fare would be $30 + 10x$.]

EXERCISE SET 3.3

1. Of all the numbers whose sum is 50, find the two which have the maximum product. That is, maximize $Q = xy$, where $x + y = 50$.

2. Of all the numbers whose sum is 70, find the two which have the maximum product. That is, maximize $Q = xy$, where $x + y = 70$.

3. In Exercise 1, can there be a minimum product? Explain.

4. In Exercise 2, can there be a minimum product? Explain.

5. Of all numbers whose difference is 4, find the two which have the minimum product.

6. Of all numbers whose difference is 6, find the two which have the minimum product.

7. Maximize $Q = xy^2$, where x and y are positive numbers such that $x + y^2 = 1$.

8. Maximize $Q = xy^2$, where x and y are positive numbers such that $x + y^2 = 4$.

9. Minimize $Q = x^2 + y^2$, where $x + y = 20$.

10. Minimize $Q = x^2 + y^2$, where $x + y = 10$.

11. Maximize $Q = xy$, where x and y are positive numbers such that $\frac{4}{3}x^2 + y = 16$.

12. Maximize $Q = xy$, where x and y are positive numbers such that $x + \frac{4}{3}y^2 = 1$.

13. A rancher wants to build a rectangular fence next to a river, using 120 yd of fencing. What dimensions of the rectangle will maximize the area? What is the maximum area? Note that the rancher does not have to fence in the side next to the river.

14. A rancher wants to enclose two rectangular areas near a river, one for sheep and one for cattle. There are 240 yd of fencing available. What is the largest total area that can be enclosed?

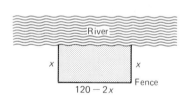

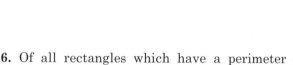

15. A carpenter is building a room with a fixed perimeter of 54 ft. What are the dimensions of the largest room that can be built? What is its area?

16. Of all rectangles which have a perimeter of 34 ft find the dimensions of the one with the largest area. What is its area?

Find the maximum profit and the number of units which must be produced and sold to yield the maximum profit.

17. $R(x) = 50x - 0.5x^2$, $C(x) = 4x + 10$

18. $R(x) = 50x - 0.5x^2$, $C(x) = 10x + 3$

19. $R(x) = 2x$, $C(x) = 0.01x^2 + 0.6x + 30$

20. $R(x) = 5x$, $C(x) = 0.001x^2 + 1.2x + 60$

21. $R(x) = 9x - 2x^2$, $C(x) = x^3 - 3x^2 + 4x + 1$; $R(x)$ and $C(x)$ are in thousands of dollars, x is in thousands of units.

22. $R(x) = 100x - x^2$, $C(x) = \frac{1}{3}x^3 - 6x^2 + 89x + 100$; $R(x)$ and $C(x)$ are in thousands of dollars, x is in thousands of units.

23. Raggs, Ltd., a clothing firm, determines that to sell x suits its price per suit must be

$$p = D(x) = 150 - 0.5x.$$

It also determines that its total cost of producing x suits is given by

$$C(x) = 4000 + 0.25x^2.$$

a) Find the total revenue $R(x)$.
b) Find the total profit $P(x)$.
c) How many suits must the company produce and sell to maximize profit?
d) What is the maximum profit?
e) What price per suit must be charged to make this maximum profit?

24. An appliance firm is marketing a new refrigerator. It determines that to sell x refrigerators its price per refrigerator must be

$$p = D(x) = 280 - 0.4x.$$

It also determines that its total cost of producing x refrigerators is given by

$$C(x) = 5000 + 0.6x^2.$$

a) Find the total revenue $R(x)$.
b) Find the total profit $P(x)$.
c) How many refrigerators must the company produce and sell to maximize profit?
d) What is the maximum profit?
e) What price per refrigerator must be charged to make this maximum profit?

25. From a thin piece of cardboard 30 in. by 30 in. square corners are cut out so the sides can be folded up to make a box. What dimensions will yield a box of maximum volume? What is the maximum volume?

26. From a thin piece of cardboard 20 in. by 20 in. square corners are cut out so the sides can be folded up to make a box. What dimensions will yield a box of maximum volume? What is the maximum volume?

27. A container company is designing an open top rectangular box with a square base which will have a volume of 62.5 cubic inches. What dimensions yield the minimum surface area? What is the minimum surface area?

28. A soup company is constructing an open top metal rectangular tank with a square base which will have a volume of 32 cubic feet. What dimensions yield the minimum surface area? What is the minimum surface area?

29. A university is trying to determine what price to charge for football tickets. At a price of $6 per ticket it averages 70,000 per game. For every increase of $1 it loses 10,000 people from the average. Every person at the game spends an average of $1.50 on concessions. What price per ticket should be charged to maximize revenue? How many people will attend at that price?

30. Suppose you are the owner of a 30-unit motel. All units are occupied when you charge $20 a day per unit. For every increase of x dollars in the daily rate, there are x units vacant. Each occupied room costs $2 per day to service and maintain. What should you charge per unit to maximize profit?

Huffman from Monkmeyer

will contain the largest volume that can be mailed? [*Hint*: There are two different girths.]

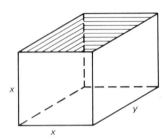

34. A rectangular play area is to be laid out in a person's back lot, and is to contain 48 square yards. The neighbor agrees to pay half the cost of the side of the play area which lines his lot. What dimensions will minimize the cost of the fence?

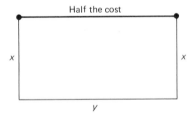

31. An apple farm yields an average of 30 bushels of apples per tree when 20 trees are planted on an acre of ground. Each time 1 more tree is planted per acre, the yield decreases 1 bu. per tree due to the extra congestion. How many trees should be planted to get the highest yield?

32. When a theater owner charges $3 for admission there is an average attendance of 100 people. For every $.10 increase in admission, there is a loss of 1 customer from the average. What admission should be charged to maximize revenue?

33. The postal service places a limit of 84 inches on the combined length and girth (distance around) of a package to be sent parcel post. What dimensions of a rectangular box with square cross section

35. A 24-inch piece of string is cut in two pieces. One piece is used to form a circle and the other to form a square. How should the string be cut so the sum of the areas is a minimum? maximum?

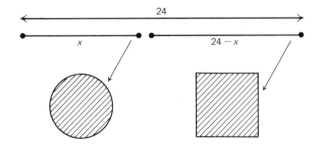

36. For what positive number is the sum of its reciprocal and four times its square a minimum?

37. A rectangular box with a volume of 320 cubic feet is to be constructed with a square base and top. The cost per square foot for the bottom is 15¢, for the top is 10¢, and for the sides is 2.5¢. What dimensions will minimize the cost?

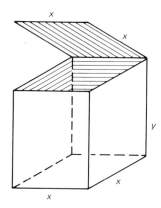

39. A Norman window is a rectangle with a semicircle on top. Suppose the perimeter of a particular Norman window is to be 24 ft. What should be its dimensions so the maximum amount of light will be allowed to enter through the window?

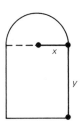

40. Solve Exercise 39, but this time the semicircle is to be stained glass which transmits only half as much light as the semicircle in Exercise 39.

41. A merchant was purchasing a display sign from a salesman. She said, "I want a sign which is 10 ft by 10 ft." The salesman responded, "That's just what we will give you, only to make it more aesthetic why don't we change it to 7 ft by 13 ft?" Comment.

38. A power line is to be constructed from a power station at point A (see the figure) to an island at point C which is directly 1 mile out in the water from a point B on shore. Point B is 4 miles downshore from the power station at A. It costs \$500 per mile to lay the power line under water and \$300 per mile to lay the line under ground. At what point S down shore from A should the line come to the shore to minimize cost? Note that S could very well be B or A. [*Hint*: The length of $\overline{CS}$ is $\sqrt{1 + x^2}$.]

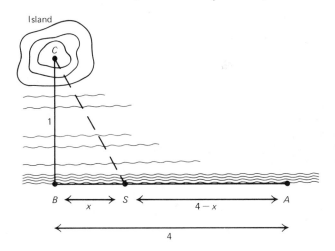

Find the Norman window.

42. The total cost function for producing x units of a certain product is given by

$$C(x) = 2x^2 + 10x + 50.$$

a) Find the marginal cost $C'(x)$.

b) Find the average cost $A(x) = \dfrac{C(x)}{x}$.

c) Find the *marginal average cost* $A'(x)$.

d) Find the minimum of $A(x)$ and the value x_0 at which it occurs. Find the marginal cost at x_0.

e) Compare $A(x_0)$ and $C'(x_0)$.

43. Consider $A(x) = \dfrac{C(x)}{x}$.

a) Find $A'(x)$ in terms of $C'(x)$ and $C(x)$.

b) Show that $A(x)$ has a minimum at that value of x_0 such that

$$C'(x_0) = A(x_0) = \frac{C(x_0)}{x_0}.$$

This shows that when marginal cost and average cost are the same, a product is being produced at the least average cost.

OBJECTIVES

You should be able, given certain inventory costs, to find how many times a year a store should reorder a product, and in what lot size, to minimize total inventory costs.

3.4 MINIMIZING INVENTORY COSTS

A retail outlet of a business is usually concerned about inventory costs. Suppose, for example, an appliance store sells 2500 TV sets per year. One way it could operate is to order all the TVs at once. But then the owners would face the carrying costs (insurance, building space, and so on) of storing all those TVs. Thus they might make several smaller orders, say 5, so that the largest number of TVs they would ever have to store is 500. On the other hand, each time they reorder there are certain reorder costs such as paperwork, delivery charges, manpower, and so on. It would therefore seem that there is some balance between carrying costs and reorder costs. We will see how calculus can help to determine what the balance might be.

How can inventory costs be minimized?   *Jan Lukas from Photo Researchers, Inc.*

We will be trying to minimize the following function.

Total inventory costs = Yearly carrying costs + Yearly reorder costs

The *lot size x* refers to the largest amount ordered each reordering period. Note the following.

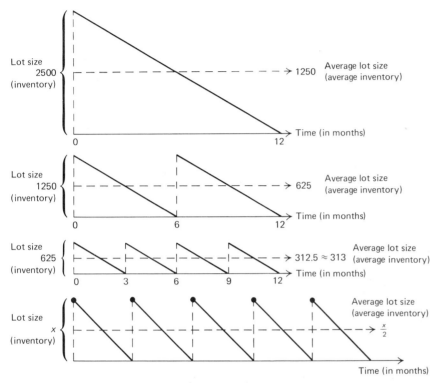

Thus if the lot size is x, then $\dfrac{x}{2}$ represents the average amount held in stock over the course of the year.

Example A retail appliance store sells 2500 TVs per year. It costs $10 to store one TV for a year. To reorder TVs there is a fixed cost of $20 plus $9 for each TV. How many times per year should the store reorder TVs, and in what lot size, so the inventory costs are minimized?

Solution Let x = the lot size. Now inventory costs are given by

$$C(x) = (\text{Yearly carrying costs}) + (\text{Yearly reorder costs}).$$

We consider each separately.

a) *Yearly carrying costs.* The average amount held in stocks is $\dfrac{x}{2}$, and it costs $10 per TV for storage. Thus

$$(\text{Yearly carrying costs}) = \begin{pmatrix} \text{Yearly cost} \\ \text{per item} \end{pmatrix} \begin{pmatrix} \text{Average number} \\ \text{of items} \end{pmatrix}$$

$$= 10 \cdot \frac{x}{2}.$$

27. (A hand-calculator problem) Without a knowledge of calculus one might make a rough estimate of the lot size which will minimize total inventory costs by completing a table like the following. Complete the table and make such an estimate.

Lot size x	Number of reorders $\frac{2500}{x}$	Average inventory $\frac{x}{2}$	Carrying costs $10 \cdot \frac{x}{2}$	Cost of each order $20 + 9x$	Reorder costs $(20 + 9x)\frac{2500}{x}$	Total inventory costs $C(x)$ $10 \cdot \frac{x}{2} + (20 + 9x)\frac{2500}{x}$
2500	1	1250	$12,500	$22,520	$22,520	$35,020
1250	2	625	$6,250	$11,270	$22,540	
500	5	250	$2,500	$4,520		
250	10	125				
167	15	84				
125	20					
100	25					
90	28					
50	50					

b) *Yearly reorder costs.* Now x = lot size, and suppose there are N reorders each year. Then $Nx = 2500$, and $N = \dfrac{2500}{x}$. Thus

$$\text{(Yearly reorder costs)} = \begin{pmatrix}\text{Cost of each}\\ \text{order}\end{pmatrix}\begin{pmatrix}\text{Number of}\\ \text{reorders}\end{pmatrix}$$

$$= (20 + 9x)\,\frac{2500}{x}.$$

c) Hence

$$C(x) = 10 \cdot \frac{x}{2} + (20 + 9x)\frac{2500}{x},$$

$$C(x) = 5x + \frac{50,000}{x} + 22,500.$$

Do Exercise 27.

d) We want to find a minimum value of C on the interval $[1, 2500]$. We first find $C'(x)$:

$$C'(x) = 5 - \frac{50,000}{x^2}.$$

e) Now $C'(x)$ exists for all x in $[1, 2500]$, so the only critical points are those x such that $C'(x) = 0$. We solve $C'(x) = 0$.

$$5 - \frac{50,000}{x^2} = 0$$

$$5 = \frac{50,000}{x^2}$$

$$5x^2 = 50,000$$

$$x^2 = 10,000$$

$$x = \pm 100$$

Now there is only one critical point in the interval $[1, 2500]$, $x = 100$, so we can use the second derivative to see if we have a maximum or minimum:

$$C''(x) = \frac{100,000}{x^3}.$$

Now $C''(x)$ is positive for all x in $[1, 2500]$, so we do have a minimum at $x = 100$.

Thus, to minimize inventory costs, the store should order TVs, $\dfrac{2500}{100}$, or 25 times per year. The lot size is 100.

Do Exercise 28.

The value of the lot size which minimizes total inventory costs is often referred to as the *economic ordering quantity*. There are three assumptions made in using the above method to determine the economic ordering quantity. The first is that the demand for the product is the same throughout the year. For televisions this may be reasonable, but for seasonable items such as clothing, or skis, this assumption may not be reasonable. The second assumption is that the time between the placing of an order and the time of its receipt should be consistent throughout the year. The third assumption is that the various costs involved, such as storage, shipping charges, and so on, do not vary. This may not be reasonable in a time of inflation, although one may account for them by anticipating what they might be and using average costs. Nevertheless, the model described above can be useful, and it allows us to analyze a seemingly difficult problem using the calculus.

28. An appliance store sells 600 refrigerators per year. It costs $30 to store one refrigerator for one year. To reorder refrigerators there is a fixed cost of $40 plus $11 for each refrigerator. How many times per year should the store order refrigerators, and in what lot size, to minimize inventory costs?

EXERCISE SET 3.4

1. A sporting goods store sells 100 pool tables per year. It costs $20 to store one pool table for one year. To reorder pool tables there is a fixed cost of $40 plus $16 for each pool table. How many times per year should the store order pool tables, and in what lot size, to minimize inventory costs?

2. A pro shop in a bowling alley sells 200 bowling balls per year. It costs $4 to store one bowling ball for one year. To reorder bowling balls there is a fixed cost of $1 plus $0.50 for each bowling ball. How many times per year should the shop order bowling balls, and in what lot size, to minimize inventory costs?

3. A retail outlet for Boxowitz Calculators sells 360 calculators per year. It costs $8 to store one calculator for one year. To reorder calculators there is a fixed cost of $10 plus $8 for each calculator. How many times per year should the store order calculators, and in what lot size, to minimize inventory costs?

4. A sporting goods store in southern California sells 720 surfboards per year. It costs $2 to store one surfboard for one year. To reorder surfboards there is a fixed cost of $5 plus $2.50 for each surfboard. How many times per year should the store order surfboards, and in what lot size, to minimize inventory costs?

You should be able to:

a) Given a reproduction curve and an initial population P_0, locate population values for subsequent years.

b) Given a reproduction curve described by a formula, find the population at which the maximum sustainable harvest occurs and the maximum sustainable harvest.

3.5 MAXIMUM SUSTAINABLE HARVEST

Reproduction Curves

In certain situations biologists are able to determine what is called a *reproduction curve*. This is a function

$$y = f(P),$$

such that if P is the population at a certain time t, then the population 1 year later, at time $t + 1$, is $f(P)$. Such a curve is shown in Fig. 3.1.

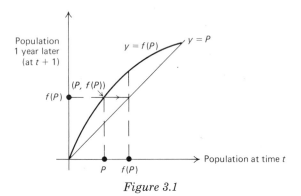

Figure 3.1

The line $y = P$ is significant for two reasons. First, if $y = P$ is a description of f, then we know the population stays the same from year to year. But the graph of f in Fig. 3.1 lies mostly above the line. Thus the population is increasing. Now if we start with a population P, we know that $f(P)$ is the population 1 year later. Given $f(P)$ we move horizontally from $(P, f(P))$ until we hit the line $y = P$, then we move down to the horizontal axis. This locates $f(P)$ on the horizontal axis, so we can find the population 2 years later. In this way we can generate a sequence of population values over a period of years.

To see how this happens look at Fig. 3.2. Suppose P_0 is some initial population. The population 1 year later is given by

$$P_1 = f(P_0).$$

The population 2 years later is given by

$$P_2 = f(P_1), \text{ and so on.}$$

We thus obtain a sequence of population values

$$P_0, P_1, P_2, P_3, \ldots.$$

If we transfer values from the horizontal axis of Fig. 3.2 to the vertical axis of Fig. 3.3, and plot points (t, P_t), where t represents time, we obtain a graph of population versus time.

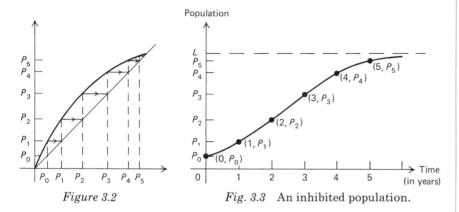

Figure 3.2   Fig. 3.3   An inhibited population.

Note in Fig. 3.3 that the population tends toward a *limiting value L*, or *equilibrium level*. This curve is called an "S-shaped curve" or "logistic curve" and is encountered in situations where the growth is inhibited by certain environmental factors, such as resources, or the size of an ecosystem. For example, a colony of bacteria in a Petri dish will grow to a certain size and stop due to waste contamination. We will consider this type of growth in more detail in Chapter 7.

Do Exercise 29.

In Fig. 3.4 the reproduction curve falls below the line $y = P$. Note that this causes the graph of population versus time to oscillate about the equilibrium level.

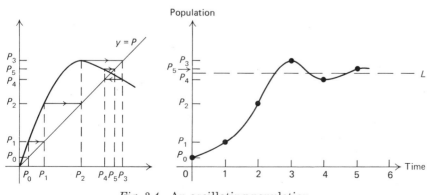

Fig. 3.4   An oscillating population.

29. In the margin on the next page is a reproduction curve.

a) Using P_0 as an initial population, locate P_1, P_2, P_3, P_4 and P_5 on both the vertical and horizontal axes.

b) Use a ruler to transfer these values to the vertical axis of the second graph. Plot the points (k, x_k) and connect them with a smooth curve. Estimate the equilibrium level and draw a line to represent it.

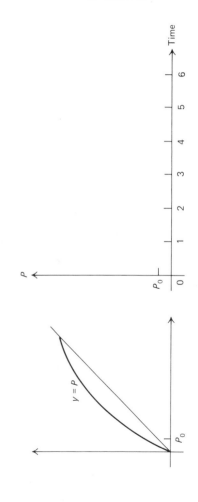

30. a) For the reproduction curve below, repeat the steps of Margin Exercise 29.

b) Is this an oscillating or cyclic population?

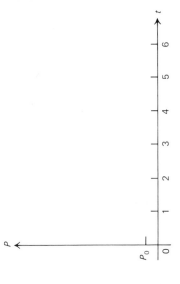

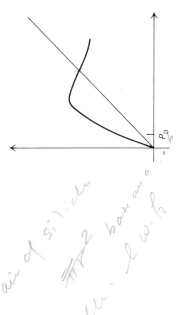

In Fig. 3.5 the reproduction curve falls even further below the line $y = P$. This causes the graph of population versus time to repeat itself in cycles, in this case of 4 years, never approaching an equilibrium level. We have drawn a line-segment graph of population versus time since this is often done in practice.

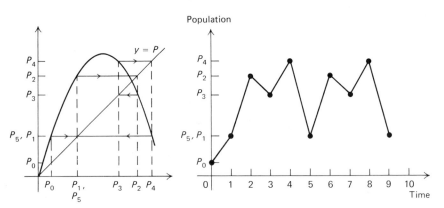

Fig. 3.5   A cyclic population.

It is known that a population of blow flies confined in a laboratory will exhibit such growth. Certain predator-prey interactions will also result in this type of growth.

Do Exercise 30.

Suppose a certain population is growing in such a way that if P is the population at a particular time, then 1 year later there will be a 2% increase. The reproduction curve is given by

$$f(P) = P + 2\%P = 1 \cdot P + 0.02P = (1 + 0.02)P = 1.02P.$$

Do Exercise 31.

The reproduction curve $f(P) = 1.02P$ is shown in Fig. 3.6 along with the graph of population versus time.

Note that the population increases indefinitely. We will study growth similar to this in Chapter 4. It is interesting that the above also models the growth of an amount, or "population" of money invested at 2% (simple interest) compounded annually.

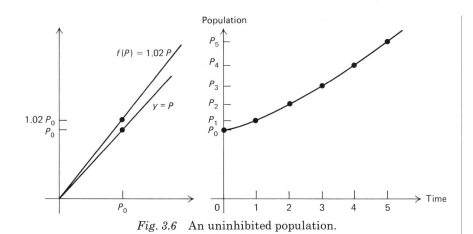

Fig. 3.6   An uninhibited population.

Example   An amount P is invested at $7\frac{1}{2}\%$ compounded annually. Find the reproduction curve.

Solution $f(P) = P + 7\frac{1}{2}\%P = 1 \cdot P + 0.075P = (1 + 0.075)P = 1.075P.$

Do Exercises 32 and 33.

Maximum Sustainable Harvest

We know that a population P will grow to $f(P)$ in one year. If this were a population of fur-bearing animals, then one could "harvest" the amount

$$f(P) - P$$

each year without depleting the initial population P. Now suppose we wanted the value of P_0 which would allow the harvest to be the largest. If we could determine that P_0, then we would let the population grow until it reached that level, and then would begin harvesting year after year the amount $f(P_0) - P_0$.

31. (A hand-calculator problem) The population of the world in 1970 was 3.6 billion. Suppose the reproduction curve is given by

$$f(P) = 1.02P.$$

Complete the table.

Year	Population
1970	3.6 billion
1971	
1972	
1973	
1974	
1975	
1976	
1977	
1978	
1979	
1980	

32. An amount P is invested at $8\frac{1}{4}\%$ compounded annually. Find the reproduction curve.

33. A certain population is growing in such a way that if P is the population, then 1 year later it will have a 1% increase. Find the reproduction curve.

Let the harvest function H be given by

$$H(P) = f(P) - P.$$

Then

$$H'(P) = f'(P) - 1.$$

Now assuming $H'(P)$ exists for all values of P and that there is only one critical point, it follows that the maximum sustainable harvest occurs at that value P_0 such that

$$H'(P_0) = f'(P_0) - 1 = 0$$

and

$$H''(P_0) = f''(P_0) < 0.$$

Or, equivalently,

The maximum sustainable harvest occurs at P_0 such that

$$f'(P_0) = 1 \quad \text{and} \quad f''(P_0) < 0,$$

and is given by

$$H(P_0) = f(P_0) - P_0.$$

Example A certain population of fur-bearing animals has the reproduction curve

$$f(P) = P(10 - P),$$

where P is measured in thousands. Find the population at which the maximum sustainable harvest occurs. Find the maximum sustainable harvest.

Solution Now

$$f(P) = 10P - P^2,$$

so

$$f'(P) = 10 - 2P$$

and

$$f''(P) = -2.$$

We set $f'(P) = 1$ and solve

$$10 - 2P = 1$$
$$-2P = -9$$
$$P = 4.5.$$

There is a maximum since the second derivative is negative for all values of P. We find the maximum sustainable harvest by substituting 4.5 into the equation $H(P) = f(P) - P = (10P - P^2) - P$:

$$H(4.5) = [10 \cdot 4.5 - (4.5)^2] - 4.5 = 24.75 - 4.5 = 20.25$$

Thus the maximum sustainable harvest is 20,250 at $P = 4500$.

Do Exercise 34.

34. A certain population of fur-bearing animals has the reproduction curve

$$f(P) = P(8 - P),$$

where P is measured in thousands. Find the population at which the maximum sustainable harvest occurs. Find the maximum sustainable harvest.

EXERCISE SET 3.5

For each reproduction curve,

a) Find the population at which the maximum sustainable harvest occurs.

b) Find the maximum sustainable harvest.

1. $f(P) = P(20 - P)$, where P is measured in thousands.

2. $f(P) = P(6 - P)$, where P is measured in thousands.

3. $f(P) = -0.025P^2 + 4P$, where P is measured in thousands. This is the reproduction curve in the Hudson Bay area for the *snowshoe hare*—a fur-bearing animal.

4. $f(P) = -0.01P^2 + 2P$, where P is measured in thousands. This is the reproduction curve in the Hudson Bay area for the *lynx*—a fur-bearing animal.

A snowshoe hare.

Ed Cesar from the National Audubon Society

A lynx.

Russ Kinne from Photo Researchers, Inc.

5. $f(P) = 1.08P$

6. $f(P) = 1.075P$

OBJECTIVES

You should be able to:

a) Given a function $y = f(x)$ and a value for Δx, find Δy.
b) Given a function $y = f(x)$, and a value for Δx, or dx, find dy.
c) Use differentials to make approximations of numbers like

$$\sqrt{27} \quad \text{or} \quad \sqrt[3]{10}.$$

3.6 APPROXIMATION

Delta Notation

Recall the difference quotient

$$\frac{f(x + h) - f(x)}{h},$$

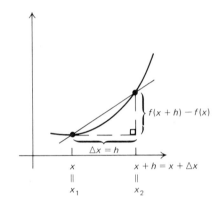

which is used to define the derivative of a function at x. The number h was considered to be a *change* in x. Another notation for such a change is Δx, read "delta x." The expression Δx is *not* the product of Δ and x, but is an entity unto itself; that is, it is a new type of variable which represents the *change* in the value of x from a *first* value to a *second*. Thus

$$\Delta x = (x + h) - x = h.$$

If subscripts are used for the first and second values of x, we would have

$$\Delta x = x_2 - x_1,$$

or

$$x_2 = x_1 + \Delta x.$$

Now Δx can be positive or negative.

Examples

a) If $x_1 = 4$ and $\Delta x = 0.7$, then $x_2 = 4.7$.

b) If $x_1 = 4$ and $\Delta x = -0.7$, then $x_2 = 3.3$.

We usually omit the subscripts and use x and $x + \Delta x$.

Now suppose we have a function given by $y = f(x)$. A change in x from x to $x + \Delta x$ yields a change in y from $f(x)$ to $f(x + \Delta x)$. The change in y is given by

$$\Delta y = f(x + \Delta x) - f(x).$$

Example 1   For $y = x^2$, $x = 4$, and $\Delta x = 0.1$, find Δy.

Solution $\Delta y = (4 + 0.1)^2 - 4^2 = (4.1)^2 - 4^2 = 16.81 - 16 = 0.81$.

Example 2   For $y = x^3$, $x = 2$, and $\Delta x = -0.1$, find Δy.

Solution $\Delta y = [2 + (-0.1)]^3 - 2^3 = (1.9)^3 - 2^3 = 6.859 - 8 = -1.141$.

Do Exercises 35 and 36.

Using delta notation, the difference quotient

$$\frac{f(x + h) - f(x)}{h}$$

becomes

$$\frac{f(x + \Delta x) - f(x)}{\Delta x} = \frac{\Delta y}{\Delta x}.$$

We can then express the derivative as

$$\frac{dy}{dx} = \lim_{\Delta x \to 0} \frac{\Delta y}{\Delta x}.$$

Note how the delta notation resembles the Leibniz notation. For values of Δx close to 0 we have the approximation

$$\frac{dy}{dx} \approx \frac{\Delta y}{\Delta x}, \quad \text{or} \quad f'(x) \approx \frac{\Delta y}{\Delta x}.$$

Multiplying both sides of the second expression by Δx we get

$$\Delta y \approx f'(x)\Delta x.$$

35. For $y = x^2$, $x = 3$, and $\Delta x = -0.1$, find Δy.

36. For $y = x^3$, $x = 2$, and $\Delta x = 1$, find Δy.

We can see this pictorially.

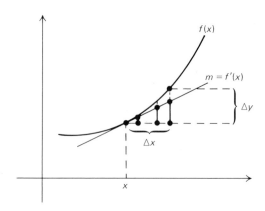

Recall that the derivative is a limit of slopes $\dfrac{\Delta y}{\Delta x}$ of secant lines. Thus as Δx gets smaller, the ratio $\dfrac{\Delta y}{\Delta x}$ gets closer to $\dfrac{dy}{dx}$. Note also that over small intervals the tangent line is a good approximation, linearly, to the function. Thus it is reasonable to assume that average rates of change $\dfrac{\Delta y}{\Delta x}$ of the function are approximately the same as the slope of the tangent line.

Let us use the fact that

$$\Delta y \approx f'(x)\, \Delta x$$

to make certain approximations, such as square roots.

Example 3   Approximate $\sqrt{27}$ using $\Delta y \approx f'(x)\, \Delta x$.

Solution   We first think of the number closest to 27 which is a perfect square. This would be 25. What we will do is approximate how y, or $\sqrt{x}$, changes when 25 changes by $\Delta x = 2$. Let

$$y = f(x) = \sqrt{x}.$$

Then

$$\Delta y = \sqrt{x + \Delta x} - \sqrt{x} = \sqrt{x + \Delta x} - y,$$

so

$$y + \Delta y = \sqrt{x + \Delta x}.$$

Now

$$f'(x)\,\Delta x = \frac{1}{2}x^{-1/2}\,\Delta x = \frac{1}{2\sqrt{x}}\,\Delta x.$$

Let $x = 25$ and $\Delta x = 2$. Then

$$f'(x)\,\Delta x = \frac{1}{2\sqrt{25}}\cdot 2 = \frac{1}{\sqrt{25}} = \frac{1}{5} = 0.2.$$

So

$$\sqrt{27} = \sqrt{x + \Delta x} = y + \Delta y \approx \sqrt{25} + 0.2 = 5 + 0.2 = 5.2.$$

To five decimal places $\sqrt{27} = 5.19615\ldots$. Thus our approximation is fairly good.

Do Exercise 37.

Suppose we have a total cost function $C(x)$. When $\Delta x = 1$, we have

$$\Delta C \approx C'(x).$$

Whether this is a good approximation depends on the function and on the values of x. Let us consider an example.

Example 4   For the total cost function

$$C(x) = 2x^3 - 12x^2 + 30x + 200.$$

a) Find ΔC and $C'(x)$ when $x = 2$ and $\Delta x = 1$.
b) Find ΔC and $C'(x)$ when $x = 100$ and $\Delta x = 1$.

Solution

a) $\Delta C = C(2 + 1) - C(2) = C(3) - C(2) = \$236 - \$228 = \$8$. Recall that $C(2)$ is the total cost of producing 2 units, and $C(3)$ is the total cost of producing 3 units, so $C(3) - C(2)$, or $\$8$, is the cost of the 3rd unit. Now

$$C'(x) = 6x^2 - 24x + 30, \qquad \text{so} \qquad C'(2) = \$6.$$

b) $\Delta C = C(100 + 1) - C(100) = C(101) - C(100) = \$58,220$. Note that this is the cost of the 101st unit. Now

$$C'(100) = \$57,630.$$

Note that in (a) we might not consider the approximation between ΔC and $C'(x)$ to be too good, while in (b) the approximation might be

37. Approximate $\sqrt{67}$ using $\Delta y \approx f'(x)\,\Delta x$. See how close the approximation is by finding $\sqrt{67}$ in Table 1 at the back of the book.

38. Consider the total cost function

$$C(x) = 0.01x^2 + 4x + 500.$$

a) Find ΔC and $C'(x)$ when $x = 5$ and $\Delta x = 1$.

b) Find ΔC and $C'(x)$ when $x = 100$ and $\Delta x = 1$.

considered quite good since the numbers are so large. We have purposely used $\Delta x = 1$ to illustrate the following:

$$C'(x) \approx C(x + 1) - C(x).$$

Marginal cost is approximately the cost of the $(x + 1)$st, or next, unit.

This is the historical interpretation which economists have given to marginal cost.

Similarly,

$$R'(x) \approx R(x + 1) - R(x).$$

Marginal revenue is approximately the revenue from the sale of the $(x + 1)$st, or next, unit.

And

$$P'(x) \approx P(x + 1) - P(x).$$

Marginal profit is approximately the profit from the production and sale of the $(x + 1)$st, or next, unit.

Do Exercise 38.

EXERCISE SET 3.6

In Exercises 1–8, find Δy and $f'(x) \, \Delta x$.

1. For $y = f(x) = x^2$, $x = 2$, and $\Delta x = 0.01$.

2. For $y = x^3$, $x = 2$, and $\Delta x = 0.01$.

3. For $y = f(x) = x + x^2$, $x = 3$, and $\Delta x = 0.04$.

4. For $y = f(x) = x - x^2$, $x = 3$, and $\Delta x = 0.02$.

5. For $y = f(x) = \dfrac{1}{x^2}$, $x = 1$, and $\Delta x = 0.5$.

6. For $y = f(x) = \dfrac{1}{x}$, $x = 1$, and $\Delta x = 0.2$.

7. For $y = f(x) = 3x - 1$, $x = 4$, and $\Delta x = 2$.

8. For $y = f(x) = 2x - 3$, $x = 8$, and $\Delta x = 0.5$.

9. For the total cost function

$$C(x) = 0.01x^2 + 0.6x + 30,$$

find ΔC and $C'(x)$ when $x = 70$ and $\Delta x = 1$.

10. For the total cost function

$$C(x) = 0.01x^2 + 1.6x + 100$$

find ΔC and $C'(x)$ when $x = 80$ and $\Delta x = 1$.

11. For the total revenue function

$$R(x) = 2x,$$

find ΔR and $R'(x)$ when $x = 70$ and $\Delta x = 1$.

12. For the total revenue function

$$R(x) = 3x,$$

find ΔR and $R'(x)$ when $x = 80$ and $\Delta x = 1$.

13. a) Using $C(x)$ of Exercise 9 and $R(x)$ of Exercise 11, find the total profit $P(x)$.

b) Find ΔP and $P'(x)$ when $x = 70$ and $\Delta x = 1$.

Approximate using $\Delta y \approx f'(x)\,\Delta x$.

15. $\sqrt{19}$ **16.** $\sqrt{10}$ **17.** $\sqrt{102}$

21. The spherical volume of a cancer tumor is given by

$$V = \tfrac{4}{3}\pi r^3,$$

where r is the radius in centimeters. By approximately how much does the volume increase when the radius is increased from 1 cm to 1.2 cm? Use 3.14 for π.

14. a) Using $C(x)$ of Exercise 10 and $R(x)$ of Exercise 12, find the total profit $P(x)$.

b) Find ΔP and $P'(x)$ when $x = 80$ and $\Delta x = 1$.

18. $\sqrt{103}$ **19.** $\sqrt[3]{10}$ **20.** $\sqrt[3]{28}$

22. The circular area of a healing wound is given by

$$A = \pi r^2,$$

where r is the radius in centimeters. By approximately how much does the area decrease when the radius is decreased from 2 cm to 1.9 cm? Use 3.14 for π.

CHAPTER 3 TEST

---

1. For $y = x^4 - 3x^2$, find $\dfrac{d^3y}{dx^3}$.

Find the maximum and minimum values, if they exist, over the indicated interval. Where no interval is specified, use the real line.

2. $f(x) = x(6 - x)$ **3.** $f(x) = x^3 + x^2 - x + 1;\ [-2, \tfrac{1}{2}]$

4. $f(x) = -x^2 + 8.6x + 10$ **5.** $f(x) = -2x + 5;\ [-1, 1]$

6. $f(x) = -2x + 5$ **7.** $f(x) = 3x^2 - x - 1$

8. $f(x) = x^2 + \dfrac{128}{x};\ (0, \infty)$

9. Of all numbers whose difference is 8, find the two which have the minimum product.

10. Minimize $Q = x^2 + y^2$, where $x - y = 10$.

11. Find the maximum profit and the number of units which must be produced and sold to yield the maximum profit.

$$R(x) = x^2 + 110x + 60, \qquad C(x) = 1.1x^2 + 10x + 80$$

12. From a piece of cardboard 60 in. by 60 in., square corners are cut out so the sides can be folded up to make a box. What dimensions will yield a box of maximum volume? What is the maximum volume?

13. A sporting goods store sells 625 tennis rackets per year. It costs $1 to store one tennis racket for one year. To reorder tennis rackets there is a fixed cost of $1 plus $0.50 for each tennis racket. How many times per year should the sporting goods store order tennis rackets, and in what lot size, to minimize inventory costs?

14. Consider the reproduction curve $f(P) = P(100 - P)$, where P is measured in thousands. Find the population at which the maximum sustainable harvest occurs. Find the maximum sustainable harvest.

15. For $y = f(x) = x^2 - 3$, $x = 5$, and $\Delta x = 0.1$, find Δy and $f'(x)\,\Delta x$.

16. Approximate $\sqrt{104}$ using $\Delta y \approx f'(x)\,\Delta x$.

What will the world population be in 1980?

4 EXPONENTIAL AND LOGARITHMIC FUNCTIONS

OBJECTIVES

You should be able to:

a) Graph equations like $y = 2^x$ and $y = \log_2 x$.

b) Given an exponential equation, write an equivalent logarithmic equation.

c) Given a logarithmic equation, write an equivalent exponential equation.

d) Given $\log_a 3 = 1.099$ and $\log_a 5 = 1.609$, find logarithms like $\log_a 15$ and $\log_a 5a$.

e) Use Table 2 to find logarithms such as $\log 546$ and $\log .0546$.

f) Given an equation like $y = a \cdot b^x$, find $\log y$.

g) Solve an equation like $e^t = 40$, for t.

h) Solve problems involving applications of logarithms.

1. Consider $y = 3^x$.

a) Complete this table of function values.

x	0	$\frac{1}{2}$	1	2	-1	-2
3^x	1	$\sqrt{3}$	3	9	$\frac{1}{3}$	$\frac{1}{9}$

b) Graph $y = 3^x$.

4.1 EXPONENTIAL AND LOGARITHMIC FUNCTIONS

Exponential Functions

The following are examples of exponential functions:

$$y = 2^x, \qquad y = (\tfrac{1}{2})^x, \qquad y = (0.4)^x.$$

Note, in contrast to power functions like $y = x^2$ or $y = x^3$, that the variable in an exponential function is in the exponent. Exponential functions have extensive application. Let us consider their graphs.

Example 1   Graph $y = 2^x$.

Solution

a) First we find some function values.

x	0	$\frac{1}{2}$	1	2	3	-1	-2
y (or 2^x)	1	1.4	2	4	8	$\frac{1}{2}$	$\frac{1}{4}$

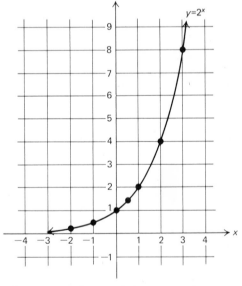

Note: For

$x = 0, y = 2^0 = 1$

$x = \tfrac{1}{2}, y = 2^{1/2} = \sqrt{2} \approx 1.4$

$x = 1, y = 2^1 = 2$

$x = 2, y = 2^2 = 4$

$x = 3, y = 2^3 = 8$

$x = -1, y = 2^{-1} = \tfrac{1}{2}$

$x = -2, y = 2^{-2} = \dfrac{1}{2^2} = \dfrac{1}{4}$

b) Next, we plot the points and connect them with a smooth curve as shown in the figure.

Do Exercise 1.

Example 2   Graph $y = (\frac{1}{2})^x$.

Solution

a) We first find some function values. Before we do this, note that

$$y = (\tfrac{1}{2})^x = (2^{-1})^x = 2^{-x}.$$

This will ease our work.

x	0	$\frac{1}{2}$	1	2	-1	-2	-3
y	1	0.7	$\frac{1}{2}$	$\frac{1}{4}$	2	4	8

Note: For,

$x = 0, y = 2^{-0} = 1$

$x = \dfrac{1}{2}, y = 2^{-1/2}$

$\quad = \dfrac{1}{\sqrt{2}} \approx \dfrac{1}{1.4} \approx 0.7$

$x = 1, y = 2^{-1} = \frac{1}{2}$

$x = 2, y = 2^{-2} = \frac{1}{4}$

$x = -1, y = 2^{-(-1)} = 2$

$x = -2, y = 2^{-(-2)} = 4$

$x = -3, y = 2^{-(-3)} = 8$

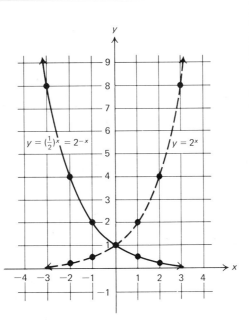

b) We plot these points and connect them with a smooth curve as shown by the solid curve in the figure. The dashed curve shows $y = 2^x$ for comparison.

Do Exercise 2.

Logarithmic Functions

The definition of logarithms is as follows:

   "$y = \log_a x$"   means   "$x = a^y$"

2. Consider $y = (\frac{1}{3})^x$.

a) Complete this table of function values.

x	0	$\frac{1}{2}$	1	2	-1	-2
y	1	$\frac{1}{\sqrt{3}}$	$\frac{1}{3}$	$\frac{1}{9}$	3	9

b) Graph $y = (\frac{1}{3})^x$.

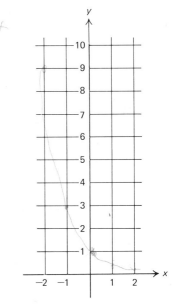

3. Write equivalent exponential equations.

a) $\log_b P = T$

b) $\log_9 3 = \frac{1}{2}$

c) $\log_{10} 1000 = 3$

d) $\log_{10} 0.1 = -1$

4. Write equivalent logarithmic equations.

a) $e^k = T$

b) $16^{1/4} = 2$

c) $10^4 = 10,000$

d) $10^{-3} = 0.001$

5. Graph $y = \log_3 x$.

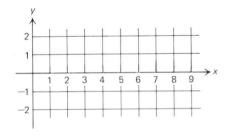

The number a is called the *logarithmic base*. Thus, for logarithms base 10, $\log_{10} x$ is that number y such that $x = 10^y$. A logarithm is thus an exponent. We can convert from a logarithmic equation to an exponential equation, and conversely, as follows.

Logarithmic equation	*Exponential equation*
$\log_a M = N$	$a^N = M$
$\log_{10} 100 = 2$	$10^2 = 100$
$\log_{10} 0.01 = -2$	$10^{-2} = 0.01$
$\log_{49} 7 = \frac{1}{2}$	$49^{1/2} = 7$

Do Exercises 3 and 4.

To graph a logarithmic equation, we can graph its equivalent exponential equation.

Example   Graph $y = \log_2 x$.

Solution   We first write the equivalent exponential equation

$$x = 2^y.$$

We select values for y and find the corresponding values of 2^y.

x (or 2^y)	1	2	4	8	$\frac{1}{2}$	$\frac{1}{4}$
y	0	1	2	3	-1	-2

Next, we plot points, remembering that x is still the first coordinate.

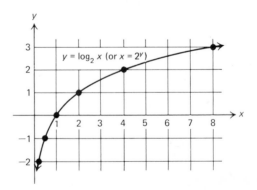

Do Exercise 5.

Basic Properties of Logarithms

The following are some basic properties of logarithms. The proofs are optional, but follow from properties of exponents.

PROPERTY 1. $\log_a MN = \log_a M + \log_a N$

PROPERTY 2. $\log_a \dfrac{M}{N} = \log_a M - \log_a N$

PROPERTY 3. $\log_a M^k = k \cdot \log_a M$

PROPERTY 4. $\log_a a = 1$

PROPERTY 5. $\log_a a^k = k$

PROPERTY 6. $\log_a 1 = 0$

Proof of 1 and 2   Let $X = \log_a M$ and $Y = \log_a N$.
Then writing the equivalent exponential equations, we have

$$M = a^X \quad \text{and} \quad N = a^Y.$$

Then by properties of exponents,

$$MN = a^X \cdot a^Y = a^{X+Y}, \quad \text{so} \quad \log_a MN = X + Y = \log_a M + \log_a N,$$

$$\frac{M}{N} = a^X \div a^Y = a^{X-Y}, \quad \text{so} \quad \log_a \frac{M}{N} = X - Y = \log_a M - \log_a N.$$

Proof of 3   Let $X = \log_a M$.

Then
$$a^X = M, \quad \text{so} \quad (a^X)^k = M^k, \quad \text{or} \quad a^{Xk} = M^k.$$
Thus
$$\log_a M^k = Xk = k \cdot \log_a M.$$

Proof of 4 $\log_a a = 1$ because $a^1 = a$.

Proof of 5 $\log_a a^k = k$ because $(a^k) = a^k$.

Proof of 6 $\log_a 1 = 0$ because $a^0 = 1$.

Let us illustrate these properties.

Examples   Given

$$\log_a 2 = 0.301$$
$$\log_a 3 = 0.477,$$

find each of the following.

a) $\log_a 6$. $\log_a 6 = \log_a (2 \cdot 3) = \log_a 2 + \log_a 3$ (Property 1)

$$= 0.301 + 0.477$$

$$= 0.778$$

$\log_a 3 + \log_a 2$

Given
$$\log_a 2 = 0.301$$
$$\log_a 5 = 0.699,$$

find each of the following.

6. $\log_a 10$

7. $\log_a \frac{2}{5}$

8. $\log_a \frac{5}{2}$

9. $\log_a \frac{1}{5}$

10. $\log_a \sqrt{a^3}$

11. $\log_a 5a$

12. $\log_a 16$

b) $\log_a \frac{2}{3}$.

$$\log_a \frac{2}{3} = \log_a 2 - \log_a 3 \qquad \text{(Property 2)}$$
$$= 0.301 - 0.477$$
$$= -0.176$$

c) $\log_a 81$.

$$\log_a 81 = \log_a 3^4 = 4\log_a 3 \qquad \text{(Property 3)}$$
$$= 4(0.477)$$
$$= 1.908$$

d) $\log_a \frac{1}{3}$.

$$\log_a \frac{1}{3} = \log_a 1 - \log_a 3 \qquad \text{(Property 2)}$$
$$= 0 - 0.477 \qquad\qquad \text{(Property 6)}$$
$$= -0.477$$

e) $\log_a \sqrt{a}$.

$$\log_a \sqrt{a} = \log_a a^{1/2} = \tfrac{1}{2} \qquad \text{(Property 5)}$$

f) $\log_a 2a$.

$$\log_a 2a = \log_a 2 + \log_a a \qquad \text{(Property 1)}$$
$$= 0.301 + 1 \qquad\qquad\quad \text{(Property 4)}$$
$$= 1.301$$

g) $\log_a 5$.

No way to find using these properties.
$$(\log_a 5 \neq \log_a 2 + \log_a 3)$$

h) $\dfrac{\log_a 3}{\log_a 2}$.

$$\frac{\log_a 3}{\log_a 2} = \frac{0.477}{0.301} = 1.58.$$

We simply divided, not using any of the properties.

Do Exercises 6 through 12.

Common Logarithms

Logarithms to the base 10 are called *common logarithms*. When we write

$$\log M,$$

with no base indicated, base 10 is to be understood. Note the following comparison of common logarithms and powers of 10.

$1000 = 10^3$	The common	$\log 1000 = 3$
$100 = 10^2$	logarithms	$\log 100 = 2$
$10 = 10^1$	at the right	$\log 10 = 1$
$1 = 10^0$	follow from	$\log 1 = 0$
$0.1 = 10^{-1}$	the powers at	$\log 0.1 = -1$
$0.01 = 10^{-2}$	the left.	$\log 0.01 = -2$
$0.001 = 10^{-3}$		$\log 0.001 = -3$

13. Find these logarithms.
a) $\log 10{,}000$
b) $\log 0.0001$

Do Exercise 13.

Now suppose we wanted to find

$$\log 524.$$

We could estimate this roughly by noting that 524 is between 100 and 1000, so log 524 is between 2 and 3. To get a closer approximation note that

$$\log 524 = \log(5.24 \cdot 100) = \log 5.24 + \log 100$$
$$= \log 5.24 + 2.$$

Now if we knew log 5.24 we would be finished. Table 2, at the back of the book, shows some values of log M for $1 \leqslant M < 10$. Part of Table 2 is shown below.

x	0	1	2	3	4	5	6	7	8	9
5.0	.6990	.6998	.7007	.7016	.7024	.7033	.7042	.7050	.7059	.7067
5.1	.7076	.7084	.7093	.7101	.7110	.7118	.7126	.7135	.7143	.7152
5.2	.7160	.7168	.7177	.7185	.7193	.7202	.7210	.7218	.7226	.7235
5.3	.7234	.7251	.7259	.7267	.7275	.7284	.7292	.7300	.7308	.7316
5.4	.7324	.7332	.7340	.7348	.7356	.7364	.7372	.7380	.7388	.7396

To find, for example, log 5.24, locate the row headed 5.2, then move across to the column headed 4. Note the shaded number in the table. Thus log 5.24 = 0.7193.

Do Exercises 14 through 18.

Thus

$$\log 524 = \log 5.24 + 2 = 0.7193 + 2 = 2.7193.$$

The number 2 is called the *characteristic*. The number 0.7193 is called the *mantissa*. In the following, as we move the decimal point, note how the mantissa recurs and the characteristic changes.

$$
\begin{array}{lll}
\log 5240   & = \quad 3 + 0.7193 = & 3.7193 \\
\log 524   & = \quad 2 + 0.7193 = & 2.7193 \\
\log 52.4   & = \quad 1 + 0.7193 = & 1.7193 \\
\log 5.24   & = \quad 0 + 0.7193 = & 0.7193 \\
\log 0.524 & = -1 + 0.7193 = & -0.2807 \\
\log 0.0524 & = -2 + 0.7193 = & -1.2807 \\
\log 0.00524 & = -3 + 0.7193 = & -2.2807 \\
\end{array}
$$

Do Exercises 19 through 21.

Use Table 2 to find the following logarithms.

14. log 7.86

15. log 3.2

16. log 9.99

17. log 1

18. log 3

19. Find these logarithms.
a) log 52,400
b) log 0.000524

20. Find these logarithms. First find log 7.86.
a) log 7860
b) log 786
c) log 78.6
d) log 7.86
e) log 0.786
f) log 0.0786
g) log 0.00786

21. Find these logarithms.
a) log 76.4
b) log 2330
c) log 0.0087

22. Find log y.

$$y = 5 \cdot 2^t$$

$y = 4, 3^t$

$\log$

23. Find log Q.

$$Q = Q_0 e^{kt}$$

Exponential Equations

In an equation where a variable occurs in an exponent, we call the equation *exponential*. Logarithms can be used to manipulate or solve exponential equations.

Example 1 Find log y. $y = 4 \cdot 3^t$.

Solution

$$y = 4 \cdot 3^t$$

$\log y = \log 4 \cdot 3^t$ (Taking the logarithm on both sides)

$\log y = \log 4 + \log 3^t$ (Using Property 1)

$\log y = \log 4 + t \cdot \log 3$ (Using Property 3)

Example 2 Find log P. $P = P_0 e^{kt}$.

Solution

$$P = P_0 e^{kt}$$

$\log P = \log P_0 e^{kt}$ (Taking the logarithm on both sides)

$\log P = \log P_0 + \log e^{kt}$ (Using Property 1)

$\log P = \log P_0 + kt \cdot \log e$ (Using Property 3)

Do Exercises 22 and 23.

The number e, which is about 2.72, will have frequent application in later work. Its common logarithm is given by

$$\log e = 0.4343.$$

You should memorize this.

Example 3 Solve for t. $e^t = 40$

Solution

$\log e^t = \log 40$ (Taking the logarithm on both sides)

$t \cdot \log e = \log 40$ (Using Property 3)

$t = \dfrac{\log 40}{\log e}$ $\left(\text{Multiplying on both sides by } \dfrac{1}{\log e}\right)$

$t = \dfrac{1.6021}{0.4343}$ $\left(\begin{array}{l}\text{We find log 40 from Table 2;} \\ \text{log } e \text{ is given as 0.4343.}\end{array}\right)$

$t \approx 3.7,$

where "$\approx$" means "approximately equal to."

Example 4   Solve for t. $e^{-0.04t} = 0.05$

Solution

$\log e^{-0.04t} = \log 0.05$ (Taking the logarithm on both sides)

$-0.04t \log e = \log 0.05$ (Using Property 3)

$$t = \frac{\log 0.05}{-0.04(\log e)} \qquad \left(\text{Multiplying on both sides} \right.$$

$$\left. \text{by } \frac{1}{-0.04(\log e)} \right)$$

$$t = \frac{-2 + 0.699}{-0.04(0.4343)} \qquad \left(\begin{array}{l} \text{We find } \log 0.05 \text{ from Table 2;} \\ \log e \text{ is given as } 0.4343. \end{array} \right)$$

$$t = \frac{-1.301}{-0.017372}$$

$$t \approx 74.9$$

Do Exercises 24 and 25.

Application

Exponential and logarithmic functions have many applications. One is to the *loudness* of sound.

The *loudness L,* in Bels*, of a sound of intensity *I* is defined to be

$$L = \log \frac{I}{I_0},$$

where I_0 is the minimum intensity detectable by the human ear (the tick of a watch at 20 feet under very quiet conditions).

When one sound is 10 times as intense as another, its loudness is 1 Bel louder. If one sound is 100 times as intense as another, it is louder by 2 Bels, and so on. This unit of loudness called the *Bel* is rather large, so in practice, a subunit $\frac{1}{10}$th as large, called a *decibel* (Db), is used.

The preceding formula for L, in Db, becomes $L = 10 \log \dfrac{I}{I_0}$. In summary,

L, in Bels $= \log \dfrac{I}{I_0}$,

L, in Db $= 10 \log \dfrac{I}{I_0}$.

* After Alexander Graham Bell.

24. Solve for t.

$$e^t = 80$$

25. Solve for t.

$$e^{-0.06t} = 0.07$$

26. Find the loudness, in decibels, of the sound in a broadcasting studio for which the intensity I is $199 \cdot I_0$.

27. Find the loudness, in decibels, of the sound of a heavy truck which has an intensity of $10^9 \cdot I_0$.

Noise Pollution. Sounds at 90 decibels and higher cause temporary, and eventually permanent, hearing loss due to deterioration of tiny cells which transmit sound from the ear to the brain.

Sounds can be interpreted as multiples of the minimum intensity I_0.

Example 1 Find the loudness, in decibels, of the sound in a library which is 2510 times as intense as the minimum intensity I_0.

Solution

$$L = 10 \log \frac{2510 \cdot I_0}{I_0} = 10(\log 2510) = 10(3.3997) \qquad \text{(Table 2)}$$
$$\approx 34 \text{ decibels}$$

Example 2 Find the loudness, in decibels, of conversational speech, having an intensity I which is $10^6 \cdot I_0$ (1 million times as intense as I_0).

Solution

$$L = 10 \log \frac{10^6 \cdot I_0}{I_0} = 10(\log 10^6) = 10 \cdot 6 \qquad \text{(Property 5)}$$
$$= 60 \text{ decibels}$$

Do Exercises 26 and 27.

EXERCISE SET 4.1

Graph.

1. $y = 4^x$ **2.** $y = 5^x$ **3.** $y = (0.4)^x$ **4.** $y = (0.2)^x$

5. $y = \log_4 x$ $: 4^y = x$ **6.** $y = \log_5 x$ $5^y = x$

Write equivalent exponential equations.

7. $\log_2 8 = 3$ $2^3 = 8$ **8.** $\log_3 81 = 4$ $3^4 = 81$ **9.** $\log_8 2 = \frac{1}{3}$ $8^{\frac{1}{3}} = 2$ **10.** $\log_{27} 3 = \frac{1}{3}$ $27^{\frac{1}{3}} = 3$

11. $\log_a K = J$ $a^J = K$ **12.** $\log_a J = K$ $a^K = J$ **13.** $\log_b T = v$ $b^v = T$ **14.** $\log_c Y = t$ $c^t = y$

Write equivalent logarithmic equations.

15. $e^M = b$ $\log_e b = M$ **16.** $e^t = p$ $\log_e p = t$ **17.** $10^2 = 100$ $\log 100 = 2$ **18.** $10^3 = 1000$ $\log 1000 = 3$

19. $10^{-1} = 0.1$ $\log .1 = -1$ **20.** $10^{-2} = 0.01$ $\log .01 = -2$ **21.** $M^p = V$ $\log_M V = p$ **22.** $Q^n = T$ $\log_Q T = n$

Given $\log_b 3 = 1.099$ and $\log_b 5 = 1.609$, find:

23. $\log_b 15$

24. $\log_b \frac{3}{5}$

25. $\log_b \frac{5}{3}$

26. $\log_b \frac{1}{3}$

27. $\log_b \frac{1}{5}$

28. $\log_b \sqrt{b}$

29. $\log_b \sqrt{b^3}$

30. $\log_b 3b$

31. $\log_b 5b$

32. $\log_b 9$

33. $\log_b 25$

34. $\log_b 75$

Using Table 2, find the following logarithms.

35. a) $\log 2130$
   b) $\log 213$
   c) $\log 21.3$
   d) $\log 2.13$
   e) $\log 0.213$
   f) $\log 0.0213$
   g) $\log 0.00213$

36. a) $\log 1880$
   b) $\log 188$
   c) $\log 18.8$
   d) $\log 1.88$
   e) $\log 0.188$
   f) $\log 0.0188$
   g) $\log 0.00188$

37. $\log 906$

38. $\log 702$

39. $\log 0.011$

40. $\log 0.033$

41. $\log 4500$

42. $\log 8100$

43. $\log 78{,}100$

44. $\log 99{,}400$

Find $\log y$.

45. $y = 3 \cdot 10^x$

46. $y = 9 \cdot 7^x$

47. $y = a \cdot b^t$

48. $y = p \cdot q^t$

Solve for t. Remember, $\log e = 0.4343$—you should memorize this!

49. $e^t = 100$

50. $e^t = 1000$

51. $e^t = 60$

52. $e^t = 80$

53. $e^{-t} = 0.1$

54. $e^{-t} = 0.01$

55. $e^{-0.02t} = 0.06$

56. $e^{-0.03t} = 0.08$

Applied Problems

57. Find the loudness, in decibels, of a dishwasher which has an intensity of $2{,}500{,}000 \cdot I_0$.

58. Find the loudness, in decibels, of an automobile which has an intensity of $3{,}100{,}000 \cdot I_0$.

59. Find the loudness, in decibels, of a three-engine jet aircraft (500 ft away) which has an intensity of $10^{12} \cdot I_0$.

60. Find the loudness, in decibels, of the threshold of sound pain for which the intensity is $10^{14} \cdot I_0$.

Daniel S. Brody from Stock, Boston

EARTHQUAKE MAGNITUDE   The magnitude R (measured on the Richter Scale) of an earthquake of intensity I is defined to be

$$R = \log \frac{I}{I_0},$$

where I_0 is a minimum intensity used for comparison. When one earthquake is 10 times as intense as another, its magnitude on the Richter Scale is 1 higher. If one earthquake is 100 times as intense as another, its magnitude on the Richter Scale is 2 higher, and so on. Thus an earthquake whose magnitude is 7 on the Richter Scale is 10 times as intense as an earthquake whose magnitude is 6. Earthquakes can be interpreted as multiples of the minimum intensity I_0.

61. The San Francisco earthquake of 1906 had an intensity of $10^{8.25} \cdot I_0$. What was its magnitude on the Richter Scale?

62. The Los Angeles earthquake of 1971 had an intensity of $10^{6.7} \cdot I_0$. What was its magnitude on the Richter Scale?

This photograph shows part of the damage of the earthquake in Anchorage, Alaska in 1964.

Pro Pix from Monkmeyer

pH: In chemistry pH is defined

$$pH = -\log[H^+],$$

where $[H^+]$ = hydrogen ion concentration in moles per liter. For example, the hydrogen ion concentration in milk is $4 \cdot 10^{-7}$ moles per liter, so

$$pH = -\log(4 \cdot 10^{-7}) = -[\log 4 + (-7)] = -[0.6021 - 7] \approx 6.4.$$

63. For eggs, $[H^+] = 1.6 \cdot 10^{-8}$. Find the pH.

64. For tomatoes, $[H^+] = 6.3 \cdot 10^{-5}$. Find the pH.

OBJECTIVES

You should be able to:

a) Graph functions like

$f(x) = 2e^x$, and $g(x) = 1 - e^{-x}$.

b) Differentiate functions involving e.
c) Solve applied problems involving exponential functions.

28. (A hand-calculator exercise—you need an a^b key.) If you have an appropriate hand calculator, complete this table. If not, perhaps your instructor will bring one to class.

r	2^r
3	
3.1	
3.14	
3.141	
3.1415	

What seems to be the value of 2^π to two decimal places?

4.2 THE EXPONENTIAL FUNCTION, BASE e

The exponential function

$$f(x) = e^x$$

and its related functions

$$f(x) = ce^{kx},$$

are some of the most important ones in mathematics and in the applications of mathematics.

The General Base a

In Chapter 1 we reviewed definitions of expressions of the type a^x, where x was a rational number. For example,

$$a^{2.34}, \text{ or } a^{234/100},$$

means "raise a to the 234th power and take the 100th root."

What about expressions with irrational exponents, such as $2^{\sqrt{2}}$, 2^π, or $2^{-\sqrt{3}}$. An irrational number is a number named by an infinite, nonrepeating decimal. Let us consider 2^π. We know π is irrational with infinite, nonrepeating decimal expansion

$$3.141592654\ldots.$$

This means that π is approached closer and closer by the rational numbers

$$3, 3.1, 3.14, 3.141, 3.1415, \ldots;$$

so it seems reasonable that 2^π should be approached closer and closer by the rational powers

$$2^3, 2^{3.1}, 2^{3.14}, 2^{3.141}, 2^{3.1415}, \ldots.$$

Do Exercise 28.

In general, a^x is approximated by the values of a^r for rational numbers r near x; a^x is the limit of a^r as r approaches x through rational values.

In summary, for $a > 0$, the definition of a^x for rational numbers x can be extended to arbitrary real numbers x in such a way that the usual laws of exponents, such as

$$a^x \cdot a^y = a^{x+y}, \qquad a^x \div a^y = a^{x-y}, \qquad (a^x)^y = a^{xy}, \qquad \text{and} \quad a^{-x} = \frac{1}{a^x},$$

still hold. Moreover, the function so obtained,

$$f(x) = a^x,$$

is continuous.

The following are some properties of the exponential function for various bases.

1. The function $f(x) = a^x$, where $a > 1$, is a positive, increasing, continuous function; and as x gets smaller, a^x approaches 0.

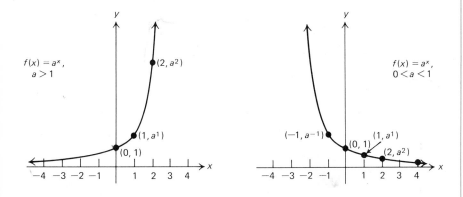

2. The function $f(x) = a^x$, where $0 < a < 1$, is a positive, decreasing, continuous function; and as x gets larger, a^x approaches 0.

When $a = 1$, $f(x) = a^x = 1^x = 1$, and is a constant function.

Let us consider finding derivatives of exponential functions.

The Derivative of a^x, the Number e

Let us consider finding the derivative of the exponential function

$$f(x) = a^x.$$

29. In order to investigate

$$\lim_{h\to 0} \frac{2^h - 1}{h}$$

we choose a sequence of numbers h, approaching 0, and compute

$$\frac{2^h - 1}{h}.$$

a) Complete this table.
Values of 2^h can be found using a calculator with a square root key. Just take successive square roots.

h	2^h	$\dfrac{2^h - 1}{h}$
$\frac{1}{2}$		
$\frac{1}{4}$		
$\frac{1}{8}$		
$\frac{1}{16}$		
$\frac{1}{32}$		

b) To the nearest tenth, what is the value of

$$\lim_{h\to 0} \frac{2^h - 1}{h}?$$

30. a) Complete this table.

h	3^h	$\dfrac{3^h - 1}{h}$
$\frac{1}{2}$		
$\frac{1}{4}$		
$\frac{1}{8}$		
$\frac{1}{16}$		
$\frac{1}{32}$		

b) To the nearest tenth, what is the value of

$$\lim_{h\to 0} \frac{3^h - 1}{h}?$$

The derivative is given by

$$f'(x) = \lim_{h\to 0} \frac{f(x + h) - f(x)}{h} \qquad \text{(Definition of the derivative)}$$

$$= \lim_{h\to 0} \frac{a^{x+h} - a^x}{h} \qquad \left(\begin{array}{l}\text{Substituting } a^{x+h} \text{ for } f(x + h) \\ \text{and } a^x \text{ for } f(x)\end{array}\right)$$

$$= \lim_{h\to 0} \frac{a^x \cdot a^h - a^x \cdot 1}{h}$$

We get

$$f'(x) = a^x \cdot \lim_{h\to 0} \frac{a^h - 1}{h}. \tag{1}$$

In particular, for $g(x) = 2^x$,

$$g'(x) = 2^x \cdot \lim_{h\to 0} \frac{2^h - 1}{h}.$$

Note that the limit does not depend on the value of x at which we are evaluating the derivative. For $g'(x)$ to exist, we must determine if

$$\lim_{h\to 0} \frac{2^h - 1}{h} \text{ exists.}$$

Let us investigate this question.

Do Exercise 29.

The margin exercise suggests that $\dfrac{2^h - 1}{h}$ has a limit as h approaches 0, and that its approximate value is 0.7, so that

$$g'(x) \approx (0.7)2^x.$$

In other words, the derivative is a constant times the function value 2^x. Similarly, for $t(x) = 3^x$,

$$t'(x) = 3^x \cdot \lim_{h\to 0} \frac{3^h - 1}{h}.$$

Again we can find an approximation for the limit which does not depend on the value of x at which we are evaluating the derivative.

Do Exercise 30.

The margin exercise suggests that $\dfrac{3^h - 1}{h}$ has a limit as h approaches 0, and that its approximate value is 1.1, so that

$$t'(x) \approx (1.1)3^x.$$

In other words, the derivative is a constant times the function value 3^x.

Do Exercises 31 and 32.

In Fig. 4.1 we have graphed $g(x) = 2^x$ and $g'(x) \approx (0.7)2^x$. Note that the graph of g' lies *below* the graph of g.

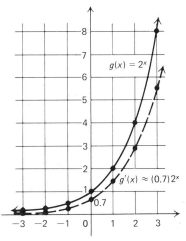

Figure 4.1

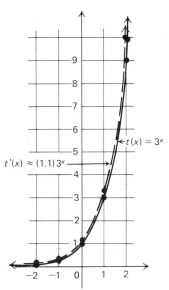

Figure 4.2

In Fig. 4.2 we have graphed $t(x) = 3^x$ and $t'(x) \approx (1.1)3^x$. Note that the graph of t' lies *above* the graph of t.

We might expect that there is exactly one base a between 2 and 3 for which a^x and its derivative have the same graph. This conjecture can be proved (though we will not do it here). We define the number e to be the unique positive real number for which

$$\lim_{h \to 0} \frac{e^h - 1}{h} = 1.$$

In the subsequent margin exercise you will not only consider an application of e, but you will find a decimal approximation.

31. a) Complete this table.

x	-3	-2	-1	0	1	2	3
2^x			0.5				
$(0.7)2^x$			0.35				

b) Using the same set of axes, graph $g(x) = 2^x$, with a solid curve; and $g'(x) \approx (0.7)2^x$ with a dashed curve.

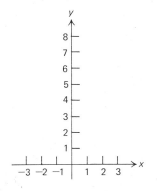

32. a) Complete this table.

x	-2	-1	0	1	2
3^x					
$(1.1)3^x$					

b) Using the same set of axes, graph $h(x) = 3^x$, with a solid line, and $h'(x) \approx (1.1)3^x$ with a dashed line.

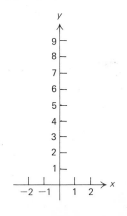

33. (A hand-calculator exercise—you will need an a^b key for part of the calculations.)

The compound interest formula which we developed in Chapter 1 is

$$P = P_0 \left(1 + \frac{i}{n}\right)^{nt},$$

where P is the amount an initial investment P_0 will be worth after t years at interest rate i, compounded n times per year.

Suppose \$1 is an initial investment at 100% interest for 1 year (no bank would pay this). The above formula becomes

$$P = \left(1 + \frac{1}{n}\right)^n.$$

Complete this table.

n	$\left(1 + \dfrac{1}{n}\right)^n$
1 (compounding annually)	
2 (compounding semiannually)	
3	
4 (compounding quarterly)	
5	
100	
365 (compounding daily)	
500	
1000	

Differentiate.

34. $6e^x$ **35.** $x^3 e^x$

36. $\dfrac{e^x}{x^2}$

Do Exercise 33.

Suppose we were to have the compounding periods n increase indefinitely. The amount in the investment of the margin exercise would be growing at interest compounded continuously, and would approach about \$2.718. The number e can be defined as a limit:

$$e = \lim_{n \to \infty} \left(1 + \frac{1}{n}\right)^n.$$

That is, e is that number which $\left(1 + \dfrac{1}{n}\right)^n$ approaches as n gets larger without bound. To ten decimal places e is given by

$$e = 2.7182818284 \ldots .$$

We have established that for the function $f(x) = e^x$, we also have $f'(x) = e^x$. Or, simply,

$$\frac{d}{dx} e^x = e^x.$$

Note that this says that the derivative (the slope of the tangent line) at any x is the same as the function value. Let us find some other derivatives.

Example 1 $\dfrac{d}{dx} 3e^x = 3e^x$

Example 2 $\dfrac{d}{dx} x^2 e^x = x^2 \cdot e^x + 2x \cdot e^x$ (Product Rule)

$\qquad\qquad\qquad = e^x(x^2 + 2x),$ or $xe^x(x + 2)$ (Factoring)

Example 3 $\dfrac{d}{dx} \left(\dfrac{e^x}{x^3}\right) = \dfrac{x^3 \cdot e^x - e^x(3x^2)}{x^6}$ (Quotient Rule)

$\qquad\qquad\qquad = \dfrac{x^2 e^x(x - 3)}{x^6}$ (Factoring)

$\qquad\qquad\qquad = \dfrac{e^x(x - 3)}{x^4}$ (Simplifying)

Do Exercises 34 through 36.

The following rule allows us to find many other derivatives.

$$\frac{d}{dx} e^{f(x)} = f'(x)e^{f(x)}, \quad \text{or} \quad \frac{d}{dx} e^{\square} = \square' \cdot e^{\square}$$

The following gives a mental way of remembering this rule.

$e^{x^2 - 5x}$

Multiply the original function by the derivative of the exponent.

$(2x - 5)e^{x^2 - 5x}$

Example 4 $\dfrac{d}{dx}\, e^{3x} = 3e^{3x}$

Example 5 $\dfrac{d}{dx}\, e^{-x^2 + 4x - 7} = (-2x + 4)e^{-x^2 + 4x - 7}$

Example 6 $\dfrac{d}{dx}\, e^{\sqrt{x^2 - 3}} = \tfrac{1}{2}(x^2 - 3)^{-1/2} \cdot 2x \cdot e^{\sqrt{x^2 - 3}}$

$$= x(x^2 - 3)^{-1/2} \cdot e^{\sqrt{x^2 - 3}}$$

$$= \frac{xe^{\sqrt{x^2 - 3}}}{\sqrt{x^2 - 3}}$$

Do Exercises 37 through 39.

Graphs of e^x, e^{-x}, and $1 - e^{-kx}$

Table 4 contains approximate values of e^x and e^{-x}. Using these we can draw graphs of these functions.

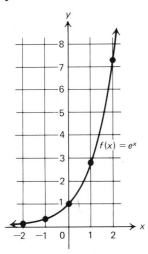

Figure 4.3

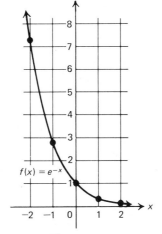

Figure 4.4

Note that the graph of e^{-x} is a reflection, or mirror image, of the graph of e^x across the y-axis.

Do Exercise 40.

Differentiate.

37. e^{-4x}

38. $e^{x^3 + 8x}$

39. $e^{\sqrt{x^2 + 5}}$

40. Graph $f(x) = 2e^{-x}$. Use Table 4. For example, for $x = 3$, $f(3) = 2e^{-3} = 2(.0498) \approx 0.1$.

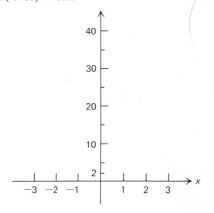

41. a) Complete this table for

$$f(x) = 1 - e^{-x}.$$

x	0	$\frac{1}{2}$	1	2	3	4
$f(x)$						

b) Graph $f(x) = 1 - e^{-x}$.

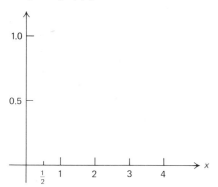

Functions of the type $f(x) = 1 - e^{-kx}$ are important later in Chapter 7, and here in Example 8.

Example 7   Graph $f(x) = 1 - e^{-2x}$, for nonnegative values of x.

Solution   We obtain these values using Table 4 at the back of the book.

x	0	$\frac{1}{2}$	1	2	3
$f(x)$	0	0.63	0.86	0.98	0.998

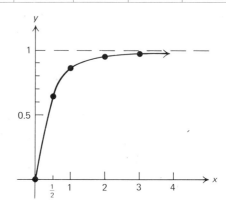

For example,

$$f(1) = 1 - e^{-2 \cdot 1}$$
$$= 1 - e^{-2}$$
$$= 1 - 0.1353 \approx 0.86$$

Do Exercise 41.

In general, the graph of $f(x) = 1 - e^{-kx}$, for $k > 0$, increases from 0 and approaches 1 as x gets larger; that is, $\lim\limits_{x \to \infty}(1 - e^{-kx}) = 1$.

Application

Example 8   A company begins a radio advertising campaign in New York City to market a new product. The percentage of the "target market" which buys a product is normally a function of the length of the advertising campaign. The radio station estimates this percentage as $(1 - e^{-.04t})$ for this type of product, where $t =$ number of days of the campaign. The target market is estimated to be 1,000,000 people and the price per unit is $.50. The costs of advertising are $1000 per day. Find the length of the advertising campaign which will result in maximum profit.

Solution   That the percentage of the target market which buys the product can be modeled by $f(t) = 1 - e^{-0.04t}$ is justified by looking at its graph.

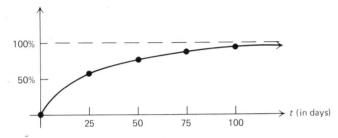

The function increases from 0(0%) towards 1(100%). The longer the advertising campaign, the larger the percentage of the market which has bought the product. (See also the discussion in Section 7.4.)

Recall the profit function (here expressed in terms of time, t):

$$\text{Profit} = \text{Revenue} - \text{Cost}$$
$$P(t) = R(t) - C(t)$$

a) Find $R(t)$.

$$R(t) = (\text{Price per unit}) \cdot (\text{Target market}) \cdot (\text{Percentage buying})$$
$$R(t) = 0.5(1{,}000{,}000)(1 - e^{-.04t}) = 500{,}000 - 500{,}000e^{-.04t}$$

b) Find $C(t)$.

$$C(t) = (\text{advertising costs per day}) \cdot (\text{number of days})$$
$$C(t) = 1000t$$

c) Find $P(t)$, and take its derivative.

$$P(t) = R(t) - C(t)$$
$$P(t) = 500{,}000 - 500{,}000e^{-.04t} - 1000t$$
$$P'(t) = (-.04)(-500{,}000e^{-.04t}) - 1000$$
$$P'(t) = 20{,}000e^{-.04t} - 1000$$

d) Set the first derivative equal to 0 and solve.

$$20{,}000e^{-.04t} - 1000 = 0$$
$$20{,}000e^{-.04t} = 1000$$
$$e^{-.04t} = \frac{1000}{20{,}000} = .05 \qquad\qquad (1)$$

42. Solve the problem in the example when the price per unit is $0.80.

From Table 4 we see that $e^{-3} \approx .05$, so the first derivative is 0 when

$$-.04t \approx -3,$$

or

$$t \approx 75.$$

If a greater degree of accuracy is desired, we can solve equation (1) using common logarithms. This is shown in Example 4 on p. 195.

e) We have only one critical point. So we can use the second derivative to determine if we have a maximum.

$$P''(t) = -.04(20{,}000e^{-.04t}) = -800e^{-.04t}$$

Now since exponential functions are positive, $e^{-.04t} > 0$ for all numbers t. Thus $-800e^{-.04t} < 0$ for all numbers t. Thus $P''(t)$ is less than 0 for $t = 75$ and we have a maximum.

Do Exercise 42.

A word of caution!   Functions of the type a^x (for example, 2^x, 3^x, and e^x) are different from functions of the type x^a (for example, x^2, x^3, $x^{1/2}$). For a^x the variable is in the exponent. For x^a the variable is in the base. The derivative of a^x is not xa^{x-1}. In particular,

$$\frac{d}{dx}\, e^x \neq xe^{x-1}, \quad \text{but} \quad \frac{d}{dx}e^x = e^x.$$

EXERCISE SET 4.2

Differentiate.

1. e^{3x} **2.** e^{2x} **3.** $5e^{-2x}$ **4.** $4e^{-3x}$ **5.** $3 - e^{-x}$ **6.** $2 - e^{-x}$

7. $-7e^x$ **8.** $-4e^x$ **9.** $\frac{1}{2}e^{2x}$ **10.** $\frac{1}{4}e^{4x}$ **11.** x^4e^x **12.** x^5e^x

13. $\dfrac{e^x}{x^4}$ **14.** $\dfrac{e^x}{x^5}$ **15.** e^{-x^2+7x} **16.** e^{-x^2+8x} **17.** $e^{-x^2/2}$ **18.** $e^{x^2/2}$

19. $e^{\sqrt{x-7}}$ **20.** $e^{\sqrt{x-4}}$ **21.** $\sqrt{e^x-1}$ **22.** $\sqrt{e^x+1}$ **23.** $xe^{-2x}+e^{-x}+x^3$

24. $e^x + x^3 - xe^x$ **25.** $1 - e^{-x}$ **26.** $1 - e^{-3x}$ **27.** $1 - e^{-kx}$ **28.** $1 - e^{-mx}$

Graph, using Table 4.

29. $f(x) = e^{2x}$ ⠀⠀⠀⠀⠀⠀**30.** $f(x) = e^{(1/2)x}$ ⠀⠀⠀⠀⠀⠀**31.** $f(x) = e^{-2x}$ ⠀⠀⠀⠀⠀⠀**32.** $f(x) = e^{-(1/2)x}$

33. $f(x) = 1 - e^{-x}$, for nonnegative values of x. ⠀⠀⠀⠀⠀⠀**34.** $f(x) = 2(1 - e^{-x})$, for nonnegative values of x.

Applied Problems

35. Solve the advertising problem where the costs of advertising are $2000 per day.

37. A company's total cost, in millions of dollars, is given by

$$C(t) = 100 - 50e^{-t},$$

where $t = $ time. Find

a) the marginal cost $C'(t)$,

b) $C'(0)$,

c) $C'(4)$.

36. Solve the advertising problem where the costs of advertising are $4000 per day.

38. A company's total cost, in millions of dollars, is given by

$$C(t) = 200 - 40e^{-t},$$

where $t = $ time. Find

a) the marginal cost $C'(t)$,

b) $C'(0)$,

c) $C'(5)$.

4.3 THE NATURAL LOGARITHM FUNCTION

Recall the definition of logarithms:

$$\text{``} y = \log_a x \text{''} \qquad \text{means} \qquad \text{``} x = a^y. \text{''}$$

Thus, for logarithms base 10, $\log_{10} x$ is that number y such that $x = 10^y$. Similarly, $\log_e x$ is that number y such that $x = e^y$. The number $\log_{10} x$ is called the *common logarithm* of x and is usually abbreviated log x. That is,

$$\log x = \log_{10} x.$$

The number $\log_e x$ is called the *natural logarithm* of x and is abbreviated ln x. That is,

$$\ln x = \log_e x.$$

Do Exercise 43.

There are two ways we might obtain the graph of

$$y = \ln x.$$

OBJECTIVES

You should be able to:

a) Given $\ln 4 = 1.3863$ and $\ln 5 = 1.6094$, find natural logarithms like $\ln 20$ and $\ln 5e$.

b) Differentiate functions involving natural logarithms.

c) Graph functions like $y = \ln x$ and $y = 2 + \ln x$, using Table 3.

d) Solve maximum-minimum problems involving natural logarithm functions.

43. Abbreviate each of the following using "ln."

a) $\log_e 7$ ⠀⠀⠀⠀⠀⠀b) $\log_e 10$

c) $\log_e M$ ⠀⠀⠀⠀⠀⠀d) $\log_e P$

44.

a) Complete, using Table 3.

x	0.5	1	2	3	4
$\ln x$			0.7		

b) Graph $y = \ln x$.

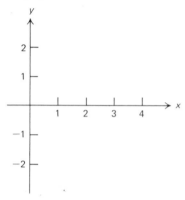

One is by writing its equivalent exponential equation

$$x = e^y.$$

Then we select values for y, and use Table 4 to find the corresponding values of e^y. Then we plot points, remembering that x still is the first coordinate.

x (or e^y)	0.4	0.1	1	2.7	7.4	20
y	-1	-2	0	1	2	3

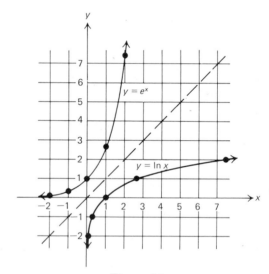

Figure 4.5

(How does this procedure compare with that used in plotting Fig. 4.3?) Note that the graph of $y = \ln x$ is a reflection, or mirror image, across the line $y = x$, of the graph of $y = e^x$.

The second way of graphing $y = \ln x$ is by using Table 3 at the back of the book, which is a table of natural logarithms. For example, $\ln 2 = 0.6931 \approx 0.7$.

Do Exercise 44.

These properties follow.

> **$\ln x$ exists only for positive number x.**
> **$\ln x < 0$ for $0 < x < 1$.**
> **$\ln x > 0$ for $x > 1$.**

The following properties were proved for general logarithmic bases in Section 4.1. We restate them in terms of natural logarithms.

PROPERTY 1. $\ln MN = \ln M + \ln N$

PROPERTY 2. $\ln \dfrac{M}{N} = \ln M - \ln N$

PROPERTY 3. $\ln a^k = k \cdot \ln a$

PROPERTY 4. $\ln e = 1$

PROPERTY 5. $\ln e^k = k$

PROPERTY 6. $\ln 1 = 0$

Let us illustrate these properties.

Examples Given
$$\ln 2 = 0.6931$$
$$\ln 3 = 1.0986,$$

find each of the following:

a) $\ln 6$. $\ln 6 = \ln(2 \cdot 3) = \ln 2 + \ln 3$ (Property 1)
$$= 0.6931 + 1.0986$$
$$= 1.7917$$

b) $\ln 81$. $\ln 81 = \ln(3^4)$
$$= 4 \ln 3 \qquad \text{(Property 3)}$$
$$= 4(1.0986)$$
$$= 4.3944$$

c) $\ln \frac{2}{3}$. $\ln \frac{2}{3} = \ln 2 - \ln 3$ (Property 2)
$$= 0.6931 - 1.0986$$
$$= -0.4055$$

d) $\ln \frac{1}{3}$. $\ln \frac{1}{3} = \ln 1 - \ln 3$ (Property 2)
$$= 0 - 1.0986 \qquad \text{(Property 6)}$$
$$= -1.0986$$

e) $\ln 2e$. $\ln 2e = \ln 2 + \ln e$ (Property 1)
$$= 0.6931 + 1 \qquad \text{(Property 4)}$$
$$= 1.6931$$

f) $\ln \sqrt{e^3}$. $\ln \sqrt{e^3} = \ln e^{3/2}$
$$= \tfrac{3}{2} \qquad \text{(Property 5)}$$

Do Exercises 45 through 51.

Given
$$\ln 2 = 0.6931$$
$$\ln 5 = 1.6094,$$

find each of the following.

45. $\ln 10$

46. $\ln \frac{2}{5}$

47. $\ln \frac{5}{2}$

48. $\ln 16$ [*Hint*: $16 = 2^4$]

49. $\ln 5e$

50. $\ln \sqrt{e}$

51. $\ln \frac{1}{5}$

52. a) Use the method of graphical differentiation developed in Section 2.3, and the graph shown in Fig. 4.6 to complete this table of values of the derivative.

x	$\frac{1}{2}$	1	2	3	4	5
$f'(x)$						

b) Look for a pattern in the table and try to discover a formula for $f'(x)$.

The Derivative of ln x

Consider $f(x) = \ln x$.

Let us try to discover a formula for $f'(x)$.

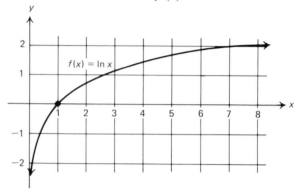

Figure 4.6

Do Exercise 52.

From the margin exercise you may have conjectured that if $f(x) = \ln x$, then $f'(x) = \dfrac{1}{x}$ (the slope of the tangent line at x is just the reciprocal of x). Let us give a proof.

We are trying to find the derivative of

$$f(x) = \ln x. \tag{1}$$

We first write its equivalent exponential equation

$$e^{f(x)} = x. \tag{2}$$

Now we differentiate both sides of this equation.

$$\frac{d}{dx} e^{f(x)} = \frac{d}{dx} x$$

$$f'(x) \cdot e^{f(x)} = 1$$

$$f'(x) \cdot x = 1 \qquad \text{[Substituting } x \text{ for } e^{f(x)} \text{ from equation (2)]}$$

$$f'(x) = \frac{1}{x}$$

Thus

$$\frac{d}{dx} \ln x = \frac{1}{x}.$$

This is true only for positive values of x, since ln x is defined only for positive numbers. Let us find some derivatives.

Example 1 $\dfrac{d}{dx}\, 3 \ln x = \dfrac{3}{x}$

Differentiate.

53. $5 \ln x$

Example 2

$\dfrac{d}{dx}(x^2 \ln x + 5x) = x^2 \cdot \dfrac{1}{x} + 2x \cdot \ln x + 5$ (Product Rule on $x^2 \ln x$)

$\qquad\qquad\qquad = x + 2x \cdot \ln x + 5$ (Simplifying)

$\qquad\qquad\qquad = x(1 + 2 \ln x) + 5$

Example 3

$\dfrac{d}{dx}\left(\dfrac{\ln x}{x^3}\right) = \dfrac{x^3 \cdot \frac{1}{x} - (\ln x)(3x^2)}{x^6}$ (Quotient Rule)

$\qquad\qquad = \dfrac{x^2 - 3x^2 \ln x}{x^6}$

$\qquad\qquad = \dfrac{x^2(1 - 3 \ln x)}{x^6}$ (Factoring)

$\qquad\qquad = \dfrac{1 - 3 \ln x}{x^4}$ (Simplifying)

54. $x^3 \ln x + 4x$

Do Exercises 53 through 55.

55. $\dfrac{\ln x}{x^2}$

The following rule allows us to find many other derivatives.

$$\dfrac{d}{dx} \ln f(x) = f'(x) \cdot \dfrac{1}{f(x)}, \quad \text{or} \quad \dfrac{d}{dx} \ln \boxed{} = \boxed{}' \cdot \dfrac{1}{\boxed{}}.$$

The following gives a mental way of remembering this rule.

$\ln(x^2 - 8x)$ 1. Differentiate the "inside" function.

$(2x - 8) \cdot \dfrac{1}{x^2 - 8x}$ 2. Multiply by the reciprocal of the "inside" function.

Example 4 $\dfrac{d}{dx} \ln 3x = 3 \cdot \dfrac{1}{3x} = \dfrac{1}{x}$

Note that we could have done this another way using Property 1:

$$\ln 3x = \ln 3 + \ln x,$$

then

$$\dfrac{d}{dx} \ln 3x = \dfrac{d}{dx} \ln 3 + \dfrac{d}{dx} \ln x = 0 + \dfrac{1}{x} = \dfrac{1}{x}.$$

Differentiate.

56. $\ln 5x$

57. $\ln(3x^2 + 4)$

58. $\ln(\ln 5x)$

59. $\ln\left(\dfrac{x^5 - 2}{x}\right)$

Example 5 $\dfrac{d}{dx}\ln(x^2 - 5) = 2x \cdot \dfrac{1}{x^2 - 5} = \dfrac{2x}{x^2 - 5}$

Example 6 $\dfrac{d}{dx}\ln(\ln x) = \dfrac{1}{x} \cdot \dfrac{1}{\ln x} = \dfrac{1}{x \ln x}$

Example 7

$\dfrac{d}{dx}\ln\left(\dfrac{x^3 + 4}{x}\right) = \dfrac{d}{dx}[\ln(x^3 + 4) - \ln x]$ $\left(\begin{array}{l}\text{Property 2. This avoids}\\ \text{using the Quotient Rule.}\end{array}\right)$

$= 3x^2 \cdot \dfrac{1}{x^3 + 4} - \dfrac{1}{x} = \dfrac{3x^2}{x^3 + 4} - \dfrac{1}{x}$

$= \dfrac{3x^2}{x^3 + 4} \cdot \dfrac{x}{x} - \dfrac{1}{x} \cdot \dfrac{x^3 + 4}{x^3 + 4}$

$= \dfrac{(3x^2)x - (x^3 + 4)}{x(x^3 + 4)} = \dfrac{3x^3 - x^3 - 4}{x(x^3 + 4)} = \dfrac{2x^3 - 4}{x(x^3 + 4)}$

Do Exercises 56 through 59.

Application

Example *Forgetting.* In a psychological experiment students were shown a set of nonsense syllables, such as *PDQ*, and asked to recall them every second thereafter. The percentage $R(t)$ who retained the syllables after t seconds was found to be given by

$$R(t) = 80 - 27 \ln t, \qquad \text{for} \quad t \geqslant 1.$$

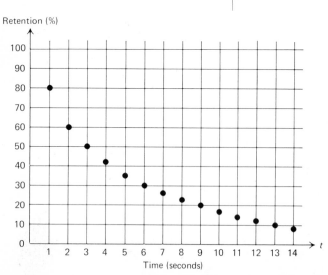

Retention (%)

Time (seconds)

Figure 4.7

Retention (%)

Time (seconds)

Figure 4.8

(Strictly speaking, the function is not continuous and has a graph as shown in Fig. 4.7. But in order to use calculus, we "fill in" the graph with a smooth curve, considering $R(t)$ to be defined for any number $t \geqslant 1$. This is not unreasonable, since we are now able to find the percentage who retained the syllables after $t = 3.417$ seconds, instead of just after integer values such as 1, 2, 3, 4, and so on.)

a) What percentage retained the syllables after 1 second?

b) Find $R'(t)$, the rate of change of R with respect to t.

c) Find maximum and minimum values, if they exist.

Conduct your own memory experiment. Study this photograph carefully. Then put it aside and write down as many items as you can. Wait a half-hour and again write down as many as you can. Do this five more times. Make a graph of the number of items you remember versus time. Does it appear to be logarithmic?

60. *Advertising.* A model for advertising response is given by

$$N(a) = 500 + 200 \ln a, \qquad a \geqslant 1,$$

where

$N(a)$ = number of units sold

a = amount spent on advertising, in thousands of dollars.

a) How many units were sold after spending 1 thousand dollars? (Substitute 1 for a, not 1000.)
b) Find $N'(a)$.
c) Find maximum and minimum values, if they exist.

Solution

a) $R(1) = 80 - 27 \cdot \ln 1 = 80 - 27 \cdot 0 = 80\%$

b) $R'(t) = -27 \cdot \dfrac{1}{t} = -\dfrac{27}{t}$

c) Now $R'(t)$ exists for all values of t in the interval $[1, \infty)$. Note that for $t \geqslant 1$, $-\dfrac{27}{t} < 0$. Thus there are no critical points and R is decreasing. Then R has a maximum value at the endpoint 1. This maximum value is $R(1)$, or 80%.

Do Exercise 60.

This problem and the one in the margin exercise are presented in reverse of how they might have come up if we were constructing models with the aid of calculus. That is, we might begin our reasoning about the rate of forgetting. It might be reasoned that the rate of forgetting $R'(t)$ is inversely proportional to time; that is, $R'(t) = -\dfrac{A}{t}$.

Then we would reason backwards to determine the function $R(t) = B - A \ln t$. Models constructed with the aid of calculus often grow out of assumptions about rates of change of quantities connected with the phenomenon to be modeled. We will do this in the subsequent three sections of this chapter and in Chapter 7.

EXERCISE SET 4.3

Given $\ln 4 = 1.3863$ and $\ln 5 = 1.6094$, find:

1. $\ln 20$ **2.** $\ln \frac{4}{5}$ **3.** $\ln \frac{5}{4}$ **4.** $\ln \frac{1}{5}$ **5.** $\ln \frac{1}{4}$ **6.** $\ln 5e$

7. $\ln 4e$ **8.** $\ln \sqrt{e^6}$ **9.** $\ln \sqrt{e^8}$ **10.** $\ln 25$ **11.** $\ln 16$ **12.** $\ln 100$

Differentiate.

13. $-6 \ln x$ **14.** $-4 \ln x$ **15.** $x^4 \ln x - \frac{1}{2}x^2$ **16.** $x^5 \ln x - \frac{1}{4}x^4$

17. $\dfrac{\ln x}{x^4}$ **18.** $\dfrac{\ln x}{x^5}$ **19.** $\ln \dfrac{x}{4}$ **20.** $\ln \dfrac{x}{2}$

[*Hint:* $\ln \dfrac{x}{4} = \ln x - \ln 4$]

21. $\ln(5x^2 - 7)$ **22.** $\ln(7x^3 + 4)$ **23.** $\ln(\ln 4x)$ **24.** $\ln(\ln 3x)$

25. $\ln\left(\dfrac{x^2 - 7}{x}\right)$ **26.** $\ln\left(\dfrac{x^2 + 5}{x}\right)$ **27.** $e^x \ln x$ **28.** $e^{2x} \ln x$

29. $\ln(e^x + 1)$ **30.** $\ln(e^x - 2)$ **31.** $(\ln x)^2$ **32.** $(\ln x)^3$
[*Hint:* The Extended Power Rule]

Applied Problems

33. *Forgetting.* Students in college botany took a final exam. They took equivalent forms of the exam in monthly intervals thereafter. The average score, $S(t)$ in percent, after t months was found to be given by
$$S(t) = 68 - 20 \ln(t + 1), \quad t \geqslant 0.$$

a) What was the average score when they initially took the test, $t = 0$?

b) What was the average score after 4 months?

c) What was the average score after 24 months?

d) What percentage of the initial score did they retain after 2 years (24 months)?

e) Find $S'(t)$.

f) Find maximum and minimum values, if they exist.

35. *Advertising.* A model for advertising response is given by
$$N(a) = 1000 + 200 \ln a, \quad a \geqslant 1,$$
where
$$N(a) = \text{number of units sold}$$
$$a = \text{amount spent on advertising,}$$
$$\text{in thousands of dollars.}$$

a) How many units were sold after spending 1 thousand dollars ($a = 1$) on advertising?

b) Find $N'(a)$, $N'(10)$.

c) Find maximum and minimum values, if they exist.

34. *Forgetting.* Students in college zoology took a final exam. They took equivalent forms of the exam in monthly intervals thereafter. The average score, $S(t)$ in percent, after t months was found to be given by
$$S(t) = 78 - 15 \ln(t + 1), \quad t \geqslant 0.$$

a) What was the average score when they initially took the test, $t = 0$?

b) What was the average score after 4 months?

c) What was the average score after 24 months?

d) What percentage of the initial score did they retain after 2 years (24 months)?

e) Find $S'(t)$.

f) Find maximum and minimum values, if they exist.

36. *Advertising.* A model for advertising response is given by
$$N(a) = 2000 + 500 \ln a, \quad a \geqslant 1,$$
where
$$N(a) = \text{number of units sold}$$
$$a = \text{amount spent on advertising,}$$
$$\text{in thousands of dollars.}$$

a) How many units were sold after spending 1 thousand dollars ($a = 1$) on advertising?

b) Find $N'(a)$, $N'(10)$.

c) Find maximum and minimum values, if they exist.

4.4 APPLICATIONS: THE UNINHIBITED GROWTH MODEL, $\dfrac{dP}{dt} = kP$

Consider the function
$$f(x) = 2e^{3x}.$$
Differentiating, we get
$$f'(x) = 3 \cdot 2e^{3x} = 3 \cdot f(x).$$

Looking at this graphically, it says that the derivative, or slope of the tangent line, is simply the constant 3 times the function value.

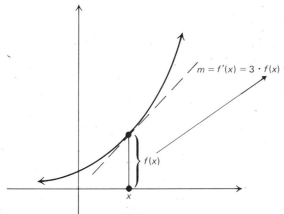

Do Exercise 61.

In general,

A function $y = f(x)$ satisfies the equation

$$\frac{dy}{dx} = ky \qquad [f'(x) = k \cdot f(x)]$$

if and only if

$$y = ce^{kx} \qquad [f(x) = ce^{kx}]$$

for some constant c.

No matter what the variables, you should be able to write the solution.

Example 1   The solution of $\dfrac{dA}{dt} = kA$ is $A = ce^{kt}$, or $A(t) = ce^{kt}$.

Example 2   The solution of $\dfrac{dP}{dt} = kP$ is $P = ce^{kt}$, or $P(t) = ce^{kt}$.

Example 3   The solution of $f'(Q) = k \cdot f(Q)$ is $f(Q) = ce^{kQ}$.

Do Exercise 62.

OBJECTIVES

You should be able to:

a) State the solution of an equation $\dfrac{dP}{dt} = kP$, as $P(t) = P_0e^{kt}$.

b) Given a growth rate find the doubling time.

c) Given the doubling time, find the growth rate.

d) Solve applied problems involving exponential growth.

61. a) Differentiate $y = 5e^{4x}$.

b) Express $\dfrac{dy}{dx}$ in terms of y.

62. a) State the solution of
$$\frac{dN}{dt} = kN.$$

b) State the solution of
$$f'(t) = k \cdot f(t).$$

63. *Exploratory Exercises—Growth*
Use a sheet of $8\frac{1}{2} \times 11$ paper. Cut it into two equal pieces. Then cut these into four equal pieces. Then cut these into eight equal pieces, and so on, performing five cutting steps.

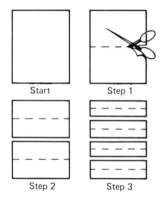

a) Place all the pieces in a stack and measure the thickness.
b) A piece of paper is typically 0.004 in. thick. Check the calculation in (a) by completing this table.

	t	$0.004 \cdot 2^t$
Start	0	$0.004 \cdot 2^0$, or 0.004
Step 1	1	$0.004 \cdot 2^1$, or 0.008
Step 2	2	$0.004 \cdot 2^2$, or 0.016
Step 3	3	
Step 4	4	
Step 5	5	

c) Compute the thickness of the paper (in miles) after 25 steps.

The equation
$$\frac{dP}{dt} = kP, \quad k > 0 \qquad [P'(t) = k \cdot P(t), \quad k > 0]$$

is the basic model of uninhibited population growth, whether it be a population of humans, a bacteria culture, or money invested at interest compounded continuously. Neglecting special inhibiting and stimulating factors, a population normally reproduces itself at a rate proportional to its size, and this is exactly what the equation $\frac{dP}{dt} = kP$ says. The solution of the equation is

$$P(t) = ce^{kt}, \tag{1}$$

where t = time. At $t = 0$, we have some "initial" population $P(0)$ which we will represent by P_0. We can rewrite equation (1) in terms of P_0 as follows:

$$P_0 = P(0) = ce^{k \cdot 0} = ce^0 = c \cdot 1 = c.$$

Thus $P_0 = c$, so we can express $P(t)$ as

$$P(t) = P_0 e^{kt}.$$

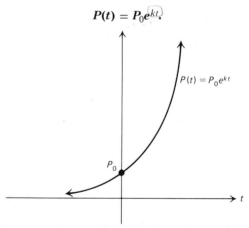

Its graph is the curve shown here. It shows how uninhibited growth results in a "population explosion."

Do Exercise 63.

The constant k is called the *rate of exponential growth*, or simply the *growth rate*. This is not the rate of change of the population size, which is

$$\frac{dP}{dt} = kP,$$

but the constant that P must be multiplied by to get its rate of change.

It is thus a different use of the word *rate*. It is like the *interest rate* paid by a bank. If the interest rate is 7%, or 0.07, we do not mean that your bank balance P is growing at the rate of 0.07 dollars per year, but at the rate of $0.07P$ dollars per year. We therefore express the rate as 7% per year, rather than 0.07 dollars per year. We could say that the rate is 0.07 dollars *per dollar* per year. When interest is compounded continuously, the interest rate *is* a true exponential growth rate.

Example 1   *Interest compounded continuously.* Suppose an amount P_0 is invested in a savings account where interest is compounded continuously at 7% per year. That is, the balance P grows at the rate given by

$$\frac{dP}{dt} = 0.07P.$$

a) Find the solution of the equation in terms of P_0 and 0.07.
b) Suppose $100 is invested. What is the balance after 1 year?
c) When will an investment of $100 double itself?

Solution

a) $P(t) = P_0 e^{0.07t}$

b) $P(1) = 100e^{0.07(1)} = 100e^{0.07} = 100(1.0725)$ (Table 4)
                           $= \$107.25$

c) We are asking at what time T does $P(T) = \$200$. The number T is called the *doubling time*. To find T we solve the equation

$$200 = 100e^{0.07 \cdot T}$$
$$2 = e^{0.07T}. \qquad \text{(Multiplying by } \tfrac{1}{100}\text{)}$$

We use natural logarithms to solve this equation since we can find ln 2 in Table 3:

$$\ln 2 = \ln e^{0.07T}$$
$$\ln 2 = 0.07T \qquad [Recall: \ln e^h = h]$$
$$\frac{\ln 2}{0.07} = T$$
$$\frac{0.6931}{0.07} = T$$
$$9.9 = T$$

Thus $100 will double itself in 9.9 years.

Do Exercise 64.

64. Suppose an amount P_0 is invested in a savings account where interest is compounded continuously at 8% per year. That is, the balance P grows at the rate given by

$$\frac{dP}{dt} = 0.08P.$$

a) Find the solution of the equation in terms of P_0 and 0.08.

b) Suppose $1000 is invested. What is the balance after 1 year?

c) When will an investment of $1000 double itself?

We can find a general expression relating the growth rate k and the doubling time T by solving the equation

$$2P_0 = P_0 e^{kT}$$
$$2 = e^{kT} \qquad \left(\text{Multiplying by } \frac{1}{P_0}\right)$$
$$\ln 2 = \ln e^{kT}$$
$$\ln 2 = kT.$$

The growth rate k and the doubling time T are related by

$$kT = \ln 2 = 0.6931,$$

or

a) $k = \dfrac{\ln 2}{T} = \dfrac{0.6931}{T}$ b) $T = \dfrac{\ln 2}{k} = \dfrac{0.6931}{k}.$

Under ideal conditions the growth rate of this population of rabbits is 15.8% per day. When will this population of rabbits double?

Julie O'Neil from Stock, Boston

Note that this relationship between k and T does not depend on P_0.

Example 2   In Canada a bank can advertise that it will double your money in 6.6 years. What is the interest rate on such an account, assuming interest to be compounded continuously?

Solution $k = \dfrac{\ln 2}{T} = \dfrac{0.6931}{6.6} = 0.105 = 10.5\%$

Do Exercise 65.

Example 3   *World population growth.* The population of the world in 1970 was 3.6 billion. On the basis of data available at that time it was estimated that the population P was growing exponentially at the rate of 2% per year. That is,

$$\frac{dP}{dt} = 0.02P, \quad \text{where } t = \text{time in years.}$$

a) Find the solution of the equation assuming $P_0 = 3.6$ and $k = 0.02$.
b) Estimate the world population in 1980 $(t = 10)$.
c) When will the population be double that in 1970?

Solution

a) $P(t) = 3.6e^{0.02t}$

b) $P(10) = 3.6e^{0.02(10)} = 3.6e^{0.2} = 3.6(1.2214)$ (Table 4)
$$\approx 4.4 \text{ billion}$$

c) $T = \dfrac{\ln 2}{k} = \dfrac{0.6931}{0.02} = \dfrac{69.31}{2} \approx 35$

Thus, according to this model, the 1970 population will double by the year 2005. No wonder ecologists are alarmed!

Do Exercise 66.

Why Would We Expect a Population P to Obey the Law $\dfrac{dP}{dt} = kP$?

Suppose, for example, that a growing colony of bacteria has size $P(t)$. Our measurements of P suggest that P grows smoothly; that is, that

65. Complete this table relating growth rate k and doubling time T.

Growth rate k (% per year)	Doubling time T (in years)
2%	
	10
4%	
	15
1%	

66. The population of the United States in 1974 was 210 million. It was estimated that the population P was growing exponentially at the rate of 1.5% per year. That is,

$$\frac{dP}{dt} = 0.015P,$$

where t = time in years.
a) Find the solution of the equation assuming $P_0 = 210$ and $k = 0.015$.

b) Estimate U.S. population in 1980 $(t = 6)$.

c) When will the population be double that in 1974?

P is a differential function of t. Let k be its growth rate when its size is 1. That is,

$$\frac{dP}{dt} = k, \quad \text{when } P = 1.$$

Now we assume, or observe, that the colony grows uniformly. That is, when the colony has grown to size n, we can picture it as composed of n identical colonies, each of size 1, and each growing (at that moment) at the rate k. So

$$\frac{dP}{dt} = kn, \quad \text{when } P = n.$$

That is,

$$\frac{dP}{dt} = kP.$$

Populations grow exponentially under certain conditions. If bacteria were confined to a Petri dish, their growth curve would be much different than $P = P_0 e^{kt}$. This is because there is only a limited amount of food, and eventually the waste products cause the population to level off. Human population growth is exponential over relatively short periods of time, say 10 to 50 years. In Chapter 7, we will study other models of population growth. If you are not going to study that chapter, you might want to read the discussion in Section 7.3 of how the world population has actually grown.

   Strictly speaking, population is an integer-valued, and hence discontinuous, function of time. Look at this small portion of a graph of $P = P_0 e^{kt}$.

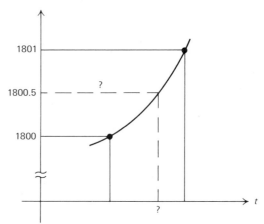

We have assumed that the graph rises from 1800 to 1801. But this implies that we have a value of t for which the population is 1800.5, which is not possible unless you count fractional parts of a pregnancy.

Donald C. Dietz from Stock, Boston

Nevertheless, estimates of population are usually all we require, and an answer like 1800.5 should cause no difficulty.

Modeling Other Phenomena

Example 4 *Alcohol absorption and the risk of having an accident.* Extensive research has provided data relating the *risk R* (%) of having an automobile accident to the *blood alcohol level b* (%). Note that the data is not a perfect fit (see the part between $b = 0$ and $b = 0.05$), but we shall approximate the data with an exponential function. The modeling assumption is that the rate of change of the risk R with respect to the blood alcohol level b is given by

$$\frac{dR}{db} = kR.$$

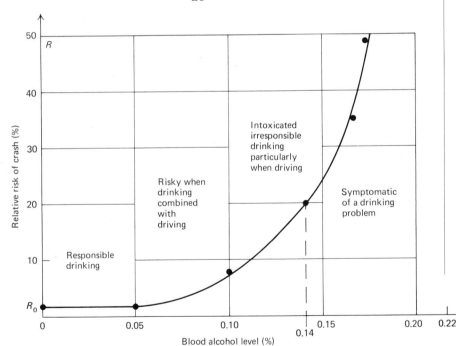

Blood alcohol level (%)

Number of 1-oz drinks of 86 proof whiskey for 160 lb man within 2 hours of eating.

*Some Myths About Alcohol.** It's a fact, the blood alcohol concentration (BAC) in the human body is measurable. And there's no cure for its effect on the central nervous system except time. It takes time for the body's metabolism to recover.

That means a cup of coffee, a cold shower and fresh air can't erase the effect of several drinks.

There are variables, of course. A person's body weight, how many drinks they've taken in a given time, whether or not they've eaten, etc. These account for different BAC levels. But the myth that some people can "handle their liquor" better than others is a gross rationalization . . . especially when it comes to driving. Some people can act more sober than others. But an automobile doesn't act, it reacts.

a) Find the solution of the equation, assuming $R_0 = 1\%$.

b) Find k, using the data point $R(0.14) = 20$. (This is how one might fit the data to an exponential equation.)

*. . . from *Indianapolis Alcohol Safety Action Project*.

67. *Electrical energy demand.* Past data on electrical energy demand in the U.S. is shown in the graph.

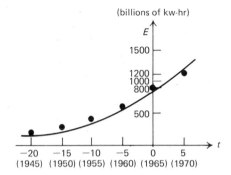

(billions of kw-hr)

It appears that we can fit an exponential function to the data. We accept the modeling assumption that the rate of change of electrical energy need E (in billion kilowatt hours, kW-hr) with respect to time is given by

$$\frac{dE}{dt} = kE.$$

a) Find the solution of the equation, assuming $E_0 = 800$ billion kW-hr. That is, at $t = 0(1965)$, $E = 800$.
b) Find k using the data point $E(5) = 1200$ billion kW-hr. That is, in 1970, 1200 billion kW-hr were used. Round to the nearest hundredth.
c) Rewrite $E(t)$ in terms of k.
d) How much electrical energy will be needed in 1995?

Daniel S. Brody from Stock, Boston

c) Rewrite $R(b)$ in terms of k.
d) At what blood alcohol level will the risk of having an accident be 100%?

Solution

a) Since both R and b are percents, we omit the % symbol for ease of computation. The solution is

$$R(b) = e^{kb}.$$

b) We solve this equation for k.

$$20 = e^{k(0.14)} = e^{0.14k}$$

We use natural logarithms to solve this equation.

$$\ln 20 = \ln e^{0.14k}$$

$$\ln 20 = 0.14k$$

$$\frac{\ln 20}{0.14} = k$$

$$\frac{2.9957}{0.14} = k$$

$$21.4 = k \qquad \text{(Rounding to the nearest tenth)}$$

c) $R(b) = e^{21.4b}$

d) We solve this equation for b.

$$100 = e^{21.4b}$$

$$\ln 100 = \ln e^{21.4b}$$

$$\ln 100 = 21.4b$$

$$\frac{\ln 100}{21.4} = b$$

$$\frac{4.6052}{21.4} = b$$

$$0.22 = b$$

Thus when the blood alcohol level is 0.22%, according to this model, the risk of an accident is 100%. From the graph, this would occur after 12 1-oz drinks of 86 proof whiskey. "Theoretically" the model tells us that after 12 drinks of whiskey one is "sure" to have an accident. This might be questioned in actuality, since a person who has had 12 drinks might not be able to drive at all.

Do Exercise 67.

EXERCISE SET 4.4

1. State the solution of $\dfrac{dQ}{dt} = kQ$ in terms of Q_0.

2. State the solution of $\dfrac{dR}{dt} = kR$ in terms of R_0.

3. Suppose P_0 is invested in a savings account where interest is compounded continuously at 9% per year. That is, the balance P grows at the rate given by

$$\frac{dP}{dt} = 0.09P.$$

a) Find the solution of the equation in terms of P_0 and 0.09.

b) Suppose $1000 is invested. What is the balance after 1 year? 2 years?

c) When will an investment of $1000 double itself?

4. Suppose P_0 is invested in a savings account where interest is compounded continuously at 10% per year. That is, the balance P grows at the rate given by

$$\frac{dP}{dt} = 0.10P.$$

a) Find the solution of the equation in terms of P_0 and 0.10.

b) Suppose $20,000 is invested. What is the balance after 1 year? 2 years?

c) When will an investment of $20,000 double itself?

5. The growth rate of the population of Central America is 3.5% per year (one of the highest in the world). What is the doubling time?

6. The growth rate of the population of Europe is 1% per year (one of the lowest in the world). What is the doubling time?

7. A bank advertises that it compounds interest continuously and that it will double your money in 10 years. What is its annual interest rate?

8. A bank advertises that it compounds interest continuously and that it will double your money in 12 years. What is its annual interest rate?

9. The population of the USSR was 209 million in 1959. It was estimated that the population P was growing exponentially at the rate of 1% per year. That is,

$$\frac{dP}{dt} = 0.01P.$$

a) Find the solution of the equation assuming $P_0 = 209$ and $k = 0.01$.

b) Estimate the population of the USSR in 1999.

c) When will the population be double that in 1959?

10. The population of Europe west of the USSR was 430 million in 1961. It was estimated that the population was growing exponentially at the rate of 1% per year. That is,

$$\frac{dP}{dt} = 0.01P.$$

a) Find the solution of the equation assuming $P_0 = 430$ and $k = 0.01$.

b) Estimate the population of Europe in 1991.

c) When will the population be double that in 1961?

11. In the example on alcohol absorption, at what blood alcohol level will the risk of an accident be 80%?

12. In the example on alcohol absorption, at what blood alcohol level will the risk of an accident be 90%?

13. A national hamburger firm is selling franchises throughout the country. The president estimates that the number of franchises N will increase at a rate of 10% per year. That is,

$$\frac{dN}{dt} = 0.10N.$$

a) Find the solution of the equation, assuming the number of franchises at $t = 0$ is 50.

b) How many franchises will there be in 20 years?

c) When will the initial number of 50 franchises double?

14. Pizza, Unltd., a national pizza firm, is selling franchises throughout the country. The president estimates that the number of franchises N will increase at a rate of 15% per year. That is,

$$\frac{dN}{dt} = 0.15N.$$

a) Find the solution of the equation, assuming the number of franchises at $t = 0$ is 40.

b) How many franchises will there be in 20 years?

c) When will the initial number of 40 franchises double itself?

15. The growth rate of the demand for oil in the United States is 10% per year. When will the demand be double that in 1976?

16. The growth rate of the demand for coal in the world is 4% per year. When will the demand be double that in 1976?

17. The population of Tempe, Arizona was 25 thousand in 1960. In 1969 it was 52 thousand. Assuming the exponential model,

a) find the value $k(P_0 = 25)$. Use common logarithms.

b) estimate the population of Tempe in 1980.

18. The population of Kansas City was 475 thousand in 1960. In 1970 it was 507 thousand. Assuming the exponential model,

a) find the value $k(P_0 = 475)$. Use common logarithms.

b) estimate the population of Kansas City in 2000.

Suppose $100 is invested at 7% compounded continuously for 1 year. We know from Example 1 that the balance will be $107.25. This is the same as if $100 were invested at 7.25% compounded once a year (simple interest). The 7.25% is called the "effective annual yield." In general, if P_0 is invested at $k(\%)$ compounded continuously, then the effective annual yield is that number i satisfying $P_0(1 + i) = P_0 e^k$. Then $1 + i = e^k$, or

Effective annual yield $= i = e^k - 1.$

19. An amount is invested at 6% per year compounded continuously. What is the effective annual yield?

20. An amount is invested at 8% per year compounded continuously. What is the effective annual yield?

21. The effective annual yield on an investment compounded continuously is 9.42%. At what rate was it invested?

22. The effective annual yield on an investment compounded continuously is 10.52%. At what rate was it invested?

23. Find an expression relating the growth rate k and the *tripling* time T_3.

24. Find an expression relating the growth rate k and the *quadrupling* time T_4.

25. Gather data concerning population growth in your city. Estimate its population in 1980, in 2000.

26. A quantity Q_1 grows exponentially with a doubling time of 1 year. A quantity Q_2 grows exponentially with a doubling time of 2 years. If the initial amounts of Q_1 and Q_2 are the same, when will Q_1 be twice the size of Q_2?

4.5 APPLICATIONS: DECAY

Do Exercise 68.

In the equation of population growth $\dfrac{dP}{dt} = kP$ the constant k is actually given by

$$k = \text{(Birth rate)} - \text{(Death rate)}.$$

Thus a population "grows" only when the *birth rate* is greater than the *death rate*. When the *birth rate* is less than the *death rate*, k will be negative so the population will be decreasing, or "decaying," at a rate proportional to its size. The equation

$$\frac{dP}{dt} = -kP \qquad \text{(where } k > 0\text{)}$$

shows P to be *decreasing* as a function of time, and the solution

$$P(t) = P_0 e^{-kt}$$

shows it to be decreasing exponentially. This is exponential *decay*. The amount present initially at $t = 0$ is again P_0.

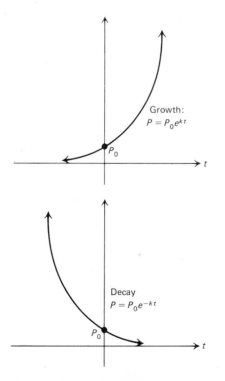

OBJECTIVES

You should be able to:

a) State the solution of an equation $\dfrac{dP}{dt} = -kP$, as $P(t) = P_0 e^{-kt}$.
b) Given a decay rate, find the half-life.
c) Given a half-life, find the decay rate.
d) Solve applied problems involving decay.
e) Solve applied problems involving Newton's Law of Cooling.

68. Using the same set of axes, graph $y = e^{2x}$ and $y = e^{-2x}$.

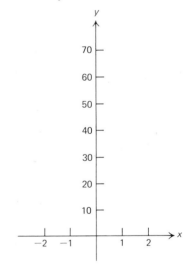

69. Xenon-133 has a decay rate of 14% per day. The rate of change of an amount N is given by

$$\frac{dN}{dt} = 0.14N.$$

a) Find the solution of the equation in terms of N_0.

b) Suppose 1000 grams of Xenon-133 is present at $t = 0$. How much will remain after 10 days?

c) After what time will half of 1000 grams remain?

Radioactive Decay

Radioactive elements decay exponentially; that is, they disintegrate at a rate which is proportional to the amount present.

Example 1   Strontium-90 has a decay rate of 2.8% per year. The rate of change of an amount N is given by

$$\frac{dN}{dt} = -0.028N.$$

a) Find the solution of the equation in terms of N_0 (the amount present at $t = 0$).

b) Suppose 1000 grams of Strontium-90 is present at $t = 0$. How much will remain after 100 years?

c) After what amount of time will half of the 1000 grams remain?

Solution

a) $N(t) = N_0 e^{-0.028t}$

b) $N(100) = 1000 e^{-0.028(100)} = 1000 e^{-2.8}$

$$= 1000(0.0608) \qquad \text{(Table 4)}$$
$$= 60.8 \text{ grams}$$

c) We are asking at what time T will $N(T) = 500$. The number T is called the *half-life*. To find T we solve the equation:

$$500 = 1000 e^{-0.028T}$$
$$\tfrac{1}{2} = e^{-0.028T}$$
$$\ln \tfrac{1}{2} = \ln e^{-0.028T}$$
$$\ln 1 - \ln 2 = -0.028T$$
$$0 - \ln 2 = -0.028T$$
$$\frac{-\ln 2}{-0.028} = T$$
$$\frac{\ln 2}{0.028} = T$$
$$\frac{0.6931}{0.028} = T$$
$$25 \approx T$$

Thus the half-life of Strontium-90 is 25 years.

Do Exercise 69.

We can find a general expression relating the decay rate k and the half-life T by solving the equation

$$\tfrac{1}{2}P_0 = P_0 e^{-kT}.$$
$$\tfrac{1}{2} = e^{-kT}$$
$$\ln \tfrac{1}{2} = \ln e^{-kT}$$
$$\ln 1 - \ln 2 = -kT$$
$$0 - \ln 2 = -kT$$
$$-\ln 2 = -kT$$
$$\ln 2 = kT$$

Again,

   The *decay rate k* and the *half-life T* are related by

   $$kT = \ln 2 = 0.6931,$$

   or

   $$\textbf{a) } k = \frac{\ln 2}{T} \qquad \textbf{b) } T = \frac{\ln 2}{k}.$$

Thus the half-life T depends only on the decay rate k. In particular, it is independent of the initial population size.

The effect of half-life is shown in this radioactive decay curve.

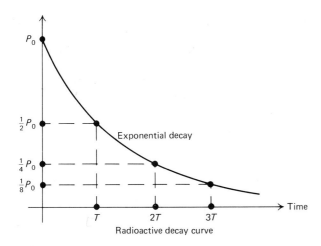

Radioactive decay curve

The exponential function gets closer to 0 as t gets larger, but never reaches 0. Thus, in theory, a radioactive substance never completely decays.

70. The decay rate of Cesium-137 is 2.3% per year. What is its half-life?

Example 2   Plutonium, a common product and ingredient of nuclear reactors, is of great concern to those who are against the building of nuclear reactors. Its decay rate is 0.003% per year. What is its half-life?

Solution $T = \dfrac{\ln 2}{k} = \dfrac{0.6931}{0.00003} = 23{,}103$ years

Do Exercises 70 and 71.

71. The half-life of Barium-140 is 13 days. What is its decay rate?

Example 3   *Carbon dating.* The radioactive element Carbon-14 has a half-life of 5750 years. The percentage of Carbon-14 present in the remains of plants and animals can be used to determine age. How old is an animal bone which has lost 30% of its Carbon-14?

Solution

a) Find the decay rate k.

$$k = \frac{\ln 2}{T} = \frac{0.6931}{5750} = 0.00012, \qquad \text{or } 0.012\% \text{ per year}$$

b) Find the exponential equation for the amount $N(t)$ which remains from an initial amount N_0 after t years.

$$N(t) = N_0 e^{-0.00012t}$$

[*Note:* This equation can be used for any subsequent carbon dating problem.]

c) If an animal bone has lost 30% of its Carbon-14 from an initial amount P_0, then 70% P_0 is the amount present. To find the age t of the bone we solve the following equation for t.

$$70\% \, P_0 = P_0 e^{-0.00012t}$$
$$0.7 = e^{-0.00012t}$$
$$\ln 0.7 = \ln e^{-0.00012t}$$
$$\ln 0.7 = -0.00012t$$
$$-0.3567 = -0.00012t \qquad \text{(Table 3)}$$
$$\frac{0.3567}{0.00012} = t$$
$$\frac{35670}{12} = t$$
$$2972.5 = t$$

How Can Scientists Determine That an Animal Bone Has Lost 30% of its Carbon-14? The assumption is that the percentage of Carbon-14 in the atmosphere and in *living* plants and animals is the same. When a plant or animal dies, the amount of Carbon-14 decays exponentially. The scientist burns the animal bone and uses a geiger counter to determine the percentage of the smoke which is Carbon-14. It is the amount this varies from the percentage in the atmosphere which tells how much Carbon-14 has been lost.

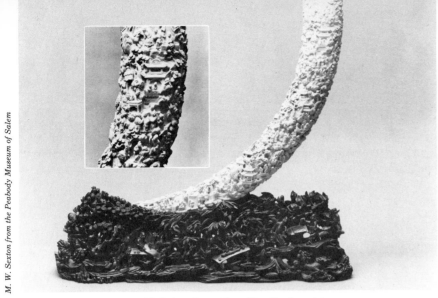

This tusk is 136 years old. It has lost 2% of its Carbon-14.

Thus, an animal bone which has lost 30% of its Carbon-14 is about 2973 years old.

Do Exercise 72.

Newton's Law of Cooling

Before you study the following do the exploratory exercises in the margin.

NEWTON'S LAW OF COOLING. *The temperature of a cooling object drops at a rate which is proportional to the difference T − C, where C is the constant temperature of the surrounding medium. Thus*

$$\frac{dT}{dt} = -k(T - C). \qquad (1)$$

The solution of (1) is

$$T = T(t) = ae^{-kt} + C. \qquad (2)$$

We can check this by differentiating:

$$\frac{dT}{dt} = -kae^{-kt} = -k(ae^{-kt}) = -k(T - C)$$

Example 1 The temperature of a cup of freshly brewed coffee is 200° and the room temperature is 70°. The temperature cools to 190° in 5 minutes.

a) What is the temperature after 10 minutes?

b) How long does it take for the temperature to cool to 90°?

72. How old is a skeleton which has lost 80% of its Carbon-14?

Exploratory Exercises—Cooling. Draw a glass of hot tap water. Place a thermometer in the glass and check the temperature. Check the temperature every 30 minutes thereafter. Plot your data on this graph and connect the points with a smooth curve.

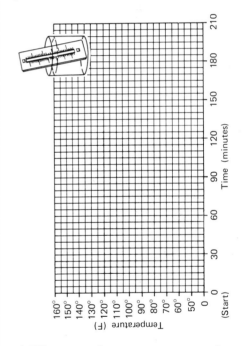

a) What was the temperature at the start?
b) At what temperature does there seem to be a leveling off of the graph?
c) What is the difference between your answers to (a) and (b)?
d) How does the temperature to (b) compare with the room temperature?

73. The temperature of a hot cup of soup is 200°. The room temperature is 70°. The temperature cools to 190° in 8 minutes.
a) Find the value of the constant a in Newton's Law of Cooling.
b) Find the value of the constant k.
c) What is the temperature after 10 minutes?
d) How long does it take for the soup to cool to 80°?

74. Return to the data you found in the exploratory exercises. Find an equation which "fits" the data. Use this equation to check values of other data points. How do they compare? Is it ever "theoretically" possible for the temperature of the water to be the same as the room temperature?

Solution

a) We first find the value of a in equation (2). At $t = 0$, $T = 200°$. We solve the following equation for a.

$$200 = ae^{-k \cdot 0} + 70$$
$$200 = a \cdot 1 + 70$$
$$130 = a$$

Now we find k using the fact that at $t = 5$, $T = 190°$. We solve the following equation for k.

$$190 = 130e^{-k \cdot 5} + 70$$
$$120 = 130e^{-5k}$$
$$\tfrac{12}{13} = e^{-5k}$$
$$\ln \tfrac{12}{13} = \ln e^{-5k} = -5k$$
$$-5k = \ln 12 - \ln 13$$
$$k = -\tfrac{1}{5}(\ln 12 - \ln 13) = -\tfrac{1}{5}(2.4849 - 2.5649) \qquad \text{(Table 3)}$$
$$= 0.016.$$

Now we find the temperature at $t = 10$.

$$T(10) = 130e^{-0.016(10)} + 70 = 130e^{-0.16} + 70$$
$$= 130(0.8521) + 70$$
$$\approx 181°$$

b) To find how long it will take for the temperature to be 90° we solve for t such that

$$90 = 130e^{-0.016t} + 70$$
$$20 = 130e^{-0.016t}$$
$$\tfrac{2}{13} = e^{-0.016t}$$
$$\ln \tfrac{2}{13} = \ln e^{-0.016t} = -0.016t$$
$$-0.016t = \ln 2 - \ln 13$$
$$t = -\tfrac{1}{0.016}(\ln 2 - \ln 13)$$
$$t = -\tfrac{1}{0.016}(0.6931 - 2.5649) \qquad \text{(Table 3)}$$
$$t \approx 117 \text{ minutes.}$$

Do Exercises 73 and 74.

The graph of

$$T(t) = ae^{-kt} + C$$

is as follows. Note that $\lim_{t \to \infty} T(t) = C$. The temperature of the object

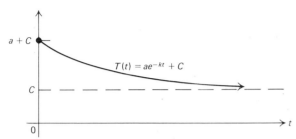

decreases toward the temperature of the surrounding medium. Mathematically, this model tells us that the temperature never reaches C, but in practice this happens eventually. At least, the temperature of the cooling object gets so close to that of the surrounding medium that no device could detect a difference. Let us now see how Newton's Law of Cooling could be used in solving a crime.

Example 2 *When was the murder committed?* The police discover the body of a calculus professor. Critical to solving the crime is determining when the murder was committed. The police call the coroner who arrives at 12:00 P.M. He immediately takes the temperature of the body and finds it to be $94.6°$. He waits 1 hour, takes the temperature again, and finds it to be $93.4°$. He also notes that the temperature of the room is $70°$. When was the murder committed?

Solution We first find a in the equation $T(t) = ae^{-kt} + C$. Assuming the temperature of the body was normal when it was murdered we have $T = 98.6°$ at $t = 0$. Thus

$$98.6° = ae^{-k \cdot 0} + 70°, \quad \text{so } a = 28.6°.$$

Thus T is given by

$$T(t) = 28.6e^{-kt} + 70.$$

We want to find the number of hours N since the murder was committed. To find N we first have to determine k. From the two temperature readings which the coroner made we have

$$94.6 = 28.6e^{-kN} + 70, \quad \text{or} \quad 24.6 = 28.6e^{-kN} \tag{1}$$

$$93.4 = 28.6e^{-k(N+1)} + 70, \quad \text{or} \quad 23.4 = 28.6e^{-k(N+1)} \tag{2}$$

Dividing equation (1) by equation (2) we get

$$\frac{24.6}{23.4} = \frac{28.6e^{-kN}}{28.6e^{-k(N+1)}} = e^{-kN + k(N+1)} = e^{-kN + kN + k} = e^k$$

or,

$$1.05 = e^k.$$

We take common logarithms since 1.05 is not in Table 3, and this gives us k.

$$\log 1.05 = \log e^k$$

$$\log 1.05 = k \log e$$

$$\frac{\log 1.05}{\log e} = k$$

$$\frac{0.0212}{0.4343} = k$$

$$0.05 \approx k$$

Models have many applications. This article, which is actually an advertisement, describes the effects of melting ice on the alcoholic content of Scotch whiskey. The graphs are of the equation describing Newton's Law of Cooling.

The Effects of Ice on Scotch

How fast a drink of Scotch whisky over rocks loses its flavor depends on the proof of the Scotch and the richness of its blend. These two factors are optimized for "on the rocks" Scotch drinkers in 90-Proof Famous Grouse, a venerable old brand from Scotland only recently introduced to America.

by Allen Mac Kenzie

In countries where Scotch has been consumed for centuries, ice and whisky rarely mingle. But on this side of the Atlantic, the picture is quite different. While a small percentage of American Scotch drinkers take it neat, better than 35% drink it "on the rocks." The rest of us add varying amounts of water, club soda, etcetera. And ice. Always plenty of ice — the great American drink requisite.

It would seem then that the American Scotch devotee, particularly our on-the-rocks fancier, has a right to raise a serious question: *Is the Scotch I drink ideally suited to enjoyment over ice?*

Pursuing a Perfect Proof

Let's turn our attention first to the proof at which Scotch whisky is bottled. Consider the hypothesis that there is indeed a better proof for on-the-rocks Scotch drinking than that of the brand you currently favor.

Practically every Scotch sold in this country is bottled at 80, 86, or 86.8 Proof. So at the instant you pour Scotch over ice, it contains between 40% and 43.4% alcohol by volume. (Proof is double the percentage of alcohol.) The chilling effect of the ice is accompanied by dilution. And when your drink has been properly cooled — in 30 seconds to a minute — you achieve what one Scotch connoisseur refers to as

"the ideal sip." From then on, the Scotch drinker's enjoyment typically runs downhill, as the drink loses its freshness.

While there is no way to preserve that fresh Scotch flavor indefinitely, we submit that you can sustain the freshness substantially longer with 90-Proof *Famous Grouse*. If you have never heard of this brand, we are not surprised. It is a well established name in Scotland, but only recently introduced to America. So far as we know, *Famous Grouse* is the only Scotch now available in this country at 90 Proof.

A Revealing Experiment

To demonstrate the merits of a slightly higher proof, we performed a simple experiment: 50 millilitres of Scotch (about 1.7 ounces) was chilled with 100 cc of ice. The ensuing dilutions at 80, 86.8 and 90 Proof are charted in the graph at left.

You'll notice that after 15 minutes on the rocks, the proof of *Famous Grouse* is diluted to a level which occurs after 12½ minutes when the Scotch is 86.8 Proof, and after 9 minutes when it is 80 Proof. In essence, the *Famous Grouse* brand has remained about 2½ minutes fresher than 86.8-Proof Scotch (Interval A on graph), 6 minutes fresher than 80-Proof Scotch (Interval B). If you "nurse" a drink beyond 15 minutes, the advantages of 90 Proof Scotch are even more pronounced.

Proof, of course, is not the only influence on the flavor of a blended Scotch. The proportion of malt to grain whiskies,

origins of the malts, aging methods — these are also important factors determining the relative richness of Scotch flavor.

The makers of *Famous Grouse* — Matthew Gloag & Son of Perth, Scotland — have been producing Scotch in the same family for six generations. And they have performed their most noble feat in the rich blend they created for *Famous Grouse* Scotch. Its flavor — so remarkable at the outset — holds firmly to its character during prolonged contact with ice.

Knowledge of Scotch, however, cannot be indefinitely pursued in the abstract. Your learning process must ultimately include a leisurely sip of *Famous Grouse* on the rocks. For Scotch drinking is one of those pleasures enjoyed most, not in the pursuit, but in the conquest. Scotland's greatest bard, Robert Burns, said it best: *"Gie me a spark o' Nature's fire, That's a' the learning I desire."*

DILUTION BY ICE OF SCOTCH AT THREE DIFFERENT PROOFS (72°F).
■■ 80 Proof ···86.8 Proof ■■ 90 Proof

Nadler & Larimer, Inc.

Now we substitute back into equation (1) and solve for N:

$$24.6 = 28.6e^{-0.05N}$$

$$\frac{24.6}{28.6} = e^{-0.05N}$$

$$0.860 = e^{-0.05N}$$

$$\log 0.860 = \log e^{-0.05N}$$

$$\log 0.860 = -0.05N \log e$$

$$\frac{\log 0.860}{-0.05(0.4343)} = N$$

$$3 \text{ hr} \approx N$$

The coroner arrived at 12:00 P.M., so the murder was committed at about 9:00 A.M.

Do Exercise 75.

75. A butcher is murdered and his body thrown in a cooler where the temperature is 40°. The coroner arrives at 3:00 P.M. He takes the temperature of the body and finds it to be 73.8°. He waits 1 hour, takes the temperature of the body again, and finds it to be 70.3°. When was the murder committed?

EXERCISE SET 4.5

1. The decay rate of Iodine-131 is 9.6% per day. What is its half-life?

2. The decay rate of Krypton-85 is 6.3% per year. What is its half-life?

3. The half-life of polonium is 3 minutes. What is its decay rate?

4. The half-life of lead is 22 yr. What is its decay rate?

5. Of an initial amount of 1000 grams of polonium, how much will remain after 20 minutes? See Exercise 3 for the value of k.

6. Of an initial amount of 1000 grams of lead, how much will remain after 100 yr? See Exercise 4 for the value of k.

7. *Carbon dating.* How old is a piece of wood which has lost 90% of its Carbon-14?

8. *Carbon dating.* How old is an ivory tusk which has lost 40% of its Carbon-14?

9. *Carbon dating.* How old is a Chinese artifact which has lost 60% of its Carbon-14?

10. *Carbon dating.* How old is a skeleton which has lost 50% of its Carbon-14?

11. In a *chemical reaction* a substance A decomposes at a rate proportional to the amount of A present.

a) Write an equation relating A to the amount left of an initial amount A_0 after time t.

b) It is found that 8 grams of A will reduce to 4 grams in 3 hours. At what time will there be only 1 gram left?

12. In a *chemical reaction* a substance A decomposes at a rate proportional to the amount of A present.

a) Write an equation relating A to the amount left of an initial amount A_0 after time t.

b) It is found that 10 lb of A will reduce to 5 lb in 3.3 hr. At what time will there be only 1 lb left?

13. *Weight loss.* The initial weight of a starving animal is W_0. Its W after t days is given by

$$W = W_0 e^{-0.008t}.$$

a) What percentage of its weight does it lose each day?

b) What percentage of its initial weight remains after 30 days?

14. *Weight loss.* The initial weight of a starving animal is W_0. Its weight after t days is given by

$$W = {'W_0} e^{-0.009t}.$$

a) What percentage of its weight does it lose each day?

b) What percentage of its initial weight remains after 30 days?

15. *Satellite power.* The power supply of a satellite is a radioisotope. The power output P, in watts, decreases at a rate proportional to the amount present. P is given by

$$P = 50e^{-0.004t},$$

where t = time in days.

a) How much power will be available after 375 days?

b) What is the half-life of the power supply?

c) The satellite's equipment cannot operate on less than 10 watts of power. How long can the satellite stay in operation?

d) How much power did the satellite have to begin with?

16. *Atmospheric pressure.* Atmospheric pressure P at altitude a is given by

$$P = P_0 e^{-0.00005a},$$

where P_0 = pressure at sea level. Assume $P_0 = 14.7$ lb/in^2 (pounds per square inch).

a) Find the pressure at an altitude of 1000 ft.

b) Find the pressure at 20,000 ft.

c) At what altitude is the pressure 1.47 lb/in^2.

17. *Salvage value.* A business estimates that the salvage value V of a piece of machinery after t years is given by

$$V(t) = \$40{,}000e^{-t}.$$

a) What did the machinery cost initially?

b) What is the salvage value after 2 years?

18. *Supply and demand.* The supply and demand for the sale of stereos by a sound company are given by

$$S(x) = e^x, \qquad D(x) = 163{,}000e^{-x},$$

where $S(x)$ = price at which the company is willing to supply x stereos, and $D(x)$ = demand price for a quantity of x stereos. Find the equilibrium point. For reference, see p. 57.

BEER-LAMBERT LAW.   A beam of light enters a medium, such as water or smoky air, with initial intensity I_0. Its intensity is decreased depending on the thickness (or concentration) of the medium. The intensity I at a depth (or concentration) of x units is given by

$$I = I_0 e^{-\mu x}.$$

The constant μ ("mu"), called the *coefficient of absorption*, varies with the medium.

19. *Light through sea water* has $\mu = 1.4$ when x is measured in meters (m).

a) What percentage of I_0 remains at a depth of sea water which is 1 m? 2 m? 3 m?

b) Plant life cannot exist below 10 meters. What percentage of I_0 remains at 10 meters?

21. The temperature of a hot liquid is 100° and the room temperature is 75°. The liquid cools to 90° in 10 minutes.

a) Find the value of the constant a in Newton's Law of Cooling.

b) Find the value of the constant k. Round to the nearest hundredth.

c) What is the temperature after 20 minutes?

d) How long does it take for the liquid to cool to 80°?

23. The coroner arrives at the scene of a murder at 11 P.M. He takes the temperature of the body and finds it to be 85.9°. He waits 1 hour, takes the temperature again and finds it to be 83.4°. He notes that the room temperature is 60°. When was the murder committed?

20. *Light through smog.* Particulate concentrations of pollution reduce sunlight. In a smoggy area $\mu = 0.01$ and $x =$ concentration of particulates measured in micrograms per cubic meter. What percentage of an initial amount I_0 of sunlight passes through smog which has a concentration of 100 micrograms per cubic meter?

22. The temperature of a hot liquid is 100° and is placed in a refrigerator where the temperature is 40°. The liquid cools to 90° in 5 minutes.

a) Find the value of the constant a in Newton's Law of Cooling.

b) Find the value of the constant k. Round to the nearest hundredth.

c) What is the temperature after 10 minutes?

d) How long does it take for the liquid to cool to 41°?

24. The coroner arrives at the scene of a murder at 2 A.M. He takes the temperature of the body and finds it to be 61.6°. He waits 1 hour, takes the temperature again, and finds it to be 57.2°. The body is in a meat freezer where the temperature is 10°. When was the murder committed?

4.6 THE DERIVATIVES OF a^x AND $\log_a x$

The Derivative of a^x

To find the derivative of a^x, for any base a, we first express it as a power of e. In order to do this we first prove the following.

PROPERTY 7. $b^{\log_b x} = x$

To prove this, let
$$y = \log_b x.$$

Then by definition of logarithms
$$b^y = x.$$

Then substituting $\log_b x$ for y we have
$$b^{\log_b x} = x.$$

OBJECTIVES

You should be able to:

a) Express a power like 2^3 as a power of e.

b) Differentiate functions involving a^x.

c) Differentiate functions involving $\log_a x$.

Express as a power of e.

76. 4^5

We can now express a^x as a power e. Using Property 7 where $b = e$ and $x = a$, we have

$$a = e^{\ln a}. \quad \text{(Remember: } \ln a = \log_e a.\text{)}$$

Raising both sides to the power x, we get

$$a^x = (e^{\ln a})^x$$
$$= e^{x \cdot \ln a} \quad \text{(Multiplying exponents)}$$

Thus

77. 2^x

$$a^x = e^{x \cdot \ln a}.$$

Examples Express as a power of e.
a) 3^2

$$3^2 = e^{2 \cdot \ln 3}$$
$$= e^{2(1.0986)} \quad \text{(Table 3)}$$
$$= e^{2.1972}$$

b) 10^x

$$10^x = e^{x \cdot \ln 10} = e^{x(2.3026)} = e^{2.3026x}$$

78. Differentiate 5^x.

Do Exercises 76 and 77.

Now we can differentiate.

Example 1 $\dfrac{d}{dx} 2^x = \dfrac{d}{dx} e^{x \cdot \ln 2}$

$$= \dfrac{d}{dx} (x \cdot \ln 2) \cdot e^{x \cdot \ln 2}$$
$$= (\ln 2)(e^{\ln 2})^x$$
$$= \ln 2 \cdot 2^x$$

We completed this by taking the derivative of $x \ln 2$, and replacing $e^{x \cdot \ln 2}$ by 2^x. Note that $\ln 2 \approx 0.7$, so the above verifies our earlier approximation of the derivative of 2^x as $(0.7)2^x$ (see p. 202).

Do Exercise 78.

In general,

$$\dfrac{d}{dx} a^x = \dfrac{d}{dx} e^{x \cdot \ln a}$$
$$= \dfrac{d}{dx} (x \cdot \ln a) \cdot e^{x \ln a}$$
$$= \ln a \cdot a^x.$$

Thus

$$\dfrac{d}{dx} a^x = \ln a \cdot a^x$$

Example 2　$\dfrac{d}{dx} 3^x = \ln 3 \cdot 3^x$

Example 3　$\dfrac{d}{dx} (1.4)^x = \ln 1.4 \cdot (1.4)^x$

Compare the formulas below.

$$\frac{d}{dx} a^x = \ln a \cdot a^x$$

$$\frac{d}{dx} e^x = e^x$$

It is the simplicity of the last formula which is a reason for the use of the base e in calculus. The many applications of e in natural phenomena provide other reasons.

Do Exercises 79 and 80.

The Derivative of $\log_a x$

Just as the derivative of a^x is expressed in terms of $\ln a$, so is the derivative of $\log_a x$. To find this derivative we first express $\log_a x$ in terms of $\ln a$ using Property 7:

$$a^{\log_a x} = x.$$

Then

$$\ln a^{\log_a x} = \ln x$$

$(\log_a x) \cdot \ln a = \ln x$　　　(Property 3; treating $\log_a x$ as an exponent.)

and

$$\log_a x = \boxed{\frac{1}{\ln a}} \cdot \ln x.$$
　　　　　　　└── constant

The derivative of $\log_a x$ follows:

$$\frac{d}{dx} \log_a x = \frac{1}{\ln a} \cdot \frac{1}{x}.$$

Comparing this with

$$\frac{d}{dx} \ln x = \frac{1}{x},$$

we again see a reason for the use of the base e in calculus.

Differentiate.

79. 4^x

80. $(4.3)^x$

Differentiate.

81. $\log_2 x$

82. $-7 \log x$

83. $x^6 \log x$

Example 1 $\dfrac{d}{dx} \log_3 x = \dfrac{1}{\ln 3} \cdot \dfrac{1}{x}$

Example 2 $\dfrac{d}{dx} \log x = \dfrac{1}{\ln 10} \cdot \dfrac{1}{x}$ $(\log x = \log_{10} x)$

Example 3 $\dfrac{d}{dx} x^2 \log x = x^2 \dfrac{1}{\ln 10} \cdot \dfrac{1}{x} + 2x \log x$ (Product rule)

$$= \dfrac{x}{\ln 10} + 2x \log x = x\left(\dfrac{1}{\ln 10} + 2 \log x\right)$$

Do Exercises 81 through 83.

EXERCISE SET 4.6

Express as a power of e.

1. 5^4 **2.** 2^3 **3.** $(3.4)^{10}$ **4.** $(5.3)^{20}$ **5.** 4^k **6.** 5^R **7.** 8^{kT} **8.** 10^{kR}

Differentiate.

9. 6^x **10.** 7^x **11.** 10^x **12.** 100^x **13.** $x(6.2)^x$ **14.** $x(5.4)^x$

15. $x^3 10^x$ **16.** $x^4 5^x$

Applied Problems

17. *Earthquake intensity.* The intensity I of an earthquake is given by

$$I = I_0 \, 10^R,$$

where

R = magnitude on the Richter Scale;
I_0 = minimum intensity, where $R = 0$, used for comparison.

(See the discussion in Exercise Set 4.1.)

a) Find I, in terms of I_0, for an earthquake of magnitude 7 on the Richter Scale.

b) Find I, in terms of I_0, for an earthquake of magnitude 8 on the Richter Scale.

c) Compare your answers to (a) and (b).

d) Find the rate of change $\dfrac{dI}{dR}$.

18. *Intensity of sound.* The intensity of a sound is given by

$$I = I_0 \, 10^{0.1L}$$

where

L = loudness of the sound as measured in decibels;
I_0 = minimum intensity detectable by the human ear.

(See the discussion in Section 4.1.)

a) Find I, in terms of I_0, for the loudness of a power mower which is 100 decibels.

b) Find I, in terms of I_0, for the loudness of just audible sound which is 10 decibels.

c) Compare your answers to (a) and (b).

d) Find the rate of change $\dfrac{dI}{dL}$.

Differentiate.

19. $\log_4 x$ **20.** $\log_5 x$ **21.** $2 \log x$ **22.** $5 \log x$

23. $\log \dfrac{x}{3}$ **24.** $\log \dfrac{x}{5}$ **25.** $x^3 \log_8 x$ **26.** $x \log_6 x$

27. *Earthquake magnitude.* The magnitude R (measured on the Richter Scale) of an earthquake of intensity I is defined to be

$$R = \log \frac{I}{I_0},$$

where

I_0 = minimum intensity (used for comparison).

(The exponential form of this definition is given in Exercise 17.)

Find the rate of change $\dfrac{dR}{dI}$.

28. *Loudness of sound.* The *loudness L* of a sound of intensity I is defined to be

$$L = 10 \log \frac{I}{I_0},$$

where

I_0 = minimum intensity detectable by the human ear;

L = loudness measured in decibels.

(The exponential form of this definition is given in Exercise 18.)

Find the rate of change $\dfrac{dL}{dI}$.

29. *Response to drug dosage.* The response y to a dosage x of a drug is given by

$$y = m \log x + b.$$

The response may be hard to measure with a number. The patient might sweat more, or have an increase in temperature, or pass out.

Find the rate of change $\dfrac{dy}{dx}$.

CHAPTER 4 TEST

Differentiate.

1. e^x **2.** $\ln x$ **3.** e^{-x^2} **4.** $\ln \dfrac{x}{7}$

5. $e^x - 5x^3$ **6.** $3e^x \ln x$ **7.** $\ln(e^x - x^3)$ **8.** $\dfrac{\ln x}{e^x}$

Given $\ln 2 = 0.6931$ and $\ln 7 = 1.9459$, find:

9. $\ln 14$.   **10.** $\ln \frac{2}{7}$.   **11.** $\ln 7e$.

12. State the solution of $\dfrac{dM}{dt} = kM$, in terms of M_0.

13. The doubling time of a certain bacteria culture is 4 hours. What is the growth rate?

14. An investment is made at 6.931% per year compounded continuously. What is the doubling time?

15. The demand for the use of fuel by the airlines is increasing at the rate of 12% per year. That is,

$$\frac{dF}{dt} = 0.12F,$$

where

$$F = \text{amount of fuel used, and } t = \text{time in years.}$$

a) The airlines used 3 billion gallons of fuel in 1960. Find the solution of the equation, assuming $F_0 = 3$ and $k = 0.12$.

b) How much fuel will be needed in 1980?

c) When will the demand be double that in 1960?

16. The half-life of tellurium is 1,000,000 years. What is its decay rate?

17. The decay rate of zirconium is 1.1% per day. What is its half-life?

18. A dose of a drug is injected into the body of a patient. The drug amount in the body decreases at the rate of 10% per hour. That is,

$$\frac{dA}{dt} = -0.1A,$$

where

$$A = \text{amount in body}, \ t = \text{time in hours}.$$

a) A dose of 5 cubic centimeters (cc) is administered. Assuming $A_0 = 5$ and $k = 0.1$, find the solution to the equation.

b) How much of the initial dose of 5 cc will remain after 10 hours?

c) At what time does half the original dose remain?

Differentiate.

19. 20^x

20. $\log_{20} x$

Georg Gerster from Rapho/Photo Researchers, Inc.

5 INTEGRATION

You should be able to:
a) Find the indefinite integral (anti-derivative) of a given function.
b) Find a function f with a given derivative and function value.
c) Solve applied problems involving antiderivatives.

5.1 THE ANTIDERIVATIVE

In Chapters 2, 3, and 4 we have considered several interpretations of the derivative. Some are listed below.

Function	Derivative
Distance	Velocity
Revenue	Marginal revenue
Cost	Marginal cost
Population	Rate of growth of population

For population we actually considered the derivative first and then the function. Many problems can be solved by doing the reverse of differentiation, called *antidifferentiation*.

The Antiderivative

Suppose y is a function of x and that the derivative is the constant 8. Can we find y? It is easy to see that one such function is $8x$. That is, $8x$ is a function whose derivative is 8. Are there other functions whose derivative is 8? Yes. Here are some examples:

$$8x + 3, \quad 8x - 10, \quad 8x + \sqrt{2}.$$

All of these functions are $8x$ plus some constant. There are no other functions having a derivative of 8 other than those of the form $8x + C$. Another way of saying this is that any two functions having a derivative of 8 must differ by a constant. This is true in general.

> If two functions F and G have the same derivative on an interval, then
> $$F(x) = G(x) + C, \quad \text{where } C \text{ is a constant.}$$

The reverse of differentiating is called *antidifferentiating*. The result of antidifferentiating is called an *antiderivative*. Above we found antiderivatives of the function 8. There are several of them, but they are all $8x$ plus some constant.

Example. Antidifferentiate (find the antiderivatives of) x^2.

Solution. One antiderivative is $\dfrac{x^3}{3}$. All other antiderivatives differ from this by a constant, so we can denote them as follows:

$$\frac{x^3}{3} + C.$$

This is the *general form* of the antiderivative.

Do Exercises 1 through 6.

Integrals and Integration

The process of antidifferentiation is, in some contexts, called *integration*, and the general form of the antiderivative is referred to as an *indefinite integral*. A common notation for the indefinite integral, due to Leibniz, is as follows:

$$\int f(x)\, dx.$$

The symbol $\int$ is called an *integral sign*. The symbol dx plays no apparent role at this point in our development, but will be useful later. In this context, $f(x)$ is called the *integrand*. We illustrate this notation using the preceding example.

Example 1 Integrate $\int x^2\, dx$.

Solution $\int x^2\, dx = \dfrac{x^3}{3} + C$

The symbol on the left is read "the integral of x^2, dx." (The "dx" is often omitted in the reading.) In this case the integrand is x^2. The constant C is called the *constant of integration*.

Example 2 Integrate $\int e^x\, dx$.

Solution $\int e^x\, dx = e^x + C$

Do Exercises 7 through 9.

1. Find three antiderivatives.
$$\frac{dy}{dx} = 7$$

2. Find three antiderivatives.
$$\frac{dy}{dx} = -2$$

Find the general form of each antiderivative.

3. x 4. x^3

5. e^x 6. $\dfrac{1}{x}$

Integrate. Don't forget the constant of integration!

7. $\int x^3\, dx$ 8. $\int x\, dx$

9. $\int \dfrac{1}{x}\, dx$

To integrate (or antidifferentiate) we make use of differentiation formulas, in effect reading them in reverse. Below are some of these, stated in reverse, as integration formulas. These can be checked by differentiating the right-hand side and noting that the result is, in each case, the integrand.

1. $\int k \, dx$, (k a constant) $= kx + C$

2. $\int x^r \, dx = \dfrac{x^{r+1}}{r+1} + C$ (provided $r \neq -1$), or

   $\int (r+1) x^r \, dx = x^{r+1} + C$

   (To integrate a power of x, other than -1, increase the power by 1 and divide by the increased power.)

3. $\int x^{-1} \, dx = \int \dfrac{1}{x} \, dx = \ln x + C$

4. $\int e^x \, dx = e^x + C$

The following rules allow us to find many other integrals. They are obtainable by reversing two familiar differentiation rules.

RULE A. $\int k \, f(x) \, dx = k \int f(x) \, dx$

(The integral of a constant times a function is the constant times the integral.)

RULE B. $\int [f(x) + g(x)] \, dx = \int f(x) \, dx + \int g(x) \, dx$

(The integral of a sum is the sum of the integrals.)

Example 1
$$\int (5x + 4x^3) \, dx = \int 5x \, dx + \int 4x^3 \, dx \quad \text{(Rule B)}$$
$$= 5\int x \, dx + \int 4x^3 \, dx \quad \text{(Rule A)}$$

(Note that we did not factor the 4 out of the second integral. This is because we can find the antiderivative of $4x^3$ directly as x^4, as shown in the second part of formula 2.)

$$= 5 \cdot \frac{x^2}{2} + x^4 + C = \frac{5}{2} x^2 + x^4 + C.$$

(Don't forget the constant of integration!)

Note:

We can always check by differentiating.

Thus, in Example 1,

$$\frac{d}{dx}\left(\frac{5}{2}x^2 + x^4 + C\right) = 2 \cdot \frac{5}{2} \cdot x + 4x^3 = 5x + 4x^3.$$

Do Exercise 10.

Example 2 $\int(e^x - \sqrt{x})\,dx = \int e^x\,dx - \int\sqrt{x}\,dx$

$$= \int e^x\,dx - \int x^{1/2}\,dx$$

$$= e^x - \frac{x^{(1/2)+1}}{\frac{1}{2}+1} + C$$

$$= e^x - \frac{x^{3/2}}{\frac{3}{2}} + C$$

$$= e^x - \tfrac{2}{3}x^{3/2} + C$$

Example 3 $\int\left(1 - \frac{3}{x} + \frac{1}{x^4}\right)dx = \int 1\,dx - 3\int\frac{dx}{x} + \int x^{-4}\,dx$

$$= x - 3\ln x + \frac{x^{-4+1}}{-4+1} + C$$

$$= x - 3\ln x - \frac{x^{-3}}{3} + C$$

Do Exercises 11 and 12.

Another Look at Antiderivatives

The graphs of the antiderivatives of x^2 are the graphs of the functions

$$y = \int x^2\,dx = \frac{x^3}{3} + C$$

for the various values of the constant C.

Do Exercise 13.

As shown in the following graphs, x^2 is the derivative of each function.

10. Integrate. Don't forget the constant of integration!

$$\int(7x^4 + 2x)\,dx$$

Integrate. Don't forget the constant of integration.

11. $\int(e^x - x^{2/5})\,dx$

12. $\int\left(\frac{5}{x} - 7 + \frac{1}{x^6}\right)dx$

13. Using the same set of axes, graph

$$y = \frac{x^3}{3}, \quad y = \frac{x^3}{3} + 1, \quad \text{and} \quad y = \frac{x^3}{3} - 1.$$

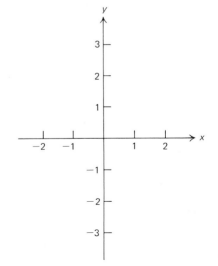

That is, the tangent line at the point $\left(a, \dfrac{a^3}{3} + C\right)$ has slope a^2. The curves $\dfrac{x^3}{3} + C$ fill up the plane, exactly one curve going through any given point (x_0, y_0).

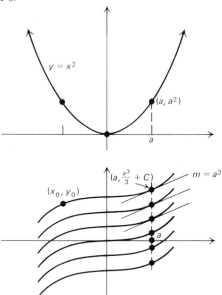

Suppose we look for an antiderivative of x^2 having a specified value at a certain point, say $f(-1) = 2$. We find that there is only one such function.

Example   Find the function f such that

$$f'(x) = x^2, \quad \text{and} \quad f(-1) = 2.$$

Solution

a) We find $f(x)$ by integrating.

$$f(x) = \int x^2 \, dx = \frac{x^3}{3} + C.$$

b) The condition $f(-1) = 2$ allows us to find C.

$$f(-1) = \frac{(-1)^3}{3} + C = 2, \qquad \text{and solving for } C \text{ we get:}$$

$$-\tfrac{1}{3} + C = 2,$$
$$C = 2 + \tfrac{1}{3}, \quad \text{or } \tfrac{7}{3}.$$

Thus $f(x) = \dfrac{x^3}{3} + \dfrac{7}{3}$.

Do Exercises 14 and 15.

Applied Problems

Example 1   A company determines that the marginal cost, C', of producing the xth unit of a certain product is given by

$$C'(x) = x^3 + 2x.$$

Find the total cost function C, assuming fixed costs (costs when 0 units are produced) are \$45.

Solution

a) We integrate to find $C(x)$, using K for the integration constant to avoid confusion with the cost function C.

$$C(x) = \int C'(x)\, dx = \int (x^3 + 2x)\, dx = \frac{x^4}{4} + x^2 + K.$$

b) Fixed costs are \$45. This means $C(0) = 45$. This allows us to determine the value of K.

$$C(0) = \frac{0^4}{4} + 0^2 + K = 45,$$

$$K = 45.$$

Thus $C(x) = \dfrac{x^4}{4} + x^2 + 45$.

Do Exercise 16.

Recall that the position coordinate, at time t, of an object moving along a number line is $s(t)$. Then

$$s'(t) = v(t) = \text{the } \textit{velocity} \text{ at time } t,$$
$$v'(t) = a(t) = \text{the } \textit{acceleration} \text{ at time } t.$$

Example 2   Suppose $v(t) = 5t^4$ and $s(0) = 9$. Find $s(t)$.

Solution

a) We find $s(t)$ by integrating.

$$s(t) = \int v(t)\, dt = \int 5t^4\, dt = t^5 + C$$

14. Find f such that

$$f'(x) = x^2, \quad \text{and} \quad f(-2) = 5.$$

15. Find g such that

$$g'(x) = 2x - 4, \quad \text{and} \quad g(2) = 9.$$

16. A company determines that the marginal cost, C', of producing the xth unit of a certain product is given by

$$C'(x) = x^2 + 5x.$$

Find the total cost function C, assuming fixed costs to be \$35.

17. Suppose $v(t) = 4t^3$ and $s(0) = 13$. Find $s(t)$.

b) The condition $s(0) = 9$ allows us to determine C.

$$s(0) = 0^5 + C = 9,$$
$$C = 9$$

Thus $s(t) = t^5 + 9$.

Do Exercise 17.

Example 3   Suppose $a(t) = 12t^2 - 6, v(0) = 5$, and $s(0) = 10$. Find $s(t)$.

Solution

a) We find $v(t)$ by integrating $a(t)$.

$$v(t) = \int a(t)\, dt = \int (12t^2 - 6)\, dt = 4t^3 - 6t + C_1$$

b) The condition $v(0) = 5$ allows us to find C_1.

$$v(0) = 4 \cdot 0^3 - 6 \cdot 0 + C_1 = 5,$$
$$C_1 = 5$$

Thus $v(t) = 4t^3 - 6t + 5$.

18. Suppose $a(t) = 24t^2 - 12$, $v(0) = 7$, and $s(0) = 8$. Find $s(t)$.

c) We find $s(t)$ by integrating $v(t)$.

$$s(t) = \int v(t)\, dt = \int (4t^3 - 6t + 5)\, dt = t^4 - 3t^2 + 5t + C_2$$

d) The condition $s(0) = 10$ allows us to find C_2.

$$s(0) = 0^4 - 3 \cdot 0^2 + 5 \cdot 0 + C_2 = 10,$$
$$C_2 = 10$$

Thus $s(t) = t^4 - 3t^2 + 5t + 10$.

Do Exercise 18.

EXERCISE SET 5.1

Integrate.

1. $\int x^6\, dx$ **2.** $\int x^7\, dx$ **3.** $\int 2\, dx$ **4.** $\int 4\, dx$ **5.** $\int x^{1/4}\, dx$ **6.** $\int x^{1/3}\, dx$

7. $\int (x^2 + x - 1)\, dx$ **8.** $\int (x^2 - x + 2)\, dx$ **9.** $\int (t^2 - 2t + 3)\, dt$ **10.** $\int (3t^2 - 4t + 7)\, dt$

11. $\int 5e^x \, dx$
12. $\int 3e^x \, dx$
13. $\int (x^3 - x^{8/7}) \, dx$
14. $\int (x^4 - x^{6/5}) \, dx$

15. $\int \frac{1000}{x} \, dx$
16. $\int \frac{500}{x} \, dx$
17. $\int \frac{dx}{x^2} \left(\text{or} \int \frac{1}{x^2} \, dx \right)$
18. $\int \frac{dx}{x^3}$

Find f.

19. $f'(x) = x - 3, f(2) = 9$
20. $f'(x) = x - 5, f(1) = 6$
21. $f'(x) = x^2 - 4, f(0) = 7$
22. $f'(x) = x^2 + 1, f(0) = 8$

(handwritten annotations in right margin:)
$f'(x) = x - 5$
$f(x) = 2x^2 - 5x + c$
$2(1)^2 - 5(1) + c$
$2 - 5 + c = 6$
$3 = 6$
$\frac{x^3}{3} + x + c$

Applied Problems

23. A company determines that the marginal cost, C', of producing the xth unit of a certain product is given by
$$C'(x) = x^3 - 2x.$$
Find the total cost function C, assuming fixed costs are $100.

24. A company determines that the marginal cost, C', of producing the xth unit of a certain product is given by
$$C'(x) = x^3 - x.$$
Find the total cost function C, assuming fixed costs are $200.

25. A company determines that the marginal revenue R', from selling the xth unit of a certain product is given by
$$R'(x) = x^2 - 3.$$
a) Find the total revenue function R, assuming $R(0) = 0$.
b) Why is $R(0) = 0$ a reasonable assumption?

26. A company determines that the marginal revenue R', from selling the xth unit of a certain product, is given by
$$R'(x) = x^2 - 1.$$
a) Find the total revenue function R, assuming $R(0) = 0$.
b) Why is $R(0) = 0$ a reasonable assumption?

Find $s(t)$.

27. $v(t) = 3t^2, s(0) = 4$
28. $v(t) = 2t, s(0) = 10$

Find $v(t)$.

29. $a(t) = 4t, v(0) = 20$
30. $a(t) = 6t, v(0) = 30$

Find $s(t)$.

31. $a(t) = -2t + 6, v(0) = 6,$ and $s(0) = 10.$
32. $a(t) = -6t + 7, v(0) = 10,$ and $s(0) = 20.$

33. For a freely falling object, $a(t) = -32$ ft/sec^2, $v(0) = v_0$, and $s(0) = s_0$. Find a general expression for $s(t)$ in terms of v_0 and s_0.

34. *Efficiency of a machine operator.* The rate at which a machine operator's efficiency E (expressed as a percentage) changes with respect to time is given by

$$\frac{dE}{dt} = 40 - 10t,$$

where $t =$ the number of hours the operator has been at work.

a) Find $E(t)$ if it is known that her efficiency after working 2 hr is 72%. That is, $E(2) = 72$.

b) Use the answer to (a) to find the operator's efficiency after 4 hr, after 8 hr.

35. *Efficiency of a machine operator.* The rate at which a machine operator's efficiency E (expressed as a percentage) changes with respect to time is given by

$$\frac{dE}{dt} = 30 - 10t,$$

where $t =$ the number of hours the operator has been at work.

a) Find $E(t)$ if it is known that his efficiency after working 2 hr is 72%. That is, $E(2) = 72$.

b) Use the answer to (a) to find the operator's efficiency after 3 hr, after 5 hr.

Donald C. Dietz from Stock, Boston

5.2 AREA

In this section we consider the application of integration to finding areas of certain regions. Consider a function whose outputs are positive in an interval (the function might be 0 at one of the endpoints). We wish to find the area of the region between the graph of the function and the *x*-axis on that interval.

OBJECTIVES

You should be able to:

a) Find the area under a graph on a given closed interval.

b) Interpret the area under a curve in two other ways.

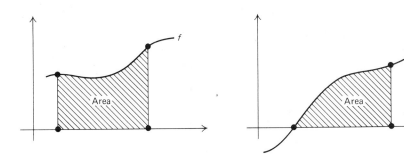

19. Consider the constant function

$$f(x) = 3.$$

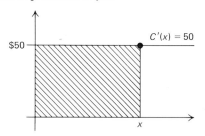

a) Find $A(x)$.
b) Find $A(1)$, $A(2)$, and $A(5)$.
c) Graph $A(x)$.
d) How do $f(x)$ and $A(x)$ compare?

20. A clothing firm, Raggs, Ltd., determines that the marginal cost of each suit it produces is $50.

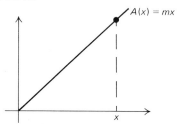

a) Find the total cost, $C(x)$, of producing x suits, assuming fixed costs are $0 (ignore fixed costs).
b) Find the area of the shaded rectangle. Compare your answer to (a).
c) Graph $C(x)$. Why is this an increasing function?

Let us first consider a constant function $f(x) = m$ on the interval from 0 to x, $[0, x]$.

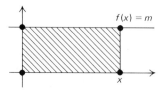

The figure formed is a rectangle, and its area is mx. Suppose we allow x to vary, giving us rectangles of different areas. The area of each rectangle is still mx. We have an area *function*,

$$A(x) = mx.$$

Its graph is shown below.

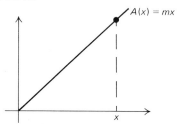

Do Exercises 19 through 21.

Let us next consider the linear function $f(x) = mx$ on the interval from 0 to x, $[0, x]$.

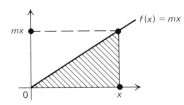

The figure formed this time is a triangle, and its area is $\frac{1}{2}$ the base times the height, $\frac{1}{2} \cdot x \cdot (mx)$, or $\frac{1}{2}mx^2$. If we allow x to vary, we again get an area function

$$A(x) = \tfrac{1}{2}mx^2.$$

Its graph is as shown below.

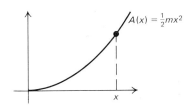

Do Exercise 22.

Now consider the linear function $f(x) = mx + b$ on the interval from 0 to x, $[0, x]$.

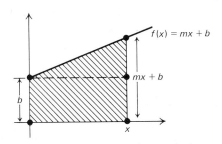

The figure formed this time is a trapezoid, and its area is $\frac{1}{2}$ the height times the sum of the lengths of its parallel sides (or, noting the dashed line, the area of the triangle plus the rectangle),

$$\tfrac{1}{2} \cdot x \cdot [b + (mx + b)], \quad \text{or } \tfrac{1}{2} \cdot x \cdot (mx + 2b), \quad \text{or } \tfrac{1}{2}mx^2 + bx.$$

21. Assuming better management Raggs Ltd., of Margin Exercise 20, is able to decrease its production costs \$10 per suit for every hundred suits it produces. This is shown below.

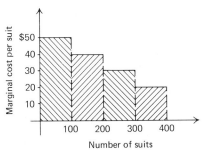

a) Find the total cost of producing 400 suits.
b) Find the total area of the rectangles. Compare your answer with (a).

22. Consider the function $f(x) = 3x$.

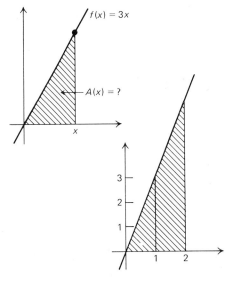

a) Find $A(x)$.
b) Find $A(1)$.
c) Find $A(2)$.
d) Find $A(3.5)$.
e) Graph $A(x)$.
f) How do $f(x)$ and $A(x)$ compare?

23. Raggs Ltd., of Margin Exercise 21, installs new sewing machines. This allows the marginal cost per suit to decrease continually in such a way that

$$C'(x) = -0.1x + 50.$$

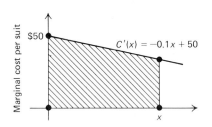

a) Find the total cost of producing x suits, ignoring fixed costs.

b) Find the area of the shaded trapezoid.

c) Find the total cost of producing 400 suits. Compare this answer with that of Margin Exercise 21.

If we allow x to vary, we again get an area function

$$A(x) = \tfrac{1}{2}mx^2 + bx.$$

Its graph is as shown below.

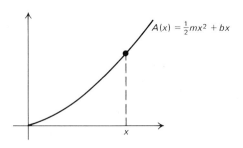

Do Exercise 23.

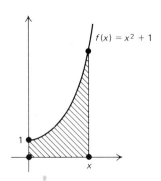

Now we consider the function $f(x) = x^2 + 1$ on the interval from 0 to x, $[0, x]$. The graph of the region in question is as shown, but it is not so easy this time to find the area function because the graph of $f(x)$ is not a straight line. Let us tabulate our previous results and look for a pattern.

$f(x)$	$A(x)$
$f(x) = 3$	$A(x) = 3x$
$f(x) = m$	$A(x) = mx$
$f(x) = 3x$	$A(x) = \tfrac{3}{2}x^2$
$f(x) = mx$	$A(x) = \tfrac{1}{2}mx^2$
$f(x) = mx + b$	$A(x) = \tfrac{1}{2}mx^2 + bx$

You may have conjectured that the area function $A(x)$ is an antiderivative of $f(x)$. In the following exploratory exercises you will investigate further.

Exploratory Exercises. Finding Areas

1. The region under the graph of

$$f(x) = x^2 + 1,$$

on the interval $[0, 2]$ is shown below.

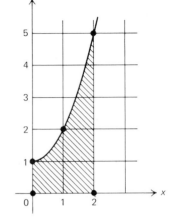

a) Make a copy of the shaded region on thin paper.

b) Cut up the shaded region in any way you wish in order to fill up squares in the grid in the middle of this page. Make an estimate of the total area.

c) Using the antiderivative

$$F(x) = \frac{x^3}{3} + x,$$

find $F(2)$.

d) Compare your answers to (b) and (c).

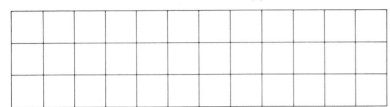

2. a), b) Repeat Exercise 1 for the shaded region at the right.

c) Using the antiderivative

$$F(x) = \frac{x^3}{3} + x,$$

find $F(3)$.

d) Compare your answers to (b) and (c).

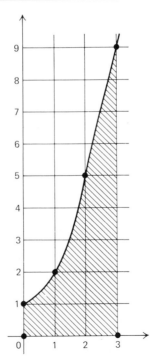

The Fundamental Theorem of Integral Calculus

The conjecture concerning areas and antiderivatives (or integrals), it turns out, is true. This result is of such importance that it is called the *Fundamental Theorem of Integral Calculus*. The theorem is as follows.

FUNDAMENTAL THEOREM OF INTEGRAL CALCULUS. Let f be a positive, continuous function on an interval $[a, b]$ and let $A(x)$ be the area of the region between the graph of f and the x-axis on the interval $[a, x]$. Then $A(x)$ is a differentiable function of x and

$$A'(x) = f(x).$$

Proof   The situation described in the theorem is shown here.

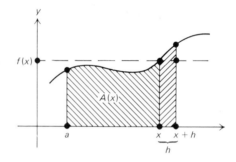

The derivative of $A(x)$ is, by definition of derivative,

$$A'(x) = \lim_{h \to 0} \frac{A(x + h) - A(x)}{h}.$$

Note, from the drawing, that

$$A(x + h) - A(x)$$

is the area of the small, shaded, vertical strip. The area of this small strip is approximately that of a rectangle of base h and height $f(x)$, especially for small values of h. Thus we have

$$A(x + h) - A(x) \approx f(x) \cdot h.$$

Now

$$A'(x) = \lim_{h \to 0} \frac{A(x + h) - A(x)}{h} = \lim_{h \to 0} \frac{f(x) \cdot h}{h} = \lim_{h \to 0} f(x) = f(x),$$

since $f(x)$ does not involve h.

The above theorem also holds if $f(x) = 0$ at one or both endpoints of the interval $[a, b]$.

Since the area function A is an antiderivative of f, and since any two antiderivatives differ by a constant, we easily conclude that the area function and any antiderivative differ by a constant.

We can think of the function A as given by

$$A(x) = \text{the area on the interval } [a, x],$$

where a is some fixed point and x varies.

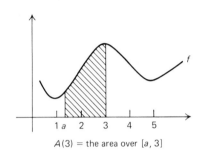

$A(3) = $ the area over $[a, 3]$

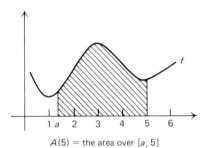

$A(5) = $ the area over $[a, 5]$

$A(3) = $ the area over $[a, 3]$ $A(5) = $ the area over $[a, 5]$

Now let us find some areas.

Example 1   Find the area under the graph of $y = x^2 + 1$ on the interval $[-1, 2]$.

Solution

a) We first make a drawing. This includes a graph of the function and the region in question.

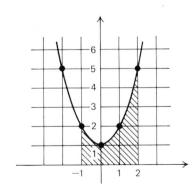

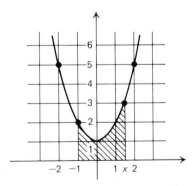

b) Second, we make a drawing showing a portion of the region from -1 to x. Now $A(x)$ is the area of this portion, that is, in the interval $[-1, x]$.

24. Find the area under the graph of $y = x^2 + 3$ on the interval $[1, 2]$.

c) Now

$$A(x) = \int (x^2 + 1)\, dx = \frac{x^3}{3} + x + C,$$

where C has to be determined. Since we know that $A(-1) = 0$ (there is no area above the number -1), we can substitute for x in $A(x)$, as follows:

$$A(-1) = \frac{(-1)^3}{3} + (-1) + C = 0,$$

$$-\tfrac{1}{3} - 1 + C = 0,$$

$$C = \tfrac{4}{3}.$$

This determines that $C = \tfrac{4}{3}$, so we have

$$A(x) = \frac{x^3}{3} + x + \frac{4}{3}.$$

Then the area in the interval $[-1, 2]$ is $A(2)$. We compute $A(2)$ as follows:

$$A(2) = \frac{2^3}{3} + 2 + \frac{4}{3} = \frac{8}{3} + 2 + \frac{4}{3} = \frac{12}{3} + 2 = 6.$$

Do Exercise 24.

Example 2 Find the area under the graph of $y = x^3$ on the interval $[0, 5]$.

Solution

a) We first make a drawing which includes a graph of the function and the region in question.

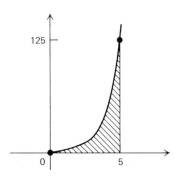 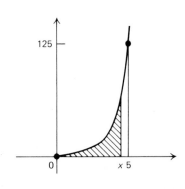

b) Second, we make a drawing showing a portion of that region from 0 to x. Now $A(x)$ is the area of this portion, that is, on the interval $[0, x]$.

c) Now

$$A(x) = \int x^3\, dx = \frac{x^4}{4} + C,$$

where C has to be determined. Since we know that $A(0) = 0$, we can substitute 0 for x in $A(x)$, as follows:

$$A(0) = \frac{0^4}{4} + C = 0,$$

$$C = 0.$$

This determines C.

So

$$A(x) = \frac{x^4}{4}.$$

Then the area in the interval $[0, 5]$ is $A(5)$. We can compute $A(5)$ as follows:

$$A(5) = \frac{5^4}{4} = \frac{625}{4} = 156\tfrac{1}{4}.$$

Do Exercise 25.

Since the area under a curve, as in the preceding examples, is an antiderivative, area can also be associated with various kinds of functions. If, for example, we have a velocity function over an interval $[0, b]$, then the area under the curve in that interval is the total distance. Suppose the velocity function is

$$v(t) = t^3.$$

In 5 hours the total distance covered is $156\tfrac{1}{4}$. This can be seen in the preceding Example 2, simply by changing the variable from x to t. For a marginal cost function over the interval $[0, x]$ the area under the curve is the total cost of producing x units, or the accumulated cost.

Example 3 Raggs, Ltd., goes even further to reduce production costs. In addition to installing new sewing machines, it installs air conditioning, and also has the president take a calculus course. This

25. Find the area under the graph of $y = x^2 + x$ on the interval $[0, 3]$.

26. In reference to Example 3,
a) Compare $10,400 to your answer for Margin Exercise 23. Has the company reduced total costs?
b) Find the total cost of producing 100 suits.

allows the marginal cost per suit to decrease rapidly in such a way that

$$C'(x) = 0.0003x^2 - 0.2x + 50.$$

Find the total cost of producing 400 suits. Ignore fixed costs.

Solution

a) We first make a drawing. This includes a graph of the function and the region in question.

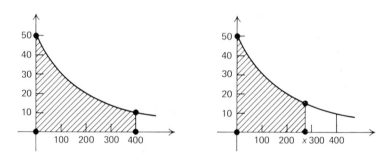

b) Second, we make a drawing showing a portion of that region from 0 to x. Now $A(x)$ is the area of that portion, that is, on the interval $[0, x]$.

c) Now

$$C(x) = A(x) = \int(0.0003x^2 - 0.2x + 50)\,dx = 0.0001x^3 - 0.1x^2 + 50x + K,$$

where K has to be determined. We are ignoring fixed costs, $K = 0$, and we have

$$C(x) = 0.0001x^3 - 0.1x^2 + 50x.$$

Then the area in the interval $[0, 400]$ is $A(400)$, or $C(400)$. We can compute $C(400)$ as follows:

$$C(400) = 0.0001 \cdot 400^3 - 0.1 \cdot 400^2 + 50 \cdot 400, \text{ or } \$10,400.$$

Do Exercise 26.

EXERCISE SET 5.2

Find the area under the given curve on the interval indicated.

1. $y = 4$; $[1, 3]$ **2.** $y = 5$; $[1, 3]$ **3.** $y = 2x$; $[1, 3]$

4. $y = x^2$; $[0, 3]$ **5.** $y = x^2$; $[0, 5]$ **6.** $y = x^3$; $[0, 2]$

7. $y = x^3$; $[0, 1]$ **8.** $y = 1 - x^2$; $[-1, 1]$ **9.** $y = 4 - x^2$; $[-2, 2]$

10. $y = e^x$; $[0, 2]$ **11.** $y = e^x$; $[0, 3]$ **12.** $y = \dfrac{1}{x}$; $[1, 2]$

13. $y = \dfrac{1}{x}$; $[1, 3]$ **14.** $y = x^2 - 4x$; $[-4, -2]$ **15.** $y = x^2 - 4x$; $[-4, -1]$

In each case give two interpretations of the shaded region.

16.
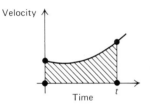
Velocity   Time

17.
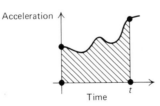
Acceleration   Time

18.
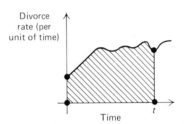
Divorce rate (per unit of time)   Time

19.
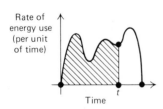
Rate of energy use (per unit of time)   Time

20.
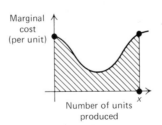
Marginal cost (per unit)   Number of units produced

21.
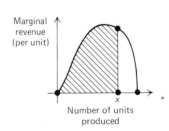
Marginal revenue (per unit)   Number of units produced

22.
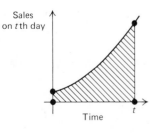
Sales on tth day   Time

23.
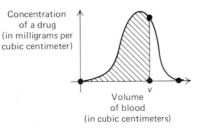
Concentration of a drug (in milligrams per cubic centimeter)   Volume of blood (in cubic centimeters)

24.
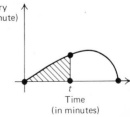
Rate of memory (in words per minute)   Time (in minutes)

25. A particle starts out from the origin. Its velocity at time t is given by

$$v(t) = 3t^2 + 2t.$$

a) Find the distance the particle has traveled after t hours.

b) Find the distance the particle has traveled after 5 hours.

27. A sound company determines that the marginal cost of producing the xth stereo is given by

$$C'(x) = 100 - 0.2x, \quad C(0) = 0.$$

It also determines that its marginal revenue from the sale of the xth stereo is given by

$$R'(x) = 100 + 0.2x, \quad R(0) = 0.$$

a) Find the total cost of producing x stereos.

b) Find the total revenue of selling x stereos.

c) Find the total profit from the production and sale of x stereos.

d) Find the total profit from the production and sale of 1000 stereos.

26. A particle starts out from the origin. Its velocity at time t is given by

$$v(t) = 4t^3 + 2t.$$

a) Find the distance the particle has traveled after t hours.

b) Find the distance the car has traveled after 2 hours.

28. A refrigeration company determines that the marginal cost of producing the xth refrigerator is given by

$$C'(x) = 50 - 0.4x, \quad C(0) = 0.$$

It also determines that its marginal revenue from the sale of the xth stereo is given by

$$R'(x) = 50 + 0.4x, \quad R(0) = 0.$$

a) Find the total cost of producing x refrigerators.

b) Find the total revenue of selling x refrigerators.

c) Find the total profit from the production and sale of x refrigerators.

d) Find the total profit from the production and sale of 1000 refrigerators.

Cary Wolinsky from Stock, Boston

The following two problems are based on factual data.

29. Find the total number of murders committed in the United States from 1967 to 1972.

30. Find the total number of robberies committed in the United States from 1967 to 1972.

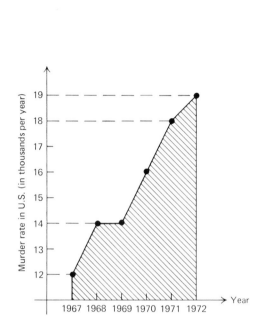

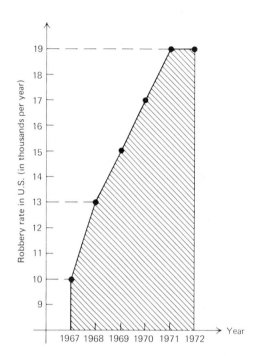

5.3 INTEGRATION ON AN INTERVAL: THE DEFINITE INTEGRAL

Let f be a positive continuous function on an interval $[a, b]$. We know that f has an antiderivative, namely $A(x)$. Let F and G be any two antiderivatives of f. Then

$$F(b) - F(a) = G(b) - G(a).$$

To see this, recall that F and G differ by a constant. That is, $F(x) = G(x) + C$. Then

$$F(b) - F(a) = [G(b) + C] - [G(a) + C] = G(b) - G(a).$$

Thus the difference

$$F(b) - F(a)$$

has the same value for all antiderivatives of f. It is called the *definite integral* of f from a to b.

OBJECTIVES

You should be able to:

a) Evaluate a definite integral.
b) Find the area under a graph on $[a, b]$.
c) Solve applied problems involving definite integrals.

Integrate.

27. $\int_a^b 2x \, dx$

28. $\int_a^b e^x \, dx$

Definite integrals are usually symbolized as follows:

$$\int_a^b f(x) \, dx.$$

This is read "the integral from a to b of $f(x) \, dx$" (the dx is sometimes omitted from the reading). From the preceding development we see that to find a definite integral $\int_a^b f(x) \, dx$ we first find an antiderivative $F(x)$. The simplest one is the one for which the constant of integration is 0. We evaluate F at b and at a and subtract.

> $\int_a^b f(x) \, dx$ **is defined to be** $F(b) - F(a)$, **where** F **is any antiderivative of** f.

Evaluating definite integrals is called *integrating*. The numbers a and b are known as the *limits of integration*.

Example 1   Integrate $\int_a^b x^2 \, dx$.

Solution   Using the antiderivative $F(x) = \dfrac{x^3}{3}$, we have

$$\int_a^b x^2 \, dx = \frac{b^3}{3} - \frac{a^3}{3}.$$

Do Exercises 27 and 28.

It is convenient to use an intermediate notation

$$\int_a^b f(x) \, dx = [F(x)]_a^b = F(b) - F(a).$$

We now evaluate several definite integrals.

Example 1
$$\int_{-1}^2 x^2 \, dx = \left[\frac{x^3}{3}\right]_{-1}^2 = \frac{2^3}{3} - \frac{(-1)^3}{3} = \frac{8}{3} - \left(-\frac{1}{3}\right) = \frac{8}{3} + \frac{1}{3} = 3$$

Example 2 $\int_0^3 e^x \, dx = [e^x]_0^3 = e^3 - e^0 = e^3 - 1$

Example 3 $\int_1^4 (x^2 - x)\, dx = \left[\dfrac{x^3}{3} - \dfrac{x^2}{2}\right]_1^4 = \left(\dfrac{4^3}{3} - \dfrac{4^2}{2}\right) - \left(\dfrac{1^3}{3} - \dfrac{1^2}{2}\right)$

$$= \left(\dfrac{64}{3} - \dfrac{16}{2}\right) - \left(\dfrac{1}{3} - \dfrac{1}{2}\right)$$

$$= \dfrac{64}{3} - 8 - \dfrac{1}{3} + \dfrac{1}{2}$$

$$= \dfrac{63}{3} - 8 + \dfrac{1}{2} = 13\tfrac{1}{2}$$

Example 4 $\int_1^e \left(1 + 2x - \dfrac{1}{x}\right) dx = [x + x^2 - \ln x]_1^e$

$$= (e + e^2 - \ln e) - (1 + 1^2 - \ln 1)$$

$$= (e + e^2 - 1) - (1 + 1 - 0)$$

$$= e + e^2 - 1 - 1 - 1 = e + e^2 - 3$$

Do Exercises 29 through 32.

The area under a curve can be expressed by a definite integral.

> **Let f be a positive continuous function over the closed interval $[a, b]$. The area under the graph of f on the interval $[a, b]$ is**
>
> $$\int_a^b f(x)\, dx.$$

Proof

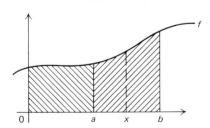

Let

$$A(x) = \text{the area of the region over } [0, x].$$

Then

$$A'(x) = f(x),$$

so $A(x)$ is an antiderivative of $f(x)$. Then

$$\int_a^b f(x)\, dx = A(b) - A(a).$$

But $A(b) - A(a)$ is the area over $[0, b]$ minus the area over $[0, a]$, which is the area over $[a, b]$.

Let us now find some areas.

Integrate.

29. $\int_1^3 2x\, dx$

30. $\int_{-2}^0 e^x\, dx$

31. $\int_0^1 (2x - x^2)\, dx$

32. $\int_1^e \left(1 + 3x^2 - \dfrac{1}{x}\right) dx$

33. Find the area under $y = x^2 + 3$ on [1, 2]. Don't forget that it helps to draw the graph. (Compare this with Margin Exercise 24.)

Example 1   Find the area under $y = x^2 + 1$ on $[-1, 2]$.

Solution $\displaystyle\int_{-1}^{2} (x^2 + 1)\, dx = \left[\frac{x^3}{3} + x\right]_{-1}^{2}$

$$= \left(\frac{2^3}{3} + 2\right) - \left(\frac{(-1)^3}{3} + (-1)\right)$$

$$= \left(\frac{8}{3} + 2\right) - \left(-\frac{1}{3} - 1\right)$$

$$= \frac{8}{3} + 2 + \frac{1}{3} + 1 = 6$$

Compare this with Example 1 on p. 263.

Do Exercise 33.

---

34. Find the area under $y = x^2 + x$ on [0, 3]. (Compare this with Margin Exercise 25.)

Example 2   Find the area under $y = x^3$ on [0, 5].

Solution $\displaystyle\int_{0}^{5} x^3\, dx = \left[\frac{x^4}{4}\right]_{0}^{5} = \frac{5^4}{4} - \frac{0^4}{4}$

$$= \frac{625}{4}$$

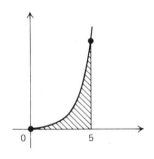

Compare this with Example 2 on p. 264.

Do Exercise 34.

Example 3 Find the area under $y = \dfrac{1}{x}$ on $[1, 4]$.

Solution $\displaystyle\int_1^4 \frac{dx}{x} = [\ln x]_1^4 = \ln 4 - \ln 1$

$$= \ln 4$$

$$\approx 1.3863 \qquad \text{(Table 3)}$$

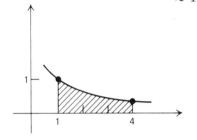

35. Find the area under $y = \dfrac{1}{x}$ on $[1, 7]$.

Example 4 Find the area under $y = \dfrac{1}{x^2}$ on $[1, b]$.

Solution $\displaystyle\int_1^b \frac{dx}{x^2} = \int_1^b x^{-2}\, dx = \left[\frac{x^{-2+1}}{-2+1}\right]_1^b$

$$= \left[\frac{x^{-1}}{-1}\right]_1^b = \left[-\frac{1}{x}\right]_1^b = \left(-\frac{1}{b}\right) - \left(-\frac{1}{1}\right)$$

$$= 1 - \frac{1}{b}$$

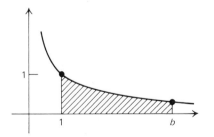

36. Find the area under $y = \dfrac{1}{x^4}$ on $[1, b]$.

Do Exercises 35 and 36.

The following properties of definite integrals follow rather easily from the definition of the definite integral and from the properties of the indefinite integral.

37. Integrate $\int_1^2 20x^3 \, dx$.

PROPERTY 1. $\int_a^b k \cdot f(x) \, dx = k \cdot \int_a^b f(x) \, dx.$

(The integral of a constant times a function is the constant times the integral of the function. That is, we can "factor out" a constant from the integrand.)

Example

$$\int_0^5 100e^x \, dx = 100 \int_0^5 e^x \, dx = 100[e^x]_0^5 = 100(e^5 - e^0) = 100(e^5 - 1)$$

Do Exercise 37.

PROPERTY 2. $\int_a^b [f(x) + g(x)] \, dx = \int_a^b f(x) \, dx + \int_a^b g(x) \, dx.$

(The integral of a sum is the sum of the integrals.)

PROPERTY 3.   For $a < c < b$,

$$\int_a^b f(x) \, dx = \int_a^c f(x) \, dx + \int_c^b f(x) \, dx.$$

(For any number c between a and b, the integral from a to b is the integral from a to c plus the integral from c to b.)

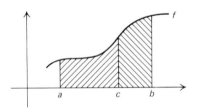

Property 3 has particular application when a function is defined in different ways over subintervals.

Example   Find the area under the graph of $y = f(x)$ from -4 to 5, where

$$f(x) = \begin{cases} 9, & \text{if } x < 3 \\ x^2, & \text{if } x \geqslant 3. \end{cases}$$

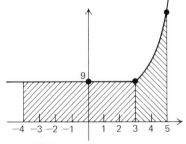

Solution

$$\int_{-4}^{5} f(x)\ dx = \int_{-4}^{3} f(x)\ dx + \int_{3}^{5} f(x)\ dx$$

$$= \int_{-4}^{3} 9\ dx + \int_{3}^{5} x^2\ dx$$

$$= 9 \int_{-4}^{3} dx + \int_{3}^{5} x^2\ dx$$

$$= 9[x]_{-4}^{3} + \left[\frac{x^3}{3}\right]_{3}^{5}$$

$$= 9[3 - (-4)] + \left(\frac{5^3}{3} - \frac{3^3}{3}\right)$$

$$= 95\tfrac{2}{3}$$

Do Exercise 38.

Applied Problem

Example The sales of a company are expected to grow continuously according to the function

$$S(t) = 100e^t,$$

where $S(t)$ = sales, in dollars, on the tth day.

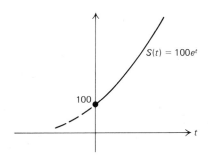

$S(t) = 100e^t$

100

a) Find the accumulated sales for the first 7 days.

b) On what day will accumulated sales pass $810,000?

Solution

a) Accumulated sales through day 7 $= \int_{0}^{7} S(t)\ dt$

$$= \int_{0}^{7} 100e^t\ dt = 100 \int_{0}^{7} e^t\ dt = 100[e^t]_{0}^{7} = 100(e^7 - e^0)$$

$$= 100(1096.6 - 1) = 100(1095.6) = \$109{,}560.$$

38. Find the area under the graph of $y = f(x)$ from -3 to 2.

$$f(x) = \begin{cases} 4, & \text{if}\quad x < 0 \\ 4 - x^2, & \text{if}\quad x \geqslant 0. \end{cases}$$

39. The sales of a company are expected to grow continuously according to the function
$$S(t) = 200e^t,$$
where $S(t)$ = sales in dollars on the tth day.
a) Find the accumulated sales for the first 8 days.
b) On what day will accumulated sales pass $300,000?
c) The accumulated sales from the 8th through the 10th day is given by
$$\int_8^{10} S(t)\, dt.$$
Find this.

b) Accumulated sales through day $k = \int_0^k S(t)\, dt$
$$= \int_0^k 100e^t\, dt = 100 \int_0^k e^t\, dt = 100[e^t]_0^k = 100(e^k - e^0) = 100(e^k - 1).$$
We set this equal to $810,000 and solve for k.
$$100(e^k - 1) = 810{,}000$$
$$e^k - 1 = 8100$$
$$e^k = 8101 \approx 8100$$

From Table 4 we see that
$$e^9 \approx 8100$$
So total sales will pass $810,000 on the 9th day.

Had the number 8100 not been close to any number in the table we could have used common logarithms to solve $e^k = 8100$, as follows:
$$e^k = 8100$$
$$\log e^k = \log 8100$$
$$k \cdot \log e = \log 8100$$
$$k = \frac{\log 8100}{\log e}$$
$$k = \frac{3.9085}{0.4343}. \quad \left(\begin{array}{l}\text{Using Table 2, } \log 8100 = 3.9085.\\ \text{Recall that } \log e = 0.4343.\end{array}\right)$$
$$k \approx 9$$
If you do not recall how to find log 8100, see p. 193. *Note:* we did not use natural logarithms, because we have not discussed how to find natural logarithms of larger numbers such as 8100. Actually, we did just find ln 8100, for if
$$e^k = 8100,$$
then
$$\ln e^k = \ln 8100$$
$$k = \ln 8100.$$
But we also know that
$$k = \frac{\log 8100}{\log e}.$$

We can find the natural logarithms from common logarithms as follows:
$$\ln N = \frac{\log N}{\log e}.$$

Do Exercise 39.

EXERCISE SET 5.3

Integrate.

1. $\int_0^1 (x - x^2)\, dx$

2. $\int_1^2 (x^2 - x)\, dx$

3. $\int_{-1}^1 (x^2 - x^4)\, dx$

4. $\int_0^b e^x\, dx$

5. $\int_a^b e^t\, dt$

6. $\int_0^a (ax - x^2)\, dx$

7. $\int_a^b 3t^2\, dt$

8. $\int_a^b 4t^3\, dt$

9. $\int_1^e \left(x + \dfrac{1}{x}\right) dx$

10. $\int_1^e \left(x - \dfrac{1}{x}\right) dx$

11. $\int_0^1 \sqrt{x}\, dx$

12. $\int_0^1 3\sqrt{x}\, dx$

13. $\int_0^1 \frac{10}{17}t^3\, dt$

14. $\int_0^1 \frac{12}{13}t^2\, dt$

Find the area under the graph on the interval indicated.

15. $y = x^3$; $[0, 2]$

16. $y = x^4$; $[0, 1]$

17. $y = x^2 + x + 1$; $[2, 3]$

18. $y = 2 - x - x^2$; $[-2, 1]$

19. $y = 5 - x^2$; $[-1, 2]$

20. $y = e^x$; $[-2, 3]$

21. $y = e^x$; $[-1, 5]$

22. $y = 2x + \dfrac{1}{x^2}$; $[1, 4]$

23. $y = 2x - \dfrac{1}{x^2}$; $[1, 3]$

Find the area under the graph on $[-2, 3]$.

24. $f(x) = \begin{cases} x^2, & \text{if } x < 1 \\ 1, & \text{if } x \geqslant 1 \end{cases}$

25. $f(x) = \begin{cases} 4 - x^2, & \text{if } x < 0 \\ 4, & \text{if } x \geqslant 0 \end{cases}$

Applied Problems

26. Raggs, Ltd. estimates that its sales will grow continuously according to the function

$$S(t) = 10e^t,$$

where $S(t)$ = sales, in dollars, on the tth day.
  a) Find the accumulated sales for the first 5 days.
  b) Find the sales from the 2nd through the 5th day.
  c) On what day will accumulated sales pass $40,000?

27. A company estimates that its sales will grow continuously according to the function

$$S(t) = 20e^t,$$

where $S(t)$ = sales, in dollars, on the tth day.
  a) Find the accumulated sales for the first 5 days.
  b) Find the sales from the 2nd through the 5th day.
  c) On what day will accumulated sales pass $20,000?

28. A particle starts out from the origin. Its velocity at time t is given by

$$v(t) = 3t^2 + 2t.$$

How far does it travel from the 2nd through the 5th hour?

29. A particle starts out from the origin. Its velocity at time t is given by

$$v(t) = 4t^3 + 2t.$$

How far does it travel from the 1st through the 3rd hour?

30. Raggs, Ltd. determines that the marginal cost per suit is given by

$$C'(x) = 0.0003x^2 - 0.2x + 50.$$

Ignoring fixed costs, find the total cost of producing the 101st through the 400th suit (integrate from $x = 100$ to $x = 400$).

31. In Exercise 30, find the cost of producing the 201st through the 400th suit (integrate from $x = 200$ to $x = 400$).

MEMORIZING   In the psychological process of memorizing, the rate of memorizing (say in words per minute) increases with respect to time, but eventually a maximum rate of memorizing is reached from which the memory rate decreases.

32. Suppose in a certain memory experiment the rate of memorizing is given by

$$m(t) = -0.009t^2 + 0.2t,$$

where $m(t)$ = memory rate in words per minute. How many words are memorized the first 10 minutes (from $t = 0$ to $t = 10$)?

33. Suppose in a certain memory experiment the rate of memorizing is given by

$$m(t) = -0.003t^2 + 0.2t,$$

where $m(t)$ = memory rate in words per minute. How many words are memorized in the first 10 minutes ($t = 0$ to $t = 10$)?

34. A company is producing a new product. However, due to the nature of the product, it is felt that the time required to produce each unit will decrease as the workers become more familiar with the production procedure. It is determined that the function for the learning process is

$$T(x) = ax^b,$$

where

$T(x)$ = cumulative average time to produce x units,
x = number of units produced,
a = hours required to produce 1st unit,
b = slope of the learning curve.

a) Find an expression for the total time required to produce 100 units.
b) Suppose $a = 100$ hr and $b = -0.322$. Find the total time required to produce 100 units.

[*Hint*: $100^{0.678} \approx 22.7$.]

5.4 THE DEFINITE INTEGRAL; AREA BETWEEN CURVES

We have considered the definite integral for functions that are positive on an interval $[a, b]$ (the function might be 0 at one or both endpoints). Now we shall consider functions which have negative values. First, let us evaluate the integral of a function without negative values.

$$\int_0^2 x^2\, dx = \left[\frac{x^3}{3}\right]_0^2 = \frac{2^3}{3} - \frac{0^3}{3} = \frac{8}{3}$$

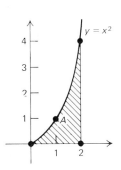

Thus the area of the shaded region is $\frac{8}{3}$.

Now let us consider the function $y = -x^2$ on the interval $[0, 2]$. Even though we have not defined the definite integral for functions with negative values, let us apply the evaluation procedures and see what we get.

$$\int_0^2 -x^2\, dx = \left[-\frac{x^3}{3}\right]_0^2$$

$$= \left[-\frac{2^3}{3} - \left(-\frac{0^3}{3}\right)\right] = -\frac{8}{3}$$

The graphs of these two functions are reflections of each other across the x-axis. Thus the areas of the shaded regions are the same; that is, $\frac{8}{3}$. The evaluation procedure in the second case gave us $-\frac{8}{3}$. This illustrates that for negative valued functions, the definite integral gives us the additive inverse of the area between the curve and the x-axis.

Do Exercises 40 and 41.

OBJECTIVES

You should be able to:

a) Evaluate the definite integral of a continuous function.
b) Find the area of a region bounded by two graphs.
c) Solve applied problems involving area between two graphs.

40. To find the area of the shaded region, integrate

$$\int_0^2 x^3\, dx.$$

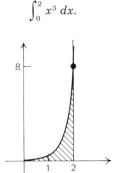

41. To find the area of the shaded region, integrate

$$\int_0^2 -x^3\, dx.$$

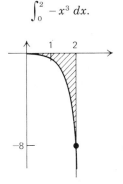

42. Integrate.

a) $\int_0^1 (x^2 - x)\, dx$

b) $\int_1^2 (x^2 - x)\, dx$

c) $\int_0^2 (x^2 - x)\, dx$

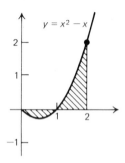

43. Integrate.

a) $\int_{-2}^0 x^3\, dx$

b) $\int_0^2 x^3\, dx$

c) $\int_{-2}^2 x^3\, dx$

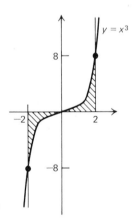

Now let us consider the function $x^2 - 1$ on $[-1, 2]$. It has both positive and negative values. We shall apply the evaluation procedures as above, even though function values are not all nonnegative. We shall do this two ways.

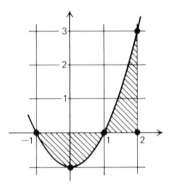

First,

$\int_{-1}^2 (x^2 - 1)\, dx$

$$= \int_{-1}^1 (x^2 - 1)\, dx + \int_1^2 (x^2 - 1)\, dx$$

$$= \left[\frac{x^3}{3} - x \right]_{-1}^1 + \left[\frac{x^3}{3} - x \right]_1^2$$

$$= \left[\left(\frac{1^3}{3} - 1 \right) - \left(\frac{(-1)^3}{3} - (-1) \right) \right] + \left[\left(\frac{2^3}{3} - 2 \right) - \left(\frac{1^3}{3} - 1 \right) \right]$$

$$= \left[-\frac{4}{3} \right] + \left[\frac{4}{3} \right]$$

$$= 0.$$

This shows that the area of the region under the x-axis is the same as the area of the region over the x-axis.

Now let us evaluate another way.

$$\int_{-1}^2 (x^2 - 1)\, dx = \left[\frac{x^3}{3} - x \right]_{-1}^2 = \left(\frac{2^3}{3} - 2 \right) - \left(\frac{(-1)^3}{3} - (-1) \right)$$

$$= \left(\frac{8}{3} - 2 \right) - \left(-\frac{1}{3} + 1 \right)$$

$$= \frac{8}{3} - 2 + \frac{1}{3} - 1$$

$$= 0.$$

This result is consistent with the first. Thus we are motivated to extend our definition of definite integral to include any continuous function, having positive, negative, or zero values.

$$\int_a^b f(x)\, dx = F(b) - F(a), \quad \text{where } F \text{ is any antiderivative of } f.$$

Do Exercises 42 and 43.

The definite integral turns out to be the area above the x-axis minus the area below.

Examples Decide whether $\int_a^b f(x)\, dx$ is positive, negative, or zero.

a) 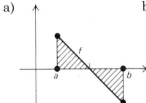   b) 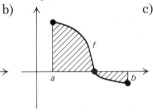   c)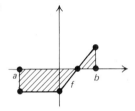

Solution

a) $\int_a^b f(x)\, dx = 0.$

   There is the same area above as below.

b) $\int_a^b f(x)\, dx > 0.$

   There is more area above.

c) $\int_a^b f(x)\, dx < 0.$

   There is more area below.

Do Exercises 44 through 47.

Area of a Region Bounded by Two Graphs

Suppose we want to find the area of a region bounded by the graphs of two functions $y = f(x)$ and $y = g(x)$.

In each exercise,

a) Decide whether $\int_a^b f(x)\, dx$ is positive, negative, or zero.

b) Express $\int_a^b f(x)\, dx$ in terms of A.

44.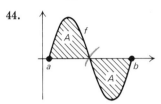

45.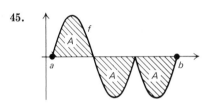

46.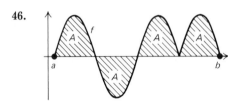

47.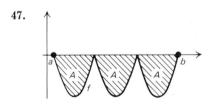

What is a simple way, not involving integration, to estimate the area between the curves formed by the sides of the staircase?

Note that the area of the region in question (I) is that of (II) minus that of (III).

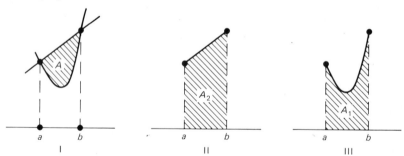

Thus

$$A = \int_a^b f(x)\, dx - \int_a^b g(x)\, dx$$

or

$$A = \int_a^b [f(x) - g(x)]\, dx.$$

In general,

> Let f and g be continuous functions and suppose $f(x) \geqslant g(x)$ over the interval $[a, b]$. Then the area of the region bounded by the graphs of the two functions is
>
> $$\int_a^b [f(x) - g(x)]\, dx.$$

Example Find the area of the region bounded by the graphs of $y = 2x + 1$ and $y = x^2 + 1$.

Solution

a) First, make a reasonably accurate sketch to insure that you have the right configuration. Note which is the *upper* graph. Here

$$(2x + 1) \geqslant x^2 + 1 \text{ over the interval } [0, 2].$$

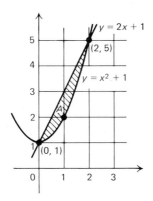

b) Second, determine the first coordinates of possible points of intersection. Usually you can do this just by looking at the graph. If not, you can solve the system of equations as follows. At the points of intersection, $y = x^2 + 1$ and $y = 2x + 1$, so

$$x^2 + 1 = 2x + 1$$
$$x^2 - 2x = 0$$
$$x(x - 2) = 0$$
$$x = 0 \quad \text{or} \quad x = 2.$$

Thus the interval with which we are concerned is $[0, 2]$.

c) Compute the area as follows:

$$\int_0^2 [(2x + 1) - (x^2 + 1)] \, dx = \int_0^2 (2x - x^2) \, dx$$
$$= \left[x^2 - \frac{x^3}{3} \right]_0^2$$
$$= \left(2^2 - \frac{2^3}{3} \right) - \left(0^2 - \frac{0^3}{3} \right)$$
$$= 4 - \frac{8}{3}$$
$$= \frac{4}{3}.$$

Do Exercise 48.

48. Find the area of the region bounded by the graphs of

$$y = x \quad \text{and} \quad y = x^2.$$

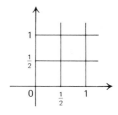

Application

Example *Emission control.* A clever college student develops an engine which she believes will meet federal standards for emission control. She determines that the rate of emission for her engine is given by

$$E(t) = 2t^2,$$

where $E(t)$ = emissions in billions of pollution particulates at time t, in years. The emission rate of a conventional engine is given by

$$C(t) = 9 + t^2.$$

The graphs are seen here.

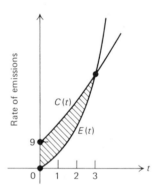

a) At what point in time will the emission rates be the same?

b) Before the time in (a), what is the reduction in emissions resulting from using the student's engine?

Solution

a) The rates of emission will be the same when $E(t) = C(t)$, or

$$2t^2 = 9 + t^2$$
$$t^2 - 9 = 0$$
$$(t - 3)(t + 3) = 0$$
$$t = 3 \quad \text{or} \quad t = -3.$$

Since negative time has no meaning in this problem, the emission rates will be the same when $t = 3$ years.

b) The reduction in emissions is represented by the area of the shaded region. It is computed as follows:

$$\int_0^3 [(9 + t^2) - 2t^2] \, dt = \int_0^3 (9 - t^2) \, dt = \left[9t - \frac{t^3}{3} \right]_0^3$$

$$= \left(9 \cdot 3 - \frac{3^3}{3} \right) - \left(9 \cdot 0 - \frac{0^3}{3} \right)$$

$$= 27 - 9 = 18 \text{ billion pollution particulates.}$$

Do Exercise 49.

49. A company determines that its marginal revenue per unit is given by

$$R'(x) = 14x, \quad R(0) = 0.$$

Its marginal cost per unit is given by

$$C'(x) = 4x - 10, \quad C(0) = 0.$$

Total profit from the production and sale of k units is given by

$$P(k) = R(k) - C(k)$$
$$= \int_0^k [R'(x) - C'(x)] \, dx.$$

a) Find $P(k)$.
b) Find $P(5)$.

EXERCISE SET 5.4

Find the area of the region bounded by the given graphs.

1. $y = x, \; y = x^3$

2. $y = x, \; y = x^4$

3. $y = x + 2, \; y = x^2$

4. $y = x^2 - 2x, \; y = x$

5. $y = 6x - x^2, \; y = x$

6. $y = x^2 - 6x, \; y = -x$

7. $y = 2x - x^2, \; y = -x$

8. $y = x^2, \; y = \sqrt{x}$

9. $y = x, \; y = \sqrt{x}$

10. $y = 3, \; y = \sqrt{x}$

11. $y = 5, \; y = \sqrt{x}$

12. $y = x^2, \; y = x^3$

13. $y = 4 - x^2, \; y = 4 - 4x$

14. $y = x^2 + 1, \; y = x^2, \; x = 1, \; x = 3$

15. $y = x^2 + 3, \; y = x^2, \; x = 1, \; x = 2$

16. A company determines that its marginal revenue per day is given by

$$R'(t) = 100e^t, \quad R(0) = 0,$$

where $R(t)$ = revenue, in dollars, on the tth day. Also, its marginal cost per day is given by

$$C'(t) = 100 - 0.2t, \quad C(0) = 0,$$

where $C(t)$ = cost, in dollars, on the tth day. Find the total profit for the $t = 0$ to $t = 10$ (the first 10 days). *Note:*

$$P(T) = R(T) - C(T) = \int_0^T [R'(t) - C'(t)] \, dt.$$

17. In a certain memory experiment, subject A is able to memorize words at the rate

$$m(t) = -0.009t^2 + 0.2t \quad \text{(words per minute).}$$

In the same memory experiment subject B is able to memorize at the rate

$$M(t) = -0.003t^2 + 0.2t \quad \text{(words per minute).}$$

a) Which subject has the higher rate of learning?
b) How many more words does that subject learn from $t = 0$ to $t = 10$ (during the first 10 minutes)?

OBJECTIVES

You should be able to:

a) Integrate using substitution.
b) Solve applied problems involving integration by substitution.

5.5 INTEGRATION TECHNIQUES: SUBSTITUTION

Recall the differentiation formulas which were considered on pp. 131, 204, and 213.

$$\frac{d}{dx}[f(x)]^n = n[f(x)]^{n-1}\frac{d}{dx}f(x),$$

$$\frac{d}{dx}e^{f(x)} = e^{f(x)}\frac{d}{dx}f(x),$$

$$\frac{d}{dx}\ln f(x) = \frac{1}{f(x)}\cdot\frac{d}{dx}f(x).$$

For simplicity let us replace $f(x)$ by u. Then the above become

$$\frac{d}{dx}u^n = n\cdot u^{n-1}\cdot\frac{du}{dx},$$

$$\frac{d}{dx}e^u = e^u\cdot\frac{du}{dx},$$

$$\frac{d}{dx}\ln u = \frac{1}{u}\cdot\frac{du}{dx}.$$

These yield the following integration formulas:

$$\int\left(n\cdot u^{n-1}\frac{du}{dx}\right)dx = u^n + C,$$

$$\int\left(e^u\frac{du}{dx}\right)dx = e^u + C,$$

$$\int\left(\frac{1}{u}\frac{du}{dx}\right)dx = \ln u + C.$$

If we assume that $\frac{du}{dx}dx = du\frac{dx}{dx}$ and that $\frac{dx}{dx}$ is a symbol for 1, then we get

A) $\int n\cdot u^{n-1}\,du = u^n + C$

B) $\int e^u\,du = e^u + C$

C) $\int\frac{1}{u}\,du = \ln u + C$

These formulas provide a basis for an integration technique called *substitution*. (Note that they also provide a motivation for using du in the integral notation.)

Integration by Substitution

In the Leibniz notation $\dfrac{dy}{dx}$ we did not give specific definitions of dy and dx. Nevertheless it will be convenient to treat $\dfrac{dy}{dx}$ as a quotient. Thus, from

$$\frac{dy}{dx} = f'(x)$$

we can derive

$$dy = f'(x)\, dx.$$

It is possible to define dy and dx, but it is not necessary for our purposes.

Example 1   For $y = f(x) = x^3$, find dy.

Solution $\dfrac{dy}{dx} = f'(x) = 3x^2$, so $dy = f'(x)\, dx = 3x^2\, dx.$

Example 2   For $u = g(x) = \ln x$, find du.

Solution $\dfrac{du}{dx} = g'(x) = \dfrac{1}{x}$, so $du = g'(x)\, dx = \dfrac{1}{x}\, dx$, or $\dfrac{dx}{x}$.

Do Exercises 50 and 51.

So far the dx in

$$\int f(x)\, dx$$

has played no role in integrating other than indicating the variable of integration. Now it will be convenient to make use of dx. Consider the integral

$$\int 2x \cdot e^{x^2}\, dx.$$

If we set

$$u = x^2,$$

then

$$du = 2x\, dx.$$

If we substitute u for x^2, and du for $2x\, dx$, the integral takes on the form

$$\int e^u\, du.$$

50. For $y = f(x) = 6x^2 + x$, find dy.

51. For $u = g(x) = x + 3$, find du.

52. Integrate.

$$\int 3x^2 e^{x^3}\, dx$$

Since

$$\int e^u\, du = e^u + C,$$

it follows that

$$\int 2x \cdot e^{x^2}\, dx = \int e^u\, du = e^u + C = e^{x^2} + C.$$

The result can be checked by differentiation. This procedure is referred to as *substitution*, or *change of variable*. It is a *trial and error* procedure; that is, if we try a substitution that doesn't result in an integrand which can be easily integrated, we try another. It will not always work! It will work if the integrand fits one of the rules A, B, or C, previously considered on p. 286.

Do Exercise 52.

53. Integrate.

$$\int \frac{2x\, dx}{5 + x^2}$$

Let us consider some further examples.

Example 1 $\displaystyle\int \frac{2x\, dx}{1 + x^2} = \int \frac{du}{u}$ Substitution $\boxed{\begin{array}{l}\text{Let } u = 1 + x^2, \\ \text{then } du = 2x\, dx.\end{array}}$

$$\Rightarrow \ln u + C$$
$$= \ln(1 + x^2) + C$$

Remember that this is a trial and error process. Suppose we had made the substitution

$$u = x^2.$$

Then

$$du = 2x\, dx,$$

and the integral becomes

$$\int \frac{du}{1 + u}.$$

This is still not easily integrated, so we would try another substitution.

Do Exercise 53.

54. Integrate.

$$\int \frac{2x\, dx}{(3 + x^2)^2}$$

Example 2 $\displaystyle\int \frac{2x\, dx}{(1 + x^2)^2} = \int \frac{du}{u^2}$ Substitution $\boxed{\begin{array}{l}u = 1 + x^2, \\ du = 2x\, dx\end{array}}$

$$= -\frac{1}{u} + C$$
$$= -\frac{1}{1 + x^2} + C$$

Do Exercise 54.

Example 3 $\displaystyle \int \frac{\ln 3x \, dx}{x} = \int u \, du$ Substitution $\boxed{\begin{array}{l} u = \ln 3x, \\ du = \dfrac{1}{x} \, dx \end{array}}$

$$= \frac{u^2}{2} + C$$

$$= \frac{(\ln 3x)^2}{2} + C$$

Do Exercise 55.

Example 4 Integrate $\int xe^{x^2} \, dx$.

Solution Suppose we try

$$u = x^2,$$

then

$$du = 2x \, dx.$$

We don't quite have $2x \, dx$. We have only $x \, dx$ and will need to supply a 2. We do this by multiplying by $\frac{1}{2} \cdot 2$ as follows.

$$\begin{aligned} \tfrac{1}{2} \cdot 2 \cdot \int xe^{x^2} \, dx &= \tfrac{1}{2}\!\int 2xe^{x^2} \, dx \\ &= \tfrac{1}{2}\!\int e^{x^2}(2x \, dx) \\ &= \tfrac{1}{2}\!\int e^u \, du \\ &= \tfrac{1}{2}e^u + C \\ &= \tfrac{1}{2}e^{x^2} + C \end{aligned}$$

Do Exercise 56.

Example 5 $\displaystyle \left.\begin{array}{l} \int e^{ax} \, dx = \dfrac{1}{a}\int ae^{ax} \, dx \\[2mm] \qquad = \dfrac{1}{a}\int e^u \, du \end{array}\right\}$ Substitution $\boxed{\begin{array}{l} u = ax, \\ du = a \, dx \end{array}}$

$$= \frac{1}{a} e^u + C$$

$$= \frac{1}{a} e^{ax} + C$$

Note that this gives us a formula for integrating e^{ax}.

Do Exercises 57 through 59.

55. Integrate.

$$\int \frac{\ln x \, dx}{x}$$

56. Integrate.

$$\int x^2 \cdot e^{x^3} \, dx$$

Integrate.

57. $\int e^{5x} \, dx$

58. $\int e^{0.02x} \, dx$

59. $\int e^{-x} \, dx$

60. Integrate.

$$\int x^3 (x^4 + 5)^{19} \, dx$$

Example 6 $\displaystyle\int \frac{dx}{x + 3} = \int \frac{du}{u}$ Substitution $\boxed{\begin{array}{l} u = x + 3, \\ du = dx \end{array}}$

$$= \ln u + C$$

$$= \ln(x + 3) + C$$

With practice, you will make certain substitutions mentally and just write down the answer. Examples 5 and 6 are good illustrations.

Example 7
$$\int x^2 (x^3 + 1)^{10} \, dx = \tfrac{1}{3}\int 3x^2(x^3 + 1)^{10} \, dx \Big\}$$ $\boxed{\begin{array}{l} u = x^3 + 1 \\ du = 3x^2 \, dx \end{array}}$

$$= \tfrac{1}{3}\int u^{10} \, du$$

$$= \frac{1}{3} \cdot \frac{u^{11}}{11} + C$$

$$= \tfrac{1}{33}(x^3 + 1)^{11} + C$$

Do Exercise 60.

---

61. Evaluate.

$$\int_1^e \frac{\ln x \, dx}{x}$$

(See Margin Exercise 55.)

Example 8   Evaluate.

$$\int_0^1 x^2 (x^3 + 1)^{10} \, dx.$$

Solution

a) First find the indefinite integral (shown in Example 7).

b) Then evaluate the definite integral on $[0, 1]$.

$$\int_0^1 x^2 (x^3 + 1)^{10} \, dx = \left[\tfrac{1}{33}(x^3 + 1)^{11}\right]_0^1$$

$$= \tfrac{1}{33}[(1^3 + 1)^{11} - (0^3 + 1)^{11}]$$

$$= \tfrac{1}{33}(2^{11} - 1^{11})$$

$$= \frac{2^{11} - 1}{33}$$

Do Exercise 61.

EXERCISE SET 5.5

Integrate. Be sure to check by differentiating!

1. $\int \dfrac{3x^2\,dx}{7+x^3}$

2. $\int \dfrac{3x^2\,dx}{1+x^3}$

3. $\int e^{4x}\,dx$

4. $\int e^{3x}\,dx$

5. $\int e^{x/2}\,dx$

6. $\int e^{x/3}\,dx$

7. $\int x^3 e^{x^4}\,dx$

8. $\int x^4 e^{x^5}\,dx$

9. $\int t^2 e^{-t^3}\,dt$

10. $\int te^{-t^2}\,dt$

11. $\int \dfrac{\ln 4x\,dx}{x}$

12. $\int \dfrac{\ln 5x\,dx}{x}$

13. $\int \dfrac{dx}{1+x}$

14. $\int \dfrac{dx}{5+x}$

15. $\int \dfrac{dx}{4-x}$

16. $\int \dfrac{dx}{1-x}$

17. $\int t^2(t^3-1)^7\,dt$

18. $\int t(t^2-1)^5\,dt$

19. $\int (x^4+x^3+x^2)^7(4x^3+3x^2+2x)\,dx$

20. $\int (x^3-x^2-x)^9(3x^2-2x-1)\,dx$

21. $\int \dfrac{e^x\,dx}{4+e^x}$

22. $\int \dfrac{e^t\,dt}{3+e^t}$

23. $\int \dfrac{\ln x^2}{x}\,dx$

24. $\int \dfrac{(\ln x)^2}{x}\,dx$

25. $\int \dfrac{dx}{x\ln x}$

26. $\int \dfrac{dx}{x\ln x^2}$

27. $\int \sqrt{ax+b}\,dx$

28. $\int x\sqrt{ax^2+b}\,dx$

29. $\int be^{ax}\,dx$

30. $\int P_0 e^{kt}\,dt$

Integrate.

31. $\int_0^1 2x\,e^{x^2}\,dx$

32. $\int_0^1 3x^2\,e^{x^3}\,dx$

33. $\int_0^1 x(x^2+1)^5\,dx$

34. $\int_1^2 x(x^2-1)^7\,dx$

35. $\int_1^3 \dfrac{dt}{1+t}$

36. $\int_1^3 e^{2x}\,dx$

37. $\int_1^4 \dfrac{2x+1}{x^2+x-1}\,dx$

38. $\int_1^3 \dfrac{2x+3}{x^2+3x}\,dx$

39. $\int_0^b e^{-x}\,dx$

40. $\int_0^b 2e^{-2x}\,dx$

41. $\int_0^b me^{-mx}\,dx$

42. $\int_0^b ke^{-kx}\,dx$

43. $\int_0^4 (x-6)^2\,dx$

44. $\int_0^3 (x-5)^2\,dx$

45. *Divorce.* It has been found that the U.S. divorce rate is approximated by

$$D(t) = 100{,}000e^{0.025t},$$

where

$D(t)$ = number of divorces occurring at time t,
 t = number of years measured from 1900.

That is, $t = 0$ corresponds to 1900, $t = 74\frac{9}{365}$ corresponds to January 9, 1974, and so on.

a) Find the total number of divorces from 1900 to 1976. Note that this is $\int_{0}^{76} D(t)\, dt$.

b) Find the total number of divorces from 1972 to 1976. Note that this is

$$\int_{72}^{76} D(t)\, dt.$$

46. *Value of an investment.* A company buys a new machine for $250,000. The marginal revenue from the sale of products produced by the machine is projected to be

$$R'(t) = 4000t.$$

The salvage value of the machine decreases at the rate of

$$V(t) = 25{,}000e^{-0.1t}.$$

The total profit from the machine after T years is given by

$$P(T) = \text{(Revenue from sale of products)}$$
$$+ \text{(Revenue from sale of machine)}$$
$$- \text{(Cost of machine)}$$
$$= \int_{0}^{T} R'(t)\, dt + \int_{0}^{T} V(t)\, dt - \$250{,}000$$

a) Find $P(T)$.

b) Find $P(10)$.

OBJECTIVES

You should be able to:

a) Integrate using integration by parts.
b) Solve applied problems involving integration by parts.
c) Integrate using a table of integration formulas.

5.6 INTEGRATION TECHNIQUES: INTEGRATION BY PARTS; TABLES

Recall the product rule for derivatives:

$$\frac{d}{dx}\, uv = \frac{du}{dx}\, v + \frac{dv}{dx}\, u = u\,\frac{dv}{dx} + v\,\frac{du}{dx}.$$

Integrating both sides, we get

$$uv = \int u\,\frac{dv}{dx} + \int v\,\frac{du}{dx}.$$

Solving for $\int u\,\dfrac{dv}{dx}$, we get

$$\int u\,\frac{dv}{dx} = uv - \int v\,\frac{du}{dx}.$$

If, for simplicity, we delete the dx in the denominators, we get

$$\int u\, dv = uv - \int v\, du.$$

This equation can be used as a formula for integrating in certain situations. These are situations in which an integrand is a product of two functions, where we already know how to integrate one of them.

For example,

$$\int xe^x \, dx$$

can be considered as follows:

$$\int x(e^x \, dx) = \int u \, dv, \quad \text{where } u = x \text{ and } dv = e^x \, dx.$$

We already know how to integrate $e^x \, dx$, or dv. The simplest anti-derivative is e^x. This is v. Now since $du = dx$, the formula gives us

$$\overset{u}{\int(x)}\overset{dv}{(e^x \, dx)} = \overset{u}{(x)}\overset{v}{(e^x)} - \int \overset{v}{(e^x)}\overset{du}{(dx)}$$

$$= xe^x - e^x + C.$$

This way of integrating is called *integration by parts* and the following is the basis of it.

INTEGRATION BY PARTS FORMULA

$$\int u \, dv = uv - \int v \, du$$

Note that integration by parts is a trial and error process, as is substitution. In the preceding example, suppose we had reversed the roles of x and e^x. We would have obtained

$$u = e^x \qquad dv = x \, dx,$$

$$du = e^x \, dx \qquad v = \frac{x^2}{2},$$

and

$$\int (e^x)(x \, dx) = (e^x)\left(\frac{x^2}{2}\right) - \int \left(\frac{x^2}{2}\right)(e^x \, dx).$$

Now the integrand on the right is more difficult to integrate than the one we started with. When we can integrate *both* factors of an integrand, and thus have a choice as to how to apply the integration by parts formula, it can happen that only one (and maybe none) of the possibilities will work.

Do Exercise 62.

Let us consider some further examples.

Example 1 Integrate

$$\int \ln x \, dx.$$

62. Integrate.

$$\int 3x \cdot e^{3x} \, dx$$

63. Integrate.

$$\int x \cdot \ln x \, dx$$

Solution   Note that $\int \dfrac{dx}{x} = \ln x + C$, but we do not yet know how to find $\int \ln x \, dx$.

Let
$$u = \ln x \qquad \text{and} \qquad dv = dx.$$
Then
$$du = \frac{1}{x} \, dx \qquad \text{and} \qquad v = x.$$

Using the integration by parts formula gives

$$\int \overset{u}{(\ln x)} \overset{dv}{(dx)} = \overset{u}{(\ln x)} \overset{v}{x} - \int \overset{v}{x} \left(\overset{\frac{1}{x} du}{\frac{1}{x} \, dx} \right)$$

$$= x \ln x - \int dx$$

$$= x \ln x - x + C.$$

Do Exercise 63.

64. Integrate.

$$\int x \sqrt{x + 3} \, dx$$

Example 2   Integrate
$$\int x \sqrt{x + 1} \, dx.$$

Solution   We let
$$u = x \qquad \text{and} \qquad dv = (x + 1)^{1/2} \, dx.$$
Then
$$du = dx \qquad \text{and} \qquad v = \tfrac{2}{3}(x + 1)^{3/2}.$$

Note that we had to use substitution to integrate dv. Using the integration by parts formula gives

$$\int x \sqrt{x + 1} \, dx = x \cdot \tfrac{2}{3}(x + 1)^{3/2} - \tfrac{2}{3}\int (x + 1)^{3/2} \, dx$$

$$= \tfrac{2}{3}x(x + 1)^{3/2} - \tfrac{2}{3} \cdot \tfrac{2}{5}(x + 1)^{5/2} + C$$

$$= \tfrac{2}{3}x(x + 1)^{3/2} - \tfrac{4}{15}(x + 1)^{5/2} + C.$$

Do Exercise 64.

Example 3   Integrate
$$\int_1^2 \ln x \, dx.$$

Solution

a) First find the indefinite integral (Example 1).

b) Then evaluate the definite integral.

$$\int_1^2 \ln x \, dx = [x \ln x - x]_1^2$$

$$= (2 \ln 2 - 2) - (1 \cdot \ln 1 - 1)$$

$$= 2 \ln 2 - 2 + 1$$

$$= 2 \ln 2 - 1$$

Do Exercise 65.

Tables of Integration Formulas

You have probably noticed that, generally speaking, integration is more difficult and "tricky" than differentiation. Because of this, integral formulas that are reasonable and/or important have been gathered into tables. Table 5, at the back of the book, though quite brief, is such an example. Entire books of integration formulas are available in libraries, and lengthy tables are also available in mathematical handbooks. Such tables are usually classified by the form of the integrand. The idea is to properly match the integral in question with a formula in the table.

Example   Integrate

$$\frac{dx}{x(3-x)}.$$

Solution   This integral fits *Formula 20* in Table 5:

$$\int \frac{1}{x(ax+b)} \, dx = \frac{1}{b} \ln\left(\frac{x}{ax+b}\right) + C.$$

In our integral, $a = -1$ and $b = 3$, so we have, by the formula,

$$\int \frac{dx}{x(3-x)} \, dx = \int \frac{dx}{x(-1 \cdot x + 3)} = \frac{1}{3} \ln\left(\frac{x}{-1 \cdot x + 3}\right) + C$$

$$= \frac{1}{3} \ln\left(\frac{x}{3-x}\right) + C.$$

Do Exercise 66.

65. Integrate.

$$\int_1^2 x \ln x \, dx$$

(See Margin Exercise 63).

66. Use Table 5. Integrate.

$$\int \frac{1}{x^2 - 25} \, dx$$

EXERCISE SET 5.6

Integrate. Use integration by parts. Do not use Table 5. Check by differentiating.

1. $\int 5xe^{5x}\,dx$ **2.** $\int 2xe^{2x}\,dx$ **3.** $\int x^3(3x^2\,dx)$ **4.** $\int x^2(2x\,dx)$ **5.** $\int xe^{2x}\,dx$

6. $\int xe^{3x}\,dx$ **7.** $\int xe^{-2x}\,dx$ **8.** $\int xe^{-x}\,dx$ **9.** $\int x^2 \ln x\,dx$ **10.** $\int x^3 \ln x\,dx$

11. $\int x \ln x^2\,dx$ **12.** $\int x^2 \ln x^3\,dx$ **13.** $\int \ln(x+3)\,dx$ **14.** $\int \ln(x+1)\,dx$

15. $\int (x+2) \ln x\,dx$ **16.** $\int (x+1) \ln x\,dx$ **17.** $\int (x-1) \ln x\,dx$ **18.** $\int (x-2) \ln x\,dx$

19. $\int x\sqrt{x+2}\,dx$ **20.** $\int x\sqrt{x+4}\,dx$ **21.** $\int x^3 \ln 2x\,dx$ **22.** $\int x^2 \ln 5x\,dx$

23. $\int x^2 e^x\,dx$ **24.** $\int (\ln x)^2\,dx$

25. a) Verify that, for any positive integer n,
$$\int x^n e^x\,dx = x^n e^x - n\int x^{n-1} e^x\,dx.$$
   b) Apply (a) repeatedly to integrate
$$\int x^3 e^x\,dx.$$

26. a) Verify that, for any positive integer n,
$$\int (\ln x)^n\,dx = x(\ln x)^n - n\int (\ln x)^{n-1}\,dx.$$
   b) Apply (a) repeatedly to integrate
$$\int (\ln x)^3\,dx.$$

Integrate. Use integration by parts. Do not use Table 5.

27. $\int_1^2 x^2 \ln x\,dx$ **28.** $\int_1^2 x^3 \ln x\,dx$ **29.** $\int_2^6 \ln(x+3)\,dx$

30. $\int_0^5 \ln(x+1)\,dx$ **31.** $\int_0^1 xe^x\,dx$ **32.** $\int_0^1 xe^{-x}\,dx$

Integrate. Use Table 5.

33. $\int xe^{-3x}\,dx$ **34.** $\int xe^{4x}\,dx$ **35.** $\int 5^x\,dx$ **36.** $\int \dfrac{1}{\sqrt{x^2-9}}\,dx$

37. $\int \dfrac{1}{16-x^2}\,dx$ **38.** $\int \dfrac{1}{x\sqrt{4+x^2}}\,dx$ **39.** $\int \dfrac{x}{5-x}\,dx$

40. $\int \dfrac{x}{(1-x)^2}\,dx$ **41.** $\int \dfrac{1}{x(5-x)^2}\,dx$ **42.** $\int \sqrt{x^2+9}\,dx$

43. *Electrical energy usage.* The number of kilowatt-hours of electrical energy used by a family in a day is given by

$$K(t) = 10te^{-t},$$

where t is the time, in hours. That is, t is in the interval [0, 24].

a) How many kilowatt-hours does the family use in the first T hours of a day ($t = 0$ to $t = T$)?

b) How many kilowatt-hours does the family use in the first 4 hours of the day?

5.7 THE DEFINITE INTEGRAL AS A LIMIT OF SUMS

We now consider approximating the area of a region by dividing it into subregions which are almost rectangles. In the drawing below [a, b] has been divided into 4 subintervals, having width Δx, or $(b - a)/4$.

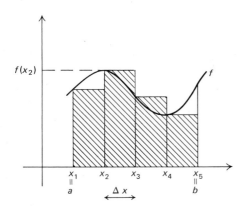

The heights of the rectangles shown are

$$f(x_1), f(x_2), f(x_3), \text{ and } f(x_4).$$

The area of the region under the curve is approximately the sum of the areas of the four rectangles,

$$f(x_1) \, \Delta x + f(x_2) \, \Delta x + f(x_3) \, \Delta x + f(x_4) \, \Delta x.$$

We can name this sum using *summation notation* which utilizes the Greek capital letter sigma, $\sum$,

$$\sum_{i=1}^{4} f(x_i) \, \Delta x.$$

This is read "the sum of the numbers $f(x_i) \, \Delta x$ from $i = 1$ to $i = 4$." To recover the original expression substitute the numbers 1 through 4 successively into $f(x_i) \, \Delta x$ and write plus signs between the results.

OBJECTIVES

You should be able to:

a) Approximate $\int_a^b f(x) \, dx$ by adding areas of rectangles.

b) Find the average value of a function over a given interval.

Write summation notation.

67. $1 + 4 + 9 + 16 + 25 + 36$

68. $e + e^2 + e^3 + e^4$

69. $P(x_1)\,\Delta x + P(x_2)\,\Delta x + \cdots + P(x_{38})\,\Delta x$

Example 1   Write summation notation for $2 + 4 + 6 + 8 + 10$.

Solution $2 + 4 + 6 + 8 + 10 = \displaystyle\sum_{i=1}^{5} 2i.$

Example 2   Write summation notation for

$$g(x_1)\,\Delta x + g(x_2)\,\Delta x + \cdots + g(x_{19})\,\Delta x.$$

Solution

$$g(x_1)\,\Delta x + g(x_2)\,\Delta x + \cdots + g(x_{19})\,\Delta x = \sum_{i=1}^{19} g(x_i)\,\Delta x.$$

Do Exercises 67 through 69.

Example 3   Express $\displaystyle\sum_{i=1}^{4} 3i$ without using summation notation.

Solution $\displaystyle\sum_{i=1}^{4} 3i = 3^1 + 3^2 + 3^3 + 3^4,$ or 120.

Express without using summation notation.

70. $\displaystyle\sum_{i=1}^{3} 4^i$

71. $\displaystyle\sum_{i=1}^{5} ie^i$

72. $\displaystyle\sum_{i=1}^{20} t(x_i)\,\Delta x$

Example 4   Express $\displaystyle\sum_{i=1}^{30} h(x_i)\,\Delta x$ without using summation notation.

Solution

$$\sum_{i=1}^{30} h(x_i)\,\Delta x = h(x_1)\,\Delta x + h(x_2)\,\Delta x + \cdots + h(x_{30})\,\Delta x.$$

Do Exercises 70 through 72.

Approximation of area by rectangles becomes better as we use more rectangles and smaller subintervals, as shown in the following drawings.

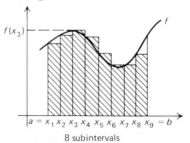

8 subintervals

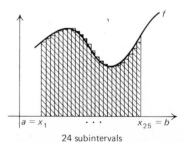

24 subintervals

In general, the interval $[a, b]$ is divided into n equal subintervals, each of width $\Delta x = (b - a)/n$.

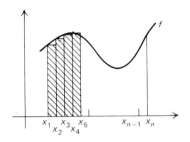

The heights of the rectangles are

$$f(x_1), f(x_2), \ldots, f(x_n).$$

The area of the region under the curve is approximated by the sum of the areas of the rectangles,

$$\sum_{i=1}^{n} f(x_i)\, \Delta x.$$

We now obtain the actual area by letting the number of intervals increase indefinitely and by taking the limit. The area is thus given by

$$A = \lim_{n \to \infty} \sum_{i=1}^{n} f(x_i)\, \Delta x.$$

By the Fundamental Theorem of Integral Calculus, the area is also given by a definite integral. Thus we have

$$\int_a^b f(x)\, dx = \lim_{n \to \infty} \sum_{i=1}^{n} f(x_i)\, \Delta x.$$

It is interesting to envision that as we take the limit on the right, the summation sign stretches into something reminiscent of an S (the integral sign) and the Δx becomes dx. This is also a motivation for the use of dx in the integral notation.

This result allows us to approximate the value of a definite integral by a sum, making it as good as we please by taking n sufficiently large.

Example 1   Raggs, Ltd., determines that the marginal cost per suit is

$$C'(x) = 0.0003x^2 - 0.2x + 50.$$

Approximate the total cost of producing 400 suits by computing the sum $\sum_{i=1}^{4} C'(x_i)\, \Delta x.$

73. In reference to Example 1 find

$$\sum_{i=1}^{8} C'(x_i) \, \Delta x,$$

where the interval $[0, 400]$ is divided into 8 equal subintervals of length

$$\Delta x = \frac{400 - 0}{8} = 50.$$

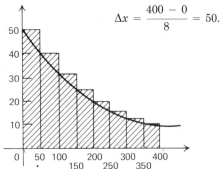

74. In (a) and (b) compute the areas of each rectangle to four decimal places. Then add them to approximate the area under the curve $y = \dfrac{1}{x}$ over $[1, 7]$.

a)

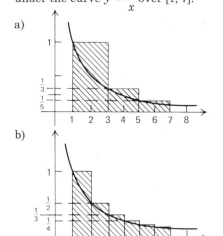

b)

c) Evaluate $\displaystyle\int_1^7 \frac{1}{x} \, dx$. Find this answer in Table 3 and compare it to (a) and (b). [*Note*: Table 3 contains approximations of natural logarithms accurate to four decimal places. Table 3 could be constructed using procedures like those in (a) and (b).]

Solution The interval $[0, 400]$ is divided into 4 subintervals, each of length $\Delta x = \dfrac{400 - 0}{4} = 100$. Now x_i is varying from $x_1 = 0$ to $x_5 = 400$.

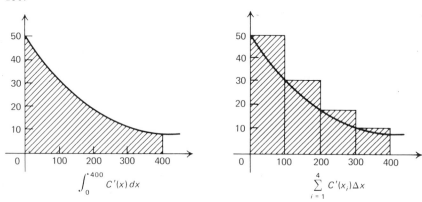

$$\sum_{i=1}^{4} C'(x_i) \, \Delta x = C'(0) \cdot 100 + C'(100) \cdot 100 + C'(200) \cdot 100 + C'(300) \cdot 100$$
$$= 50 \cdot 100 + 33 \cdot 100 + 22 \cdot 100 + 17 \cdot 100$$
$$= \$12,200$$

Now

$$\int_0^{400} C'(x) \, dx = \$10,400. \text{ (See Example 3 on p. 266.)}$$

Thus this approximation is not too far off, even though the number of subintervals is small. In Margin Exercise 73 you will obtain a better approximation using 8 subintervals.

___

Do Exercises 73 and 74.

The fact that an integral can be approximated by a sum is useful when the antiderivative of a function does not have an elementary formula. For example, for the function $e^{-x^2/2}$, important in probability, there is no formula for the antiderivative. So, tables of approximate values of its integral have been computed using summation methods.

The Average Value of a Function

Suppose that

$$T = f(t)$$

is the temperature at time t recorded at a weather station on a certain day. The station uses a 24-hour clock, so the domain of the temperature function is the interval [0, 24].

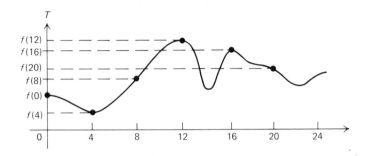

To find the average temperature for the given day, we might take six temperature readings at 4-hour intervals, starting at midnight:

$$T_0 = f(0), \quad T_1 = f(4), \quad T_2 = f(8), \quad T_3 = f(12), \quad T_4 = f(16), \quad T_5 = f(20).$$

The average reading would then be the sum of these six readings divided by 6:

$$T_{av} = \frac{T_0 + T_1 + T_2 + T_3 + T_4 + T_5}{6}.$$

This computation of the average temperature may not give the most useful answer: For example, suppose it is a hot summer day, and that at 2:00 in the afternoon (hour 14 on the 24-hour clock) there is a short thunderstorm that cools the air for an hour between our readings. This temporary dip would not show up in the average computed above. What can we do? We could take 48 readings at $\frac{1}{2}$-hour intervals. This should give a better result. In fact, the shorter the time between readings, the better the result should be. If we let the time interval approach 0, the result will be given by

$$\frac{1}{24} \int_0^{24} f(t)\, dt.$$

This is the *average value* of the function f over [0, 24].

> Let f be a continuous function over a closed interval [a, b]. Its *average value*, y_{av}, is given by
>
> $$y_{av} = \frac{1}{b - a} \int_a^b f(x)\, dx.$$

75. Find the average value of $f(x) = x^3$ over the interval $[0, 2]$.

Example 1   Find the average value of $f(x) = x^2$ over the interval $[0, 2]$.

Solution   The average value is

$$\frac{1}{2}\int_0^2 x^2\,dx = \frac{1}{2}\left[\frac{x^3}{3}\right]_0^2$$

$$= \frac{1}{2}\left(\frac{2^3}{3} - \frac{0^3}{3}\right)$$

$$= \frac{1}{2}\cdot\frac{8}{3}$$

$$= \frac{4}{3},\text{ or }1\tfrac{1}{3}$$

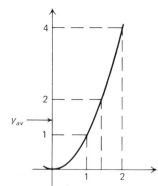

Note that while the values of $f(x)$ increase from 0 to 4, we would not expect the average value to be 2 because we see from the graph that $f(x)$ is less than 2 over more than half the interval.

Do Exercise 75.

Let us consider average value in another way. If we multiply on both sides of

$$y_{av} = \frac{1}{b-a}\int_a^b f(x)\,dx$$

by $b - a$, we get

$$(b-a)y_{av} = \int_a^b f(x)\,dx.$$

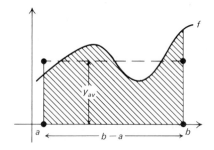

Now the expression on the left will give the area of a rectangle of length $b - a$ and height y_{av}. The area of such a rectangle is the same as the area bounded by $y = f(x)$ on the interval $[a, b]$.

Example 2   The emissions of an engine are given by

$$E(t) = 2t^2,$$

where $E(t)$ = emissions in billions of pollution particulates at time t, in years. Find the average emissions from $t = 1$ to $t = 5$.

Solution   The average emissions are

$$\frac{1}{5-1}\int_1^5 2t^2\, dt = \frac{1}{4}\left[\frac{2}{3}t^3\right]_1^5 = \frac{1}{4}\cdot\frac{2}{3}(5^3 - 1^3) = \frac{1}{6}(125 - 1)$$
$$= 20\tfrac{2}{3}\ \text{billion pollution particulates.}$$

Do Exercise 76.

76. The sales of a company are expected to grow according to the function

$$S(t) = 100t + t^2,$$

where $S(t)$ = sales, in dollars, on the tth day. Find the average sales from $t = 1$ to $t = 4$ (from the 1st to the 4th day).

EXERCISE SET 5.7

1. a) Approximate $\int_1^7 \dfrac{dx}{x^2}$ by computing the area of each rectangle to four decimal places and adding.

   b) Evaluate $\int_1^7 \dfrac{dx}{x^2}$. Compare the answer to (a).

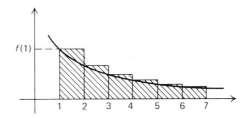

2. a) Approximate $\int_0^5 (x^2 + 1)\, dx$ by computing the area of each rectangle and adding.

   b) Evaluate $\int_0^5 (x^2 + 1)\, dx$. Compare the answer to (a).

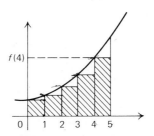

Find the average value over the given interval.

3. $y = 2x^3$; $[-1, 1]$ **4.** $y = 4 - x^2$; $[-2, 2]$ **5.** $y = e^x$; $[0, 1]$

6. $y = e^{-x}$; $[0, 1]$ **7.** $y = x^2 - x + 1$; $[0, 2]$ **8.** $y = x^2 + x - 2$; $[0, 4]$

9. $y = 3x + 1$; $[2, 6]$ **10.** $y = 4x + 1$; $[3, 7]$ **11.** $y = x^n$; $[0, 1]$ **12.** $y = x^n$; $[1, 2]$

13. A student's score on a test is a function

$$S(t) = t^2, \quad t \text{ in } [0, 10],$$

where $S(t)$ = score after t hours of study.

a) Find the maximum score the student can achieve and how many hours he must study to attain it.

b) Find the average score over the 10-hour interval.

14. A typist's speed over a 4-minute interval is given by

$$W(t) = -6t^2 + 12t + 90, \quad t \text{ in } [0, 4],$$

where $W(t)$ = speed in words per minute at time t.

a) Find the speed at the beginning of the interval.

b) Find the maximum speed and when it occurs.

c) Find the average speed over the 4-minute interval.

CHAPTER 5 TEST

Integrate.

1. $\int dx$

2. $\int 1000x^4 \, dx$

3. $\int \left(e^x + \dfrac{1}{x} + x^{3/8} \right) dx$

Find the area under the curve on the interval indicated.

4. $y = x - x^2$;   [0, 1]

5. $y = \dfrac{4}{x}$;   [1, 3]

6. Give two interpretations of the shaded area.

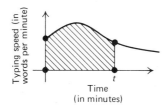

Integrate.

7. $\displaystyle\int_{-1}^{2} (2x + 3x^2) \, dx$

8. $\displaystyle\int_{0}^{1} e^{-2x} \, dx$

9. $\displaystyle\int_{a}^{b} \dfrac{dx}{x}$

Decide if $\displaystyle\int_{a}^{b} f(x) \, dx$ is positive, negative, or zero.

10.

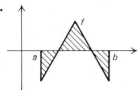

11.

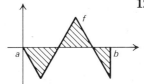

12.

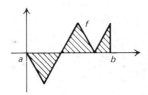

Integrate. Use substitution. Do not use Table 5.

13. $\int \dfrac{dx}{x + 8}$

14. $\int e^{-0.5x} \, dx$

15. $\int t^3 (t^4 + 1)^9 \, dt$

Integrate. Use integration by parts. Do not use Table 5.

16. $\int xe^{5x}\,dx$

17. $\int x^3 \ln x^4\,dx$

Integrate. Use Table 5.

18. $\int 2^x\,dx$

19. $\int \dfrac{dx}{x(7-x)}$

20. Find the average value of $y = 4t^3 + 2t$ over $[-1, 2]$.

21. Find the area of the region bounded by $y = x$ and $y = x^5$.

22. Approximate $\int_0^5 (25 - x^2)\,dx$, by computing the area of each rectangle and adding.

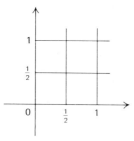

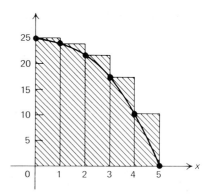

23. An air conditioning company determines that the marginal cost of the xth air conditioner is given by

$$C'(x) = -0.2x + 500, \quad C(0) = 0.$$

Find the total cost of producing 100 air conditioners.

24. A typist's speed over a 4-minute interval is given by

$$W(t) = -6t^2 + 12t + 90, \quad t \text{ in } [0, 4],$$

where

$W(t) =$ speed in words per minute at time t.

How many words does he type during the second minute (from $t = 1$ to $t = 2$)?

Assuming no new oil discoveries, when will the world reserves of oil be exhausted?

6 INTEGRATION AND APPLICATIONS

1. Evaluate.

$$\int_0^k 100e^{0.25t} \, dt$$

6.1 THE MODEL $\int_0^T P_0 e^{kt} \, dt$

In this chapter we will make frequent use of the integration formula

$$\int be^{ax} \, dx = \frac{b}{a} e^{ax} + C. \tag{1}$$

You should memorize it. It can be easily verified by differentiating the right-hand side and obtaining the integrand.

Example 1   Evaluate $\int_0^k 1000e^{0.08t} \, dt$.

Solution

$$\int_0^k 1000e^{0.08t} \, dt = \left[\frac{1000}{0.08} e^{0.08t} \right]_0^k = 12{,}500(e^{0.08k} - e^{0.08 \cdot 0})$$

$$= 12{,}500(e^{0.08k} - 1)$$

Do Exercise 1.

Recall the basic model of exponential growth (p. 220):

$$P'(t) = k \cdot P(t) \qquad \left(\text{or, } \frac{dP}{dt} = kP \right).$$

The solution of the equation is

$$P(t) = P_0 e^{kt}. \tag{2}$$

Thus $P(t)$ is an antiderivative of $kP_0 e^{kt}$, as we can see by using (1):

$$\int kP_0 e^{kt} \, dt = \frac{kP_0}{k} e^{kt} = P_0 e^{kt}.$$

One application of equation (2) is computing the balance in a savings account after t years, from an initial investment of P_0 at continuous interest rate k.

Example 2   Find the balance in a savings account after 3 years from an initial investment of $1000 at interest rate 8% compounded continuously.

Solution   Using equation (2) we have

$$P(3) = 1000e^{0.08(3)} = 1000e^{0.24} \approx 1000(1.2712) \qquad \text{(Table 4)}$$

$$= \$1271.20.$$

Do Exercise 2.

The Integral $\displaystyle\int_0^T P_0 e^{kt} \, dt$

Let us consider the integral of $P_0 e^{kt}$ over the interval $[0, T]$.

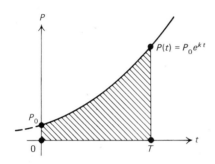

$$\int_0^T P_0 e^{kt} \, dt = \left[\frac{P_0}{k} \cdot e^{kt} \right]_0^T = \frac{P_0}{k} (e^{kT} - e^{k \cdot 0}) = \frac{P_0}{k} (e^{kT} - 1).$$

Thus

$$\int_0^T P_0 e^{kt} \, dt = \frac{P_0}{k} (e^{kT} - 1). \qquad \textbf{(3)}$$

Here is an application of this definite integral. In the case of $1000 compounded continuously at 8% over 3 years we have

$$\int_0^3 1000 e^{0.08t} \, dt = \left[\frac{1000}{0.08} e^{0.08t} \right]_0^3$$

$$= 12{,}500(e^{0.08 \cdot 3} - 1)$$

$$= 12{,}500(e^{0.24} - 1)$$

$$= 12{,}500(1.2712 - 1)$$

$$= 12{,}500(0.2712)$$

$$= \$3390.$$

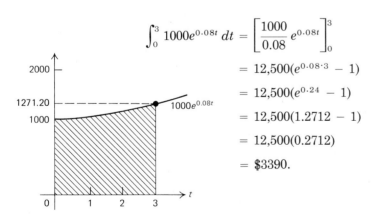

The \$3390 represents what economists call the *total money flow* over 3 years.

Do Exercise 3.

2. Find the balance in a savings account after 2 years from an initial investment of \$1000 at an interest rate of 7.5%, compounded continuously.

3. An initial investment of \$1000 is deposited in a savings account for 2 years at interest rate 7.5%, compounded continuously. Find the total money flow.

The Amount of an Annuity

An *annuity* is a series of equal payments made at equal time intervals. Rent payments are an example of an annuity. Deposits in a savings account can also be an annuity. For example, suppose a person makes a deposit of $1000 annually in a savings account on which interest is compounded continuously at 8%. The amount in the account at the end of a certain time is called the *amount of the annuity*. Let us find the amount of the given annuity for a period of 5 years. The following time diagram can help. Note that we do not consider a deposit at the end of the 5th year.

Each $1000 grows over a different time period. The total amount in the account after 5 years, the amount of the annuity, is given by

$$1000e^{0.08(5)} + 1000e^{0.08(4)} + 1000e^{0.08(3)} + 1000e^{0.08(2)} + 1000e^{0.08(1)}$$
$$= \$1491.80 + \$1377.13 + \$1271.25 + \$1173.51 + \$1083.29$$
$$= \$6396.98.$$

The amount of an annuity is also the sum

$$\sum_{i=1}^{5} 1000e^{0.08t_i} \, \Delta t,$$

where $\Delta t = 1$, $t_1 = 5$ and $t_5 = 1$. This sum can be *approximated* by integrating the function $1000e^{0.08t}$ over the interval $[0, 5]$:

$$\int_0^5 1000e^{0.08t} \, dt = \left[\frac{1000}{0.08} e^{0.08t} \right]_0^5 = 12{,}500(e^{0.08 \cdot 5} - e^{0.08 \cdot 0})$$
$$= 12{,}500(e^{0.4} - 1)$$
$$= 12{,}500(1.4918 - 1)$$
$$= \$6147.50.$$

This is very close to the actual amount of the annuity. Note here that the integral provides an approximation to a sum, in contrast to a sum approximating an integral.

In general,

> The *amount of an annuity,* where P_0 dollars per year is being invested at interest rate k, compounded continuously, over T years is approximated by
>
> $$A_T = \frac{P_0}{k}\,(e^{kT} - 1).$$

Example 3   Find the amount of an annuity where $1000 per year is being invested at 8%, compounded continuously, for 15 years.

Solution

$$A_{15} = \frac{1000}{0.08}\,(e^{0.08(15)} - 1) = 12{,}500(e^{1.2} - 1)$$

$$= 12{,}500(3.3201 - 1)$$
$$= \$29{,}001.25$$

Do Exercise 4.

Example 4   What annual payment P_0 should be made so the amount of an annuity over 20 years at interest rate 8%, compounded continuously, will be $10,000?

Solution   We find P_0 such that

$$10{,}000 = \frac{P_0}{0.08}\,(e^{0.08(20)} - 1).$$

Solving, we get

$$800 = P_0(e^{1.6} - 1)$$
$$800 = P_0(4.9530 - 1)$$
$$800 = P_0(3.9530)$$
$$\$202.98 = P_0.$$

Do Exercise 5.

4. Find the amount of an annuity where $2000 per year is being invested at 7.5%, compounded continuously, for 10 years.

5. What annual payment P_0 should be made so that the amount of an annuity over 20 years at interest rate 7.5%, compounded continuously, will be $10,000?

6. *The demand for oil.* In 1973 ($t = 0$) the world use of oil was

20,300 million barrels,

and the demand for it was growing exponentially at the rate of

10% per year.

If the demand continues at this rate, how many barrels of oil will the world use from 1973 to 1983?

Depletion of Natural Resources

Another application of the integral of exponential growth concerns

$$P(t) = P_0 e^{kt}$$

as a model of the demand for natural resources. Suppose P_0 represents the amount of a natural resource (such as coal, oil, and so on) used at time $t = 0$, and suppose the growth rate for the use of this resource is k. Then, assuming exponential growth (which is the case for many resources), the amount to be used at time t is $P(t)$, given by

$$P(t) = P_0 e^{kt}.$$

The total amount used during an interval $[0, T]$ is given by

$$\int_0^T P_0 e^{kt}\, dt = \frac{P_0}{k}\, (e^{kT} - 1). \qquad (4)$$

Example 5   *The demand for copper.* In 1973 ($t = 0$) the world use of copper was

7,700,000 tons,

and the demand for it was growing exponentially at the rate of 8% per year. If the growth continues at this rate, how many tons of copper will the world use from 1973 to 1983?

Solution   Using equation (4), we have

$$\int_0^{10} 7{,}700{,}000 e^{0.08t}\, dt = \frac{7{,}700{,}000}{0.08}\, (e^{0.08 \cdot 10} - 1)$$

$$= 96{,}250{,}000(e^{0.8} - 1)$$

$$= 96{,}250{,}000(2.2255 - 1) \qquad \text{(Table 4)}$$

$$= 96{,}250{,}000(1.2255)$$

$$= 117{,}954{,}375$$

Thus from 1973 to 1983 the world will use 117,954,375 tons of copper.

Do Exercise 6.

Example 6   *The depletion of copper.* The world reserves of copper are

370,000,000 tons.

Assuming the growth rate in Example 5 continues and that no new reserves are discovered, when will the world reserves of copper be exhausted?

7. *The depletion of oil.* The world reserves of oil are

625,200 million barrels.

In 1973 ($t = 0$) the world use of oil was

20,300 million barrels,

and the growth rate for the use of oil was 10%. Assuming this growth rate continues and that no new reserves are discovered, when will the world reserves of oil be exhausted?

Solution   Using equation (4) we want to find T such that

$$370,000,000 = \frac{7,700,000}{0.08}(e^{0.08T} - 1).$$

We solve for T as follows:

$370,000,000 = 96,250,000(e^{0.08T} - 1)$

$\dfrac{370,000,000}{96,250,000} = e^{0.08T} - 1$

$3.8 = e^{0.08T} - 1$ (Rounding to the nearest tenth)

$4.8 = e^{0.08T}$

$\ln 4.8 = \ln e^{0.08T}$ (Taking the natural logarithm on both sides)

$\ln 4.8 = 0.08T$ (Recall: $\ln e^k = k$.)

$\dfrac{\ln 4.8}{0.08} = T$

$\dfrac{1.5686}{0.08} = T$ (Table 3)

$20 = T.$ (Rounding to the nearest one)

Thus 20 years from 1973, or by 1993, the world reserves of copper will be exhausted.

Do Exercise 7.

EXERCISE SET 6.1

1. Find the amount in a savings account after 3 years from an initial investment of $100 at 9%, compounded continuously.

3. In Exercise 1, find the total money flow.

5. Find the amount of an annuity where $100 per year is being invested at 9%, compounded continuously, for 20 years.

7. What annual payment should be made so that the amount of an annuity over 30 years at interest rate 9%, compounded continuously, will be $40,000?

9. *The demand for aluminum ore.* In 1973 ($t = 0$) the world use of aluminum ore was

$$69,500,000 \text{ tons,}$$

and the demand for it was growing exponentially at the rate of 12% per year. If the demand continues to grow at this rate, how many tons of aluminum ore will the world use from 1973 to 1983?

11. *The depletion of aluminum ore.* The world reserves of aluminum ore are

$$15,500,000,000 \text{ tons.}$$

Assuming the growth rate of Exercise 9 continues and that no new reserves are discovered, when will the world reserves of aluminum ore be exhausted?

2. Find the amount in a savings account after 4 years from an initial investment of $100 at 10%, compounded continuously.

4. In Exercise 2, find the total money flow.

6. Find the amount of an annuity where $100 per year is being invested at 10%, compounded continuously, for 20 years.

8. What annual payment should be made so that the amount of an annuity over 30 years at interest rate 10%, compounded continuously, will be $40,000?

10. *The demand for natural gas.* In 1973 ($t = 0$) the world use of natural gas was

$$44,600 \text{ billion cubic feet,}$$

and the demand for it was growing exponentially at the rate of 4% per year. If the demand continues to grow at this rate, how many cubic feet of natural gas will the world use from 1973 to 1983?

12. *The depletion of natural gas.* The world reserves of natural gas are

$$1,897,000 \text{ billion cubic feet.}$$

Assuming the growth rate of Exercise 10 continues and that no new reserves are discovered, when will the world reserves of natural gas be exhausted?

OBJECTIVES

You should be able to find:

a) The present value of an investment due t years later at a certain interest rate, compounded continuously.
b) The capital value of a rental property.

6.2 THE MODEL $\int_0^T Pe^{-kt}\, dt$

A representative of a financial institution is often asked to solve a problem like the following.

Example 1   A parent, following the birth of a child, wants to make an initial investment of P_0 which will grow to $10,000 by the child's 20th birthday. Interest is compounded continuously at 8%. What should the initial investment be?

Solution   Using the equation $P = P_0 e^{kt}$, we find P_0 such that

$$10{,}000 = P_0 e^{0.08 \cdot 20},$$

or

$$10{,}000 = P_0 e^{1.6}.$$

Now

$$\frac{10{,}000}{e^{1.6}} = P_0,$$

or

$$10{,}000 e^{-1.6} = P_0,$$

and using Table 4 we have

$$P_0 = 10{,}000 e^{-1.6} = 10{,}000(0.2019) = \$2019.00.$$

Thus the parent must deposit \$2019.00 to grow to \$10,000 by the child's 20th birthday.

Economists call \$2019 the *present value* of \$10,000 due 20 years from now at 8% compounded continuously.*

Do Exercise 8.

In general, the present value P_0 of an amount P due t years later is found by solving the following equation for P_0:

$$P_0 e^{kt} = P,$$

$$P_0 = \frac{P}{e^{kt}} = Pe^{-kt}.$$

The *present value* of an amount P due t years later at interest rate k, compounded continuously, is given by

$$P_0 = Pe^{-kt}.$$

Note this can be interpreted as exponential decay from the future back to the present.

Do Exercise 9.

Suppose a person owns a rental property that earns \$100 a month. The going interest rate (amount being charged for loans or being paid for investments) is 9%, compounded continuously. The *capital*

8. A parent, following the birth of a child, wants to make an initial investment P_0 which will grow to \$10,000 by the child's 20th birthday. Interest is compounded continuously at 7.5%. What should this initial investment be?

9. Find the present value of \$40,000 due 5 years later at 10%, compounded continuously.

---

* The process of computing the present value is called *discounting*.

value of the property over some time period is the sum of all the present values of the rental payments. Thus for 6 months the capital value is found as follows:

Payment	Present value	
1	$100e^{-0.09(1/12)}$ =	$99.25
2	$100e^{-0.09(2/12)}$ =	98.51
3	$100e^{-0.09(3/12)}$ =	97.78
4	$100e^{-0.09(4/12)}$ =	97.04
5	$100e^{-0.09(5/12)}$ =	96.31
6	$100e^{-0.09(6/12)}$ =	95.60
	Capital value =	$584.49

Thus the capital value is the sum

$$\sum_{i=1}^{6} 100e^{-0.09t_i},$$

where $t_i = \dfrac{i}{12}$ and i runs from 1 to 6. Now $100 = 100 \cdot \dfrac{12}{12} = (100 \cdot 12) \cdot \dfrac{1}{12} = 1200 \cdot \frac{1}{12}$. So the preceding sum can be expressed as

$$\sum_{i=1}^{6} 1200e^{-0.09t_i} \, \Delta t, \quad \text{where} \quad \Delta t = \frac{1}{12}.$$

Now this sum can be approximated by integrating the function $1200e^{-0.09t}$ over the half-year interval $[0, 0.5]$. Now

$$\int_0^{0.5} 1200e^{-0.09t} \, dt = \left[\frac{1200}{-0.09} e^{-0.09t} \right]_0^{0.5}$$

$$= -13{,}333.33(e^{-0.09(0.5)} - e^{-0.09 \cdot 0})$$

$$= -13{,}333.33(0.9560 - 1)$$

$$= \$586.67$$

This is very close to the actual capital value.

In general, suppose a rental property has an annual rent of R dollars paid in n equal payments per year. The capital value of the property over some time T is given by

$$\sum_{i=1}^{nT} \frac{R}{n} e^{-kt_i},$$

where the payment $\dfrac{R}{n}$ is made at time t_i and the going interest rate is k, compounded continuously. This can be expressed as

$$\sum_{i=1}^{nT} R e^{-kt_i}\, \Delta t, \quad \text{where} \quad \Delta t = \frac{1}{n}.$$

This sum can be approximated by the definite integral

$$\int_0^T R e^{-kt}\, dt.$$

Evaluating this integral, we get

$$\int_0^T R e^{-kt}\, dt = \frac{R}{-k}\left(e^{-kT} - e^{-k\cdot 0}\right) = \frac{R}{k}\left(1 - e^{-kT}\right).$$

The **capital value** of a property over T years is approximated by

$$\mathbf{A}_T = \frac{R}{k}\,(1 - e^{-kT}),$$

where R **is the annual rent, or income, and** k **is the going interest rate.**

Example 2 Find the capital value of a rental property over a 5-year period where the annual rent is \$2400 and the going interest rate is 8%.

Solution

$$A_5 = \frac{2400}{0.08}\,(1 - e^{-0.08\cdot 5}) = 30{,}000(1 - e^{-0.4})$$

$$= 30{,}000(1 - 0.6703)$$

$$= \$9891$$

Do Exercise 10.

The previous example is an application of the model

$$\int_0^T P e^{-kt}\, dt = \frac{P}{k}\,(1 - e^{-kT}).$$

Another application of this model is provided by the buildup of radioactive material in the atmosphere, when a certain amount is being released into the atmosphere annually. Some of the material decays, but more keeps being released. The amount present at time T is given by the above integral.

10. Find the capital value of a rental property over a 20-year period where the annual rent is \$1800 and the going interest rate is 10%.

EXERCISE SET 6.2

1. A parent, following the birth of a child, wants to make an initial investment P_0 which will grow to $5000 by the child's 20th birthday. Interest is compounded continuously at 9%. What should the initial investment be?

2. A parent, following the birth of a child, wants to make an initial investment P_0 which will grow to $5000 by the child's 20th birthday. Interest is compounded continuously at 10%. What should this initial investment be?

3. Find the present value of $60,000 due 8 years later at 5%, compounded continuously.

4. Find the present value of $50,000 due 16 years later at 5%, compounded continuously.

5. Find the capital value of a rental property over a 10-yr period where the annual rent is $2700 and the going interest rate is 9%.

6. Find the capital value of a rental property over a 10-yr period where the annual rent is $2700 and the going interest rate is 10%.

7. A woman accepts the position of president of a company at the age of 35. Assuming she retires at the age of 65 and that her annual salary is $45,000, what is her capital value? The going interest rate is 8%.

8. A man takes a job as a truck driver at the age of 25. Assuming he retires at the age of 65 and that his annual salary is $14,000, what is his capital value? The going interest rate is 7%.

OBJECTIVES

You should be able to determine whether an improper integral is convergent or divergent, and calculate its value if convergent.

6.3 IMPROPER INTEGRALS

Let us try to find the area of the region under the graph of $y = \dfrac{1}{x^2}$ on the interval $[1, \infty)$.

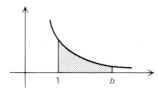 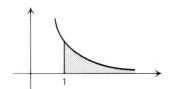

Note that this region is of infinite extent. We have not yet considered how to find the area of such a region. Let us find the area under the curve on the interval from 1 to b, and then see what happens as b gets very large. The area on $[1, b]$ is

$$\int_1^b \frac{dx}{x^2} = \left[-\frac{1}{x}\right]_1^b = \left(-\frac{1}{b}\right) - \left(-\frac{1}{1}\right) = -\frac{1}{b} + 1 = 1 - \frac{1}{b}.$$

Then

$$\lim_{b\to\infty} [\text{area from 1 to } b] = \lim_{b\to\infty}\left(1 - \frac{1}{b}\right).$$

Let us investigate this limit.

Do Exercise 11.

Note that as $b \to \infty$, $\frac{1}{b} \to 0$, so $\left(1 - \frac{1}{b}\right) \to 1$. Thus

$$\lim_{b \to \infty} [\text{area from 1 to } b] = \lim_{b \to \infty} \left(1 - \frac{1}{b}\right) = 1.$$

We *define* the area from 1 to ∞ to be this limit. Here we have an example of an infinitely long region with a finite area.

Do Exercise 12.

Such areas may not always be finite. Let us try to find the area of the region under the graph of $y = \frac{1}{x}$ on the interval $[1, \infty)$.

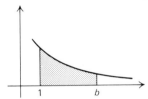 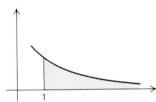

By definition, the area A from 1 to ∞ is the limit as $b \to \infty$ of the area from 1 to b, so

$$A = \lim_{b \to \infty} \int_1^b \frac{dx}{x} = \lim_{b \to \infty} [\ln x]_1^b = \lim_{b \to \infty} (\ln b - \ln 1) = \lim_{b \to \infty} \ln b.$$

On p. 210 of Chapter 4 we can see that since $\ln b$ increases indefinitely as b increases, this limit does not exist.

Thus we have an infinitely long region with an infinite area. Note that the graphs of $y = \frac{1}{x^2}$ and $y = \frac{1}{x}$ have similar shapes, but the region under one of them has a finite area and the other does not.

Do Exercise 13.

An integral such as

$$\int_a^\infty f(x)\, dx, \quad \text{with an upper limit of } \infty,$$

is called an *improper integral*. Its value is defined to be the following limit.

$$\int_a^\infty f(x)\, dx = \lim_{b \to \infty} \int_a^b f(x)\, dx$$

11. Complete.

b	$1 - \dfrac{1}{b}$
2	$1 - \frac{1}{2}$, or $\frac{1}{2}$
3	
10	
100	
200	

12. Find the area of the region under the graph of $y = \frac{1}{x^2}$ on the interval $[2, \infty)$.

13. Find the area under the graph of $y = \frac{1}{x}$ from $x = 2$ to $x = \infty$.

Determine whether each of the following improper integrals is convergent or divergent, and calculate its value if convergent.

14. $\int_0^\infty 5e^{-5x}\,dx$

15. $\int_0^\infty 2x\,dx$

If the limit exists, then we say that the improper integral *converges*. If the limit does not exist, we say that the improper integral *diverges*. Thus

$$\int_1^\infty \frac{dx}{x^2} = 1 \quad converges; \text{ and} \quad \int_1^\infty \frac{dx}{x} = \infty \quad diverges.$$

Example

$$\int_0^\infty 2e^{-2x}\,dx = \lim_{b\to\infty} \int_0^b 2e^{-2x}\,dx = \lim_{b\to\infty} [2(-\tfrac{1}{2})e^{-2x}]_0^b$$

$$= \lim_{b\to\infty} [-e^{-2x}]_0^b$$

$$= \lim_{b\to\infty} [-e^{-2b} - (-e^{-2\cdot0})]$$

$$= \lim_{b\to\infty} (-e^{-2b} + 1)$$

$$= \lim_{b\to\infty} \left(1 - \frac{1}{e^{2b}}\right)$$

Now as $b \to \infty$, $e^{2b} \to \infty$ (from Chapter 4), so $\dfrac{1}{e^{2b}} \to 0$ and $\left(1 - \dfrac{1}{e^{2b}}\right) \to 1$. Thus

$$\int_0^\infty 2e^{-2x}\,dx = 1. \qquad \text{(The integral is convergent)}$$

Do Exercises 14 and 15.

The following are definitions of two other types of improper integrals.

$$\int_{-\infty}^b f(x)\,dx = \lim_{a\to-\infty} \int_a^b f(x)\,dx$$

$$\int_{-\infty}^\infty f(x)\,dx = \int_{-\infty}^c f(x)\,dx + \int_c^\infty f(x)\,dx$$

For $\int_{-\infty}^\infty f(x)\,dx$ to converge, both integrals on the right above must converge.

Applications

In Section 6.2 we learned that the capital value of a rental property over T years is approximated by

$$A_T = \int_0^T Re^{-kt}\,dt = \frac{R}{k}(1 - e^{-kT}),$$

where R is the annual rent and k is the going interest rate. Suppose that the rent is paid perpetually. Then under this assumption the capital value over this infinite time period would be

$$\lim_{T \to \infty} A_T = \int_0^\infty Re^{-kt}\, dt = \lim_{T \to \infty} \int_0^T Re^{-kt}\, dt = \lim_{T \to \infty} \frac{R}{k}(1 - e^{-kT})$$

$$= \lim_{T \to \infty} \frac{R}{k}\left(1 - \frac{1}{e^{kT}}\right)$$

$$= \frac{R}{k}.$$

The capital value of a property for which the annual rent, or income, is being paid, or received, perpetually is

$$\frac{R}{k},$$

where k is the going interest rate compounded continuously.

Example   An annual rent of $2000 is being paid for a property for which there is a permanent lease. The going interest rate is 8%. Find the capital value.

Solution   The capital value is $\dfrac{2000}{0.08}$, or $25,000.

Do Exercise 16.

When an amount P of radioactive material is being released into the atmosphere annually, the amount present at time T is given by

$$A_T = \int_0^T Pe^{-kt}\, dt = \frac{P}{k}(1 - e^{-kT}).$$

As $T \to \infty$ (the radioactivity is to be released forever), $A_T \to \dfrac{P}{k}$. That is, the buildup of radioactive material approaches a limiting value $\dfrac{P}{k}$.

$A_T = \frac{P}{k}(1 - e^{-kt})$

16. An annual rent of $2400 is being paid for a property for which there is a permanent lease. The going interest rate is 12%. Find the capital value.

EXERCISE SET 6.3

Determine whether each of the following improper integrals is convergent or divergent, and calculate its value if convergent.

1. $\int_3^\infty \dfrac{dx}{x^2}$ **2.** $\int_4^\infty \dfrac{dx}{x^2}$ **3.** $\int_3^\infty \dfrac{dx}{x}$ **4.** $\int_4^\infty \dfrac{dx}{x}$

5. $\int_0^\infty 3e^{-3x}\,dx$ **6.** $\int_0^\infty 4e^{-4x}\,dx$ **7.** $\int_1^\infty \dfrac{dx}{x^3}$ **8.** $\int_1^\infty \dfrac{dx}{x^4}$

9. $\int_0^\infty \dfrac{dx}{1+x}$ **10.** $\int_0^\infty \dfrac{4\,dx}{1+x}$ **11.** $\int_1^\infty 5x^{-2}\,dx$ **12.** $\int_1^\infty 7x^{-2}\,dx$

13. $\int_0^\infty e^x\,dx$ **14.** $\int_0^\infty e^{2x}\,dx$ **15.** $\int_3^\infty x^2\,dx$ **16.** $\int_5^\infty x^4\,dx$

17. $\int_0^\infty xe^x\,dx$ **18.** $\int_0^\infty \ln x\,dx$ **19.** $\int_0^\infty me^{-mx}\,dx,\quad m>0$ **20.** $\int_0^\infty ke^{-kx}\,dx,\quad k>0$

21. $\int_0^\infty Be^{-kt}\,dt,\quad k>0$ **22.** $\int_0^\infty Qe^{-kt}\,dt,\quad k>0$

23. An annual rent of \$3600 is being paid for a property for which there is a permanent lease. The going interest rate is 12%. Find the capital value.

24. An annual rent of \$4500 is being paid for a property for which there is a permanent lease. The going interest rate is 9%. Find the capital value.

OBJECTIVES

You should be able to:

a) Verify that a given function satisfies the property

$$\int_a^b f(x)\,dx = 1,$$

for being a probability density function.

b) Find k such that a function like

$$f(x) = kx^2$$

is a probability density function over an interval $[a, b]$.

c) Solve applied problems involving probability density functions.

6.4 PROBABILITY

The definite integral plays a role in the theory of probability. Briefly, the *probability* of an event is a number from 0 to 1 which represents its chances of occurring. It is the "relative frequency" of occurrence—the percentage of times an event will occur in a large number of trials.

Example 1   What is the probability of drawing an ace from a well-shuffled deck of cards?

Solution   Since there are 52 possible outcomes, and each card has the same chance of being drawn, and there are 4 aces, the probability of drawing an ace is

$$\tfrac{4}{52}, \quad \text{or}\quad \tfrac{1}{13}, \quad \text{or about}\quad 7.7\%.$$

Owen Franken from Stock, Boston

A desire to calculate odds in games gave rise to the theory of probability.

In practice we may not draw an ace 7.7% of the time, but in a large number of trials, after shuffling the cards and drawing one, shuffling the cards and drawing one, we would expect to get an ace about 7.7% of the time. That is, the more draws we make, the closer we get to the 7.7%.

Example 2   A bag contains 7 black balls, 6 yellow balls, 4 green balls, and 3 red balls. The bag is shaken well and 1 ball is removed without looking. What is the probability that it is red? white?

Solution   There are 20 balls altogether and of these 3 are red, so the probability of drawing a red ball is $\frac{3}{20}$. There are no white balls, so the probability of drawing a white one is $\frac{0}{20}$, or 0.

Do Exercises 17 and 18.

17. In Example 2, what is the probability that the ball is
a) black?   b) yellow?
c) green?   d) chartreuse?

18. Consider this dartboard.

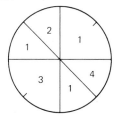

You throw a dart at the board without aiming at any particular region. What is the probability that you will score a

a) 1?   b) 2?
c) 3?   d) 4?

Let us consider a table of probabilities from Example 2.

Color	Probability
Black (B)	$\frac{7}{20}$
Yellow (Y)	$\frac{6}{20}$
Green (G)	$\frac{4}{20}$
Red (R)	$\frac{3}{20}$

Note that the sum of these probabilities is 1. We are certain that we will draw either a black, yellow, green, or blue ball. The probability of that event is 1. Let us arrange this data from the table into what is called a frequency graph. It shows the fraction of times each event occurs (the probability of each event).

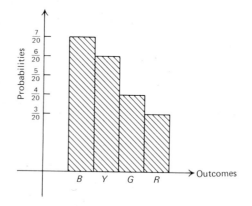

If we assign a width of 1 to each rectangle, then the sum of the areas of the rectangles is 1.

Continuous Random Variables

Suppose we throw a dart at a number line in such a way that it always lands in the interval [1, 3].

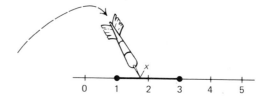

Let x be the number that the dart hits. Note that x is a quantity which can be observed (or measured) repeatedly and whose possible values consist of an entire interval of real numbers. Such a variable is called a *continuous random variable*. Suppose we throw the dart a large number of times and it lands in the subinterval [1.6, 2.8] 43% of the time. Then the probability that the dart lands in that interval is 0.43.

Let us consider some other examples of continuous random variables.

Example 1 Suppose x is the arrival time of buses at a bus stop in a three-hour period from 2 P.M. to 5 P.M. The interval is [2, 5].

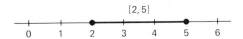

Then x is a continuous random variable distributed over the interval [2, 5].

Example 2 Suppose x is the corn acreage of each farm in the U.S. and Canada. The interval is [0, a], where a is the highest acreage. Or, not knowing what the highest acreage might be, the interval might be [0, ∞) to allow for all possibilities.

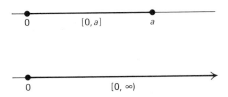

[*Note*: It might be argued that some values in [0, a] or [0, ∞) are not taken on by any farm, but for practical purposes this is often disregarded.]

Then x is a continuous random variable distributed over the interval [0, a], or [0, ∞).

Do Exercise 19.

Suppose, considering Example 1 on the arrival times of buses, that we wanted to know the probability that a bus will arrive between 4 P.M. and 5 P.M., as represented by

$$P([4, 5]), \quad \text{or} \quad P(4 \leqslant x \leqslant 5).$$

19. Suppose
a) x is the dosage of a drug from 15 milligrams to 25 milligrams. What interval is determined?
b) x is the distance between successive cars on a highway. What interval is determined?

20. Find the probability that a bus will arrive between 2:30 P.M. and 4:30 P.M.

In some cases it is possible to find a function over $[2, 5]$ such that areas over subintervals give the probabilities that a bus will arrive during these subintervals. For example, suppose we had a constant function $f(x) = \frac{1}{3}$ which will give us these probabilities. Look at its graph.

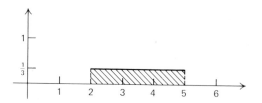

The area under the curve is $3 \cdot \frac{1}{3}$, or 1. The probability that a bus will arrive between 4 P.M. and 5 P.M. is that fraction of the large area which lies over the interval $[4, 5]$. That is,

$$P([4, 5]) = \tfrac{1}{3} = 33\tfrac{1}{3}\%.$$

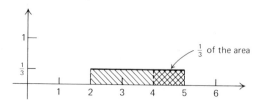

The probability that a bus will arrive between 2:00 P.M. and 4:30 P.M. is $\frac{5}{6}$, or $83\frac{1}{3}\%$.

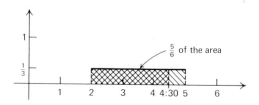

Do Exercise 20.

Note that any interval of length 1 has probability $\frac{1}{3}$. This may not always happen. Suppose we have a function

$$f(x) = \frac{3}{117} x^2$$

whose definite integral over the interval $[4, 5]$ would yield the probability that a bus will arrive between 4 P.M. and 5 P.M. Then

$$P([4, 5]) = \int_4^5 f(x) \, dx = \int_4^5 \frac{3}{117} x^2 \, dx$$

$$= \left[\frac{3}{117} \cdot \frac{1}{3} x^3 \right]_4^5$$

$$= \frac{1}{117} (5^3 - 4^3)$$

$$= \frac{61}{117} \approx 0.52.$$

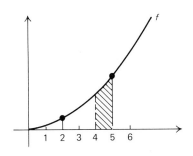

Thus 52% of the time you will be able to catch a bus between 4 P.M. and 5 P.M. The function f is called a *probability density function*. Its integral over *any* subinterval gives the probability that x "lands" in that subinterval.

Let x be a continuous random variable distributed over some interval $[a, b]$. A function f is said to be a *probability density function* for x if

1. f is nonnegative over $[a, b]$, that is, $f(x) \geqslant 0$ for all x in $[a, b]$;

2. for any subinterval $[c, d]$ of $[a, b]$, the probability $P([c, d])$, or $P(c \leqslant x \leqslant d)$, that x lands in that subinterval is given by

$$P([c, d]) = \int_c^d f(x) \, dx; \quad \text{and}$$

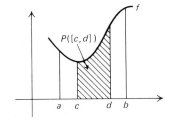
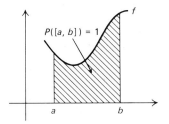

3. the probability that x lands in $[a, b]$ is 1:

$$\int_a^b f(x) \, dx = 1.$$

21. Verify property 3 of the definition of a probability density function for

$$f(x) = \tfrac{2}{3}x \quad \text{over } [1, 2].$$

That is, we are "certain" that x is in the interval $[a, b]$.

Example 1   Verify property 3 of the above definition for

$$f(x) = \frac{3}{117}\, x^2.$$

Solution   The "big" interval under consideration is $[2, 5]$. So

$$\int_2^5 \frac{3}{117} x^2 \, dx = \left[\frac{3}{117} \cdot \frac{1}{3} x^3 \right]_2^5 = \frac{1}{117}(5^3 - 2^3) = \frac{117}{117} = 1.$$

Do Exercise 21.

---

22. In reference to Example 2,
a) Verify property 3 of the definition of a probability density function.

Example 2   A company produces transistors. It determines that the life t of a transistor is from 3 to 6 years and that the probability density function for t is given by

$$f(t) = \frac{24}{t^3}, \quad \text{for} \quad 3 \leqslant t \leqslant 6.$$

a) Find the probability that a transistor will last no more than 4 years.
b) Find the probability that a transistor will last from 4 to 5 years.

b) Find the probability that a transistor will last no more than 5 years.

Solution
a) The probability that a transistor will last no more than 4 years is

$$P(3 \leqslant t \leqslant 4) = \int_3^4 \frac{24}{t^3}\, dt = \left[24\left(-\frac{1}{2}t^{-2}\right)\right]_3^4 = \left[-\frac{12}{t^2}\right]_3^4 = -12\left(\frac{1}{4^2} - \frac{1}{3^2}\right)$$

$$= -12\left(\frac{1}{16} - \frac{1}{9}\right) = -12\left(-\frac{7}{144}\right) = \frac{7}{12} \approx 0.58.$$

b) The probability that a transistor will last from 4 to 5 years is

$$P(4 \leqslant t \leqslant 5) = \int_4^5 \frac{24}{t^3}\, dt = \left[24\left(-\frac{1}{2}t^{-2}\right)\right]_4^5 = \left[-\frac{12}{t^2}\right]_4^5 = -12\left(\frac{1}{5^2} - \frac{1}{4^2}\right)$$

c) Find the probability that a transistor will last from 4 to 6 years.

$$= -12\left(\frac{1}{25} - \frac{1}{16}\right) = -12\left(-\frac{9}{400}\right) = \frac{27}{100} = 0.27.$$

Do Exercise 22.

Constructing Probability Density Functions

Suppose you have an arbitrary nonnegative function $f(x)$ whose definite integral over some interval $[a, b]$ is K. Then

$$\int_a^b f(x)\, dx = K.$$

Now multiply on both sides by $\dfrac{1}{K}$.

$$\frac{1}{K} \int_a^b f(x)\, dx = \frac{1}{K} \cdot K = 1$$

Or,

$$\int_a^b \frac{1}{K} \cdot f(x)\, dx = 1.$$

Thus when we multiply the function $f(x)$ by $\dfrac{1}{K}$ we have a function whose area over the given interval is 1.

Example   Find k such that

$$f(x) = kx^2$$

is a probability density function over the interval $[2, 5]$.

Solution

$$\int_2^5 x^2\, dx = \left[\frac{x^3}{3}\right]_2^5 = \frac{5^3}{3} - \frac{2^3}{5} = \frac{125}{3} - \frac{8}{3} = \frac{117}{3}$$

Thus $k = \dfrac{1}{\frac{117}{3}} = \dfrac{3}{117}$, and $f(x) = \dfrac{3}{117} x^2.$

Do Exercises 23 and 24.

Uniform Distributions

Suppose the probability density function of a continuous random variable is constant. How is it described? Consider the following graph.

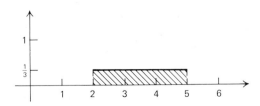

23. Find k such that

$$f(x) = kx^2$$

is a probability density function over the interval $[1, 3]$.

24. Find k such that

$$f(x) = kx^3$$

is a probability density function over the interval $[0, 1]$.

25. A number x is selected at random from the interval $[7, 15]$. The probability density function for x is given by

$$f(x) = \tfrac{1}{8}, \quad \text{for} \quad 7 \leqslant x \leqslant 15.$$

Find the probability that a number selected is in the subinterval $[11, 13]$.

The length of the shaded rectangle is the length of the interval $[2, 5]$ which is 3. For the shaded area to be 1, the height of the rectangle must be $\tfrac{1}{3}$. Thus $f(x) = \tfrac{1}{3}$. For the general case consider the following graph.

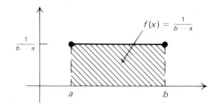

The length of the shaded rectangle is the length of the interval $[a, b]$ which is $b - a$. For the shaded area to be 1, the height of the rectangle must be $\dfrac{1}{b - a}$. Thus $f(x) = \dfrac{1}{b - a}$.

A continuous random variable x is said to be **_uniformly distributed_** over an interval $[a, b]$ if it has a probability density function f given by

$$f(x) = \frac{1}{b - a}, \quad \text{for} \quad a \leqslant x \leqslant b.$$

Example 1   A number x is selected at random from the interval $[40, 50]$. The probability density function for x is given by

$$f(x) = \tfrac{1}{10}, \quad \text{for} \quad 40 \leqslant x \leqslant 50.$$

Find the probability that a number selected is in the subinterval $[42, 48]$.

Solution   The probability is

$$P(42 \leqslant x \leqslant 48) = \int_{42}^{48} \tfrac{1}{10} \, dx = \tfrac{1}{10}[x]_{42}^{48} = \tfrac{1}{10}(48 - 42) = \tfrac{6}{10} = 0.6.$$

Do Exercise 25.

Example 2   A company produces guitars for a rock concert. The maximum loudness L of the guitars ranges from 70 to 100 decibels. The probability density for L is

$$f(L) = \tfrac{1}{30}, \quad \text{for} \quad 70 \leqslant L \leqslant 100.$$

A guitar is selected at random off the assembly line. Find the probability that its maximum loudness is 70 to 92 decibels.

Jeff Albertson from Stock, Boston

Solution   The probability is

$$P(70 \leqslant L \leqslant 92) = \int_{70}^{92} \tfrac{1}{30} \, dL = \tfrac{1}{30}[L]_{70}^{92} = \tfrac{1}{30}(92 - 70) = \tfrac{22}{30} = \tfrac{11}{15} \approx 0.73.$$

Do Exercise 26.

Exponential Distributions

The duration of a phone call, the distance between successive cars on a highway, and the amount of time required to learn a task are all examples of exponentially distributed random variables. That is, their probability density functions are exponential.

> A continuous random variable is *exponentially distributed* if it has a probability density function given by
>
> $$f(x) = ke^{-kx}, \quad \text{over the interval } [0, \infty).$$

The function

$$f(x) = 2e^{-2x}$$

is such a probability density function. That

$$\int_{0}^{\infty} 2e^{-2x} \, dx = 1$$

is shown in Section 6.3. The verification for the general case

$$\int_{0}^{\infty} ke^{-kx} \, dx = 1$$

can be done in a similar way.

26. A person arrives at a bus stop. The waiting time t for a bus is 0 to 20 minutes. The probability density function for t is

$$f(t) = \tfrac{1}{20}, \quad \text{for} \quad 0 \leqslant t \leqslant 20.$$

What is the probability that the person will have to wait no more than 5 minutes for a bus?

27. A transportation planner determines that the average distance between cars on a certain stretch of highway is 125 ft. What is the probability that the distance between cars is 50 ft or less?

Stock, Boston

Why is it reasonable to assume that distance between cars is exponentially distributed? This is because there are many more cases in which distances are small. The same argument holds for the duration of a phone call. That is, there are more short calls than long ones.

Example 1 *Transportation planning.* The distance x, in feet, between successive cars on a certain stretch of highway has probability density function

$$f(x) = ke^{-kx}, \quad \text{for} \quad 0 \leqslant x < \infty,$$

where $k = \dfrac{1}{a}$ and a = average distance between successive cars over some period of time.

A transportation planner determines that the average distance between cars on a certain stretch of highway is 166 ft. What is the probability that the distance between cars is 50 ft or less?

Solution   We first determine k.

$$k = \tfrac{1}{166} \approx 0.006$$

The probability density function for x is

$$f(x) = 0.006e^{-0.006x}, \quad \text{for} \quad 0 \leqslant x < \infty.$$

The probability that the distance between cars is 50 ft or less is

$$
\begin{aligned}
P(0 \leqslant x \leqslant 50) &= \int_0^{50} 0.006e^{-0.006x}\, dx \\
&= \left[\frac{0.006}{-0.006} e^{-0.006x} \right]_0^{50} \\
&= \left[-e^{-0.006x} \right]_0^{50} \\
&= \left(-e^{-0.006 \cdot 50} \right) - \left(-e^{0.006 \cdot 0} \right) \\
&= -e^{-0.3} + 1 \\
&= 1 - e^{-0.3} \\
&= 1 - 0.7408 \qquad \text{(Table 4)} \\
&= 0.2592
\end{aligned}
$$

Do Exercise 27.

EXERCISE SET 6.4

Verify property 3 of the definition of a probability density function over the given interval.

1. $f(x) = 2x$, $[0, 1]$

2. $f(x) = \frac{1}{4}x$, $[1, 3]$

3. $f(x) = \frac{1}{3}$, $[4, 7]$

4. $f(x) = \frac{1}{4}$, $[9, 13]$

5. $f(x) = \frac{3}{26}x^2$, $[1, 3]$

6. $f(x) = \frac{3}{64}x^2$, $[0, 4]$

7. $f(x) = \frac{1}{x}$, $[1, e]$

8. $f(x) = \frac{1}{e-1}e^x$, $[0, 1]$

9. $f(x) = \frac{3}{2}x^2$, $[-1, 1]$

10. $f(x) = \frac{1}{3}x^2$, $[-2, 1]$

11. $f(x) = 3e^{-3x}$, $[0, \infty)$

12. $f(x) = 4e^{-4x}$, $[0, \infty)$

Find k such that each function is a probability density function over the given interval.

13. $f(x) = kx$, $[1, 3]$

14. $f(x) = kx$, $[1, 4]$

15. $f(x) = kx^2$, $[-1, 1]$

16. $f(x) = kx^2$, $[-2, 2]$

17. $f(x) = k$, $[2, 7]$

18. $f(x) = k$, $[3, 9]$

19. $f(x) = k(2 - x)$, $[0, 2]$

20. $f(x) = k(4 - x)$, $[0, 4]$

21. $f(x) = \frac{k}{x}$, $[1, 3]$

22. $f(x) = \frac{k}{x}$, $[1, 2]$

23. $f(x) = ke^x$, $[0, 3]$

24. $f(x) = ke^x$, $[0, 2]$

25. A dart is thrown at a number line in such a way that it always lands in the interval $[0, 10]$. Let $x = $ the number the dart hits. Suppose the probability density function for x is given by

$$f(x) = \tfrac{1}{50}x, \quad \text{for} \quad 0 \leqslant x \leqslant 10.$$

Find $P(2 \leqslant x \leqslant 6)$, the probability that it lands in $[2, 6]$.

26. Suppose, in reference to Exercise 25, that the dart always lands in the interval $[0, 5]$, and that the probability density function for x is given by

$$f(x) = \tfrac{3}{125}x^2, \quad \text{for} \quad 0 \leqslant x \leqslant 5.$$

Find $P(1 \leqslant x \leqslant 4)$, the probability that it lands in $[1, 4]$.

27. A number x is selected at random from the interval $[4, 20]$. The probability density function for x is given by

$$f(x) = \tfrac{1}{16}, \quad \text{for} \quad 4 \leqslant x \leqslant 20.$$

Find the probability that a number selected is in the subinterval $[9, 17]$.

28. A number x is selected at random from the interval $[5, 29]$. The probability density function for x is given by

$$f(x) = \tfrac{1}{24}, \quad \text{for} \quad 5 \leqslant x \leqslant 29.$$

Find the probability that a number selected is in the subinterval $[13, 29]$.

29. A transportation planner determines that the average distance between cars on a certain highway is 100 ft. What is the probability that the distance between cars is 40 ft or less?

30. A transportation planner determines that the average distance between cars on a certain highway is 200 ft. What is the probability that the distance between cars is 10 ft or less?

31. A telephone company determines the duration t of a phone call is an exponentially distributed random variable with probability density function

$$f(t) = 2e^{-2t}, \quad 0 \leqslant t < \infty.$$

Find the probability that a phone call will last no more than 5 minutes.

32. In Exercise 31 find the probability that a phone call will last no more than 2 minutes.

33. In a psychology experiment, the time t, in seconds, that it takes a rat to learn its way through a maze is an exponentially distributed random variable with probability density function

$$f(t) = 0.02e^{-0.02t}, \quad 0 \leqslant t < \infty.$$

Find the probability that a rat will learn its way through a maze in 150 seconds, or less.

34. In Exercise 33 find the probability that a rat will learn its way through a maze in 50 seconds, or less.

35. *The time to failure t*, in hours, of a certain machine can often be assumed to be exponentially distributed with probability density function

$$f(t) = ke^{-kt}, \quad 0 \leqslant t < \infty$$

where $k = \dfrac{1}{a}$, and a = average time which will pass before a failure occurs. Suppose the average time that will pass before a failure occurs is 100 hours. What is the probability that a failure will occur in 50 hours, or less?

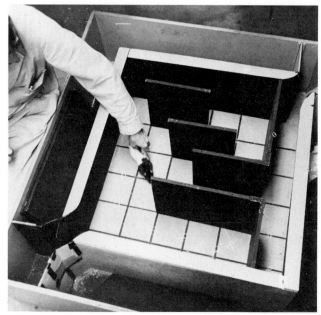

Sol Schwartz from Monkmeyer

36. The *reliability* of the machine (probability that it will work) in Exercise 35 is defined to be

$$R(T) = 1 - \int_0^T 0.01e^{-0.01t}\, dt,$$

where $R(T)$ is the reliability at time T. Find $R(T)$.

37. The function $f(x) = x^3$ is a probability density on $[0, b]$. What is b?

38. The function $f(x) = 12x^2$ is a probability density on $[-a, a]$. What is a?

6.5 PROBABILITY: EXPECTED VALUE, THE NORMAL DISTRIBUTION EXPECTED VALUE

Let us again consider throwing a dart at a number line in such a way that it always lands in the interval [1, 3].

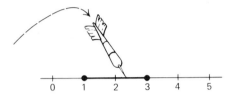

Suppose we throw the dart at the line 100 times and keep track of the numbers it hits. Then suppose we calculate the arithmetic mean (or average) $\bar{x}$ of all these numbers.

$$\bar{x} = \frac{x_1 + x_2 + x_3 + \cdots + x_{100}}{100} = \frac{\sum_{i=1}^{100} x_i}{100} = \sum_{i=1}^{100} x_i \cdot \frac{1}{100}$$

The expression

$$\sum_{i=1}^{n} x_i \cdot \frac{1}{n}$$

is analogous to the integral

$$\int_{1}^{3} x \cdot f(x) \, dx,$$

where f is the probability density function for x. That is, $\frac{1}{n}$ gives a weight to x_i, and similarly $f(x)$ gives a weight to x. We add all the $x_i \cdot \frac{1}{n}$ values when we find $\sum_{i=1}^{n} x_i \cdot \frac{1}{n}$; and similarly we add all the $x \cdot f(x)$ values when we find $\int_{1}^{3} x \cdot f(x) \, dx$. Suppose $f(x) = \frac{1}{4}x$. Then

$$\int_{1}^{3} x \cdot f(x) \, dx = \int_{1}^{3} x \cdot \frac{1}{4} x \, dx = \left[\frac{1}{4} \cdot \frac{x^3}{3} \right]_{1}^{3} = \left[\frac{x^3}{12} \right]_{1}^{3}$$

$$= \frac{1}{12}(3^3 - 1^3) = \frac{26}{12} \approx 2.17.$$

Suppose we keep throwing the dart and computing averages. The more times we throw the dart, the closer we expect the averages to come to 2.17.

You should be able to:

a) Given a probability density, find $E(x)$, $E(x^2)$, the mean, variance, and standard deviation.

b) Use Table 6 to evaluate probabilities involving a normal distribution.

28. Given the probability density function

$$f(x) = 2x, \quad \text{over } [0, 1],$$

find $E(x)$ and $E(x^2)$.

Let x be a continuous random variable over the interval $[a, b]$ with probability density function f.

The expected value of x is defined by

$$E(x) = \int_a^b x \cdot f(x) \, dx.$$

The notion of expected value generalizes to other functions of x. Suppose $y = g(x)$. Then

The expected value of $g(x)$ is defined by

$$E(g(x)) = \int_a^b g(x) \cdot f(x) \, dx.$$

For example,

$$E(x) = \int_a^b x f(x) \, dx, \quad E(x^2) = \int_a^b x^2 f(x) \, dx, \quad E(e^x) = \int_a^b e^x f(x) \, dx,$$

and

$$E(2x + 3) = \int_a^b (2x + 3) f(x) \, dx.$$

Example 1   Given the probability density function

$$f(x) = \tfrac{1}{2}x, \quad \text{over } [0, 2],$$

find $E(x)$ and $E(x^2)$.

Solution

$$E(x) = \int_0^2 x \cdot \frac{1}{2} x \, dx = \int_0^2 \frac{1}{2} x^2 \, dx = \frac{1}{2} \left[\frac{x^3}{3} \right]_0^2$$

$$= \frac{1}{2} \left(\frac{2^3}{3} - \frac{0^3}{3} \right) = \frac{1}{2} \cdot \frac{8}{3} = \frac{4}{3}$$

$$E(x^2) = \int_0^2 x^2 \cdot \frac{1}{2} x \, dx = \int_0^2 \frac{1}{2} x^3 \, dx = \frac{1}{2} \left[\frac{x^4}{4} \right]_0^2$$

$$= \frac{1}{2} \left(\frac{2^4}{4} - \frac{0^4}{4} \right) = \frac{1}{2} \cdot \frac{16}{4} = 2.$$

Do Exercise 28.

The *mean* μ of a continuous random variable is defined to be $E(x)$. That is,

$$\mu = E(x) = \int_a^b x \, f(x) \, dx.$$

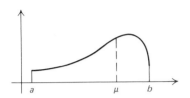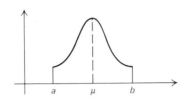

If we could imagine cutting out the region under the curve, the mean is the balance point. The symbol μ is the lower case Greek letter "mu." Note that the mean can be thought of as an average on the x-axis in contrast to the "average value of a function" which lies on the y-axis.

The *variance* σ^2 **of a continuous random variable is defined**

$$\sigma^2 = E(x^2) - \mu^2 = E(x^2) - [E(x)]^2$$

$$= \int_a^b x^2 f(x)\, dx - \left[\int_a^b x f(x)\, dx \right]^2.$$

The *standard deviation* σ **of a continuous random variable is defined**

$$\sigma = \sqrt{\text{variance}}.$$

The symbol σ is the lower case Greek letter "sigma."

Example 2   Given the probability density function

$$f(x) = \tfrac{1}{2}x, \quad \text{over } [0, 2],$$

find the mean, variance, and standard deviation.

Solution   From Example 1,

$$E(x) = \tfrac{4}{3} \quad \text{and} \quad E(x^2) = 2.$$

Then

$$\text{the } mean = \mu = E(x) = \tfrac{4}{3};$$

$$\text{the } variance = \sigma^2 = E(x^2) - [E(x)]^2$$

$$= 2 - \left(\tfrac{4}{3}\right)^2$$

$$= 2 - \tfrac{16}{9}$$

$$= \tfrac{18}{9} - \tfrac{16}{9}$$

$$= \tfrac{2}{9};$$

$$\text{the } standard\ deviation = \sigma = \sqrt{\tfrac{2}{9}} = \tfrac{1}{3}\sqrt{2} \approx 0.47.$$

29. Given the probability density function

$$f(x) = 2x, \quad \text{over } [0, 1],$$

find the mean, variance, and standard deviation.

Loosely speaking, the standard deviation is a measure of how close the graph of f is to the mean. Note these examples.

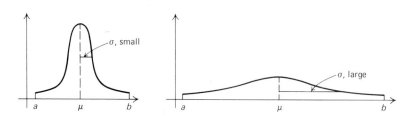

Do Exercise 29.

The Normal Distribution

Suppose the average on a test is 70. Usually there are about as many scores above the average as there are below; and the further away from the average, the fewer people there are who get a given score. For example, more people would score in the 80's than in the 90's; and more people would score in the 60's than in the 50's. Test scores, heights of human beings, weights of human beings are all examples of random variables which may be *normally* distributed.

Consider the function

$$g(x) = e^{-x^2/2}, \quad \text{over the interval } (-\infty, \infty).$$

This function has the entire set of real numbers as domain. Its graph is the bell-shaped curve which follows. Function values are found using Table 4.

$$y = e^{-x^2/2}$$

x	0	1	2	3	-1	-2	-3
y	1	0.6	0.1	0.01	0.6	0.1	0.01

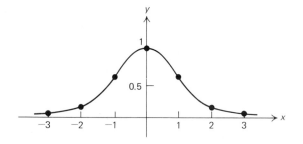

This function has an antiderivative, but that antiderivative has no elementary formula. Nevertheless, it has been shown that its improper integral converges over the interval $(-\infty, \infty)$, and

$$\int_{-\infty}^{\infty} e^{-x^2/2}\, dx = \sqrt{2\pi}.$$

That is, while an expression for the antiderivative cannot be found, there is a numerical value for the improper integral evaluated over the set of real numbers. Note that since the area is not 1, the function g is not a probability density function; but the following is:

$$\frac{1}{\sqrt{2\pi}}\, e^{-x^2/2}.$$

A continuous random variable x has a *standard normal distribution* if its probability density function is

$$f(x) = \frac{1}{\sqrt{2\pi}}\, e^{-x^2/2}, \quad \textbf{over } (-\infty, \infty).$$

This distribution has a mean of 0 and standard deviation 1. Its graph is shown below.

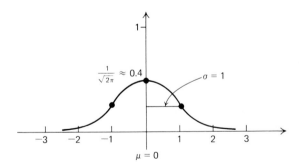

The general case is defined as follows.

A continuous random variable x is *normally distributed* with mean μ and standard deviation σ if its probability density function is given by

$$f(x) = \frac{1}{\sigma\sqrt{2\pi}} \cdot e^{-(1/2)[(x-\mu)/\sigma]^2}, \quad \textbf{over } (-\infty, \infty).$$

The graph is a transformation of the graph of the standard density. This is done by translating the graph along the x-axis and changing the way the graph is clustered about the mean. Some examples are shown below.

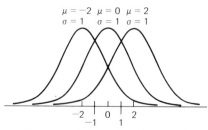

Normal distributions with same standard deviations but different means.

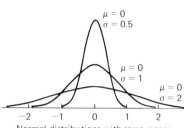

Normal distributions with same means but different standard deviations.

The normal distribution is extremely important in statistics. Much of the research done in the behavioral and social sciences has some underlying assumption regarding a normal distribution. Because of this, tables of approximate values of the definite integral of the standard density functions have been prepared. Table 6 is such a table. It contains values of

$$P(0 \leqslant x \leqslant t) = \int_0^t \frac{1}{\sqrt{2\pi}} e^{-x^2/2} \, dx.$$

The symmetry of the graph about the mean allows many types of probabilities to be computed from the table.

Examples   Let x be a continuous random variable with standard normal density. Using Table 6, find:

a) $P(0 \leqslant x \leqslant 1.68)$,   b) $P(-0.97 \leqslant x \leqslant 0)$,

c) $P(-2.43 \leqslant x \leqslant 1.01)$,   d) $P(1.90 \leqslant x \leqslant 2.74)$,

e) $P(-2.98 \leqslant x \leqslant -0.42)$,   f) $P(x \geqslant 0.61)$.

Solutions

a) $P(0 \leqslant x \leqslant 1.68)$ is the area bounded by the standard normal curve and the lines $x = 0$ and $x = 1.68$. We look this up in Table 6 by going down the left column to 1.6, then moving to the right to the column headed 0.08. There we read 0.4535. Thus

$$P(0 \leqslant x \leqslant 1.68) = 0.4535.$$

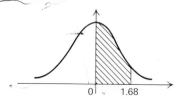

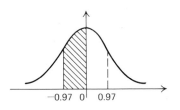

30. Let x be a continuous random variable with standard normal density. Using Table 6, find:

a) $P(0 \leqslant x \leqslant 2.17)$

b) Due to the symmetry of the graph,

$$P(-0.97 \leqslant x \leqslant 0) = P(0 \leqslant x \leqslant 0.97) = 0.3340.$$

b) $P(-1.76 \leqslant x \leqslant 0)$

c) $P(-2.43 \leqslant x \leqslant 1.01)$
$= P(-2.43 \leqslant x \leqslant 0) + P(0 \leqslant x \leqslant 1.01)$
$= P(0 \leqslant x \leqslant 2.43) + P(0 \leqslant x \leqslant 1.01)$
$= 0.4925 + 0.3438$
$= 0.8363$

c) $P(-1.77 \leqslant x \leqslant 2.53)$

d) $P(1.90 \leqslant x \leqslant 2.74)$
$= P(0 \leqslant x \leqslant 2.74) - P(0 \leqslant x \leqslant 1.90)$
$= 0.4969 - 0.4713$
$= 0.0256$

d) $P(0.49 \leqslant x \leqslant 1.75)$

e) $P(-2.98 \leqslant x \leqslant -0.42)$
$= P(0.42 \leqslant x \leqslant 2.98)$
$= P(0 \leqslant x \leqslant 2.98) - P(0 \leqslant x \leqslant 0.42)$
$= 0.4986 - 0.1628$
$= 0.3358$

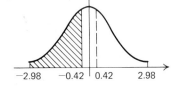

e) $P(-1.66 \leqslant x \leqslant -1.00)$

f) $P(x \geqslant 0.61)$
$= P(x \geqslant 0) - P(0 \leqslant x \leqslant 0.61)$
$= 0.5000 - 0.2291$

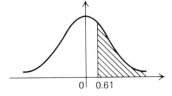

f) $P(x \geqslant 1.87)$

(Because of the symmetry about the line $x = 0$, half the area is on each side of the line, and since the entire area is 1, $P(x \geqslant 0) = 0.5000$).
$= 0.2709$

Do Exercise 30.

In many applications, a normal distribution is not standard. It would be a hopeless task to make tables for all values of the mean, μ, and the standard deviation, σ. In such cases, the transformation

$$X = \frac{x - \mu}{\sigma}$$

standardizes the distribution, allowing the use of Table 6 at the back of the book. That is,

$$P(a \leqslant x \leqslant b) = P\left(\frac{a - \mu}{\sigma} \leqslant X \leqslant \frac{b - \mu}{\sigma}\right),$$

and the probability on the right can be found using Table 6.

To see this, consider

$$P(a \leqslant x \leqslant b) = \int_a^b \frac{1}{\sigma\sqrt{2\pi}} e^{-(1/2)[(x-\mu)/\sigma]^2}\, dx,$$

and make the substitution

$$X = \frac{x - \mu}{\sigma} = \frac{x}{\sigma} - \frac{\mu}{\sigma}.$$

Then

$$dX = \frac{1}{\sigma}\, dx.$$

When $x = a$, $X = \dfrac{a - \mu}{\sigma}$, and when $x = b$, $X = \dfrac{b - \mu}{\sigma}$. Then

$$P(a \leqslant x \leqslant b) = \int_a^b \frac{1}{\sigma\sqrt{2\pi}} e^{-(1/2)[(x-\mu)/\sigma]^2}\, dx$$

$$= \int_{(a-\mu)/\sigma}^{(b-\mu)/\sigma} \frac{1}{\sqrt{2\pi}} e^{-(1/2)X^2}\, dX \qquad \text{(The integrand is now in the form of the standard density.)}$$

$$= P\left(\frac{a - \mu}{\sigma} \leqslant X \leqslant \frac{b - \mu}{\sigma}\right). \qquad \text{(We can look this up in Table 6.)}$$

Example   The weights w of the students in a calculus class are normally distributed with mean 150 lb and standard deviation 25 lb. Find the probability that a student's weight is from 160 lb to 180 lb.

Solution We first standardize the weights:

$$180 \text{ is standardized to } \frac{b - \mu}{\sigma} = \frac{180 - 150}{25} = 1.2.$$

$$160 \text{ is standardized to } \frac{a - \mu}{\sigma} = \frac{160 - 150}{25} = 0.4.$$

Then

$$
\begin{aligned}
P(160 \leqslant w \leqslant 180) &= P(0.4 \leqslant X \leqslant 1.2) \quad \text{(Now we can use Table 6.)} \\
&= P(0 \leqslant X \leqslant 1.2) - P(0 \leqslant X \leqslant 0.4) \\
&= 0.3849 - 0.1554 \\
&= 0.2295
\end{aligned}
$$

Thus the probability that a student's weight is from 160 lb to 180 lb is 0.2295. That is, about 23% of the students have weights from 160 lb to 180 lb.

31. The daily profits p of a small firm are normally distributed with mean \$200 and standard deviation \$40. Find the probability that the daily profit will be from \$230 to \$250.

Do Exercise 31.

EXERCISE SET 6.5

For each probability density, over the given interval, find $E(x)$, $E(x^2)$, the mean, variance, and standard deviation.

1. $f(x) = \frac{1}{3}$, $[2, 5]$

2. $f(x) = \frac{1}{4}$, $[3, 7]$

3. $f(x) = \frac{2}{9}x$, $[0, 3]$

4. $f(x) = \frac{1}{8}x$, $[0, 4]$

5. $f(x) = \frac{2}{3}x$, $[1, 2]$

6. $f(x) = \frac{1}{4}x$, $[1, 3]$

7. $f(x) = \frac{1}{3}x^2$, $[-2, 1]$

8. $f(x) = \frac{3}{2}x^2$, $[-1, 1]$

9. $f(x) = \frac{1}{\ln 3} \cdot \frac{1}{x}$, $[1, 3]$

10. $f(x) = \frac{1}{\ln 2} \cdot \frac{1}{x}$, $[1, 2]$

11. The uniform probability density

$$f(x) = \frac{1}{b - a}, \quad \text{over } [a, b].$$

12. The exponential probability density

$$f(x) = ke^{-kx}, \quad \text{over } [0, \infty).$$

Let x be a continuous random variable with standard normal density. Using Table 6, find:

13. $P(0 \leqslant x \leqslant 2.69)$

14. $P(0 \leqslant x \leqslant 0.04)$

15. $P(-1.11 \leqslant x \leqslant 0)$

16. $P(-2.61 \leqslant x \leqslant 0)$ **17.** $P(-1.89 \leqslant x \leqslant 0.45)$ **18.** $P(-2.94 \leqslant x \leqslant 2.00)$

19. $P(1.76 \leqslant x \leqslant 1.86)$ **20.** $P(0.76 \leqslant x \leqslant 1.45)$ **21.** $P(-1.45 \leqslant x \leqslant -0.69)$

22. $P(-2.45 \leqslant x \leqslant -1.69)$ **23.** $P(x \geqslant 3.01)$ **24.** $P(x \geqslant 1.01)$

25. a) $P(-1 \leqslant x \leqslant 1)$ **26.** a) $P(-2 \leqslant x \leqslant 2)$
   b) What percentage of the area is from -1 to 1?   b) What percentage of the area is from -2 to 2?

Let x be a continuous random variable which is normally distributed with mean $\mu = 22$ and standard deviation $\sigma = 5$. Using Table 6, find:

27. $P(24 \leqslant x \leqslant 30)$ **28.** $P(22 \leqslant x \leqslant 27)$ **29.** $P(19 \leqslant x \leqslant 25)$ **30.** $P(18 \leqslant x \leqslant 26)$

31. The heights h of the students in a calculus class are normally distributed with mean 65 in. and standard deviation 10 in.

a) Find the probability that a student's height is from 67 to 73 in.

b) Find the probability that a student's height is from 60 to 70 in.

c) Find the probability that a student's height is more than 6 ft (72 in).

32. The daily production N of stereos by a recording company is normally distributed with mean 1000 and standard deviation 50. The company promises to pay bonuses to its employees on those days when the production of stereos is 1100 or more. What percentage of the days will the company have to pay a bonus?

33. The number of daily orders N received by a mail order firm is normally distributed with mean 250 and standard deviation 20. The company has to hire extra help or pay overtime on those days when the number of orders received is 300 or higher. What percentage of the days will a company have to hire extra help or pay overtime?

34. The scores S on a psychology test are normally distributed with mean 65 and standard deviation 20. A score of 80 to 89 is a B. What is the probability of getting a B?

6.6 ECONOMIC APPLICATION—CONSUMER'S SURPLUS

Consumer's Surplus

Recall that the consumer's demand curve $D(x)$ gives the demand price per unit that the consumer is willing to pay for x units. The producer's supply curve $S(x)$ gives the price per unit at which the producer is willing to supply x units. The equilibrium point (x_E, p_E) is the intersection of the two curves.

OBJECTIVES

Given a demand function $D(x)$ and a supply function $S(x)$, you should be able to find the equilibrium point and the consumer's surplus.

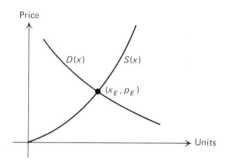

Suppose the following figure represents the supply and demand of college students for movies.

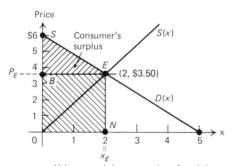

Units per week (average number of movies)

Here we might think of $6 as the price the consumer is willing to pay rather than see no movies at all, and 5 (on the x-axis) is the number of movies per week that the students would go to see if they were free. The area of rectangle $OBEN$ is $2 \cdot 3.50$, or $7.00. This represents the amount the consumer pays out to see 2 movies a week at $3.50 each. But the consumer actually gets utility or pleasure in terms of the area of trapezoid $OSEN$ which is

$$\tfrac{1}{2} \cdot 2 \cdot (\$6 + \$3.50), \quad \text{or } \$9.50.$$

The area of triangle *SEB* is defined to be *consumer's surplus* and is

$$\tfrac{1}{2} \cdot 2 \cdot \$2.50, \quad \text{or } \$2.50,$$

and represents the bonus the consumer receives because of living in a competitive society. That is, consumers get more than they pay for. To see this more clearly look at the following graphs.

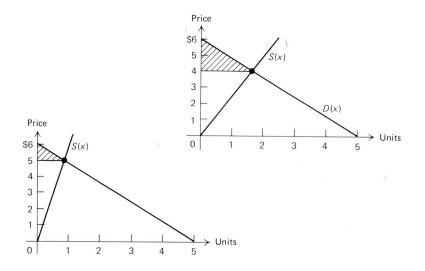

Assuming that one movie-maker is monopolizing the movies over competitive movie-makers, prices are raised. Note how consumer's surplus decreases.

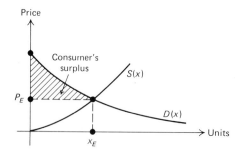

Consumer's surplus is defined as

$$\int_0^{x_E} D(x)\, dx - x_E p_E,$$

where $D(x)$ is the demand curve.

Example Given
$$D(x) = (x - 5)^2$$
$$S(x) = x^2 + x + 3,$$

find (a) the equilibrium point and (b) the consumer's surplus.

Solution

a) To find the equilibrium point we set $D(x) = S(x)$ and solve.

$$(x - 5)^2 = x^2 + x + 3$$
$$x^2 - 10x + 25 = x^2 + x + 3$$
$$-10x + 25 = x + 3$$
$$22 = 11x$$
$$\tfrac{22}{11} = x$$
$$2 = x$$

Thus $x_E = 2$ units. To find p_E we substitute x_E into $D(x)$ or $S(x)$. We use $D(x)$. Then

$$p_E = D(x_E) = D(2) = (2 - 5)^2 = (-3)^2 = \$9 \text{ per unit.}$$

Thus the equilibrium point is (2, $9).

b) The consumer's surplus is

$$\int_0^{x_E} D(x)\, dx - x_E p_E,$$

or

$$\int_0^2 (x - 5)^2\, dx - 2 \cdot 9$$
$$= \left[\frac{(x - 5)^3}{3} \right]_0^2 - 18$$
$$= \frac{(2 - 5)^3}{3} - \frac{(0 - 5)^3}{3} - 18$$
$$= \frac{(-3)^3}{3} - \frac{(-5)^3}{3} - 18$$
$$= -\frac{27}{3} + \frac{125}{3} - \frac{54}{3}$$
$$= \frac{44}{3}$$
$$= \$14.67$$

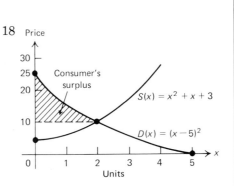

Do Exercise 32.

32. Given
$$D(x) = (x - 6)^2,$$
$$S(x) = x^2 + x + 10,$$

find
a) the equilibrium point, and
b) the consumer's surplus.

EXERCISE SET 6.6

In each exercise find (a) the equilibrium point and (b) the consumer's surplus.

1. $D(x) = -\frac{5}{6}x + 10$, $S(x) = \frac{1}{2}x + 2$

2. $D(x) = -2x + 8$, $S(x) = x + 2$

3. $D(x) = (x - 4)^2$, $S(x) = x^2 + 2x + 6$

4. $D(x) = (x - 3)^2$, $S(x) = x^2 + 2x + 1$

5. $D(x) = (x - 6)^2$, $S(x) = x^2$

6. $D(x) = (x - 5)^2$, $S(x) = x^2$

OBJECTIVES

You should be able to use integration to find the volume of a solid of revolution.

Select a bottle. Determine the curve that is rotated to form the solid of revolution.

Cary Wolinsky from Stock, Boston

6.7 VOLUME

Consider the graph of $y = f(x)$. If the upper half-plane is rotated about the x-axis, then each point on the graph has a circular path, and the whole graph sweeps out a certain surface, called a *surface of revolution*.

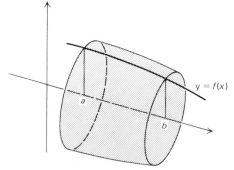

The plane region between the graph, the x-axis, and the interval $[a, b]$, sweeps out a *solid of revolution*. To calculate the volume of this solid we first approximate it by a finite sum of thin right circular cylinders. We divide the interval $[a, b]$ into equal subintervals each of length Δx. Thus the height of each cylinder is Δx. The radius of each cylinder is $f(x_i)$, where x_i is the right-hand endpoint of the subinterval that gives that cylinder.

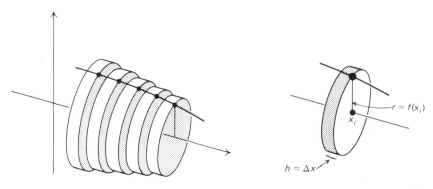

Since the volume of a right circular cylinder is

$$V = \pi r^2 h,$$

each of the approximating cylinders has volume

$$\pi[f(x_i)]^2 \, \Delta x.$$

The volume of the solid of revolution is approximated by the sum of all the cylinders:

$$V \approx \sum_{i=1}^{n} \pi[f(x_i)]^2 \, \Delta x.$$

The actual volume is the limit as the thickness of the cylinders approaches 0, or the number of them approaches infinity:

$$V = \lim_{n \to \infty} \sum_{i=1}^{n} \pi[f(x_i)]^2 \, \Delta x.$$

This is just the definite integral of the function $y = \pi[f(x)]^2$. That is,

$$V = \int_a^b \pi[f(x)]^2 \, dx \qquad \textit{Volume of a solid of revolution}$$

Example 1 Find the volume of the solid of revolution generated by rotating the region under the graph of

$$y = \sqrt{x},$$

from $x = 0$ to $x = 1$.

Solution

$$V = \int_0^1 \pi[f(x)]^2 \, dx$$

$$= \int_0^1 \pi[\sqrt{x}]^2 \, dx$$

$$= \int_0^1 \pi x \, dx$$

$$= \left[\frac{\pi x^2}{2} \right]_0^1$$

$$= \pi \left(\frac{1^2}{2} - \frac{0^2}{2} \right)$$

$$= \frac{\pi}{2}$$

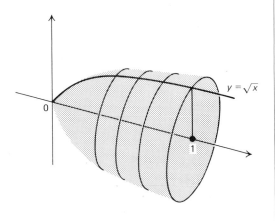

Do Exercise 33.

33. Find the volume of the solid of revolution generated by rotating the region under the graph of

$$y = x,$$

from $x = 0$ to $x = 1$.

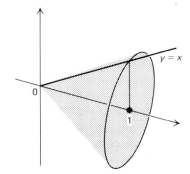

34. Find the volume of the solid of revolution generated by rotating the region under the graph of

$$y = e^x,$$

from $x = -2$ to $x = 1$.

Example 2   Find the volume of the solid of revolution generated by rotating the region under the graph of

$$y = e^x,$$

from $x = -1$ to $x = 2$.

Solution

$$V = \int_{-1}^{2} \pi[f(x)]^2 \, dx$$

$$= \int_{-1}^{2} \pi[e^x]^2 \, dx$$

$$= \int_{-1}^{2} \pi e^{2x} \, dx$$

$$= \left[\frac{\pi}{2} e^{2x} \right]_{-1}^{2}$$

$$= \frac{\pi}{2} (e^{2 \cdot 2} - e^{2(-1)})$$

$$= \frac{\pi}{2} (e^4 - e^{-2})$$

Do Exercise 34.

EXERCISE SET 6.7

Find the volume generated by revolving about the x-axis the regions bounded by the following graphs.

1. $y = \sqrt{x}, x = 0, x = 3$

2. $y = \sqrt{x}, x = 0, x = 2$

3. $y = x, x = 1, x = 2$

4. $y = x, x = 1, x = 3$

5. $y = e^x, x = -2, x = 5$

6. $y = e^x, x = -3, x = 2$

7. $y = \frac{1}{x}, x = 1, x = 3$

8. $y = \frac{1}{x}, x = 1, x = 4$

9. $y = \frac{1}{\sqrt{x}}, x = 1, x = 3$

10. $y = \frac{1}{\sqrt{x}}, x = 1, x = 4$

11. $y = 4, x = 1, x = 3$

12. $y = 5, x = 1, x = 3$

13. $y = x^2, x = 0, x = 2$

14. $y = x^2, x = 0, x = 1$

15. $y = x + 1, x = -1, x = 2$

16. $y = x + 2, x = -2, x = 1$

17. $y = \sqrt{1 + x}, x = 2, x = 10$

18. $y = \sqrt{3 + x}, x = 4, x = 6$

19. $y = 2\sqrt{x}, x = 1, x = 2$

20. $y = 3\sqrt{x}, x = 1, x = 2$

21. $y = \sqrt{4 - x^2}, x = -2, x = 2$

22. $y = \sqrt{1 - x^2}, x = -1, x = 1$

23. $y = \sqrt{r^2 - x^2}, x = -r, x = r$. Make drawings for Exercises 21 and 22. Here you will derive a general formula for the volume of a sphere.

CHAPTER 6 TEST

1. Find the amount of an annuity where $1200 per year is being invested at 6%, compounded continuously, for 15 years.

2. What annual payment should be made so that the amount of an annuity over 25 years at interest rate 6%, compounded continuously, will be $20,000?

3. *The demand for iron ore.* In 1973 ($t = 0$) the world use of iron ore was 810,000 thousand tons, and the demand for it was growing exponentially at the rate of 6% per year. If the demand continues to grow at this rate, how many tons of iron ore will the world use from 1973 to 1983?

4. *The depletion of iron ore.* The world reserves of iron ore are 108,304,000 tons. Assuming the growth rate of 6% per year continues, and that no new reserves are discovered, when will the world reserves of iron ore be exhausted?

5. A parent, following the birth of a child, wants to make an initial investment P_0 which will grow to $10,000 by the child's 20th birthday. Interest is compounded continuously at 7%. What should the initial investment be?

6. Find the capital value of a rental property over a 20-year period where the annual rent is $1200 and the going interest rate is 8%.

7. Find the capital value of the rental property in Question 6 if the rent is to be paid perpetually.

Determine whether each of the following improper integrals is convergent or divergent, and calculate its value if convergent.

8. $\int_1^\infty \frac{dx}{x^5}$

9. $\int_0^\infty \frac{3}{1 + x}\, dx$

10. Find k such that $f(x) = kx^3$ is a probability density function over the interval $[0, 2]$.

11. A telephone company determines that the length of time t of a phone call is an exponentially distributed random variable with probability density function

$$f(t) = 2e^{-2t}, \quad 0 \leqslant t \leqslant \infty.$$

Find the probability that a phone call will last no more than 1 minute.

Given the probability density function

$$f(x) = 3x^2, \text{ over } [0, 1],$$

find:

12. $E(x)$ **13.** $E(x^2)$ **14.** the mean.

15. the variance.   **16.** the standard deviation.

Let x be a continuous random variable with standard normal density. Using Table 6, find:

17. $P(0 \leqslant x \leqslant 1.5)$ **18.** $P(0.12 \leqslant x \leqslant 2.32)$ **19.** $P(-1.61 \leqslant x \leqslant 1.76)$

20. The price per pound p of T-bone steak at various stores in a certain city is normally distributed with mean $3.75 and standard deviation $.25. What is the probability that the price per pound is $3.80 or more?

Given the demand and supply functions

$$D(x) = (x - 7)^2, \quad S(x) = x^2 + x + 4,$$

find:

21. the equilibrium point.   **22.** the consumer's surplus.

Find the volume generated by revolving about the x-axis the regions bounded by the following graphs.

23. $y = \dfrac{1}{\sqrt{x}}, x = 1, x = 5$ **24.** $y = \sqrt{2 + x}, x = 0, x = 1$

Waves can be represented by differential equations.

7 DIFFERENTIAL EQUATIONS

OBJECTIVES

You should be able to:

a) Solve certain differential equations giving both general and particular solutions.
b) Solve certain differential equations given a condition $f(a) = b$.
c) Verify that a given function is a solution of a given differential equation.

1. Solve
$$y' = 3x^2.$$

7.1 DIFFERENTIAL EQUATIONS

A *differential equation* is an equation which involves derivatives or differentials. In Chapter 4 we studied one very important differential equation

$$\frac{dP}{dt} = kP,$$

where P, or $P(t)$, is the population at time t. This equation is a model of uninhibited population growth. Its solution is

$$P = P_0 e^{kt},$$

where the constant P_0 is the size of the initial population; that is, at $t = 0$. As this one equation illustrated, differential equations are rich in application.

Solving Certain Differential Equations

In this chapter we will frequently use the notation y' for a derivative—mainly because it is simple. Thus, if $y = f(x)$, then

$$y' = \frac{dy}{dx} = f'(x).$$

We have already found solutions of certain differential equations when we found antiderivatives or indefinite integrals. The differential equation

$$\frac{dy}{dx} = g(x), \quad \text{or} \quad y' = g(x),$$

has the solution

$$y = \int g(x)\, dx + C.$$

Example 1 Solve $y' = 2x$.

Solution
$$y = \int 2x\, dx + C = x^2 + C$$

Do Exercise 1.

Look again at the solution to Example 1. Note the constant of integration. This solution is called a *general solution* because taking all values of C gives *all* the solutions.

Taking specific values of C gives particular solutions. For example, the following are particular solutions of $y' = 2x$:

$$y = x^2 + 3,$$
$$y = x^2,$$
$$y = x^2 - 3.$$

2. For

$$y' = 3x^2$$

a) Write the general solution.
b) Write three particular solutions.

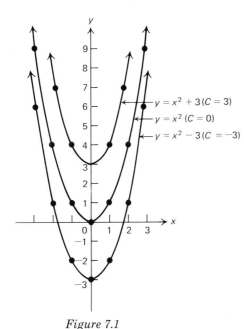

Figure 7.1

Figure 7.1 shows graphs of a few particular solutions. The general solution can be envisioned as the set of all particular solutions, a *family* of curves.

Do Exercise 2.

Knowing the value of a function at a particular point may allow us to select a particular solution from the general solution.

3. Solve

$$y' = 2x$$

given that $y = 7$ when $x = 1$.

4. Solve

$$f'(x) = \frac{1}{x} - 2x + x^{1/2}$$

given that $f(1) = 4$.

5. Show that

$$y = 2e^x - 7e^{3x}$$

is a solution of

$$y'' - 4y' + 3y = 0.$$

6. Show that

$$y = xe^{2x}$$

is a solution of

$$\frac{dy}{dx} - 2y = e^{2x}.$$

At the 1968 Olympic Games in Mexico City, Bob Beamon made what was believed to be a miracle long jump of 29 ft $2\frac{1}{2}$ in. Many believed this was due to the altitude which was 7400 ft. Using differential equations for analysis, the altitude theory was refuted in the article by M. N. Bearley, "The Long Jump Miracle of Mexico City," *Mathematics Magazine* **45**, (November 1972): 241–246. Bearley argues that the world record jump was a result of Beamon's exceptional speed (9.5 seconds in the 100 yd dash) and the fact that he hit the take-off board in the perfect position.

Wide World Photos

Example 2   Solve $f'(x) = e^x + 5x - x^{1/2}$, given that $f(0) = 8$.

Solution

a) First find the general solution.

$$f(x) = \int f'(x)\, dx + C = e^x + \tfrac{5}{2}x^2 - \tfrac{2}{3}x^{3/2} + C$$

b) Since $f(0) = 8$, we substitute to find C.

$$8 = e^0 + \tfrac{5}{2} \cdot 0^2 - \tfrac{2}{3} \cdot 0^{3/2} + C$$
$$8 = 1 + C$$
$$7 = C$$

Thus the solution is $f(x) = e^x + \tfrac{5}{2}x^2 - \tfrac{2}{3}x^{3/2} + 7$.

Do Exercises 3 and 4.

Verifying Solutions

To verify that a function is a solution of a differential equation we find the necessary derivatives and substitute.

Example   Show that $y = 4e^x + 5e^{3x}$ is a solution of

$$y'' - 4y' + 3y = 0.$$

Solution

a) We first find y' and y''.

$$y' = 4e^x + 15e^{3x}$$
$$y'' = 4e^x + 45e^{3x}$$

b) Then we substitute as follows in the differential equation.

$$y'' - 4y' + 3y = 0$$

$(4e^x + 45e^{3x}) - 4(4e^x + 15e^{3x}) + 3(4e^x + 5e^{3x})$	0
$4e^x + 45e^{3x} - 16e^x - 60e^{3x} + 12e^x + 15e^{3x}$	
	0

Do Exercises 5 and 6.

EXERCISE SET 7.1

Find the general solution and three particular solutions.

1. $y' = 4x^3$ **2.** $y' = 6x^5$ **3.** $y' = e^{2x} + x$ **4.** $y' = e^{3x} - x$

5. $y' = \dfrac{3}{x} - x^2 + x^5$ **6.** $y' = \dfrac{5}{x} + x^2 - x^4$

Find the particular solution determined by the given condition.

7. $y' = x^2 + 2x - 3$; $y = 4$ when $x = 0$ **8.** $y' = 3x^2 - x + 5$; $y = 6$ when $x = 0$

9. $f'(x) = x^{2/3} - x$; $f(1) = -6$ **10.** $f'(x) = x^{2/5} + x$; $f(1) = -7$

11. Show that $y = x \ln x + 3x - 2$ is a solution of $y'' - \dfrac{1}{x} = 0$.

12. Show that $y = x \ln x - 5x + 7$ is a solution of $y'' - \dfrac{1}{x} = 0$.

13. Show that $y = e^x + 3xe^x$ is a solution of $y'' - 2y' + y = 0$.

14. Show that $y = -2e^x + xe^x$ is a solution of $y'' - 2y' + y = 0$.

15. Marginal cost for a certain product is $C'(x) = 2.6 - 0.02x$. Find the total cost function $C(x)$ and the average cost $A(x)$, assuming fixed costs are $120; that is, $C(0) = \$120$.

16. Marginal revenue for a certain product is $R'(x) = 300 - 2x$. Find the total revenue function $R(x)$ assuming $R(0) = 0$.

7.2 SEPARATION OF VARIABLES

Consider the differential equation

$$\frac{dy}{dx} = 2xy. \tag{1}$$

We treat $\dfrac{dy}{dx}$ as a quotient, as we did in Chapter 5. We multiply equation (1) by dx and then by $\dfrac{1}{y}$ and get

$$\frac{dy}{y} = 2x \, dx. \tag{2}$$

OBJECTIVE

You should be able to solve certain differential equations using separation of variables.

7. Use separation of variables to solve

$$\frac{dy}{dx} = 3x^2y.$$

We say that we have *separated the variables*, meaning that all the expressions involving y are on one side, and those involving x are on the other. We then integrate both sides of equation (2).

$$\int \frac{dy}{y} = \int 2x \, dx + C$$

We use only one constant because any two antiderivatives differ by a constant.

$$\ln y = x^2 + C \qquad\qquad (y \geqslant 0)$$
$$y = e^{x^2+C} = e^{x^2} \cdot e^C$$

Thus the solution of differential equation (1) is

$$y = C_1 e^{x^2}, \quad \text{where } C_1 = e^C.$$

Do Exercise 7.

Example 1   Solve

$$3y^2 \frac{dy}{dx} + x = 0.$$

Solution   We first separate the variables as follows.

$$3y^2 \frac{dy}{dx} = -x, \qquad 3y^2 \, dy = -x \, dx$$

8. Solve

$$3y^2 \frac{dy}{dx} - 2x = 0.$$

We integrate both sides.

$$\int 3y^2 \, dy = \int -x \, dx + C$$
$$y^3 = -\frac{x^2}{2} + C = C - \frac{x^2}{2}$$
$$y = \sqrt[3]{C - \frac{x^2}{2}} \qquad \text{(Taking the cube root)}$$

Do Exercise 8.

Example 2   Solve

$$\frac{dy}{dx} = \frac{x}{y}.$$

Solution   We first separate variables as follows.

$$y \frac{dy}{dx} = x$$
$$y \, dy = x \, dx$$

We integrate both sides:

$$\int y\, dy = \int x\, dx + C$$

$$\frac{y^2}{2} = \frac{x^2}{2} + C$$

$$y^2 = x^2 + 2C$$

$$y^2 = x^2 + C_1,$$

where $C_1 = 2C$. We make this substitution to simplify the equation. We then obtain the solutions

$$y = \sqrt{x^2 + C_1} \quad \text{and} \quad y = -\sqrt{x^2 + C_1}.$$

Do Exercise 9.

Example 3   Solve

$$y' = x - xy.$$

Solution   Before we separate variables we replace y' by $\dfrac{dy}{dx}$:

$$\frac{dy}{dx} = x - xy.$$

Now we separate variables.

$$dy = (x - xy)\, dx$$

$$dy = x(1 - y)\, dx$$

$$\frac{dy}{1 - y} = x\, dx$$

Now we integrate both sides.

$$\int \frac{dy}{1 - y} = \int x\, dx + C$$

$$-\ln(1 - y) = \frac{x^2}{2} + C \qquad (1 - y > 0)$$

$$\ln(1 - y) = -\frac{x^2}{2} - C$$

$$1 - y = e^{-x^2/2 - C}$$

$$-y = e^{-x^2/2 - C} - 1$$

$$y = -e^{-x^2/2 - C} + 1 = -e^{-x^2/2} \cdot e^{-C} + 1$$

Thus
$$y = 1 + C_1 e^{-x^2/2} \qquad (\text{where } C_1 = -e^{-C})$$

Do Exercise 10.

9. Solve

$$\frac{dy}{dx} = \frac{5}{y}.$$

10. Solve

$$y' = 2x + xy.$$

A Psychological Application—Reaction to a Stimulus

THE WEBER-FECHNER LAW   In psychology, one model of stimulus-response asserts that the rate of change $\dfrac{dR}{dS}$ of the reaction R with respect to a stimulus S is inversely proportional to the stimulus. That is,

$$\frac{dR}{dS} = \frac{k}{S},$$

where k is some positive constant. To solve this equation we first separate the variables:

$$dR = k \cdot \frac{dS}{S}.$$

We integrate both sides.

$$\int dR = \int k \cdot \frac{dS}{S} + C$$

$$R = k \ln S + C \tag{1}$$

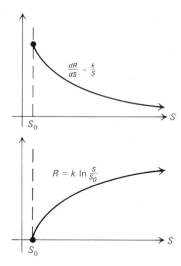

Now suppose we let S_0 be the lowest level of the stimulus which can be detected consistently, called the *threshold value*, or *detection threshold*. For example, the lowest level of sound which can be consistently detected is the tick of a watch at 20 feet, under very quiet conditions. If S_0 is the lowest level of sound which can be detected, it seems reasonable that the reaction to it would be 0. That is, $R(S_0) = 0$.

Substituting this condition in equation (1) we get

$$0 = k \ln S_0 + C, \quad \text{or} \quad -k \ln S_0 = C.$$

Replacing C in equation (1) by $-k \ln S_0$, we get

$$R = k \cdot \ln S - k \cdot \ln S_0$$
$$R = k(\ln S - \ln S_0).$$

Using a property of logarithms we have

$$R = k \cdot \ln \frac{S}{S_0}.$$

Compare this equation with that for the loudness of sound and the magnitude of an earthquake given on pp. 195–199. Look at the graphs of $\frac{dR}{dS}$ and R given previously. Note that as the stimulus gets larger the rate of change decreases; that is, the reaction becomes smaller as one receives stronger stimulation. For example, suppose you are in a room with one lamp and that lamp has a 50-watt bulb in it. If the bulb were suddenly changed to 100 watts you would probably notice it quite a bit. That is, your reaction would be strong. If the bulb were changed to a 150-watt, your change in reaction would not be as great as it was going from the 50 to the 100-watt bulb. From the 150- to a 200-watt bulb your change in reaction would be even less, and so on.

For your interest, here are some other detection thresholds.

Stimulus	Detection Threshold
Light	The flame of a candle 30 miles away on a dark night
Taste	Water diluted with sugar in the ratio of 1 teaspoon to two gallons.
Smell	One drop of perfume diffused into the volume of three average size rooms.
Touch	The wing of a bee dropped on your cheek at a distance of 1 centimeter (about $\frac{3}{8}$ of an inch).

Do Exercise 11.

11. *The Brentano-Stevens Law.* The Weber-Fechner Law has been the subject of great debate among psychologists as to its validity. The model

$$\frac{dR}{dS} = k \cdot \frac{R}{S},$$

where k is a positive constant, has also been conjectured and experimented with. Find the general solution of this equation. This has also been referred to as the *Power Law of Stimulus-Response.*

EXERCISE SET 7.2

Solve.

1. $\dfrac{dy}{dx} = 4x^3y$ 2. $\dfrac{dy}{dx} = 5x^4y$ 3. $3y^2\,\dfrac{dy}{dx} = 5x$ 4. $3y^2\,\dfrac{dy}{dx} = 7x$

5. $\dfrac{dy}{dx} = \dfrac{2x}{y}$ 6. $\dfrac{dy}{dx} = \dfrac{x}{2y}$ 7. $\dfrac{dy}{dx} = \dfrac{3}{y}$ 8. $\dfrac{dy}{dx} = \dfrac{4}{y}$

9. $y' = 3x + xy$ 10. $y' = 2x - xy$ 11. $y' = 5y^{-2}$ 12. $y' = 7y^{-2}$

13. $\dfrac{dy}{dx} = 3y$ 14. $\dfrac{dy}{dx} = 4y$ 15. $\dfrac{dP}{dt} = 2P$ 16. $\dfrac{dP}{dt} = 4P$

17. a) Use separation of variables to solve the differential equation model of uninhibited growth.

$$\frac{dP}{dt} = kP$$

b) Rewrite the solution in terms of the condition $P_0 = P(0)$.

18. *Domar's Capital Expansion Model is*

$$\frac{dI}{dt} = hkI$$

where

I = investment, h = investment productivity (constant), k = marginal productivity to consume (constant), and t = time.

a) Use separation of variables to solve the differential equation.

b) Rewrite the solution in terms of the condition $I_0 = I(0)$.

19. *Utility.* The reaction R in pleasure units, by a consumer receiving S units of a product can be modeled by the differential equation

$$\frac{dR}{dS} = \frac{k}{S + 1},$$

where k is a positive constant.

a) Use separation of variables to solve the differential equation.

b) Rewrite the solution in terms of the initial condition $R(0) = 0$.

c) Explain why the condition $R(0) = 0$ is reasonable.

20. *Newton's Law of Cooling.* The temperature T of a cooling object drops at a rate which is proportional to the difference $T - M$, where M is the constant temperature of the surrounding medium. Thus

$$\frac{dT}{dt} = -k(T - M),$$

where k is a positive constant and t is time.

a) Solve the differential equation.

b) Rewrite the solution in terms of the condition $T(0) = 200°$.

7.3 APPLICATIONS: THE INHIBITED GROWTH MODEL, $\dfrac{dP}{dt} = kP(L - P)$

Recall the model of uninhibited growth

$$\frac{dP}{dt} = kP$$

with solution

$$P = P_0 e^{kt}.$$

A more realistic model of population growth will take into account factors other than the size of the population. For example, there may be some compelling reason why the population P can never grow beyond a limiting value L, due perhaps to a limitation on food, living space, or other natural resources. In such cases we would expect the *growth rate* to lessen as the population size increases, and to approach 0 as P approaches L.

Example Buy an ant colony at a pet shop. Place a fixed amount of food and water in the colony (enough to last a long period of time) and close it up. The growth rate of the ants is inhibited by the fixed amount of food and water.

The simplest model for such an inhibition to express itself is for the growth rate $\dfrac{dP}{dt}$ to be directly proportional to *both* the population size P and to its remaining possible room for growth $L - P$. Then the

Model of Inhibited Growth is $\dfrac{dP}{dt} = kP(L - P),$

where $L = $ *limiting value* and $k > 0.$

Work through the following exploratory exercise set, either on your own or in class with your instructor.

OBJECTIVES

You should be able to:

a) State the differential equation

$$\frac{dP}{dt} = kP(L - P)$$

for the inhibited growth model.

b) State the solution to the inhibited growth model

$$P(t) = \frac{P_0 L}{P_0 + e^{-Lkt}(L - P_0)}$$

c) Given the point of inflection, find the limiting value.

d) Given the values of the constants for the equation in (b),
1) write the equation for $P(t)$ in terms of the given constant.
2) sketch a graph of $P(t)$, given the time t at which the point of inflection occurs.
3) find t such that $P(t) = M$, for number M.

e) Given certain constants and function values find the value of k in the formula in (b).

The population of this island is probably close to its limiting value.

Exploratory Exercises.   *Shipwrecked on an Island*

A ship carrying 100 passengers wrecks on an island never to be rescued. The population grows over the next 120 years as indicated in the table.

a) Complete the table.

b) Plot P versus t. Use solid dots and connect them with a smooth curve.

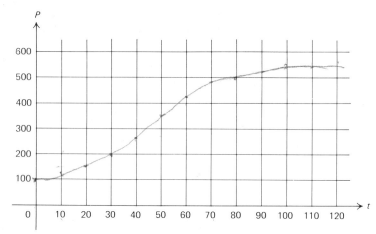

t	P	$\dfrac{\Delta P}{\Delta t}$
(in years)	(population)	(growth rate)
0	100	0 (assumed)
10	120	2
20	150	3
30	200	6
40	270	7
50	350	8
60	420	2
70	470	5
80	500	3
90	520	2
100	530	1
110	535	$\frac{1}{2}$
120	538	$\frac{1}{3}$

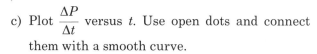

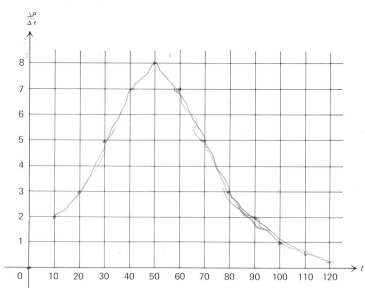

c) Plot $\dfrac{\Delta P}{\Delta t}$ versus t. Use open dots and connect them with a smooth curve.

d) Does P resemble the graph of an exponential function of the type $P(t) = P_0 e^{kt}$?

e) Between what values of t is $\dfrac{\Delta P}{\Delta t}$ increasing?

f) Between what values of t is $\dfrac{\Delta P}{\Delta t}$ decreasing?

g) Is there a point of inflection? Where?

h) Does there appear to be a limiting value to the population growth? If so, what is it?

Now let us solve the differential equation

$$\frac{dP}{dt} = kP(L - P).$$

Note that this equation defines P as a function of t implicitly. That is, it is assumed that P is a function of t even though t does not appear on the right side of the equation. We first separate variables:

$$dP = kP(L - P)\,dt$$

$$\frac{dP}{P(L - P)} = k\,dt$$

Now we integrate both sides. We use Table 5 to integrate the left side. A similar example appears on p. 295.

$$\int \frac{dP}{P(L - P)} = \int k\,dt + C$$

$$\frac{1}{L}\ln\frac{P}{L - P} = kt + C$$

To solve for P we first find an expression for $\dfrac{P}{L - P}$.

$$\ln\frac{P}{L - P} = Lkt + LC$$

$$\frac{P}{L - P} = e^{Lkt + LC} = e^{Lkt} \cdot e^{LC}$$

Now, letting $C_1 = e^{LC}$, we have

$$\frac{P}{L - P} = C_1 e^{Lkt}.$$

We complete the solution for P as follows, dropping the subscript from C_1 for simplicity.

$$P = Ce^{Lkt}(L - P)$$

$$P = CLe^{Lkt} - PCe^{Lkt}$$

$$P + PCe^{Lkt} = CLe^{Lkt}$$

$$P(1 + Ce^{Lkt}) = CLe^{Lkt}$$

$$P = \frac{CLe^{Lkt}}{1 + Ce^{Lkt}}$$

12. Let $C = 1$, $L = 1$, and $k = 1$, then equation (2) becomes

$$P(t) = \frac{e^t}{1 + e^t}.$$

We want to graph $P(t)$, but to ease computations we multiply by 1 as follows:

$$P(t) = \frac{e^t}{1 + e^t} \cdot \frac{e^{-t}}{e^{-t}} = \frac{e^t \cdot e^{-t}}{1 \cdot e^{-t} + e^t \cdot e^{-t}}$$

$$P(t) = \frac{1}{e^{-t} + 1}$$

a) Use Table 4 and complete this table of function values.

t	-3	-2	-1	0	1	2	3
$P(t)$							.95

For example

$$P(3) = \frac{1}{e^{-3} + 1} = \frac{1}{0.05 + 1}$$

$$= \frac{1}{1.05} \approx .95.$$

b) Graph $P(t)$.

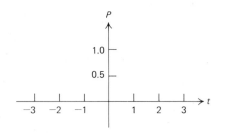

The *Model of Inhibited Growth*

$$\frac{dP}{dt} = kP(L - P) \tag{1}$$

has the solution

$$P(t) = \frac{CLe^{LKt}}{1 + Ce^{Lkt}}. \tag{2}$$

Do Exercise 12.

For each value of the constant C we get an S-shaped curve. These curves fill up the strip $0 < P < L$. See Fig. 7.2.

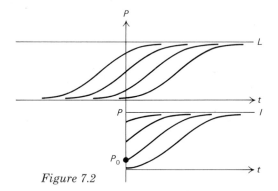

Figure 7.2

If we don't project these curves into the past (that is, if we don't use *negative time*), then the solution curves are confined to the part of the strip for which $t \geqslant 0$. For any initial population P_0, there is a growth curve emanating from $(0, P_0)$, showing the evolution of that population. That is, $P = P_0$ at $t = 0$ is a condition that picks out a unique solution. We can eliminate the constant C and express P in terms of P_0 as follows.

$$P_0 = P(0) = \frac{CLe^{Lk0}}{1 + Ce^{Lk0}} = \frac{CL}{1 + C}. \tag{3}$$

Solving for C, we get

$$C = \frac{P_0}{L - P_0}. \tag{4}$$

$$P = \frac{P_0 Le^{Lkt}}{P_0 e^{Lkt} + (L - P_0)}$$

We can simplify this further by multiplying by $\dfrac{e^{-Lkt}}{e^{-Lkt}}$.

Do Exercise 13.

The *Model of Inhibited Growth*

$$\frac{dP}{dt} = kP(L - P)$$

has the solution

$$P(t) = \frac{P_0 L}{P_0 + e^{-Lkt}(L - P_0)}.$$

Recall that an inflection point is a point where the graph changes concavity (see p. 142). The inflection point on the graph of $P(t)$ is important in application. The following tells us where the inflection point of P occurs.

P has an inflection point at that value of t where

$$P = \tfrac{1}{2}L.$$

The following example is based on an actual experiment.*

Example 1 Prior to 1937 there were no pheasants on Protection Island off the coast of Washington state. In 1937 eight pheasants, 2 cocks and 6 hens, were released on the island. The following curve shows the growth of the pheasant population over the next six years.

13. Given

$$P = \frac{CLe^{Lkt}}{1 + Ce^{Lkt}} \qquad (1)$$

and

$$C = \frac{P_0}{L - P_0} \qquad (2)$$

a) Replace C in (1) by the right side of (2) and show your work in simplifying to get

$$P = \frac{P_0 Le^{Lkt}}{P_0 e^{Lkt} + (L - P_0)}. \qquad (3)$$

b) Simplify (3) by multiplying by $\dfrac{e^{-Lkt}}{e^{-Lkt}}$.

Russ Kinne from Photo Researchers

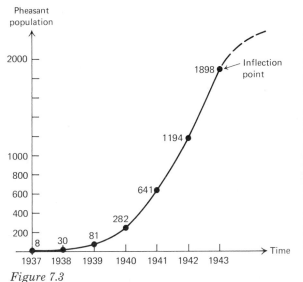

Figure 7.3

A ring-neck pheasant.

---

* A. S. Einarsen, "Some Factors Affecting Ring-neck Pheasant Population Density," *Murrelet*, **26** (1945): 2–9, 39–44.

14. The following shows the growth of an ant colony with a point of inflection at P_1. What is the limiting value?

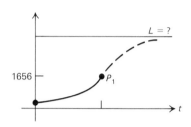

In 1943 the army arrived and started shooting the pheasants. It was theorized on the basis of the data that the population had reached its point of inflection. That is, the growth would stop turning upward and start turning downward as it approached its limiting value. What was the limiting value of the pheasant population?

Solution At the inflection point

$$P = \tfrac{1}{2}L.$$

Now $P = 1898$ from the graph, so

$$1898 = \tfrac{1}{2}L.$$
$$3796 = L.$$

Do Exercise 14.

The spread of an epidemic can also be described by the model of inhibited growth.

Example 2 *Spread of an epidemic.* In a town whose total population is 2000, the disease *Rottenich* creates an epidemic. The initial number of people infected is 10. The rate of spread of the infection follows the inhibited growth model

$$\frac{dP}{dt} = kP(L - P),$$

where

$\quad\quad P =$ the number of people infected after time t (in weeks),
$\quad\quad L = 2000$, the total population of the town,
$\quad\quad k = 0.003$, and
$\quad\quad P_0 =$ the number of people initially infected $= 10$.

a) Write the equation for $P(t)$ in terms of the given constants.
b) Sketch a graph of $P(t)$ given that the point of inflection occurs at $t = 0.882$ wk.
c) At what time t are 1600 people affected?

Solution

a) $P(t) = \dfrac{P_0 L}{P_0 + e^{-Lkt}(L - P_0)} = \dfrac{10 \cdot 2000}{10 + e^{-2000(.003)t}(2000 - 10)}$

$P(t) = \dfrac{20{,}000}{10 + 1990e^{-6t}}$

b) We first mark the limiting value 2000 on the vertical axis in the figure and draw a horizontal line through it. Then mark P_0, or 10, on the vertical axis and the inflection point (0.882, 1000). Finally, we draw an S-shaped curve from P_0 through the inflection point, and upward approaching the limiting value.

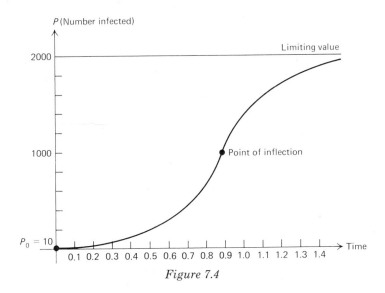

Figure 7.4

c) We solve the following equation for t.

$$1600 = \dfrac{20{,}000}{10 + 1990e^{-6t}}$$

$$1600(10 + 1990e^{-6t}) = 20{,}000$$

$$10 + 1990e^{-6t} = \dfrac{20{,}000}{1600} = 12.5$$

$$1990e^{-6t} = 2.5$$

$$e^{-6t} = \dfrac{2.5}{1990}$$

15. A town whose population is 4000 is struck by the disease *Andromedamama*. The initial number of people infected is 20. The rate of spread of the infection followed the inhibited growth model

$$\frac{dP}{dt} = kP(L - P),$$

where

P = number infected after t (months),

L = 4000, the total population of the town,

k = 0.0005, and

P_0 = 20, the number of people initially infected.

a) Write the equation for $P(t)$ in terms of the given constants.

b) Sketch a graph of $P(t)$, given that the point of inflection occurs at t = 2.9 mo. Use graph paper.

c) At what time t, are 800 people infected?

16. State the solution, $Q(y)$, of

$$\frac{dQ}{dy} = rQ(M - Q).$$

We use common logarithms to solve this equation.

$$\log e^{-6t} = \log \frac{2.5}{1990}$$

$$-6t \cdot \log e = \log 2.5 - \log 1990$$

$$t = \frac{\log 2.5 - \log 1990}{-6 \cdot \log e}$$

$$t = \frac{\log 2.5 - \log 1990}{-6(0.4343)} \qquad (e \approx 2.71, \log e \approx 0.4343)$$

$$t = 1.113 \text{ wk}$$

Do Exercise 15.

As you will have seen after you do the exercises in this section, and as you have already seen in the preceding example, the differential equation $\frac{dP}{dt} = kP(L - P)$ has many applications. The solution of the equation, however, can be used in all of the applications. Of course, different variables or constants are used in different applications. For example, the solution of $\frac{dN}{dw} = cN(K - N)$ is

$$N(w) = \frac{N_0 K}{N_0 + e^{-Kcw}(K - N_0)}.$$

Do Exercise 16.

Population Growth—Some Comments

Can a J-shaped curve (graph of the equation $P = P_0 e^{kt}$) or an S-shaped curve be used to model world population growth? To find out let us look at a log-log graph* of population growth over the last 1 million years. (See following page.)

What happens is that we get a series of S-shaped curves. At three intervals there are surges of growth. These smaller intervals could be modeled by J-shaped curves. Following each surge there seems to be a leveling off, but an advance in technology causes another surge. One comes after the *tool-making revolution*. Another comes after the *agricultural revolution*, and another comes after the *industrial revolu-*

---

* The axes are scaled using logarithms of the numbers in question. This condenses the graph. For more on this see Appendix A.

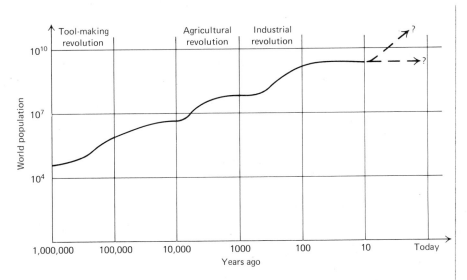

tion. Judging from the graph, and from the current concerns about availability of food, energy, and other resources, it might be speculated that we are in the midst of a leveling off period where the birth-rate and the death-rate are about the same, or will be by the year 2000.

EXERCISE SET 7.3

For the inhibited growth model,

1. $P = 450$ at the point of inflection. What is the limiting value?

2. $P = 670$ at the point of inflection. What is the limiting value?

3. In an experiment* it was found that the rate or growth of yeast cells in a laboratory satisfied the inhibited growth model

$$\frac{dP}{dt} = kP(L - P)$$

where

P = the number of cells present after time t (in hours),
L = 700, the limiting value,
k = 0.0008, and
P_0 = 10.

a) Write the equation for $P(t)$ in terms of the given constants.

b) Sketch a graph of $P(t)$ given that the point of inflection occurs at $t = 8$.

c) At what time t are 500 cells present?

---

* G. F. Gause, *The Struggle For Existence*, Baltimore: Williams and Wilkins, 1934.

4. A company introduced a new product on a trial run in a city. They advertised the product on TV and gathered data concerning the percentage P of people who bought the product in relation to the number of times the product was advertised on TV. The graph of the data resembled an S-shaped curve, so they hypothesized that it satisfied the inhibited growth model

$$\frac{dP}{dt} = kP(L - P)$$

where

P = the percentage of people who buy the product.
t = the number of times the product is advertised on TV,
L = 100%, or 1, the highest percentage of people who could buy the product,
k = 0.13, and
P_0 = 2%, or .02, the percentage who bought the product without having seen an ad.

a) Write the equation for $P(t)$ in terms of the given constants.

b) Sketch a graph of $P(t)$ given that the point of inflection (50%) occurs at $t = 30$.

c) How many times t would the company have to advertise its product so that 80% of the people would buy?

In Exercises 5 and 6 you will study two problems concerning the *diffusion of information*. This is a sociological term for the spread of information such as a rumor, or news of some new fashion rage, or news of some new product or medicine. In a limited population L the rate of diffusion of the information is proportional to the number who have heard the information N, and to the number who have not heard the information $L - N$.

5. *Spread of a rumor.* In a college with a student population of 800, a group of 6 students spread the rumor "Men go for women who study calculus, and women go for men who study calculus!" The rate at which the rumor spreads satisfies the differential equation

$$\frac{dN}{dt} = kN(L - N)$$

where

N = number of people who have heard the rumor after t minutes,
L = 800, and
N_0 = 6, the number of people who started the rumor.

a) Write the equation for $N(t)$, the solution of the differential equation, in terms of the given constants. Note that we do not yet know k.

b) The point of inflection occurs at $t = 12.2$; that is, $N(12.2) = 400$. Use this to find k,

c) After what time t have 700 students heard the rumor?

6. *Acceptance of hybrid corn.* The rate of acceptance of hybrid corn in Kentucky* followed the differential equation

$$\frac{dC}{dt} = kC(L - C)$$

---

* *Agricultural Statistics*, U.S. Department of Agriculture, Washington, D.C., 1961.

where

C = percentage of corn acreage in hybrid at time t in years (after 1938),

$L = 100\%$, or 1,

$C_0 = 3\%$, the percent of the corn acreage at $t = 0$ (1938).

a) Write the equation for $C(t)$, the solution of the differential equation, in terms of the given constants. Note that we do not yet know k.

b) The point of inflection occurs at $t = 7$; that is, $C(7) = 50\%$, or 0.5. Use this to find k.

c) After what time t is 80% of the acreage in hybrid corn?

Exploratory Exercises.   A Psychology Experiment on Perception

Preparation

a) Find a 100 gram ("gram" is abbreviated "g") weight to be used as a *standard*.

b) Find rocks (or other objects) which respectively weigh about 85 g, 90 g, 95 g, 100 g, 105 g, 110 g, and 115 g.

Carrying Out the Experiment   The experiment can be performed by the instructor or a student on the rest of the class.

a) Arrange the rocks in random order. Pick one. Hand the standard and the rock to each member of the class and ask the question "Is the rock heavier than the standard?"

b) Repeat (a) with each rock and keep track of the responses in a table such as the following:

Weight of rock (g)	Students						% who responded "Yes"
	1	2	3	4	5	. . .	
105	Yes	No	Yes				80
85	No	No	No				5
110							
100							
90							
95							
115							

c) Plot the data points using the axes below and connect them with a smooth curve.

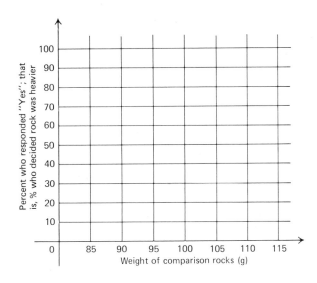

d) Answer the following discussion questions.
   1) Does the graph resemble an *S*-shaped curve?
   2) Does a small percent of the class respond "Yes" when handed the 85 g rock? Does this seem reasonable?
   3) Does a large percent of the class respond "Yes" when handed the 115 g rock? Does this seem reasonable?
   4) What percent respond "Yes" to the 100 g rock? Does this seem reasonable? Why?
   5) How could the experiment be repeated to improve the shape of the curve?

---

7. A *perception* experiment in psychology is done as in the preceding exploratory exercises. If you have not done the experiment, you should read it over. The percentage *P* who respond "Yes" to a rock of weight *w* satisfies the differential equation

$$\frac{dP}{dw} = kP(L - P)$$

where

   P = % who respond "Yes" to a rock of weight w,
   L = 100%, or 1,
   P_{85} = 4%, percent who respond "Yes" to the weight of w = 85 g (gram).

Look the graph over. Doesn't it seem reasonable that only 4% would have judged the 85-g rock to be heavier than the 100-g rock? As the weight of the comparison rocks gets to the standard, the percent increases. When the comparison weighs 100 g, the same as the standard, 50% say it is heavier. That is, half would say it is heavier and half would say it isn't. Then as the comparison rock gets heavier and heavier, the percent of "Yes" responses increases towards 100%.

a) Write the equation for $P(w)$, the solution of the differential equation, in terms of the given constants. Note that $w = 0$ means (85 g), $w = 1$ means (90 g), $w = 2$ means (95 g), and so on. Note that we have not yet determined k.

b) Use the fact that $P = 50\% = 0.5$ at $w = 3$ (100 g) to find k.

c) Rewrite the equation for $P(w)$ in terms of k and the other constants.

d) At what weight w does 80% respond "Yes"?

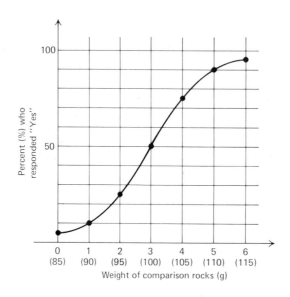

OBJECTIVES

You should be able to:

a) State the solution to the growth model $\dfrac{dP}{dt} = k(L - P)$.

b) Use Table 4 to graph equations of the type

$$P(t) = L(1 - e^{-kt}).$$

c) Given L and a function value for the equation in (b), find k.

d) Given L and k for the equation in (b), find a certain function value $P(t)$.

e) Given L and k for the equation in (b), find t such that $P(t) = M$, for some given number M.

7.4 APPLICATIONS: THE GROWTH MODEL $\dfrac{dP}{dt} = k(L - P)$

We have considered two models of growth:

1. $\dfrac{dP}{dt} = kP,$ *Uninhibited growth model*

2. $\dfrac{dP}{dt} = kP(L - P),$ *Inhibited growth model*

A third kind of growth assumes a limited population L, but assumes that the growth rate $\dfrac{dP}{dt}$ is directly proportional only to its remaining possible room for growth $L - P$, independent of the number who already exist. The model is

3. $\dfrac{dP}{dt} = k(L - P)$,   where $P = 0$ when $t = 0$.

This model has not proved suitable to describe biological population growth. Thus we will not consider that here. It is applicable to other areas. Before solving the differential equation we consider one such application in Margin Exercise 17.

Do Exercise 17.

We have considered a problem similar to this before in Exercise 4 of Exercise Set 7.3 where an S-shaped curve was encountered. In Margin Exercise 17 the graph did not resemble an S-shaped curve. In most advertising applications a curve like that in Margin Exercise 17 is what occurs. Models can vary, of course.

Now let us solve the differential equation

$$\frac{dP}{dt} = k(L - P).$$

We first separate the variables.

$$\frac{dP}{L - P} = k \, dt$$

Now we integrate both sides.

$$\int \frac{dP}{L - P} = \int k \, dt + C$$

$$-\ln(L - P) = kt + C$$

$$\ln(L - P) = -kt - C$$

$$L - P = e^{-kt - C} = e^{-kt} \cdot e^{-C}$$

Letting $C_1 = e^{-C}$, we have

$$L - P = C_1 e^{-kt}$$

$$-P = -L + C_1 e^{-kt}$$

$$P = L - C_1 e^{-kt}.$$

Now $P = 0$ when $t = 0$, so

$$0 = L - C_1 e^{-k \cdot 0} = L - C_1 \cdot 1 = L - C_1.$$

17. *Exploratory exercises. Advertising.* A company introduces a new product on a trial run in a city. It advertises the product on TV and gathers data concerning the percentage P of the people in the city who bought the product after it was advertised a certain number of times.

a) The following table contains the data. Complete the calculations in the table.

t (Number of times Ad run)	P (% who bought product)	$\dfrac{\Delta P}{\Delta t}$ (Rate of change) %
0	0	undefined
10	50	5
20	75	
30	87	
40	94	
50	97	

b) Plot P versus t. Connect the points with a smooth curve.

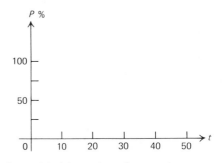

Steps (c)–(g) continued on next page.

c) Plot $\dfrac{\Delta P}{\Delta t}$ versus t. Connect the points with a smooth curve.

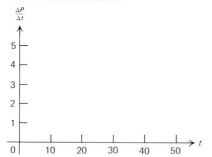

d) Does P resemble an S-shaped curve?
e) Does there seem to be a point of inflection for P?
f) What appears to be the limiting value for P?
g) Does the slope appear to be increasing? decreasing? neither?

---

18. Let $L = 3$, and $k = 1$, so

$$P(t) = 3(1 - e^{-t}).$$

a) Use Table 4 and complete this table of function values.

t	0	1	2	3	4	5
$P(t)$			2.6			

For example,

$$P(2) = 3(1 - e^{-2})$$
$$= 3(1 - 0.1353), \text{ by Table 4}$$
$$= 2.5941 \approx 2.6.$$

b) Graph $P(t)$.

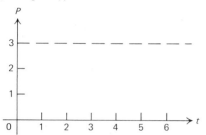

Thus $L = C_1$, and

$$P = L - Le^{-kt} = L(1 - e^{-kt}).$$

The solution of

$$\frac{dP}{dt} = k(L - P) \tag{3}$$

is

$$P(t) = L(1 - e^{-kt}). \tag{4}$$

Do Exercise 18.

As Exercise 18 illustrates, the following is a graph of $P(t)$. Note that the graph starts at $(0, 0)$ and increases upward toward the limiting value L. The slope is decreasing and there is no point of inflection.

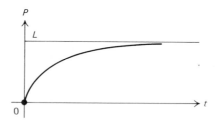

Now let us reconsider the problem on advertising in Margin Exercise 17.

Example   Reread Margin Exercise 17.

a) Suppose we want to "fit" equation (4) to this data. We know that $L = 100\%$, or 1, so

$$P(t) = 1 - e^{-kt}.$$

Thus we must determine a value for k. A way to do this is to arbitrarily pick a data point, substitute, and solve for k. We use $(10, 50\%)$; that is, $P(10) = 50\%$, or 0.5. Substituting and solving, we have

$$0.5 = 1 - e^{-k \cdot 10}$$
$$-0.5 = -e^{-10k}$$
$$0.5 = e^{-10k}.$$

Since ln 0.5 can be found in Table 3, we can use natural logarithms to solve this equation. Otherwise we can use common logarithms.

$$\ln 0.5 = \ln e^{-10k}$$
$$9.3069 - 10 = -10k$$
$$-0.6931 = -10k$$
$$0.06931 = k$$
$$0.07 \approx k$$

b) Rewrite $P(t)$ in terms of k. $P(t) = 1 - e^{-0.07t}$.

c) Use the equation in (b) and Table 4 to find $P(50)$.

$$P(50) = 1 - e^{-0.07 \cdot 50} = 1 - e^{-3.5} = 1 - 0.0302 = 0.9698$$

Note that this is close to the data value of 97%. This may not always happen in practice.

d) How many times must the product be advertised so that 99% of the people will buy it?

We solve
$$.99 = 1 - e^{-0.07t}$$

for t and get $t \approx 66$.

Do Exercise 19.

19. a) In another advertising experiment it was determined that $L = 100\%$, so
$$P(t) = 1 - e^{-kt}.$$
One of the data points was
$$P(10) = 40\%, \text{ or } 0.4.$$
Use this value to determine k. Round to the nearest hundredth.
b) Rewrite $P(t)$ in terms of k.
c) Use the equation in (b) and Table 4 to find $P(60)$.
d) How many times must the product be advertised so that 99% of the people will buy it?

EXERCISE SET 7.4

Graph.

1. $P(t) = 4(1 - e^{-t})$ 2. $P(t) = 2(1 - e^{-t})$ 3. $P(t) = 1 - e^{-2t}$ 4. $P(t) = 1 - e^{-3t}$

5. In a different advertising experiment it was determined that $L = 50\%$, or 0.5; that is, no matter how much a company advertised the percentage of people who bought the product would never reach or exceed 50%.

a) Express $P(t)$ in terms of $L = 0.5$.
b) It was determined that $P(10) = 25\%$, or .25. Use this to determine k. Round to the nearest hundredth.
c) Rewrite $P(t)$ in terms of k.
d) Use the equation in (c) to find $P(30)$.
e) How many times must the product be advertised so that 49% of the people will buy it?

6. *Acceptance of a new medicine.* A different model for the diffusion of information, for example, awareness of a new medicine by doctors, is the differential equation

$$\frac{dP}{dt} = k(L - P),$$

where

$P =$ percentage of doctors who are aware of the new medicine after time t (in months),
$L = 100\%$, or 1,
$k =$ constant.

a) Write the equation for $P(t)$, the solution of the differential equation, in terms of L and k.

b) Suppose $P(4) = 50\%$, or 0.5. Use this to determine k. Round to the nearest tenth.

c) Rewrite $P(t)$ in terms of k.

d) Use the equation in (c) to find $P(6)$.

e) How many months will it take for 90% of the doctors to become aware of the new medicine?

8. *Yield due to the spread of fertilizer.* A farmer is growing soybeans in a field. The more fertilizer he spreads, the greater his yield up to some limiting value L. A model for this, relative to a certain farm, is

$$\frac{dY}{dn} = k(L - Y),$$

where

$Y =$ the yield, in bushels per acre, upon spreading n pounds of fertilizer per acre,
$L = 60$ bushels per acre, and
$k =$ constant.

a) Write the solution $Y(n)$ in terms of L and k.

b) Suppose $P(10) = 21$. Use this to determine k. Round to the nearest hundredth.

c) Rewrite $Y(n)$ in terms of k.

d) Use the equation in (c) to find $Y(5)$.

e) How many pounds of fertilizer, per acre, must be spread to yield 42 bushels per acre?

[*Note:* This model is not completely valid in the sense that there usually is a certain amount of fertilizer which would kill the crop resulting in no yield.

7. The *Hullian Model of Learning* is

$$\frac{dP}{dt} = k(L - P)$$

where

$P =$ probability of mastery of a certain concept after t learning trials,
$L = 1$, the limiting value of mastery of the learning, and
$k =$ constant.

a) Write the solution $P(t)$ in terms of L and k.

b) Suppose $P(5) = 0.6$. Use this to determine k. Round to the nearest hundredth.

c) Rewrite $P(t)$ in terms of k.

d) Use the equation in (c) to find $P(10)$.

e) Find t such that $P(t) = 0.90$. That is, how many trials are necessary for the probability of mastery of learning to be 0.90?

9. Atomic blasts and nuclear reactors cause a buildup of radioactive material in the atmosphere which satisfies

$$\frac{dM}{dt} = k\left(\frac{p}{k} - M\right), \qquad M = 0 \text{ when } t = 0;$$

where

M = mass of radioactive material in the atmosphere after time t (in years),

p = rate at which the radioactive material is introduced into the atmosphere,

k = annual decay rate of the radioactive material.

Find the solution, $M(t)$, of the differential equation in terms of p and k.

10. The *growth rate of a certain stock* is modeled by

$$\frac{dV}{dt} = k(L - V), \qquad V = \$20 \text{ when } t = 0;$$

where

V = value of stock, per share, after time t (in months),

L = \$24.81, the limiting value of the stock, and

k = constant.

Find the solution of the differential equation in terms of L and k.

Nuclear power station at Rowe, Massachusetts.

CHAPTER 7 TEST

1. Solve the differential equation $y' = x^2 + 3x - 5$, given the condition $y = 7$ when $x = 0$.

Solve these differential equations.

2. $\dfrac{dy}{dx} = 8x^7y$

3. $\dfrac{dy}{dx} = \dfrac{9}{y}$

4. $\dfrac{dy}{dt} = 6y$

5. For the inhibited growth model, $P = 680$ at the point of inflection. What is the limiting value?

6. The growth rate for a certain population of bacteria cells is given by

$$\frac{dP}{dt} = kP(L - P),$$

where

P = the number of cells present after time t (in hours).
$L = 800$, the limiting value,
$k = 0.0009$,
$P_0 = 20$.

a) Write the solution, $P(t)$, in terms of the given constants.

b) Sketch a graph of $P(t)$ given that the point of inflection occurs at $t = 5$.

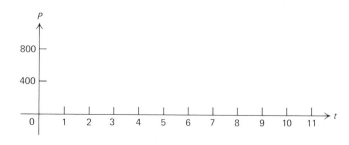

c) At what time t are 500 cells present?

7. Graph $P(t) = 5(1 - e^{-t})$.

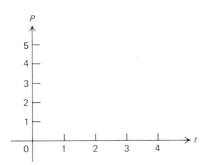

8. The growth rate of a company is modeled by

$$\frac{dS}{dt} = k(L - S),\ S = \$0 \quad \text{when } t = 0;$$

where

S = total sales, in millions of dollars, in the tth year of operation,
L = \$20 million, the limiting value,
k = constant.

a) Write the solution $S(t)$ in terms of L and k.

b) Suppose $S(2) = \$4$ million; that is, sales during the 2nd year are \$4 million. Use this to determine k. Round to the nearest hundredth.

c) Rewrite $S(t)$ in terms of k.

d) Use the equation in (c) to find $S(10)$, the sales in the 10th year.

e) In what year will the sales be \$15 million?

Jean-Claude Lejeune from Stock, Boston

8 FUNCTIONS OF SEVERAL VARIABLES

OBJECTIVES

You should be able to:

a) Find a function value for a function of several variables.
b) Find the partial derivatives of a given function.
c) Evaluate the partial derivatives of a function at a given point.

1. For $P(x, y) = 4x + 6y$,

a) find $P(14, 12)$ and interpret its meaning.

b) find $P(0, 8)$ and interpret its meaning.

2. For $A(x, y) = xy$, find $A(7, 20)$.

8.1 PARTIAL DERIVATIVES

Functions of Several Variables

Suppose a one-product firm produces x items of its product at a profit of \$4 per item. Then its total profit $P(x)$ is given by

$$P(x) = 4x.$$

This is a function of *one* variable.

Suppose a two-product firm produces x items of one product at a profit of \$4 per item, and y items of a second at a profit of \$6 per item. Then its total profit P is a function of the *two* variables x and y and is given by

$$P(x, y) = 4x + 6y.$$

This function assigns to the input pair (x, y) a unique output number $4x + 6y$.

Example 1   For $P(x, y) = 4x + 6y$, find $P(25, 10)$.

Solution

$P(25, 10)$ is defined to be the value of the function found by substituting 25 for x and 10 for y:

$$P(25, 10) = 4 \cdot 25 + 6 \cdot 10 = 100 + 60 = 160.$$

For the two-product firm this means that by selling 25 items of the first product and 10 of the second it will make a profit of \$160.

Do Exercise 1.

The following are further examples of functions of several variables, that is, functions of two or more variables.

Example 2   The area of a rectangle is given by

$$A(x, y) = xy,$$

where x represents the length and y the width. Find $A(7, 9)$.

Solution
$$A(7, 9) = 7 \cdot 9 = 63$$

Do Exercise 2.

Example 3   The volume of a rectangular solid is given by

$$V(x, y, z) = xyz,$$

where x is the length, y the width, and z the height. This is a function of three variables.

Do Exercise 3.

Example 4   The production of a company is given by

$$f(x, y, z, w) = 4x^2 - 5y + z - w,$$

where x dollars are spent for labor, y dollars are spent for raw materials, z dollars are spent for advertising, and w dollars are spent for machinery. This is a function of four variables.

Find $f(3, 2, 0, 10)$.

Solution   We substitute 3 for x, 2 for y, 0 for z, and 10 for w.

$$
\begin{aligned}
f(3, 2, 0, 10) &= 4 \cdot 3^2 - 5 \cdot 2 + 0 - 10 \\
&= 4 \cdot 9 - 10 + 0 - 10 \\
&= 16
\end{aligned}
$$

Do Exercise 4.

Example 5   Suppose an amount P_0 is invested in a savings account, where interest is compounded continuously at interest rate k. The balance after t years is given by

$$P(P_0, k, t) = P_0 e^{kt}.$$

Find $P(\$100, 0.07, 1)$.

Solution $P(\$100, 0.07, 1) = 100e^{0.07(1)} = 100(1.0725)$, by Table 4
$$= \$107.25$$

Do Exercise 5.

---

3. For $V(x, y, z) = xyz$, find $V(5, 10, 40)$.

4. For the function f of Example 4, find
a) $f(9, 5, 3, 0)$
b) $f(1, 2, 3, 4)$

5. For the function of Example 5, find
$$P(\$1000, 0.08, 2).$$

6. The constant function g is given by

$$g(x, y) = 4$$

for all inputs x and y. Find
a) $g(-9, 10)$ b) $g(560, 43)$.

Example 6   *The gravity model.* The number of telephone calls between two cities is given by

$$N(d, P_1, P_2) = \frac{2.8 P_1 P_2}{d^{2.4}},$$

where d is the distance between the cities, and P_1 and P_2 are their populations.

Sociologists say that as the communication between two cities increases, the cities tend to merge.

A constant can also be thought of as a function of several variables.

Example 7   The constant function f is given by

$$f(x, y) = -3, \quad \text{for all inputs } x \text{ and } y.$$

Find $f(5, 7)$ and $f(-2, 0)$.

Solution   Since this is a constant function, it has the value -3 for any x and y.

So $f(5, 7) = -3$ and $f(-2, 0) = -3$.

Do Exercise 6.

Partial Derivatives

Consider the function f given by

$$z = f(x, y) = x^2y^3 + xy + 4y^2.$$

Suppose for the moment that we fix y at 3. Then

$$f(x, 3) = x^23^3 + x3 + 4 \cdot 3^2 = 27x^2 + 3x + 36.$$

Note that we now have a function of only one variable. Taking the first derivative with respect to x, we have

$$54x + 3.$$

Do Exercise 7.

Now, without replacing y by a specific number, let us consider y fixed. Then f becomes a function of x alone and we can calculate its derivative with respect to x. This derivative is called the *partial derivative of f with respect to x*. Notation for this partial derivative is

$$\frac{\partial f}{\partial x}, \quad \text{or} \quad \frac{\partial z}{\partial x}.$$

Thus fixing y (treating it as a constant) and calculating the derivative with respect to x, we have

$$\frac{\partial f}{\partial x} = \frac{\partial z}{\partial x} = 2xy^3 + y.$$

Do Exercise 8.

Similarly, we find $\dfrac{\partial f}{\partial y}$, or $\dfrac{\partial z}{\partial y}$, by fixing x (treating it as a constant) and calculating the derivative with respect to y. We have

$$\frac{\partial f}{\partial y} = \frac{\partial z}{\partial y} = 3x^2y^2 + x + 8y.$$

Do Exercise 9.

7. Consider

$$f(x, y) = 1 - x^2 - y^2.$$

a) Fix y at 4 and find $f(x, 4)$.
b) The answer to (a) could be interpreted as a function of one variable x. Find the first derivative.

8. For

$$f(x, y) = 1 - x^2 - y^2,$$

find $\dfrac{\partial f}{\partial x}$.

9. For

$$z = 3x^2y + 5x^3,$$

a) find $\dfrac{\partial z}{\partial x}$,

b) find $\dfrac{\partial z}{\partial y}$.

10. For $t = xy + xz + x^2 + y^3$, find

a) $\dfrac{\partial t}{\partial x}$,   b) $\dfrac{\partial t}{\partial y}$,   c) $\dfrac{\partial t}{\partial z}$.

Partial differentiation can be done for any number of variables.

Example   For $w = x^2 - xy + y^2 + 2yz + 2z^2 + z$, find $\dfrac{\partial w}{\partial x}$, $\dfrac{\partial w}{\partial y}$, and $\dfrac{\partial w}{\partial z}$.

Solution

$$\frac{\partial w}{\partial x} = 2x - y$$

$$\frac{\partial w}{\partial y} = -x + 2y + 2z$$

$$\frac{\partial w}{\partial z} = 2y + 4z + 1$$

Do Exercise 10.

11. For $f(x, y) = 3x^3y + 2xy$, find

a) f_x,   b) $f_x(-4, 1)$,
c) f_y,   d) $f_y(2, 6)$.

We will often make use of a simpler notation f_x for the partial derivative of f with respect to x, and f_y for the partial derivative of f with respect to y.

Example   For $f(x, y) = 3x^2y + xy$, find f_x and f_y.

Solution

$$f_x = 6xy + y, \qquad f_y = 3x^2 + x$$

For the function in the preceding example let us evaluate f_x at $(2, -3)$.

$$f_x(2, -3) = 6 \cdot 2 \cdot (-3) + (-3) = -39$$

Using the notation $\dfrac{\partial z}{\partial x} = 6xy + y$, where $z = 3x^2y + xy$, the value of the partial derivative at $(2, -3)$ is given by

$$\left.\frac{\partial z}{\partial x}\right|_{(2, -3)} = 6 \cdot 2 \cdot (-3) + (-3) = -39,$$

but this notation is not as convenient as $f_x(2, -3)$.

Do Exercise 11.

Geometric Interpretations

Consider a function of two variables

$$z = f(x, y).$$

Recall the mapping interpretation of function which we considered in Chapter 1. As a mapping, a function of two variables can be thought of as mapping a point (x_1, y_1) in an xy-plane onto a point z_1 on a number line:

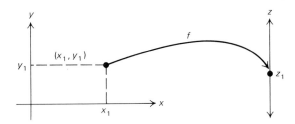

To graph a function of two variables we need a three-dimensional coordinate system. The axes are usually placed as follows. The line z, called the z-axis, is placed perpendicular to the xy-plane at the origin.

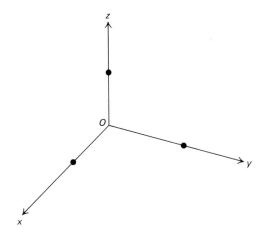

To help visualize this, think of looking into the corner of a room, where the floor is the xy-plane and the z-axis is the intersection of two walls. To plot a point (x_1, y_1, z_1) we locate the point (x_1, y_1) in the xy-plane, and move up or down in space according to the value of z_1.

12. Using the axes shown below, graph $P_1(3, 2, 5)$, $P_2(2, 3, 1)$, and $P_3(-3, 2, 0)$.

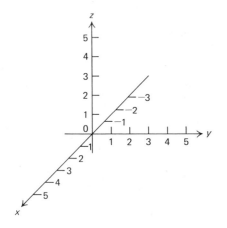

Examples   Plot the points $P_1(2, 3, 5)$, $P_2(2, -2, -4)$, and $P_3(0, 5, 2)$.

Solution

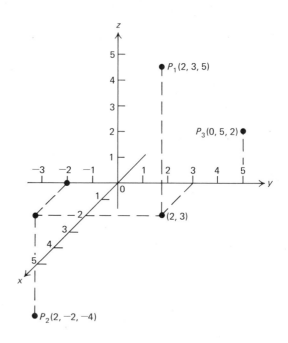

Do Exercise 12.

The *graph* of a function of two variables

$$z = f(x, y)$$

consists of ordered triples (x_1, y_1, z_1), where $z_1 = f(x_1, y_1)$. The domain of f is a region D in the xy-plane, and the graph of f is a surface S, as shown below.

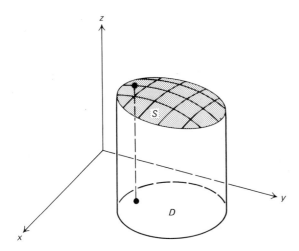

Now suppose we hold x fixed, say at the value a. The set of all points for which $x = a$ is a plane parallel to the yz-plane, so when x is fixed at a, y and z vary along the plane as shown in the following figure.

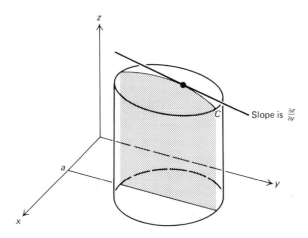

Slope is $\frac{\partial z}{\partial y}$

The plane shown cuts the surface S in some curve C as shown. The partial derivative f_y gives the slopes of tangent lines to this curve. Similarly, if we hold y fixed, say at the value b, we obtain a curve C' as shown in the following figure. The partial derivative f_x gives the slopes of tangent lines to this curve.

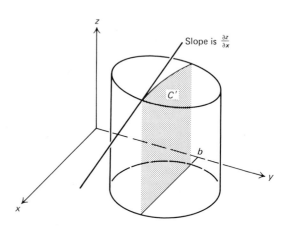

EXERCISE SET 8.1

1. For $f(x, y) = x^2 - 2xy$, find $f(0, -2)$, $f(2, 3)$, and $f(10, -5)$.

2. For $f(x, y) = y^2 + 3xy$, find $f(-2, 0)$, $f(3, 2)$, and $f(-5, 10)$.

3. For $f(x, y) = 3^x + 7xy$, find $f(0, -2)$, $f(-2, 1)$, and $f(2, 1)$.

4. For $f(x, y) = \log_{10} x - 5y^2$, find $f(10, 2)$, $f(1, -3)$, and $f(100, 4)$.

5. For $f(x, y) = \ln x + y^3$, find $f(e, 2)$, $f(e^2, 4)$, and $f(e^3, 5)$.

6. For $f(x, y) = 2^x - 3^y$, find $f(0, 0)$, $f(1, 1)$, and $f(2, 2)$.

7. For $f(x, y, z) = x^2 - y^2 + z^2$, find $f(-1, 2, 3)$ and $f(2, -1, 3)$.

8. For $f(x, y, z) = 2^x + 5zy - x$, find $f(0, 1, -3)$ and $f(1, 0, -3)$.

Find $\dfrac{\partial z}{\partial x}$, $\dfrac{\partial z}{\partial y}$, $\dfrac{\partial z}{\partial x}\Big|_{(-2,-3)}$, and $\dfrac{\partial z}{\partial y}\Big|_{(0,-5)}$.

9. $z = 2x - 3xy$

10. $z = 5y + 2xy$

11. $z = 3x^2 - 2xy + y$

12. $z = 2x^3 + 3xy - x$

Find f_x, f_y, $f_x(-2, 4)$, and $f_y(4, -3)$.

13. $f(x, y) = 2x - 3y$

14. $f(x, y) = 5x + 7y$

Find f_x, f_y, $f_x(-2, 1)$, and $f_y(-3, -2)$.

15. $f(x, y) = \sqrt{x^2 + y^2}$

16. $f(x, y) = \sqrt{x^2 - y^2}$

Find f_x and f_y.

17. $f(x, y) = e^{2x+3y}$

18. $f(x, y) = e^{3x-2y}$

19. $f(x, y) = e^{xy}$

20. $f(x, y) = e^{2xy}$

21. $f(x, y) = y \ln(x + y)$

22. $f(x, y) = x \ln(x + y)$

23. $f(x, y) = x \ln(xy)$

24. $f(x, y) = y \ln(xy)$

25. $f(x, y) = \dfrac{x}{y} - \dfrac{y}{x}$

26. $f(x, y) = \dfrac{x}{y} + \dfrac{y}{x}$

27. $f(x, y) = 3(2x + y - 5)^2$

28. $f(x, y) = 4(3x + y - 8)^2$

Find f_x, f_y, and f_λ.

29. $f(x, y, \lambda) = 3xy - \lambda(2x + y - 8)$

30. $f(x, y, \lambda) = 4xy - \lambda(3x - y + 7)$

31. $f(x, y, \lambda) = x^2 + y^2 - \lambda(10x + 2y - 4)$

32. $f(x, y, \lambda) = x^2 - y^2 - \lambda(4x - 7y - 10)$

Find $\dfrac{\partial f}{\partial b}$ and $\dfrac{\partial f}{\partial m}$.

33. $f(b, m) = (m + b - 4)^2 + (2m + b - 5)^2 + (3m + b - 6)^2$

34. $f(b, m) = (m + b - 6)^2 + (2m + b - 8)^2 + (3m + b - 9)^2$

OBJECTIVES

You should be able to find the four second partial derivatives of a function.

13. Consider

$$z = 3xy^2 + 2xy + x^2.$$

a) Find $\dfrac{\partial z}{\partial y}$.

b) For the function in (a), find the first partial derivative with respect to x.

c) For the function in (a), find the first partial derivative with respect to y; that is, differentiate "twice" with respect to y.

14. Consider

$$f(x, y) = 3xy^2 + 2xy + x^2.$$

a) Find f_y.

b) For the function in (a), find the first partial derivative with respect to x. Denote this f_{yx}.

c) For the function in (a), find the first partial derivative with respect to y. Denote this f_{yy}.

8.2 HIGHER-ORDER PARTIAL DERIVATIVES

Consider

$$z = f(x, y) = 3xy^2 + 2xy + x^2. \tag{1}$$

Then

$$\frac{\partial z}{\partial x} = \frac{\partial f}{\partial x} = 3y^2 + 2y + 2x. \tag{2}$$

Suppose we find the first partial derivative of function (2) with respect to y. This will be a *second-order partial derivative*. Notation for it is as follows.

$$\frac{\partial}{\partial y}\left(\frac{\partial z}{\partial x}\right) = \frac{\partial}{\partial y}\left(\frac{\partial f}{\partial x}\right) = \frac{\partial^2 z}{\partial y\, \partial x} = \frac{\partial^2 f}{\partial y\, \partial x} = 6y + 2.$$

Do Exercise 13.

We could also denote the preceding partial derivative using the notation f_{xy}. Then

$$f_{xy} = 6y + 2.$$

Note that in the notation f_{xy}, x and y are in the order (left to right) in which the differentiation is done. In the other symbolisms that order is reversed, but the meaning is not.

Do Exercise 14.

Notation for the four second-order partial derivatives is as follows:

$$\frac{\partial^2 z}{\partial x\, \partial x} = \frac{\partial^2 f}{\partial x\, \partial x} = \frac{\partial^2 z}{\partial x^2} = \frac{\partial^2 f}{\partial x^2} = f_{xx}$$

(Take the partial with respect to x, and then with respect to x again.)

$$\frac{\partial^2 z}{\partial y\, \partial x} = \frac{\partial^2 f}{\partial y\, \partial x} = f_{xy}$$

(Take the partial with respect to x, and then with respect to y.)

$$\frac{\partial^2 z}{\partial x\, \partial y} = \frac{\partial^2 f}{\partial x\, \partial y} = f_{yx}$$

(Take the partial with respect to y, and then with respect to x.)

$$\frac{\partial^2 z}{\partial y\, \partial y} = \frac{\partial^2 f}{\partial y\, \partial y} = \frac{\partial^2 z}{\partial y^2} = \frac{\partial^2 f}{\partial y^2} = f_{yy}$$

(Take the partial with respect to y, and then with respect to y again.)

Example   For

$$z = f(x, y) = x^2 y^3 + x^4 y$$

find the four second-order partial derivatives.

Solution

a) $\dfrac{\partial^2 f}{\partial x^2} = \dfrac{\partial}{\partial x}\,(2xy^3 + 4x^3 y) = 2y^3 + 12x^2 y$

   (Differentiate twice with respect to x.)

b) $\dfrac{\partial^2 f}{\partial y\, \partial x} = \dfrac{\partial}{\partial y}\,(2xy^3 + 4x^3 y) = 6xy^2 + 4x^3$

   (Differentiate with respect to x, then with respect to y.)

c) $\dfrac{\partial^2 f}{\partial x\, \partial y} = \dfrac{\partial}{\partial x}\,(3x^2 y^2 + x^4) = 6xy^2 + 4x^3$

   (Differentiate with respect to y, then with respect to x.)

d) $\dfrac{\partial^2 f}{\partial y^2} = \dfrac{\partial}{\partial y}\,(3x^2 y^2 + x^4) = 6x^2 y$

   (Differentiate twice with respect to y.)

Do Exercise 15.

Note by comparing (b) and (c) above that

$$\frac{\partial^2 f}{\partial y\, \partial x} = \frac{\partial^2 f}{\partial x\, \partial y} \text{ (and similarly, } f_{xy} = f_{yx}).$$

This will be true for all functions which we consider in this text, but is *not* true for all functions.

15. For

$$z = f(x, y) = 3xy^2 + 2xy + x^2$$

find the four second-order partial derivatives.

EXERCISE SET 8.2

Find the four second-order partial derivatives.

1. $f(x, y) = 3x^2 - xy + y$ **2.** $f(x, y) = 5x^2 + xy - x$

3. $f(x, y) = 3xy$ **4.** $f(x, y) = 4xy$

5. $f(x, y) = x^5y^4 + x^3y^2$ **6.** $f(x, y) = x^4y^3 - x^2y^3$

Find f_{xx}, f_{yx}, f_{xy}, and f_{yy}. (Remember, f_{yx} means differentiate with respect to y, then x).

7. $f(x, y) = 2x - 3y$ **8.** $f(x, y) = 3x + 5y$

9. $f(x, y) = e^{2xy}$ **10.** $f(x, y) = e^{xy}$

11. $f(x, y) = x + e^y$ **12.** $f(x, y) = y - e^x$

13. $f(x, y) = y \ln x$ **14.** $f(x, y) = x \ln y$

15. Consider $f(x, y) = \ln(x^2 + y^2)$. Show that f is a solution of the partial differential equation

$$\frac{\partial^2 f}{\partial x^2} + \frac{\partial^2 f}{\partial y^2} = 0.$$

16. Consider $f(x, y) = x^3 - 5xy^2$. Show that f is a solution of the partial differential equation

$$xf_{xy} - f_y = 0.$$

OBJECTIVES

You should be able to find maximum and minimum values of functions of two variables.

8.3 MAXIMUM-MINIMUM PROBLEMS

In this section we shall find maximum and minimum values of functions of two variables.

 DEFINITION. **A function f of two variables,**

  i) **has a relative maximum at (a, b) if**

$$f(x, y) \leq f(a, b)$$

  for all points in a circular region containing (a, b).

  ii) **has a relative minimum at (a, b) if**

$$f(x, y) \geq f(a, b)$$

  for all points in a circular region containing (a, b).

This definition is illustrated below.

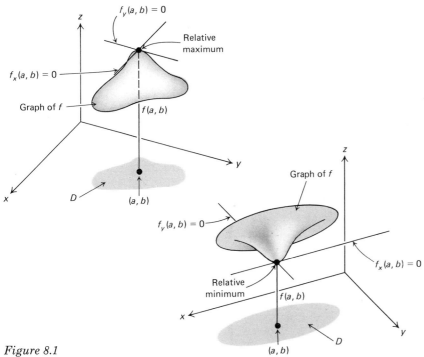

Figure 8.1

A relative maximum (minimum) may not be an "absolute" maximum (minimum) as illustrated below.

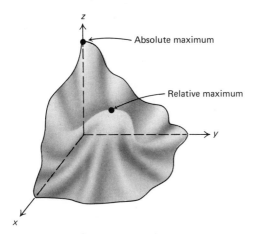

Figure 8.2

Determining Maximum and Minimum Values

Suppose a function f assumes a relative maximum (or minimum) value at some point (a, b) inside its domain. If we hold y constant at the value b then $f(x, b)$ is a function of one variable x having its relative maximum value at $x = a$, so its derivative must be 0 there. That is, $f_x = 0$ at the point (a, b). Similarly, $f_y = 0$ at (a, b). The equations

$$f_x = 0, \qquad f_y = 0$$

are thus satisfied by the point (a, b) at which the relative maximum occurs. We call a point (a, b) where both partial derivatives are 0 a *critical point*. This is comparable to the earlier definition for functions of one variable. Thus one strategy for finding relative maximum or minimum values is to solve the above system of equations to find critical points. Just as for functions of one variable, this strategy does *not* guarantee that we will have a relative maximum or minimum value. We have argued only that *if* f has a maximum or minimum value at (a, b), *then* both its partial derivatives must be 0 at that point. Look at Fig. 8.1. That this does not hold in all cases is shown in Fig. 8.3.

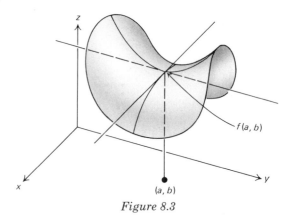

Figure 8.3

Now suppose we fix y at a point b. Then $f(x, b)$, considered as a function of one variable, has a maximum at a, but f does not. Similarly, if we fix x at a, then $f(a, y)$, considered as a function of one variable, has a minimum at b, but f does not. The point $f(a, b)$ is called a *saddle point*. In other words, $f_x(a, b) = 0$ and $f_y(a, b) = 0$ [the point (a, b) is a critical point], but f does not attain a relative maximum or minimum at (a, b).

A test for finding relative maximum and minimum values which involves the use of first- and second-order partial derivatives is stated
below. We shall not prove this theorem.

THEOREM. *The D-test.* **To find the relative maximum and minimum
values of f,**
1. **Find f_x, f_y, f_{xx}, f_{yy}, and f_{xy}.**
2. **Solve the system of equations $f_x = 0$, $f_y = 0$.**
   Let (a, b) represent a solution.
3. **Evaluate D where $D = f_{xx}(a, b) \cdot f_{yy}(a, b) - [f_{xy}(a, b)]^2$.**
4. **Then**
   i) f has a maximum at (a, b) if $D > 0$ and $f_{xx}(a, b) < 0$.
   ii) f has a minimum at (a, b) if $D > 0$ and $f_{xx}(a, b) > 0$.
   iii) f has neither a maximum nor a minimum at (a, b) if $D < 0$.
   The function has a *saddle point* at (a, b). See Fig. 8.3.
   iv) This test is not applicable if $D = 0$.

A relative maximum or minimum *may not be an absolute maximum or
minimum.* Tests for absolute maximum or minimum are rather com-
plicated. We shall restrict our attention to finding *relative* maximum
or minimum values. Fortunately, in most applications relative maximum and minimum values turn out to be absolute maximum and
minimum values.

Example 1 Find the relative maximum and minimum values of

$$f(x, y) = x^2 + xy + y^2 - 3x.$$

Solution
1. Find f_x, f_y, f_{xx}, f_{yy}, and f_{xy}.

$$f_x = 2x + y - 3, \qquad f_y = x + 2y,$$
$$f_{xx} = 2, \qquad\qquad f_{yy} = 2,$$
$$f_{xy} = 1$$

2. Solve the system of equations $f_x = 0$, $f_y = 0$:

$$2x + y - 3 = 0 \qquad\qquad (1)$$
$$x + 2y = 0 \qquad\qquad (2)$$

Solving equation (2) for x we get $x = -2y$. Substituting $-2y$ for x in
equation (1) and solving we get

$$2(-2y) + y - 3 = 0$$
$$-4y + y - 3 = 0$$
$$-3y - 3 = 0$$
$$y = -1$$

16. Find the relative maximum and minimum values of

$$f(x, y) = x^2 + 2xy + 2y^2 - 6y.$$

To find x when $y = -1$ we substitute -1 for y in either equation (1) or equation (2). We use equation (2):

$$x + 2(-1) = 0$$
$$x = 2$$

Thus $(2, -1)$ is our candidate for a maximum or minimum.

3. We have to check to see if $f(2, -1)$ is a maximum or minimum.

$$D = f_{xx}(2, -1) \cdot f_{yy}(2, -1) - [f_{xy}(2, -1)]^2$$

$$= 2 \cdot 2 - [1]^2$$

$$= 3$$

4. Thus $D = 3$ and $f_{xx}(2, -1) = 2$. Since $D > 0$ and $f_{xx}(2, -1) > 0$, it follows that f has a relative minimum at $(2, -1)$ and that minimum is found as follows:

$$f(2, -1) = 2^2 + 2(-1) + (-1)^2 - 3 \cdot 2$$
$$= 4 - 2 + 1 - 6 = -3$$

Do Exercise 16.

Example 2 Find the relative maximum and minimum values of

$$f(x, y) = xy - x^3 - y^2.$$

Solution

1. Find f_x, f_y, f_{xx}, f_{yy}, and f_{xy}:

$$f_x = y - 3x^2, \qquad f_y = x - 2y,$$
$$f_{xx} = -6x, \qquad f_{yy} = -2,$$
$$f_{xy} = 1$$

2. Solve the system of equations $f_x = 0, f_y = 0$:

$$y - 3x^2 = 0 \tag{1}$$
$$x - 2y = 0 \tag{2}$$

Solving equation (1) for y, we get $y = 3x^2$. Substituting $3x^2$ for y in equation (2) and solving, we get

$$x - 2(3x^2) = 0$$
$$x - 6x^2 = 0$$
$$x(1 - 6x) = 0 \qquad \text{(factoring)}$$

Setting each factor equal to 0 and solving, we have

$$x = 0 \quad \text{or} \quad 1 - 6x = 0$$
$$x = 0 \quad \text{or} \quad x = \tfrac{1}{6}.$$

To find y when $x = 0$ we substitute 0 for x in either equation (1) or equation (2). We use equation (2):

$$0 - 2y = 0$$
$$-2y = 0$$
$$y = 0.$$

Thus $(0, 0)$ is one critical value (candidate for a maximum or minimum). To find the other critical value we substitute $\tfrac{1}{6}$ for x in either equation (1) or (2). We use (2).

$$\tfrac{1}{6} - 2y = 0$$
$$-2y = -\tfrac{1}{6}$$
$$y = \tfrac{1}{12}$$

Thus $(\tfrac{1}{6}, \tfrac{1}{12})$ is another critical point.

3. We have to check both $(0, 0)$ and $(\tfrac{1}{6}, \tfrac{1}{12})$ as to whether they yield maximum or minimum values.

For $(0, 0)$: $\quad D = f_{xx}(0, 0) \cdot f_{yy}(0, 0) - [f_{xy}(0, 0)]^2$
$$= [-6 \cdot 0] \cdot [-2] - [1]^2$$
$$= -1$$

Since $D < 0$, it follows that $f(0, 0)$ is neither a maximum nor a minimum.

For $(\tfrac{1}{6}, \tfrac{1}{12})$: $\quad D = f_{xx}(\tfrac{1}{6}, \tfrac{1}{12})f_{yy}(\tfrac{1}{6}, \tfrac{1}{12}) - [f_{xy}(\tfrac{1}{6}, \tfrac{1}{12})]^2$
$$= [-6 \cdot \tfrac{1}{6}] \cdot [-2] - [1]^2$$
$$= -1(-2) - 1$$
$$= 1$$

4. Thus $D = 1$ and $f_{xx}(\tfrac{1}{6}, \tfrac{1}{12}) = -1$. Since $D > 0$ and $f_{xx}(\tfrac{1}{6}, \tfrac{1}{12}) < 0$, it follows that f has a relative maximum at $(\tfrac{1}{6}, \tfrac{1}{12})$ and that maximum is found as follows:

$$f(\tfrac{1}{6}, \tfrac{1}{12}) = \tfrac{1}{6} \cdot \tfrac{1}{12} - (\tfrac{1}{6})^3 - (\tfrac{1}{12})^2$$
$$= \tfrac{1}{72} - \tfrac{1}{216} - \tfrac{1}{144} = \tfrac{1}{432}$$

Do Exercise 17.

17. Find the relative maximum and minimum values of

$$f(x, y) = 2xy - 4x^3 - y^2.$$

From *Chariots of the Gods*
    by Erich Von Daniken

Green Bank Conference*

It is no longer a secret that in November, 1961, in the National Radio Astronomy Observatory at Green Bank, West Virginia, eleven authorities met at a secret conference. Here, too, the theme of the conference was the question of the existence of extraterrestrial intelligences. The scientists, among them Giuseppe Cocconi, Su Shu Huang, Philip Morrison, Frank Drake, Otto Struve, and Carl Sagan, as well as the Nobel Prize winner Melvin Calvin, collaborated at the end of the conference on what is known as the Green Bank Formula. According to this formula there are at any moment in our galaxy alone 50,000,000 different civilizations which are either trying to get in touch with us or waiting for a sign from other planets.

The terms of the Green Bank Formula take into account all the aspects in question, but in addition the scientists allotted two values to each term: a normal value admissible according to our present state of knowledge and an **absolute minimum** value.

$$N = R_+ f_p n_e f_1 f_i f_c L$$

In this formula:

R_+ = the average annual number of new stars that are like our sun;

f_p = the number of stars with possible living beings;

n_e = the average number of planets which orbit the ecosphere of their sun and so have adequate premises for the development of life by human standards;

f_1 = the number of planets favored in this way on which life has actually developed;

f_i = the number of planets which are populated by intelligences with their own ability to act during the lifetime of their sun;

f_c = the number of planets inhabited by intelligences that already have a developed technical civilization;

L = the life-span of a civilization, for only very long-lasting civilizations could encounter each other, given the vast distances in the universe.

If we take the lowest possible figures for all terms in this formula, we get: $N = 40$.

But if we take the admissible **maximum value**, we get: $N = 50,000,000$.

In other words, in the most unfavorable case the fantastic Green Bank Formula calculates that there are forty groups of intelligences in our Milky Way who are seeking contact with other intelligences.

The most audacious possibility gives 50,000,000 unknown intelligences who are waiting for a sign from the cosmos. All the Green Bank calculations are based not on present astronomical figures but on the number of stars in our Milky Way since it existed.

* Erich Von Daniken, *Chariots of the Gods*, New York, Bantam Books, 1971, pp. 139–141. Reprinted by permission of G. P. Putnam's Sons. English translation copyright © 1969 by Michael Heron and Souvenir Press of London.

Lick Observatory

EXERCISE SET 8.3

Find the relative maximum and minimum values.

1. $f(x, y) = x^2 + xy + y^2 - y$

2. $f(x, y) = x^2 + xy + y^2 - 5y$

3. $f(x, y) = 2xy - x^3 - y^2$

4. $f(x, y) = 4xy - x^3 - y^2$

5. $f(x, y) = x^3 + y^3 - 3xy$

6. $f(x, y) = x^3 + y^3 - 6xy$

7. $f(x, y) = x^2 + y^2 - 2x + 4y - 2$

8. $f(x, y) = x^2 + 2xy + 2y^2 - 6y$

9. $f(x, y) = x^2 + y^2 + 2x - 4y$

10. $f(x, y) = 4y + 6x - x^2 - y^2$

11. $f(x, y) = 4x^2 - y^2$

12. $f(x, y) = x^2 - y^2$

In these problems assume that relative maximum and minimum values are absolute maximum and minimum values.

13. A one-product company found that its profit in millions of dollars is a function P given by

$$P(a, p) = 2ap + 80p - 15p^2 - \tfrac{1}{10}a^2p - 100,$$

where a = amount spent on advertising, in millions of dollars, and p = price charged per item of the product, in dollars. Find the maximum value of P and the values of a and p at which it is attained.

14. A one-product company finds that its profit in millions of dollars is a function P given by

$$P(a, n) = -5a^2 - 3n^2 + 48a - 4n + 2an + 300,$$

where a = amount spent on advertising, in millions of dollars, and n = number of items sold. Find the maximum value of P and the values of a and n at which it is attained.

15. *Two variable revenue maximization.* Boxowitz, Inc., a computer firm, markets two kinds of electronic calculators which compete with one another. Their demand functions are expressed by the following relationships

$$q_1 = 78 - 6p_1 - 3p_2, \tag{1}$$

$$q_2 = 66 - 3p_1 - 6p_2, \tag{2}$$

where

p_1, p_2 = the price of each calculator in multiples of $10,

q_1, q_2 = quantity of each calculator demanded in hundreds of units.

16. Repeat Exercise 15, where

$$q_1 = 64 - 4p_1 - 2p_2,$$
$$q_2 = 56 - 2p_1 - 4p_2.$$

a) Find a formula for the total revenue function R in terms of the variables p_1 and p_2. [*Hint:* $R = p_1q_1 + p_2q_2$, then substitute expressions from equations (1) and (2) to find $R(p_1, p_2)$.]

b) What prices p_1 and p_2 should be charged for each product in order to maximize total revenue?

c) How many units will be demanded?

d) What is the maximum total revenue?

8.4 APPLICATION—THE LEAST SQUARES TECHNIQUE

The problem of fitting an equation to a set of data occurs frequently. We considered one procedure for doing this in Section 1.6. Such an equation provides a model of the phenomena from which predictions can be made. For example, in business one might want to predict future sales based on past data. In ecology, one might want to predict future demands for natural gas based on past need. Suppose we are trying to determine a linear equation

$$y = mx + b$$

to fit the data. To determine this equation is to determine the values of m and b. But how? Let us consider some factual data on life expectancy of the female in the U.S.

Year—x	1. 1950	2. 1960	3. 1970	4. 1980
Life expectancy of female (in years)—y	72	73	75	?

Chester Higgins, Jr. from Rapho Guillumette Pictures

OBJECTIVES

You should be able to find the regression line for a given set of data points and use the regression line to make predictions regarding further data.

What is the life expectancy of the female in 1980?

18. a) Use Fig. 8.5 to predict life expectancy of the female in 1980.
   b) Use Fig. 8.6 to predict life expectancy of the female in 1980.
   c) Compare your answers.

Suppose we plot these points and try to draw a line which fits. Note
that there are several ways this might be done. Each would give a
different estimate of life expectancy in 1980.

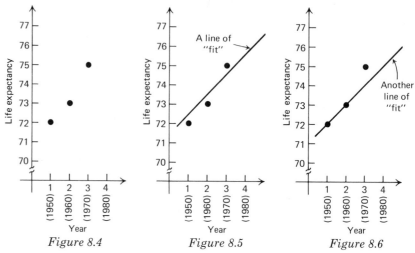

Figure 8.4   Figure 8.5   Figure 8.6

Do Exercise 18.

The time is in increments of ten years. Computation will be easier if
we take time in *tens* of years. Consider the data points (1, 72), (2, 73),
and (3, 75) as plotted in Fig. 8.7.

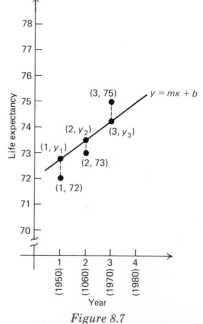

Figure 8.7

We will try to fit this data with a line

$$y = mx + b$$

by determining values of m and b. Note the y-errors, or y-deviations, $y_1 - 72$, $y_2 - 73$, and $y_3 - 75$ between the observed points $(1, 72)$, $(2, 73)$, and $(3, 75)$ and the points $(1, y_1)$, $(2, y_2)$, and $(3, y_3)$ on the line. We would like, somehow, to minimize these deviations, in order to have a good fit. One way of minimizing the deviations is based on the so-called *least squares assumption*, as follows.

LEAST SQUARES ASSUMPTION. The line of best fit is the line for which the sum of squares of the y-deviations is a minimum. This is called the *regression line*.

Using the least squares assumption for the life expectancy data, we would minimize

$$(y_1 - 72)^2 + (y_2 - 73)^2 + (y_3 - 75)^2 \tag{1}$$

and since the points $(1, y_1)$, $(2, y_2)$, and $(3, y_3)$ must be solutions of $y = mx + b$, it follows that

$$y_1 = m1 + b = m + b$$
$$y_2 = m2 + b = 2m + b$$
$$y_3 = m3 + b = 3m + b.$$

Substituting $m + b$ for y_1, $2m + b$ for y_2, and $3m + b$ for y_3 in (1), we have

$$(m + b - 72)^2 + (2m + b - 73)^2 + (3m + b - 75)^2.$$

Thus, to find the regression line for the given set of data we must find the values of m and b which minimize the function S given by $S(b, m) = (m + b - 72)^2 + (2m + b - 73)^2 + (3m + b - 75)^2$.

To apply the D-test, we first find the partial derivatives $\dfrac{\partial S}{\partial b}$ and $\dfrac{\partial S}{\partial m}$.

$$\frac{\partial S}{\partial b} = 2(m + b - 72) + 2(2m + b - 73) + 2(3m + b - 75)$$

$$= 12m + 6b - 440$$

$$\frac{\partial S}{\partial m} = 2(m + b - 72) + 2(2m + b - 73)2 + 2(3m + b - 75)3$$

$$= 28m + 12b - 886$$

We set these derivatives equal to 0 and solve the resulting system.

$$\begin{array}{ccc} 12m + 6b - 440 = 0 & & 6m + 3b = 220 \quad (2) \\ & \text{or} & \\ 28m + 12b - 886 = 0 & & 14m + 6b = 443 \quad (3) \end{array}$$

19. Consider this factual data on life expectancy of males in the United States.

Year—x	1. 1950	2. 1960	3. 1970	4. 1980
Life expectancy of male (in years)—y	65	67	68	?

$y = mx + b.$

a) Find the regression line

b) Use the regression line to predict life expectancy of the male in 1980.

The solution of this system is $b = \frac{211}{3} = 70\frac{1}{3}$, $m = \frac{3}{2}$. We leave it to the reader to complete the D-test to verify that $(70\frac{1}{3}, \frac{3}{2})$ does, in fact, yield the minimum of S. We need not bother to compute $S(70\frac{1}{3}, \frac{3}{2})$. The values of m and b are all we need to determine $y = mx + b$. The regression line is

$$y = \tfrac{3}{2}x + 70\tfrac{1}{3}, \quad \text{or } y = 1.5x + 70.3 \text{ (rounded)}.$$

We can extrapolate from the data to find a predicted life expectancy in 1980.

$$y = 1.5 \cdot 4 + 70.3$$
$$= 6 + 70.3$$
$$= 76.3$$

Thus, life expectancy in 1980 is 76.3 years.

Do Exercise 19.

The method of least squares was illustrated here with only three data points, much fewer than one would use in practice. It should be pointed out that the method of least squares can also be used to fit functions other than linear functions to a set of data.

(Optional) The Regression Line for an Arbitrary Collection of Data Points (c_1, d_1), (c_2, d_2), . . . , (c_n, d_n).

Look again at the regression line

$$y = \tfrac{3}{2}x + \tfrac{211}{3}$$

for the data points (1, 72), (2, 73), and (3, 75). Let us consider the arithmetic averages, or means, of the x-coordinates, denoted $\bar{x}$; and the y-coordinates, denoted $\bar{y}$.

$$\bar{x} = \frac{1 + 2 + 3}{3} = 2, \qquad \bar{y} = \frac{72 + 73 + 75}{3} = \frac{220}{3}$$

It turns out that the point $(\bar{x}, \bar{y})$, or $(2, \frac{220}{3})$, is on the regression line for

$$\frac{220}{3} = \frac{3}{2} \cdot 2 + \frac{211}{3}.$$

Thus the regression line is as follows

$$y - \bar{y} = m(x - \bar{x}), \quad \text{or} \quad y - \frac{220}{3} = m(x - 2).$$

All that remains, in general, is to determine m. Suppose we wanted to find the regression line for an arbitrary number of points (c_1, d_1), $(c_2, d_2), \ldots, (c_n, d_n)$.

To do so, find the values m and b which minimize the function S given by

$$S(b, m) = (y_1 - d_1)^2 + (y_2 - d_2)^2 + \cdots + (y_n - d_n)^2 = \sum_{i=1}^{n} (y_i - d_i)^2,$$

where $y_i = mc_i + b$.

Using a procedure like the one we used earlier to minimize S, it can be shown that $y = mx + b$ takes the form

$$y - \bar{y} = m(x - \bar{x}),$$

where

$$\bar{x} = \frac{\sum_{i=1}^{n} c_i}{n}, \quad \bar{y} = \frac{\sum_{i=1}^{n} d_i}{n}, \quad \text{and} \quad m = \frac{\sum_{i=1}^{n} (c_i - \bar{x})(d_i - \bar{x})}{\sum_{i=1}^{n} (c_i - \bar{x})^2}.$$

Let us see how this works out for the life expectancy example done previously.

c_i	d_i	$c_i - \bar{x}$	$(c_i - \bar{x})^2$	$(d_i - \bar{y})$	$(c_i - \bar{x})(d_i - \bar{y})$
1	72	-1	1	-1.3	1.3
2	73	0	0	-0.3	0
3	75	1	1	1.7	1.7

$\sum_{i=1}^{3} c_i = 6,$ $\sum_{i=1}^{3} d_i = 220$ $\sum_{i=1}^{3} (c_i - \bar{x})^2 = 2$ $\sum_{i=1}^{3} (c_i - \bar{x})(d_i - \bar{y}) = 3$

$\bar{x} = 2$ $\bar{y} = 73.3$ $m = \frac{3}{2}$

Thus the regression line is

$$y - 73.3 = \tfrac{3}{2}(x - 2)$$

which simplifies to

$$y = \tfrac{3}{2}x + 70.3.$$

Do Exercise 20.

20. Repeat Margin Exercise 19(a) using the procedure outlined in this optional part of the section.

EXERCISE SET 8.4

1. Use the regression line $y = 1.5x + 70.3$ to predict life expectancy of the female in the year 2000.

3. Consider this factual data regarding natural gas demand.

Year-x	1. 1950	2. 1960	3. 1970	4. 1980
Demand-y (in quadrillion BTU)	19	21	22	?

a) Find the regression line $y = mx + b$.

b) Use the regression line to predict gas demand in 1980.

c) Use the regression line to predict gas demand in 2000.

5. Consider this data relating cricket chirps per minute to Fahrenheit temperature.

Chirps per minute-x	60	76	88	100
Fahrenheit temperature-y	55°	59°	62°	65°

a) Find the regression line $y = mx + b$. [*Hint*: The y-deviations are $60m + b - 55$, $76m + b - 59$, and so on.]

b) One night the crickets chirped 84 times per minute. Use the regression line to determine the temperature that night.

2. Use the regression line $y = 1.5x + 63.7$ to predict life expectancy of the male in the year 2000.

4. A student wanted to predict his final examination score, based on what his midterm test score was. He decided to base his data on scores of three students the previous semester in the same course with the same instructor. Below is this data.

Midterm score (%)-x	70	60	85
Final exam score (%)-y	75	62	89

a) Find the regression line $y = mx + b$. [*Hint*: The y-deviations are $70m + b - 75$, $60m + b - 62$, and so on.]

b) The midterm score of the student was 81. Use the regression line to predict his final exam score.

6. Consider this data regarding the total sales of a company during the first 4 years of operation.

Year-x	1	2	3	4
Sales-y (in millions)	$22	$34	$44	$60

a) Find the regression line $y = mx + b$.

b) Use the regression line to predict sales in the 5th year.

The formula relating temperature to cricket chirps is discussed in *Deep-river Jim's Wilderness Trail Book*, Boston: Open Road Publishing Co., p. 138.

8.5 CONSTRAINED MAXIMUM AND
MINIMUM VALUES-LAGRANGE MULTIPLIERS

Before we get into detail let us look at a problem we considered in Chapter 3.

Example 1 A hobby store has 20 ft of fencing to fence off a rectangular electric train area in one corner of its display room. What dimensions of the rectangle will maximize the area?

We maximize the function
$$A = xy$$

subject to the condition, or *constraint* $x + y = 20$. Note that A is a function of two variables:
$$A(x, y) = xy.$$

OBJECTIVES

You should be able to:

a) Find a maximum or minimum value of a given function subject to a given constraint, using the Method of LaGrange Multipliers.
b) Solve applied problems involving LaGrange Multipliers.

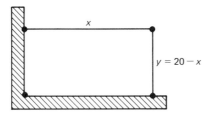

When we solved this earlier, we first solved the constraint for y:
$$y = 20 - x.$$
We then substituted $20 - x$ for y to obtain
$$A(x, 20 - x) = x(20 - x) = 20x - x^2,$$

which is a function of one variable. We then proceeded to find a maximum value using Maximum-Minimum Principle 1 (see p. 156). By itself, the function of two variables
$$A(x, y) = xy$$

has no maximum value. This can be checked using the D-test. But, with the constraint $x + y = 20$, the function does have a maximum.

We see this pictorially in the following figure.

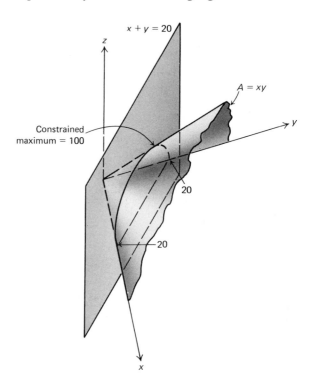

It may be quite difficult to solve a constraint for one variable. A procedure, outlined below, allows us to proceed without solving a constraint for one variable.

METHOD OF LAGRANGE MULTIPLIERS.   To find a maximum or minimum value of a function $f(x, y)$ subject to the constraint $g(x, y) = 0$,
1. **Form a new function:**

$$F(x, y, \lambda) = f(x, y) - \lambda g(x, y).$$

2. **Find the partial derivatives F_x, F_y, and F_λ.**
3. **Solve the system**

$$F_x = 0, \quad F_y = 0, \quad \text{and } F_\lambda = 0.$$

Let (a, b) represent a solution. One would still have to determine that (a, b) yields a maximum or minimum, but we will assume one or the other in the problems considered here.

The variable λ (lambda) is called a *LaGrange Multiplier*. We first illustrate the Method of LaGrange Multipliers in Example 1.

Example 2 Find the maximum value of

$$A(x, y) = xy$$

subject to the constraint $x + y = 20$.

Solution

1. We form the new function F given by

$$F(x, y, \lambda) = xy - \lambda \cdot (x + y - 20).$$

Note that we first had to express $x + y = 20$ as $x + y - 20 = 0$.

2. We find the first partial derivatives.

$$F_x = y - \lambda,$$
$$F_y = x - \lambda,$$
$$F_\lambda = -(x + y - 20)$$

3. We set these derivatives equal to 0 and solve the resulting system.

$$y - \lambda = 0 \qquad\qquad (1)$$

$$x - \lambda = 0 \qquad\qquad (2)$$

$$x + y - 20 = 0 \qquad\qquad (3)$$

[If $-(x + y - 20) = 0$, then $x + y - 20 = 0$.]

From equations (1) and (2) it follows that

$$x = y = \lambda.$$

Substituting λ for x and y in equation (3) we get

$$\lambda + \lambda - 20 = 0,$$
$$2\lambda = 20,$$
$$\lambda = 10.$$

Thus $x = \lambda = 10$, and $y = \lambda = 10$. The maximum occurs at $(10, 10)$ and is

$$A(10, 10) = 10 \cdot 10 = 100.$$

Do Exercise 21.

21. A rancher has 50 ft of fencing to fence off a rectangular animal pen in the corner of a barn. What dimensions of the rectangle will yield the maximum area?

a) Express the area as a function of two variables with a constraint.

b) Find the maximum value of the function in (a) using the Method of LaGrange Multipliers.

Example 3   Find the maximum value of

$$f(x, y) = 3xy$$

subject to the constraint

$$2x + y = 8.$$

[*Note*: f could be interpreted as a production function with budget constraint $2x + y = 8$.]

Solution

1. We form the new function F given by

$$F(x, y, \lambda) = 3xy - \lambda(2x + y - 8),$$

Note that we had to express $2x + y = 8$ as $2x + y - 8 = 0$.

2. We find the first partial derivatives.

$$F_x = 3y - 2\lambda$$
$$F_y = 3x - \lambda$$
$$F_\lambda = -(2x + y - 8)$$

3. We set these derivatives equal to 0 and solve the resulting system

$$3y - 2\lambda = 0 \qquad\qquad (1)$$
$$3x - \lambda = 0 \qquad\qquad (2)$$
$$-(2x + y - 8) = 0, \quad \text{or } 2x + y - 8 = 0 \qquad\qquad (3)$$

Solving equation (1) for y, we get

$$y = \frac{2}{3}\lambda.$$

Solving equation (2) for x, we get

$$x = \frac{\lambda}{3}.$$

Substituting $\frac{2}{3}\lambda$ for y and $\frac{\lambda}{3}$ for x in equation (3), we get

$$2\left(\frac{\lambda}{3}\right) + \left(\frac{2}{3}\lambda\right) - 8 = 0$$
$$\tfrac{4}{3}\lambda = 8$$
$$\lambda = \tfrac{3}{4} \cdot 8 = 6.$$

Then

$$x = \frac{\lambda}{3} = \frac{6}{3} = 2 \qquad \text{and} \qquad y = \frac{2}{3}\lambda = \frac{2}{3} \cdot 6 = 4.$$

The maximum of f subject to the constraint occurs at $(2, 4)$ and is

$$f(2, 4) = 3 \cdot 2 \cdot 4 = 24.$$

Do Exercise 22.

Example 4 *The beverage can problem.* The standard beverage can has a volume of 12 oz, or 26 in^3. What dimensions yield the minimum surface area? Find the minimum surface area.

Solution We want to minimize the function s given by

$$s(h, r) = 2\pi rh + 2\pi r^2$$

subject to the volume constraint

$$\pi r^2 h = 26, \quad \text{or } \pi r^2 h - 26 = 0.$$

We might point out that s does not have a minimum without the constraint.

1. We form the new function S given by

$$S(h, r, \lambda) = 2\pi rh + 2\pi r^2 - \lambda(\pi r^2 h - 26).$$

2. We find the first partial derivatives.

$$\frac{\partial S}{\partial h} = 2\pi r - \lambda \pi r^2$$

$$\frac{\partial S}{\partial r} = 2\pi h + 4\pi r - 2\lambda \pi rh$$

$$\frac{\partial S}{\partial \lambda} = -(\pi r^2 h - 26)$$

22. Find the maximum value of

$$f(x, y) = 5xy$$

subject to the constraint

$$4x + y = 20.$$

23. Repeat Example 4 for a can of 16 oz, or 35 in³.

3. We set these derivatives equal to 0 and solve the resulting system.

$$2\pi r - \lambda \pi r^2 = 0 \tag{1}$$

$$2\pi h + 4\pi r - 2\lambda \pi r h = 0 \tag{2}$$

$$-(\pi r^2 h - 26) = 0, \quad \text{or } \pi r^2 h - 26 = 0 \tag{3}$$

Note that equation (1) can be solved for r:

$$\pi r(2 - \lambda r) = 0$$

$$\pi r = 0 \quad \text{or} \quad 2 - \lambda r = 0$$

$$r = 0 \quad \text{or} \qquad r = \frac{2}{\lambda}$$

Now $r = 0$ cannot be a solution to the original problem, so we continue by substituting $\frac{2}{\lambda}$ for r in equation (2):

$$2\pi h + 4\pi \cdot \frac{2}{\lambda} - 2\lambda \pi \cdot \frac{2}{\lambda} \cdot h = 0$$

$$2\pi h + \frac{8\pi}{\lambda} - 4\pi h = 0$$

$$\frac{8\pi}{\lambda} - 2\pi h = 0$$

$$- 2\pi h = -\frac{8\pi}{\lambda}, \quad \text{so } h = \frac{4}{\lambda}.$$

Since $h = \frac{4}{\lambda}$ and $r = \frac{2}{\lambda}$ it follows that $h = 2r$. Substituting $2r$ for h in equation (3) yields

$$\pi r^2(2r) - 26 = 0$$

$$2\pi r^3 - 26 = 0$$

$$2\pi r^3 = 26$$

$$\pi r^3 = 13$$

$$r^3 = \frac{13}{\pi}$$

$$r = \sqrt[3]{\frac{13}{\pi}} \approx 1.6 \text{ in.} \quad \text{(Use Table 1.)}$$

So when $r = 1.6$ in., $h = 3.2$ in., the surface area is a minimum and is about $2\pi(1.6)(3.2) + 2\pi(1.6)^2$, or 48.3 in².

Do Exercise 23.

EXERCISE SET 8.5

Find the maximum value of f subject to the given constraint.

1. $f(x, y) = xy$; $2x + y = 8$

2. $f(x, y) = 2xy$; $4x + y = 16$

3. $f(x, y) = 4 - x^2 - y^2$; $x + 2y = 10$

4. $f(x, y) = 3 - x^2 - y^2$; $x + 6y = 37$

Find the minimum value of f subject to the given constraint.

5. $f(x, y) = x^2 + y^2$; $2x + y = 10$

6. $f(x, y) = x^2 + y^2$; $x + 4y = 17$

7. $f(x, y) = 2y^2 - 6x^2$; $2x + y = 4$

8. $f(x, y) = 2x^2 + y^2 - xy$; $x + y = 8$

9. $f(x, y, z) = x^2 + y^2 + z^2$; $y + 2x - z = 3$

10. $f(x, y, z) = x^2 + y^2 + z^2$; $x + y + z = 1$

Use the *Method of LaGrange Multipliers* to solve these problems.

11. Of all numbers whose sum is 70, find the two which have the maximum product.

12. Of all numbers whose sum is 50, find the two which have the maximum product.

13. Of all numbers whose difference is 6, find the two which have the minimum product.

14. Of all numbers whose difference is 4, find the two which have the minimum product.

15. A standard piece of typing paper has a perimeter of 39 in. Find the dimensions of the paper which will give the most typing area, subject to the perimeter constraint of 39 in. What is its area?

16. A carpenter is building a room with a fixed perimeter of 80 ft. What are the dimensions of the largest room that can be built? What is its area?

17. An oil drum of standard size has a volume of 200 gal or 27 ft³. What dimensions yield the minimum surface area? Find the minimum surface area.

Do the drums appear to be made in such a way as to minimize surface area?

Peter Menzel from Stock, Boston

18. A juice can of standard size has a volume of 99 in³. What dimensions yield the minimum surface area? Find the minimum surface area.

20. The total sales S of a one-product firm is given by

$$S(L, M) = 2ML - L^2,$$

where M = cost of materials, and L = cost of labor. Find the maximum value of this function subject to the budget constraint

$$M + L = 60.$$

22. A container company is going to construct a shipping container of volume 12 cubic feet with a square bottom and top. The cost of the top and sides is \$2 per square foot, and \$3 per square foot for the bottom. What dimensions will minimize the cost of the container?

19. The total sales S of a one-product firm is given by

$$S(L, M) = ML - L^2,$$

where M = cost of materials, and L = cost of labor. Find the maximum value of this function subject to the budget constraint

$$M + L = 80.$$

21. A company is planning to construct a warehouse whose cubic footage is to be 252,000 ft³. Construction costs are estimated to be

walls: \$3.00 per sq. ft.
floor: \$4.00 per sq. ft.
ceiling: \$3.00 per sq. ft.

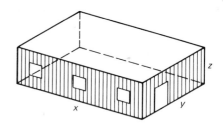

a) The total cost of the building is a function $C(x, y, z)$, where x is the length, y is the width, and z is the height. Find a formula for $C(x, y, z)$.

b) What dimensions of the building will minimize total cost? What is the minimum cost?

23. Suppose $p(x, y)$ represents the production of a two product firm. We give no formula for p. The company produces x items of the first product at a cost c_1 of each, and y items of the second product at a cost c_2 of each. The budget constraint B is given by

$$B = c_1 x + c_2 y.$$

Find the value of λ in the LaGrange Multiplier method in terms of p_x, p_y, c_1, and c_2. The resulting equation is called the *Law of Equimarginal Productivity*.

8.6 MINIMIZING TRAVEL TIME IN A BUILDING

In multi-level building design one consideration is travel time between remotest points in a rectangular building with a square base. Let us suppose each floor has a square grid of hallways as shown below.

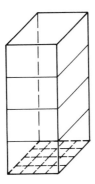

Suppose you are standing at the remotest point P in the top northeast corner of such a building with 12 floors. How long will it take to reach the southwest corner on the first floor? You will be going from point P to point Q in the illustration.

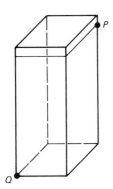

Let us call the time t. We find a formula for t in two steps.

i) You are to go from the twelfth floor to the first floor. This is a move in a *vertical direction*; and

ii) You need to go across the first floor. This is a move in a *horizontal direction*.

OBJECTIVES

You should be able to find the dimensions of a building of fixed floor area, with a square base, which will minimize travel time from remotest points in the building.

The vertical time is h, the height of the top floor from the ground, divided by a, the speed at which you can travel in a vertical direction (elevator speed). So, vertical time is $\dfrac{h}{a}$.

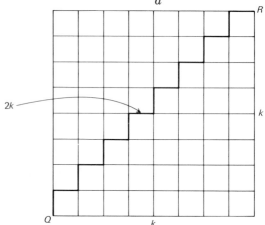

The horizontal time is the time it takes to go across the first level, by way of the square grid of hallways (from R to Q below). If each floor is a square with side of length k, then the distance from R to Q is $2k$. If the walking speed is b, then the horizontal time is $\dfrac{2k}{b}$. Thus, the time it will take to go from P to Q is a function of two variables, h and k, given by

$$t(h,\,k) = \text{vertical time} + \text{horizontal time} = \frac{h}{a} + \frac{2k}{b}.$$

Now, what happens if we have to choose between two (or more) building plans with the same total floor area, but with different dimensions? Will the travel time be the same, or will it be different for the two buildings? First of all, what is the total floor area of a given building? Suppose the building has n floors each a square of side k. Then, the total floor area is given by

$$A = nk^2.$$

Note that the area of the root is not included.

If h is the height of the top floor from the ground and c is the height of each floor, then $n = \dfrac{h}{c}$. So,

$$A = \frac{h}{c}k^2.$$

Let us return to the problem of the two buildings with the same total floor area, but with different dimensions, and see what happens to $t(h,\,k)$. Let us explore this.

Exploratory Exercises.   (A Hand Calculator Would be Helpful.)

For each case, let the elevator speed $a = 10$ ft/sec; walking speed $b = 4$ ft/sec; and the height of each floor $c = 15$ ft. Complete the following table.

Case	Building	Number of levels (n)	Floor length (k)	Total area (A)	Height $h = cn$	Travel time $t(h, k)$
1	B_1	2	40 ft	3200 ft²	30 ft	23 sec
	B_2	3	32.66 ft	3200 ft²	45 ft	20.83 sec
2	B_1	2	60 ft			
	B_2	3	48.99 ft			
3	B_1	4	40 ft			
	B_2	5	35.777 ft			
4	B_1	5	60 ft			
	B_2	10	42.246 ft			
5	B_1	5	150 ft			
	B_2	10	106.066 ft			
6	B_1	10	40 ft			
	B_2	17	30.679 ft			
7	B_1	10	80 ft			
	B_2	17	61.357 ft			
8	B_1	17	40 ft			
	B_2	26	32.344 ft			
9	B_1	17	50 ft			
	B_2	26	40.43 ft			
10	B_1	26	77 ft			
	B_2	50	55.525 ft			

a) What did you notice about $t(h, k)$ when h and k were very nearly the same?

b) What about when h and k were very large?

c) Do you think there are values of h and k for a building with a given floor area which will minimize travel time?

Now let us use calculus to solve a building planning problem.

Example   *Minimizing travel time.* The objective is to find the dimensions of a rectangular building with a square base that will minimize travel time t between the remotest points in the building. Each floor has a square grid of hallways. The height of the top floor from the ground is h, and the length of a side of each floor is k. The elevator speed is 10 ft/sec and the average speed of a person walking is 4 ft/sec. The total floor area of the building is 40,000 ft². The height of each floor is 8 ft.

Solution   We want to find values of h and k which will minimize the function t given by

$$t(h, k) = \frac{h}{10} + \frac{2k}{4} = \frac{1}{10} h + \frac{1}{2} k,$$

subject to the constraint

$$\frac{h}{8} k^2 = 40{,}000, \quad \text{or } hk^2 = 320{,}000.$$

We first form the new function T given by

$$T(h, k, \lambda) = \frac{1}{10} h + \frac{1}{2} k - \lambda(hk^2 - 320{,}000).$$

We take the first partial derivatives and set them equal to 0.

$$T_h = \tfrac{1}{10} - \lambda k^2 = 0 \tag{1}$$

$$T_k = \tfrac{1}{2} - 2\lambda hk = 0 \tag{2}$$

$$T_\lambda = -(hk^2 - 320{,}000) = 0, \quad \text{or } hk^2 - 320{,}000 = 0 \tag{3}$$

To clear of fractions, we multiply the first equation by 10 and the second by 2.

$$1 - 10\lambda k^2 = 0 \tag{4}$$

$$1 - 4\lambda hk = 0 \tag{5}$$

$$hk^2 - 320{,}000 = 0 \tag{6}$$

Solving equation (4) for λ, we get

$$\lambda = \frac{1}{10k^2}.$$

Solving equation (5) for λ, we get

$$\lambda = \frac{1}{4hk}.$$

Thus

$$\frac{1}{10k^2} = \frac{1}{4hk}. \tag{7}$$

Now k must be nonzero in the original problem. Assuming $k \neq 0$, we multiply equation (7) by k to simplify it and get

$$\frac{1}{10k} = \frac{1}{4h}.$$

Solving this equation for k, we get

$$k = \tfrac{2}{5}h. \tag{8}$$

Substituting $\tfrac{2}{5}h$ for k in equation (6) we get

$$h(\tfrac{2}{5}h)^2 - 320{,}000 = 0$$
$$\tfrac{4}{25}h^3 - 320{,}000 = 0$$
$$\tfrac{4}{25}h^3 = 320{,}000$$
$$h^3 = 320{,}000 \cdot \tfrac{25}{4} = 2{,}000{,}000$$
$$h = \sqrt[3]{2{,}000{,}000}$$
$$h \approx 126 \text{ ft.} \qquad \text{(Use Table 1, a hand}$$
$$\text{calculator, or logarithms.)}$$

Then from equation (8) we find k.

$$k = \tfrac{2}{5} \cdot 126 \approx 50 \text{ ft}$$

The height of the building is 126 ft plus 8 ft. The height of the top floor is added on. Thus the dimensions of the building are 50 ft by 50 ft by 134 ft.

Do Exercise 24.

24. Solve the example when the total floor area is 100,000 ft^2 and the height of each floor is 10 ft.

EXERCISE SET 8.6

Given the conditions in Exercises 1–3, find the values of h and k which minimize travel time

$$t(h, k) = \frac{h}{a} + \frac{2k}{b}$$

subject to the floor area constraint A given by

$$A = \frac{h}{c} k^2,$$

where

$$h = \text{height of top floor from the ground (ft)}$$
$$k = \text{length of side of base (ft)}$$
$$a = \text{elevator speed (ft/sec)}$$
$$b = \text{average speed of humans walking in building (ft/sec)}$$
$$c = \text{height of each floor (ft)}.$$

Then find the dimensions of the building.

1. $a = 20, b = 5, c = 8, A = 80{,}000$ ft^2

2. $a = 20, b = 5, c = 10, A = 60{,}000$ ft^2

3. Find a general solution in terms of a, b, c, and A.

CHAPTER 8 TEST

Given $f(x, y) = e^x + 2x^3y + y$, find:

1. $\dfrac{\partial f}{\partial x}$ **2.** $\dfrac{\partial f}{\partial y}$ **3.** $\dfrac{\partial^2 f}{\partial x^2}$ **4.** $\dfrac{\partial^2 f}{\partial x\, \partial y}$ **5.** $\dfrac{\partial^2 f}{\partial y\, \partial x}$ **6.** $\dfrac{\partial^2 f}{\partial y^2}$

7. Find the relative maximum and minimum values.

$$f(x, y) = x^2 - xy + y^3 - x$$

8. Find the relative maximum and minimum values.

$$f(x, y) = y^2 - x^2$$

9. Consider this data regarding total sales of a company during the first three years of operation.

Year-x	1	2	3
Sales-y (in millions)	$10	$15	$19

  a) Find the regression line $y = mx + b$.

  b) Use the regression line to predict sales in the 4th year.

10. Find the maximum value of

$$f(x, y) = 6xy - 4x^2 - 3y^2$$

subject to the constraint $x + 3y = 19$.

FINAL
EXAMINATION

Chapter 1

1. Write an equation of the line with slope -4 and containing the point $(-7, 1)$.

2. For $f(x) = x^2 - 5$, find $f(x + h)$.

Chapter 2

3. Find $\lim\limits_{x \to -4} \dfrac{x^2 - 16}{x + 4}$

Differentiate.

4. $-9x + 3$

5. $x^2 - 7x + 3$

6. $x^{1/4}$

7. x^{-6}

8. $(x - 3)(x + 1)^5$

9. $\dfrac{x^3 - 1}{x^5}$

Chapter 3

Find maximum and minimum values, if they exist, over the indicated interval. If no interval is indicated, use the real line.

10. $f(x) = 3x^2 - 6x - 4$

11. $f(x) = -5x + 1$

12. $f(x) = \frac{1}{3}x^3 - x^2 - 3x + 5; [-2, 0]$

13. For a certain product the total revenue and total cost functions are given by

$$R(x) = 4x^2 + 11x + 110,$$
$$C(x) = 4.2x^2 + 5x + 10.$$

Find the number of units that must be produced and sold to maximize profit.

14. An appliance store sells 450 pocket radios each year. It costs $4 to store one radio for one year. To order radios there is a fixed cost of $1 plus $.75 for each radio. How many times per year should the store reorder radios, and in what lot size, to minimize inventory costs?

15. A certain population of fur-bearing animals has the reproduction curve

$$f(P) = P(400 - P),$$

where P is measured in thousands. Find the population at which the maximum sustainable harvest occurs, and find the maximum sustainable harvest.

16. For $f(x) = 3x^2 - 7$, $x = 5$, and $\Delta x = 0.1$, find Δy and $f'(x)\,\Delta x$.

Chapter 4

Differentiate.

17. $\dfrac{e^x + x}{e^x}$

18. $\ln(x^2 + 5)$

19. $e^{\ln x}$

20. $e^{3x} + x^2$

21. The demand for oil in the world is increasing at the rate of 10% per year; that is,

$$\frac{dA}{dt} = 0.1A,$$

where

$$A = \text{the amount of oil used, and}$$
$$t = \text{time in years.}$$

a) 20,300 million barrels were used in 1973. Find the solution of the equation assuming $A_0 = 20{,}300$ and $k = 0.1$.

b) How much oil will be used in 1980?

Chapter 5

Integrate.

22. $\displaystyle\int 3x^5\,dx$

23. $\displaystyle\int_{-1}^{0} (2e^x + 1)\,dx$

24. Find the area under the graph of $y = x^2 + 3x$ on the interval $[1, 5]$.

25. Integrate. Use substitution. Do not use Table 5.

$$\int x^3 e^{x^4} \, dx$$

26. Integrate. Use integration by parts. Do not use Table 5.

$$\int (x + 3)\ln x \, dx$$

27. Integrate. Use Table 5.

$$\int \frac{x}{(7 - 3x)^2} \, dx$$

Chapter 6

28. What annual payment should be made so the amount of an annuity over 30 years at 9%, compounded continuously, will be $81,000?

29. Find the capital value of a rental property over a 50-year period where the annual rent is $4500 and the going interest rate is 9%.

30. Determine whether the following improper integral is convergent or divergent, and calculate its value if convergent.

$$\int_3^\infty \frac{1}{x^7} \, dx$$

31. Given the probability density function

$$f(x) = \frac{3}{2x^2} \text{ over } [1, 3],$$

find $E(x)$.

32. Let x be a continuous random variable which is normally distributed with mean $\mu = 3$ and standard deviation $\sigma = 5$. Using Table 6, find $P(-2 \leqslant x \leqslant 8)$.

33. Given the demand and supply functions

$$D(x) = (x - 20)^2 \quad \text{and} \quad S(x) = x^2 + 10x + 50,$$

find the equilibrium point and the consumer's surplus.

34. Find the volume of the solid of revolution generated by rotating the region under the graph of

$$y = e^{-x} \quad \text{from} \quad x = 0 \quad \text{to} \quad x = 5.$$

Chapter 7

35. Solve the differential equation $\dfrac{dy}{dx} = xy$.

36. In an advertising experiment it was determined that

$$\frac{dP}{dt} = k(L - P),$$

where

P = percentage of the people in the city who bought the product after the ad was run t times, and

$L = 100\%$, or 1.

a) Express $P(t)$ in terms of $L = 1$.

b) It was determined that $P(10) = 70\%$. Use this to determine k. Round your answer to the nearest hundredth.

c) Rewrite $P(t)$ in terms of k.

d) Use the equation in (c) to find $P(20)$.

Chapter 8

Given $f(x, y) = e^y + 4x^2y^3 + 3x$, find:

37. f_x **38.** f_{yy}

39. Find the relative maximum and minimum values of

$$f(x, y) = 8x^2 - y^2.$$

40. Maximize

$$f(x, y) = 4x + 2y - x^2 - y^2 + 4$$

subject to the constraint $x + 2y = 9$.

APPENDIXES
A THROUGH D

Appendix A

SEMILOGARITHMIC GRAPHING

Suppose we are graphing a set of data and the y values are very large. Then it is convenient to use what is known as *semilogarithmic* graphing. In effect, one graphs the logarithms of the y values. For example, consider the exponential equation

$$y = 8 \cdot 5^x.$$

Suppose we compute some values, where, for convenience, x is nonnegative.

x	0	1	2	3
y	8	40	200	1000

(1)

Note that the y values get larger and for larger values of x they get even larger. It would be awkward to construct a graph with the y-axis scaled in the usual manner. Let us take the common logarithms of the y values.

x	0	1	2	3
$\log y$	0.9	1.6	2.3	3

(2)

Note that this graph would be more convenient to construct. In semilogarithmic graphing the y-axis is scaled in distances proportional to the logarithms of the numbers in question. The distances between numbers are not the same.

Example 1   Graph $y = 8 \cdot 5^x$ on semilogarithmic paper.

Solution   We compute the values in (1) above. We plot the points from that table on semilogarithmic paper. We do not need to compute the logarithms since the vertical axis is scaled logarithmically.

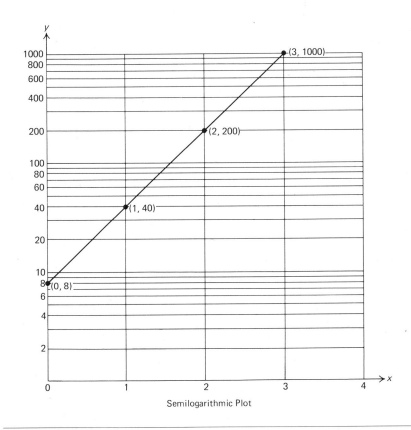

Semilogarithmic Plot

Note that the semilogarithmic graph of $y = 8 \cdot 5^x$ is a straight line. Let us see why. If we take the common logarithm of both sides of

$$y = 8 \cdot 5^x$$

we get

$$\log y = \log 8 \cdot 5^x = \log 8 + x \log 5. \quad \text{(See Section 4.1.)}$$

Note that log 8 and log 5 are constants. So if we replace log y by a new variable Y, the equation takes the form of a linear function

$$Y = mx + b,$$

where

$$m = \log 5 \quad \text{and} \quad b = \log 8.$$

This holds for any exponential equation.

The semilogarithmic graph of an exponential equation $y = k \cdot a$ is a straight line $Y = mx + b$, where $Y = \log y$, $m = \log a$, and $b = \log k$.

1. Consider $y = 4 \cdot 3^x$.
a) Complete this table.

x	0	1	2	3	4	5
y						

b) Graph $y = 4 \cdot 3^x$ on semilogarithmic paper.
c) Transform $y = 4 \cdot 3^x$ to a linear equation by taking the common logarithm of both sides.

The converse of this result is often applied to a set of data from an experiment. The data is plotted on semilogarithmic paper. If the graph is close to being a straight line, it is hypothesized that the data can be modeled by an exponential function.

Do Exercise 1.

When both sets of numbers become large, it is convenient to scale both axes logarithmically. The resulting graph is a *log-log* graph, or a *logarithmic* graph.

Example 2　Graph the following set of data on log-log paper.

A	10	20	40	60	80	100	120	140	160	180
S	4	9	18	60	150	380	770	1300	2600	4700

A = amount spent on advertising, in thousands, and S = sales, in thousands.

Solution

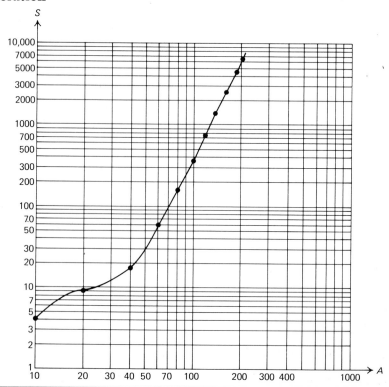

A log-log plot of a power function

$$y = ax^m$$

will be a straight line. Let us see why. If we take the common logarithm of both sides we get

$$\log y = \log ax^m = \log a + m \cdot \log x.$$

The numbers $\log a$ and m are constants. If we replace $\log y$ by Y and $\log x$ by X we get a linear equation

$$Y = mX + b.$$

The log-log graph of the power function $y = ax^m$ is a straight line $Y = mX + b$, where $Y = \log y$, $X = \log x$, and $b = \log a$.

The converse of this result is often applied to the results of an experiment. The data is plotted on semilogarithmic paper, but the graph is not a straight line. It then may be plotted on log-log paper. If a straight line is obtained, it is hypothesized that the data can be modeled by a power function.

Do Exercise 2.

2. Consider $y = x^3$.

a) Complete this table.

x	1	2	3	4	5	6	7	8	9	10
y										

b) Graph $y = x^3$ on log-log paper.

c) Transform $y = x^3$ to a linear equation by taking the common logarithm of both sides.

Appendix B
LINEAR
PROGRAMMING

OBJECTIVES

You should be able to:

a) Graph inequalities in two variables in the plane.
b) Graph systems of linear inequalities and find vertices if they exist.
c) Find the maximum and minimum values, if they exist, of a linear function subject to a system of constraints.
d) Solve applied problems involving a linear function and a system of constraints.

INEQUALITIES IN TWO VARIABLES

We want to consider graphs of inequalities in two variables such as

$$y < x, \qquad 3x - 2y \leqslant 6, \qquad \text{and} \qquad y > -3x + 5.$$

A *solution* of such an inequality is an ordered pair, as with equations in two variables. For example, $(-3, 2)$ is a solution of $5x - 4y \leqslant 13$ because $5(-3) - 4 \cdot 2 \leqslant 13$, or $-23 \leqslant 13$, is true. But $(0, -7)$ is not a solution because $5 \cdot 0 - 4(-7) \leqslant 13$, or $28 \leqslant 13$, is false. A *graph* of such an inequality is a geometric representation of all of its solutions.

Example 1 Graph $3y - 2x > 1$.

Solution

METHOD 1. Solve for y:

$$y > \frac{2x + 1}{3}.$$

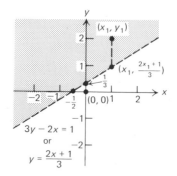

Now graph the line $y = \dfrac{2x + 1}{3}$. Any pair (x_1, y_1) which is a solution of

$y > \dfrac{2x + 1}{3}$ must be such that the second coordinate y_1 is greater than

$\dfrac{2x_1 + 1}{3}$. Thus any point (x_1, y_1) above $\left(x_1, \dfrac{2x_1 + 1}{3}\right)$ is a solution. The

graph consists of the shaded area above the line $y = \dfrac{2x + 1}{3}$, called a

half-plane. The dashed line indicates that $y = \dfrac{2x + 1}{3}$ is *not* part of the

graph. (A solid line would be used if we were graphing $3y - 2x \geqslant 1$.)

METHOD 2.   Graph $3y - 2x = 1$. The intercepts are $(0, \frac{1}{3})$ and $(-\frac{1}{2}, 0)$.
We try one point off the line. The origin $(0, 0)$ is easy to use. Since
$3 \cdot 0 - 2 \cdot 0 > 1$ is false, the origin is not in the graph. This means
that we shade the upper half-plane. (If the origin is on the line, we
pick another point.) Had the sentence been true, we would have
shaded the lower half-plane, since the origin would be in the graph.

Do Exercises 1 through 3.

A graph on a line of the inequality $x \leqslant 3$ is shown below.

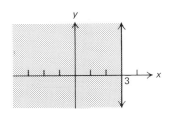

A graph in the plane of $x \leqslant 3$ can be thought of as a graph of $x + 0y \leqslant 3$.
It consists of all ordered pairs whose first coordinate is less than or
equal to 3. The graph is as follows.

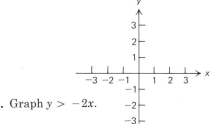

1. Graph $y > -2x$.

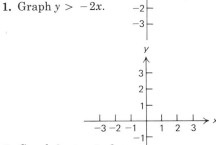

2. Graph $2x + y \geqslant 2$.

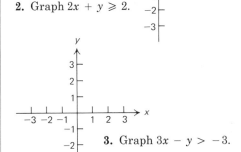

3. Graph $3x - y > -3$.

4. Graph $x \leqslant -1$.

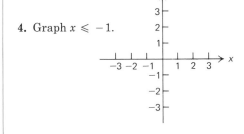

5. Graph $y > -\frac{1}{2}$.

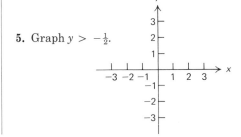

Do Exercises 4 and 5.

6. Graph $-4 \leqslant x < 1$.

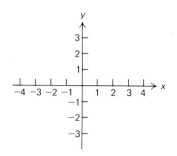

7. Graph $1 \leqslant y \leqslant 2\frac{1}{2}$.

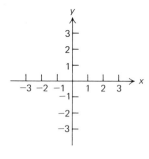

Example 2 Graph $-1 < y \leqslant 2$.

Solution The graph consists of all ordered pairs whose second coordinate is greater than -1 and less than or equal to 2. It is shown below.

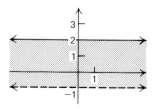

Do Exercises 6 and 7.

SYSTEMS OF INEQUALITIES

In Example 2 we were actually graphing the *system* of inequalities

$$-1 < y \quad and \quad y \leqslant 2.$$

It consists of those ordered pairs which are solutions of *both* inequalities. In general, the graph of a system (or set) of inequalities consists of those ordered pairs which are solutions of *all* the inequalities.

Example 3 Graph the system and find the vertices.

$$2x + y \geqslant 2$$
$$4x + 3y < 12$$
$$\tfrac{1}{2} \leqslant x \leqslant 2$$
$$y \geqslant 0$$

Solution   The separate graphs are shown on the left and the graph of the system is shown at the right.

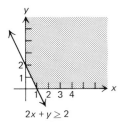

$2x + y \geq 2$

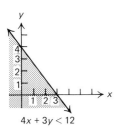

$4x + 3y < 12$

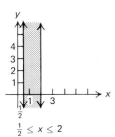

$\frac{1}{2} \leq x \leq 2$

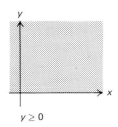

$y \geq 0$

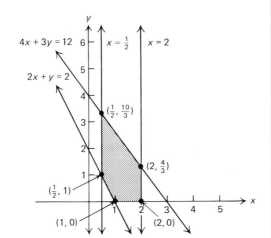

We find the vertex $(\frac{1}{2}, 1)$ by solving the system

$$2x + y = 2$$
$$x = \tfrac{1}{2}.$$

Graph each system and find the vertices.

8. $x + y \geqslant 1$

$\quad y - x \geqslant 2$

9. $5x + 6y \leqslant 30$

$\quad 0 \leqslant y \leqslant 3$

$\quad 0 \leqslant x \leqslant 4$

We find the vertex (1, 0) by solving the system

$$2x + y = 2$$
$$y = 0.$$

We find the vertex (2, 0) from the system

$$x = 2$$
$$y = 0.$$

The vertices $(2, \frac{4}{3})$ and $(\frac{1}{2}, \frac{10}{3})$ were found by solving, respectively, the systems

$$x = 2 \qquad \qquad x = \frac{1}{2}$$
$$4x + 3y = 12 \quad \text{and} \quad 4x + 3y = 12.$$

Do Exercises 8 and 9.

LINEAR PROGRAMMING

Have you ever taken a test where some of the items were worth a certain number of points and others were worth more points? Usually the problems worth more points took more time. Did you wonder how many of each kind you should do to get the best score? Let's consider such a problem.

Example 1 You are taking a test in which problems of type A are worth 10 points and those of type B are worth 15 points. It takes 3 minutes to do a problem of type A and 6 minutes to do a problem of type B and the testing time is 60 minutes. You are not allowed to do more than 16 questions. Assuming the items attempted are correct, how many of each type should you do to get the maximum score?

Solution Let x = number of items of type A and y = number of items of type B.

The total score T is a function of the two variables x and y, given by

$$T = 10x + 15y.$$

This is a linear function, since x and y are both to the first power. Now this function is subject to the following constraints:

Number of questions allowed:	$x + y \leqslant 16$
Time:	$3x + 6y \leqslant 60$
Number of items of type A:	$x \geqslant 0$
Number of items of type B:	$y \geqslant 0$

Suppose we graph the system of constraints and find the vertices. Though we cannot prove it here, the maximum is obtained at one of the vertices. We need only substitute the (x, y) values at the vertices in $T = 10x + 15y$ to find this maximum.

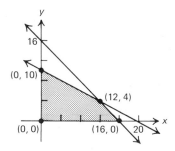

Vertices (x, y)	Score $T = 10x + 15y$
$(0, 0)$	0
$(16, 0)$	160
$(12, 4)$	180
$(0, 10)$	150

Thus the best score you could get would be 180 points, doing 12 questions of type A and 4 of type B. If you knew such information prior to a test, you could use this method to plan your strategy.

We have used a powerful result of a branch of mathematics known as *linear programming*. It has ever-increasing application to such fields as economics, business, psychology, and the natural sciences. To formulate our methods more carefully, we will use the facts of the following theorem, which we will not prove here.

THEOREM. **Any linear function $F = ax + by + c$ defined on a system of linear inequalities (called constraints) attains its maximum and minimum values (if it has any) at the vertices of that system of constraints.**

Example 1 Maximize and minimize $F = 9x + 40y$, subject to

$$y - x \geqslant 1$$
$$y - x \leqslant 3$$
$$2 \leqslant x \leqslant 5.$$

10. Maximize and minimize

$$F = 34x + 6y$$

subject to

$$x + y \leqslant 6$$
$$x + y \geqslant 1$$
$$1 \leqslant x \leqslant 3$$

11. Maximize and minimize

$$G = 3x - 5y + 27$$

subject to

$$x + 2y \leqslant 8$$
$$0 \leqslant y \leqslant 3$$
$$0 \leqslant x \leqslant 6.$$

Solution

Vertices (x, y)	$F = 9x + 40y$
(2, 3)	138
(2, 5)	218
(5, 6)	285
(5, 8)	365

The *maximum* of F is 365 when $x = 5$, $y = 8$.
The *minimum* of F is 138 when $x = 2$, $y = 3$.

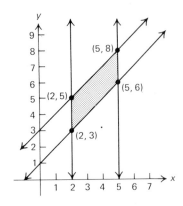

Do Exercises 10 and 11.

Example 2   A company manufactures motorcycles and bicycles. To stay in business it must produce each month at least 10 motorcycles but does not have facilities to produce more than 60 motorcycles. It also does not have facilities to produce more than 120 bicycles. The total production of motorcycles and bicycles cannot exceed 160. The profit on a motorcycle is $134 and on a bicycle is $20. Find the number of each which should be manufactured to maximize profit.

Solution   Let $x =$ number of motorcycles to be produced, and $y =$ number of bicycles to be produced.

The profit P is given by

$$P = \$134x + \$20y,$$

subject to the constraints

$$10 \leqslant x \leqslant 60$$
$$0 \leqslant y \leqslant 120$$
$$x + y \leqslant 160.$$

Vertices (x, y)	Profit $P = \$134x + \$20y$
(10, 0)	$ 1340
(60, 0)	$ 8040
(60, 100)	$10,040
(40, 120)	$ 7760
(10, 120)	$ 3740

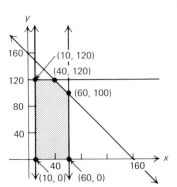

Thus the company will make a maximum profit of $10,040 by producing 60 motorcycles and 100 bicycles.

Do Exercise 12.

EXERCISE SET, APPENDIX B

1. Maximize and minimize

$$F = 4x + 28y$$

subject to

$$5x + 3y \leqslant 34$$
$$3x + 5y \leqslant 30$$
$$x \geqslant 0$$
$$y \geqslant 0.$$

2. Maximize and minimize

$$G = 14x + 16y$$

subject to

$$3x + 2y \leqslant 12$$
$$7x + 5y \leqslant 29$$
$$x \geqslant 0$$
$$y \geqslant 0.$$

3. Maximize and minimize

$$P = 16x - 2y + 40$$

subject to

$$6x + 8y \leqslant 48$$
$$0 \leqslant y \leqslant 4$$
$$0 \leqslant x \leqslant 7.$$

4. Maximize and minimize

$$Q = 24x - 3y + 52$$

subject to

$$5x + 4y \geqslant 20$$
$$0 \leqslant y \leqslant 4$$
$$0 \leqslant x \leqslant 3.$$

5. You are about to take a test which contains questions of type A worth 4 points and questions of type B worth 7 points. You must do at least 5 questions of type A but time restricts doing more than 10. You must do at least 3 questions of type B but time restricts doing more than 10. In total, you can do no more than 18 questions. How many of each type of question must you do to maximize your score? What is this maximum score?

6. You are about to take a test which contains questions of type A worth 10 points and questions of type B worth 25 points. You must do at least 3 questions of type A but time restricts doing more than 12. You must do at least 4 questions of type B but time restricts doing more than 15. In total you can do no more than 20 questions. How many of each type of question must you do to maximize your score? What is this maximum score?

7. A man is planning to invest up to $22,000 in bank X or bank Y or both. He wants to invest at least $2000 but no more than $14,000 in bank X. Bank Y does not insure more than a $15,000 investment so he will invest no more than that in bank Y. The interest in bank X is 6% and in bank Y it is $6\frac{1}{2}\%$ and this will be simple interest for one year. How much should he invest in each bank to maximize his income? What is the maximum income?

12. A college snack bar cooks and sells hamburgers and hot dogs during the lunch hour. To stay in business it must sell at least 10 hamburgers but cannot cook more than 40. It must also sell at least 30 hot dogs but cannot cook more than 70. It cannot cook more than 90 sandwiches altogether. The profit on a hamburger is $0.33 and on a hot dog it is $0.21. How many of each kind of sandwich should they sell to make the maximum profit?

8. A woman is planning to invest up to $40,000 in corporate or municipal bonds or both. The least she is allowed to invest in corporate bonds is $6000 and she does not want to invest more than $22,000 in corporate bonds. She also does not want to invest more than $30,000 in municipal bonds. The interest on corporate bonds is 8% and on municipal bonds $7\frac{1}{2}$%. This is simple interest for one year. How much should she invest in each type of bond to maximize her income? What is the maximum income?

9. It takes a tailoring firm 2 hr of cutting and 4 hr of sewing to make a knit suit. To make a worsted suit it takes 4 hr of cutting and 2 hr of sewing. At most, 20 hr per day are available for cutting and, at most, 16 hr per day are available for sewing. The profit on a knit suit is $34 and on a worsted suit is $31. How many of each kind of suit should be made to maximize profit? What is the maximum profit?

10. A pipe tobacco company has 3000 lb of English tobacco, 2000 lb of Virginia tobacco and 500 lb of Latakia tobacco. To make one batch of *Smello* tobacco it takes 12 lb of English tobacco and 4 lb of Latakia. To make one batch of *Roppo* tobacco it takes 8 lb of English and 8 lb of Virginia tobacco. The profit is $10.56 per batch for *Smello* and $6.40 for *Roppo*. How many batches of each kind of tobacco should be made to yield maximum profit? What is the maximum profit?

Table 1 Powers, roots, and reciprocals

n	n^2	n^3	$\sqrt{n}$	$\sqrt[3]{n}$	$\sqrt{10n}$	$\dfrac{1}{n}$	n	n^2	n^3	$\sqrt{n}$	$\sqrt[3]{n}$	$\sqrt{10n}$	$\dfrac{1}{n}$
1	1	1	1.000	1.000	3.162	1.0000	51	2,601	132,651	7.141	3.708	22.583	.0196
2	4	8	1.414	1.260	4.472	.5000	52	2,704	140,608	7.211	3.733	22.804	.0192
3	9	27	1.732	1.442	5.477	.3333	53	2,809	148,877	7.280	3.756	23.022	.0189
4	16	64	2.000	1.587	6.325	.2500	54	2,916	157,464	7.348	3.780	23.238	.0185
5	25	125	2.236	1.710	7.071	.2000	55	3,025	166,375	7.416	3.803	23.452	.0182
6	36	216	2.449	1.817	7.746	.1667	56	3,136	175,616	7.483	3.826	23.664	.0179
7	49	343	2.646	1.913	8.367	.1429	57	3,249	185,193	7.550	3.849	23.875	.0175
8	64	512	2.828	2.000	8.944	.1250	58	3,364	195,112	7.616	3.871	24.083	.0172
9	81	729	3.000	2.080	9.487	.1111	59	3,481	205,379	7.681	3.893	24.290	.0169
10	100	1,000	3.162	2.154	10.000	.1000	60	3,600	216,000	7.746	3.915	24.495	.0167
11	121	1,331	3.317	2.224	10.488	.0909	61	3,721	226,981	7.810	3.936	24.698	.0164
12	144	1,728	3.464	2.289	10.954	.0833	62	3,844	238,328	7.874	3.958	24.900	.0161
13	169	2,197	3.606	2.351	11.402	.0769	63	3,969	250,047	7.937	3.979	25.100	.0159
14	196	2,744	3.742	2.410	11.832	.0714	64	4,096	262,144	8.000	4.000	25.298	.0156
15	225	3,375	3.873	2.466	12.247	.0667	65	4,225	274,625	8.062	4.021	25.495	.0154
16	256	4,096	4.000	2.520	12.648	.0625	66	4,356	287,496	8.124	4.041	25.690	.0152
17	289	4,913	4.123	2.571	13.038	.0588	67	4,489	300,763	8.185	4.062	25.884	.0149
18	324	5,832	4.243	2.621	13.416	.0556	68	4,624	314,432	8.246	4.082	26.077	.0147
19	361	6,859	4.359	2.668	13.784	.0526	69	4,761	328,509	8.307	4.102	26.268	.0145
20	400	8,000	4.472	2.714	14.142	.0500	70	4,900	343,000	8.367	4.121	26.458	.0143
21	441	9,261	4.583	2.759	14.491	.0476	71	5,041	357,911	8.426	4.141	26.646	.0141
22	484	10,648	4.690	2.802	14.832	.0455	72	5,184	373,248	8.485	4.160	26.833	.0139
23	529	12,167	4.796	2.844	15.166	.0435	73	5,329	389,017	8.544	4.179	27.019	.0137
24	576	13,824	4.899	2.884	15.492	.0417	74	5,476	405,224	8.602	4.198	27.203	.0135
25	625	15,625	5.000	2.924	15.811	.0400	75	5,625	421,875	8.660	4.217	27.386	.0133
26	676	17,576	5.099	2.962	16.125	.0385	76	5,776	438,976	8.718	4.236	27.568	.0132
27	729	19,683	5.196	3.000	16.432	.0370	77	5,929	456,533	8.775	4.254	27.749	.0130
28	784	21,952	5.292	3.037	16.733	.0357	78	6,084	474,552	8.832	4.273	27.928	.0128
29	841	24,389	5.385	3.072	17.029	.0345	79	6,241	493,039	8.888	4.291	28.107	.0127
30	900	27,000	5.477	3.107	17.321	.0333	80	6,400	512,000	8.944	4.309	28.284	.0125
31	961	29,791	5.568	3.141	17.607	.0323	81	6,561	531,441	9.000	4.327	28.460	.0123
32	1,024	32,768	5.657	3.175	17.889	.0312	82	6,724	551,368	9.055	4.344	28.636	.0122
33	1,089	35,937	5.745	3.208	18.166	.0303	83	6,889	571,787	9.110	4.362	28.810	.0120
34	1,156	39,304	5.831	3.240	18.439	.0294	84	7,056	592,704	9.165	4.380	28.983	.0119
35	1,225	42,875	5.916	3.271	18.708	.0286	85	7,225	614,125	9.220	4.397	29.155	.0118
36	1,296	46,656	6.000	3.302	18.974	.0278	86	7,396	636,056	9.274	4.414	29.326	.0116
37	1,369	50,653	6.083	3.332	19.235	.0270	87	7,569	658,503	9.327	4.431	29.496	.0115
38	1,444	54,872	6.164	3.362	19.494	.0263	88	7,744	681,472	9.381	4.448	29.665	.0114
39	1,521	59,319	6.245	3.391	19.748	.0256	89	7,921	704,969	9.434	4.465	29.833	.0112
40	1,600	64,000	6.325	3.420	20.000	.0250	90	8,100	729,000	9.487	4.481	30.000	.0111
41	1,681	68,921	6.403	3.448	20.248	.0244	91	8,281	753,571	9.539	4.498	30.166	.0110
42	1,764	74,088	6.481	3.476	20.494	.0238	92	8,464	778,688	9.592	4.514	30.332	.0109
43	1,849	79,507	6.557	3.503	20.736	.0233	93	8,649	804,357	9.644	4.531	30.496	.0108
44	1,936	85,184	6.633	3.530	20.976	.0227	94	8,836	830,584	9.695	4.547	30.659	.0106
45	2,025	91,125	6.708	3.557	21.213	.0222	95	9,025	857,375	9.747	4.563	30.822	.0105
46	2,116	97,336	6.782	3.583	21.448	.0217	96	9,216	884,736	9.798	4.579	30.984	.0104
47	2,209	103,823	6.856	3.609	21.679	.0213	97	9,409	912,673	9.849	4.595	31.145	.0103
48	2,304	110,592	6.928	3.634	21.909	.0208	98	9,604	941,192	9.899	4.610	31.305	.0102
49	2,401	117,649	7.000	3.659	22.136	.0204	99	9,801	970,299	9.950	4.626	31.464	.0101
50	2,500	125,000	7.071	3.684	22.361	.0200	100	10,000	1,000,000	10.000	4.642	31.623	.0100

Table 2   Common logarithms

x	0	1	2	3	4	5	6	7	8	9
1.0	.0000	.0043	.0086	.0128	.0170	.0212	.0253	.0294	.0334	.0374
1.1	.0414	.0453	.0492	.0531	.0569	.0607	.0645	.0682	.0719	.0755
1.2	.0792	.0828	.0864	.0899	.0934	.0969	.1004	.1038	.1072	.1106
1.3	.1139	.1173	.1206	.1239	.1271	.1303	.1335	.1367	.1399	.1430
1.4	.1461	.1492	.1523	.1553	.1584	.1614	.1644	.1673	.1703	.1732
1.5	.1761	.1790	.1818	.1847	.1875	.1903	.1931	.1959	.1987	.2014
1.6	.2041	.2068	.2095	.2122	.2148	.2175	.2201	.2227	.2253	.2279
1.7	.2304	.2330	.2355	.2380	.2405	.2430	.2455	.2480	.2504	.2529
1.8	.2553	.2577	.2601	.2625	.2648	.2672	.2695	.2718	.2742	.2765
1.9	.2788	.2810	.2833	.2856	.2878	.2900	.2923	.2945	.2967	.2989
2.0	.3010	.3032	.3054	.3075	.3096	.3118	.3139	.3160	.3181	.3201
2.1	.3222	.3243	.3263	.3284	.3304	.3324	.3345	.3365	.3385	.3404
2.2	.3424	.3444	.3464	.3483	.3502	.3522	.3541	.3560	.3579	.3598
2.3	.3617	.3636	.3655	.3674	.3692	.3711	.3729	.3747	.3766	.3784
2.4	.3802	.3820	.3838	.3856	.3874	.3892	.3909	.3927	.3945	.3962
2.5	.3979	.3997	.4014	.4031	.4048	.4065	.4082	.4099	.4116	.4133
2.6	.4150	.4166	.4183	.4200	.4216	.4232	.4249	.4265	.4281	.4298
2.7	.4314	.4330	.4346	.4362	.4378	.4393	.4409	.4425	.4440	.4456
2.8	.4472	.4487	.4502	.4518	.4533	.4548	.4564	.4579	.4594	.4609
2.9	.4624	.4639	.4654	.4669	.4683	.4698	.4713	.4728	.4742	.4757
3.0	.4771	.4786	.4800	.4814	.4829	.4843	.4857	.4871	.4886	.4900
3.1	.4914	.4928	.4942	.4955	.4969	.4983	.4997	.5011	.5024	.5038
3.2	.5051	.5065	.5079	.5092	.5105	.5119	.5132	.5145	.5159	.5172
3.3	.5185	.5198	.5211	.5224	.5237	.5250	.5263	.5276	.5289	.5307
3.4	.5315	.5328	.5340	.5353	.5366	.5378	.5391	.5403	.5416	.5428
3.5	.5441	.5453	.5465	.5478	.5490	.5502	.5514	.5527	.5539	.5551
3.6	.5563	.5575	.5587	.5599	.5611	.5623	.5635	.5647	.5658	.5670
3.7	.5682	.5694	.5705	.5717	.5729	.5740	.5752	.5763	.5775	.5786
3.8	.5798	.5809	.5821	.5832	.5843	.5855	.5866	.5877	.5888	.5899
3.9	.5911	.5922	.5933	.5944	.5955	.5966	.5977	.5988	.5999	.6010
4.0	.6021	.6031	.6042	.6053	.6064	.6075	.6085	.6096	.6107	.6117
4.1	.6128	.6138	.6149	.6160	.6170	.6180	.6191	.6201	.6212	.6222
4.2	.6232	.6243	.6253	.6263	.6274	.6284	.6294	.6304	.6314	.6325
4.3	.6335	.6345	.6355	.6365	.6375	.6385	.6395	.6405	.6415	.6425
4.4	.6435	.6444	.6454	.6464	.6474	.6484	.6493	.6503	.6513	.6522
4.5	.6532	.6542	.6551	.6561	.6571	.6580	.6590	.6599	.6609	.6618
4.6	.6628	.6637	.6646	.6656	.6665	.6675	.6684	.6693	.6702	.6712
4.7	.6721	.6730	.6739	.6749	.6758	.6767	.6776	.6785	.6794	.6803
4.8	.6812	.6821	.6830	.6839	.6848	.6857	.6866	.6875	.6884	.6893
4.9	.6902	.6911	.6920	.6928	.6937	.6946	.6955	.6964	.6972	.6981
5.0	.6990	.6998	.7007	.7016	.7024	.7033	.7042	.7050	.7059	.7067
5.1	.7076	.7084	.7093	.7101	.7110	.7118	.7126	.7135	.7143	.7152
5.2	.7160	.7168	.7177	.7185	.7193	.7202	.7210	.7218	.7226	.7235
5.3	.7243	.7251	.7259	.7267	.7275	.7284	.7292	.7300	.7308	.7316
5.4	.7324	.7332	.7340	.7348	.7356	.7364	.7372	.7380	.7388	.7396
x	0	1	2	3	4	5	6	7	8	9

Table 2—*(cont.)*

x	0	1	2	3	4	5	6	7	8	9
5.5	.7404	.7412	.7419	.7427	.7435	.7443	.7451	.7459	.7466	.7474
5.6	.7482	.7490	.7497	.7505	.7513	.7520	.7528	.7536	.7543	.7551
5.7	.7559	.7566	.7574	.7582	.7589	.7597	.7604	.7612	.7619	.7627
5.8	.7634	.7642	.7649	.7657	.7664	.7672	.7679	.7686	.7694	.7701
5.9	.7709	.7716	.7723	.7731	.7738	.7745	.7752	.7760	.7767	.7774
6.0	.7782	.7789	.7796	.7803	.7810	.7818	.7825	.7832	.7839	.7846
6.1	.7853	.7860	.7868	.7875	.7882	.7889	.7896	.7903	.7910	.7917
6.2	.7924	.7931	.7938	.7945	.7952	.7959	.7966	.7973	.7980	.7987
6.3	.7993	.8000	.8007	.8014	.8021	.8028	.8035	.8041	.8048	.8055
6.4	.8062	.8069	.8075	.8082	.8089	.8096	.8102	.8109	.8116	.8122
6.5	.8129	.8136	.8142	.8149	.8156	.8162	.8169	.8176	.8182	.8189
6.6	.8195	.8202	.8209	.8215	.8222	.8228	.8235	.8241	.8248	.8254
6.7	.8261	.8267	.8274	.8280	.8287	.8293	.8299	.8306	.8312	.8319
6.8	.8325	.8331	.8338	.8344	.8351	.8357	.8363	.8370	.8376	.8382
6.9	.8388	.8395	.8401	.8407	.8414	.8420	.8426	.8432	.8439	.8445
7.0	.8451	.8457	.8463	.8470	.8476	.8482	.8488	.8494	.8500	.8506
7.1	.8513	.8519	.8525	.8531	.8537	.8543	.8549	.8555	.8561	.8567
7.2	.8573	.8579	.8585	.8591	.8597	.8603	.8609	.8615	.8621	.8627
7.3	.8633	.8639	.8645	.8651	.8657	.8663	.8669	.8675	.8681	.8686
7.4	.8692	.8698	.8704	.8710	.8716	.8722	.8727	.8733	.8739	.8745
7.5	.8751	.8756	.8762	.8768	.8774	.8779	.8785	.8791	.8797	.8802
7.6	.8808	.8814	.8820	.8825	.8831	.8837	.8842	.8848	.8854	.8859
7.7	.8865	.8871	.8876	.8882	.8887	.8893	.8899	.8904	.8910	.8915
7.8	.8921	.8927	.8932	.8938	.8943	.8949	.8954	.8960	.8965	.8971
7.9	.8976	.8982	.8987	.8993	.8998	.9004	.9009	.9015	.9020	.9025
8.0	.9031	.9036	.9042	.9047	.9053	.9058	.9063	.9069	.9074	.9079
8.1	.9085	.9090	.9096	.9101	.9106	.9112	.9117	.9122	.9128	.9133
8.2	.9138	.9143	.9149	.9154	.9159	.9165	.9170	.9175	.9180	.9186
8.3	.9191	.9196	.9201	.9206	.9212	.9217	.9222	.9227	.9232	.9238
8.4	.9243	.9248	.9253	.9258	.9263	.9269	.9274	.9279	.9284	.9289
8.5	.9294	.9299	.9304	.9309	.9315	.9320	.9325	.9330	.9335	.9340
8.6	.9345	.9350	.9555	.9360	.9365	.9370	.9375	.9380	.9385	.9390
8.7	.9395	.9400	.9405	.9410	.9415	.9420	.9425	.9430	.9435	.9440
8.8	.9445	.9450	.9455	.9460	.9465	.9469	.9474	.9479	.9484	.9489
8.9	.9494	.9499	.9504	.9509	.9513	.9518	.9523	.9528	.9533	.9538
9.0	.9542	.9547	.9552	.9557	.9562	.9566	.9571	.9576	.9581	.9586
9.1	.9590	.9595	.9600	.9605	.9609	.9614	.9619	.9624	.9628	.9633
9.2	.9638	.9643	.9647	.9652	.9657	.9661	.9666	.9671	.9675	.9680
9.3	.9685	.9689	.9694	.9699	.9703	.9708	.9713	.9717	.9722	.9727
9.4	.9731	.9736	.9741	.9745	.9750	.9754	.9759	.9763	.9768	.9773
9.5	.9777	.9782	.9786	.9791	.9795	.9800	.9805	.9809	.9814	.9818
9.6	.9823	.9827	.9832	.9836	.9841	.9845	.9850	.9854	.9859	.9863
9.7	.9868	.9872	.9877	.9881	.9886	.9890	.9894	.9899	.9903	.9908
9.8	.9912	.9917	.9921	.9926	.9930	.9934	.9939	.9943	.9948	.9952
9.9	.9956	.9961	.9965	.9969	.9974	.9978	.9983	.9987	.9991	.9996
x	0	1	2	3	4	5	6	7	8	9

Table 3   Natural logarithms of numbers

n	$\log_e n$	n	$\log_e n$	n	$\log_e n$
0.0	*	4.5	1.5041	9.0	2.1972
0.1	7.6974	4.6	1.5261	9.1	2.2083
0.2	8.3906	4.7	1.5476	9.2	2.2192
0.3	8.7960	4.8	1.5686	9.3	2.2300
0.4	9.0837	4.9	1.5892	9.4	2.2407
0.5	9.3069	5.0	1.6094	9.5	2.2513
0.6	9.4892	5.1	1.6292	9.6	2.2618
0.7	9.6433	5.2	1.6487	9.7	2.2721
0.8	9.7769	5.3	1.6677	9.8	2.2824
0.9	9.8946	5.4	1.6864	9.9	2.2925
1.0	0.0000	5.5	1.7047	10	2.3026
1.1	0.0953	5.6	1.7228	11	2.3979
1.2	0.1823	5.7	1.7405	12	2.4849
1.3	0.2624	5.8	1.7579	13	2.5649
1.4	0.3365	5.9	1.7750	14	2.6391
1.5	0.4055	6.0	1.7918	15	2.7081
1.6	0.4700	6.1	1.8083	16	2.7726
1.7	0.5306	6.2	1.8245	17	2.8332
1.8	0.5878	6.3	1.8405	18	2.8904
1.9	0.6419	6.4	1.8563	19	2.9444
2.0	0.6931	6.5	1.8718	20	2.9957
2.1	0.7419	6.6	1.8871	25	3.2189
2.2	0.7885	6.7	1.9021	30	3.4012
2.3	0.8329	6.8	1.9169	35	3.5553
2.4	0.8755	6.9	1.9315	40	3.6889
2.5	0.9163	7.0	1.9459	45	3.8067
2.6	0.9555	7.1	1.9601	50	3.9120
2.7	0.9933	7.2	1.9741	55	4.0073
2.8	1.0296	7.3	1.9879	60	4.0943
2.9	1.0647	7.4	2.0015	65	4.1744
3.0	1.0986	7.5	2.0149	70	4.2485
3.1	1.1314	7.6	2.0281	75	4.3175
3.2	1.1632	7.7	2.0142	80	4.3820
3.3	1.1939	7.8	2.0541	85	4.4427
3.4	1.2238	7.9	2.0669	90	4.4998
3.5	1.2528	8.0	2.0794	95	4.5539
3.6	1.2809	8.1	2.0919	100	4.6052
3.7	1.3083	8.2	2.1041		
3.8	1.3350	8.3	2.1163		
3.9	1.3610	8.4	2.1282		
4.0	1.3863	8.5	2.1401		
4.1	1.4110	8.6	2.1518		
4.2	1.4351	8.7	2.1633		
4.3	1.4586	8.8	2.1748		
4.4	1.4816	8.9	2.1861		

* Subtract 10 from $\log_e n$ entries for $n < 1.0$.

Table 4   Exponential functions

x	e^x	e^{-x}	x	e^x	e^{-x}	x	e^x	e^{-x}
0.00	1.0000	1.0000	0.55	1.7333	0.5769	3.6	36.598	0.0273
0.01	1.0101	0.9900	0.60	1.8221	0.5488	3.7	40.447	0.0247
0.02	1.0202	0.9802	0.65	1.9155	0.5220	3.8	44.701	0.0224
0.03	1.0305	0.9704	0.70	2.0138	0.4966	3.9	49.402	0.0202
0.04	1.0408	0.9608	0.75	2.1170	0.4724	4.0	54.598	0.0183
0.05	1.0513	0.9512	0.80	2.2255	0.4493	4.1	60.340	0.0166
0.06	1.0618	0.9418	0.85	2.3396	0.4274	4.2	66.686	0.0150
0.07	1.0725	0.9324	0.90	2.4596	0.4066	4.3	73.700	0.0136
0.08	1.0833	0.9231	0.95	2.5857	0.3867	4.4	81.451	0.0123
0.09	1.0942	0.9139	1.0	2.7183	0.3679	4.5	90.017	0.0111
0.10	1.1052	0.9048	1.1	3.0042	0.3329	4.6	99.484	0.0101
0.11	1.1163	0.8958	1.2	3.3201	0.3012	4.7	109.95	0.0091
0.12	1.1275	0.8869	1.3	3.6693	0.2725	4.8	121.51	0.0082
0.13	1.1388	0.8781	1.4	4.0552	0.2466	4.9	134.29	0.0074
0.14	1.1503	0.8694	1.5	4.4817	0.2231	5	148.41	0.0067
0.15	1.1618	0.8607	1.6	4.9530	0.2019	6	403.43	0.0025
0.16	1.1735	0.8521	1.7	5.4739	0.1827	7	1096.6	0.0009
0.17	1.1853	0.8437	1.8	6.0496	0.1653	8	2981.0	0.0003
0.18	1.1972	0.8353	1.9	6.6859	0.1496	9	8103.1	0.0001
0.19	1.2092	0.8270	2.0	7.3891	0.1353	10	22026	0.00005
0.20	1.2214	0.8187	2.1	8.1662	0.1225	11	59874	0.00002
0.21	1.2337	0.8106	2.2	9.0250	0.1108	12	162,754	0.000006
0.22	1.2461	0.8025	2.3	9.9742	0.1003	13	442,413	0.000002
0.23	1.2586	0.7945	2.4	11.023	0.0907	14	1,202,604	0.0000008
0.24	1.2712	0.7866	2.5	12.182	0.0821	15	3,269,017	0.0000003
0.25	1.2840	0.7788	2.6	13.464	0.0743			
0.26	1.2969	0.7711	2.7	14.880	0.0672			
0.27	1.3100	0.7634	2.8	16.445	0.0608			
0.28	1.3231	0.7558	2.9	18.174	0.0550			
0.29	1.3364	0.7483	3.0	20.086	0.0498			
0.30	1.3499	0.7408	3.1	22.198	0.0450			
0.35	1.4191	0.7047	3.2	24.533	0.0408			
0.40	1.4918	0.6703	3.3	27.113	0.0369			
0.45	1.5683	0.6376	3.4	29.964	0.0334			
0.50	1.6487	0.6065	3.5	33.115	0.0302			

Table 5 Integration formulas

(Whenever ln X is used it is assumed that $X > 0$.)

1. $\int x^n \, dx = \dfrac{x^{n+1}}{n+1} + C, n \neq -1$

2. $\int \dfrac{dx}{x} = \ln x + C$

3. $\int u \, dv = uv - \int v \, du$

4. $\int e^x \, dx = e^x + C$

5. $\int e^{ax} \, dx = \dfrac{1}{a} \cdot e^{ax} + C$

6. $\int x e^{ax} \, dx = \dfrac{1}{a^2} \cdot e^{ax}(ax - 1) + C$

7. $\int x^n e^{ax} \, dx = \dfrac{x^n e^{ax}}{a} - \dfrac{n}{a} \int x^{n-1} e^{ax} \, dx$

8. $\int \ln x \, dx = x \ln x - x + C$

9. $\int (\ln x)^n \, dx = x(\ln x)^n - n \int (\ln x)^{n-1} \, dx, n \neq -1$

10. $\int x^n \ln x \, dx = x^{n+1} \left[\dfrac{\ln x}{n+1} - \dfrac{1}{(n+1)^2} \right] + C, n \neq -1$

11. $\int a^x \, dx = \dfrac{a^x}{\ln a} + C, a > 0, a \neq 1$

12. $\int \dfrac{1}{\sqrt{x^2 + a^2}} \, dx = \ln(x + \sqrt{x^2 + a^2}) + C$

13. $\int \dfrac{1}{\sqrt{x^2 - a^2}} \, dx = \ln(x + \sqrt{x^2 - a^2}) + C$

14. $\int \dfrac{1}{x^2 - a^2} \, dx = \dfrac{1}{2a} \ln \left(\dfrac{x - a}{x + a} \right) + C$

15. $\int \dfrac{1}{a^2 - x^2} \, dx = \dfrac{1}{2a} \ln \left(\dfrac{a + x}{a - x} \right) + C$

16. $\int \dfrac{1}{x\sqrt{a^2 + x^2}} \, dx = -\dfrac{1}{a} \ln \left(\dfrac{a + \sqrt{a^2 + x^2}}{x} \right) + C$

17. $\int \dfrac{1}{x\sqrt{a^2 - x^2}} \, dx = -\dfrac{1}{a} \ln \left(\dfrac{a + \sqrt{a^2 - x^2}}{x} \right) + C, 0 < x < a$

18. $\int \dfrac{x}{ax + b} \, dx = \dfrac{b}{a^2} + \dfrac{x}{a} - \dfrac{b}{a^2} \ln (ax + b) + C$

19. $\int \dfrac{x}{(ax + b)^2} \, dx = \dfrac{b}{a^2(ax + b)} + \dfrac{1}{a^2} \ln (ax + b) + C$

20. $\int \dfrac{1}{x(ax + b)} \, dx = \dfrac{1}{b} \ln \left(\dfrac{x}{ax + b} \right) + C$

21. $\int \dfrac{1}{x(ax + b)^2} \, dx = \dfrac{1}{b(ax + b)} + \dfrac{1}{b^2} \ln \left(\dfrac{x}{ax + b} \right) + C$

22. $\int \sqrt{x^2 \pm a^2} \, dx$

$\qquad = \frac{1}{2}[x\sqrt{x^2 \pm a^2} \pm a^2 \ln(x + \sqrt{x^2 \pm a^2})] + C$

Table 6 Areas for a standard normal Distribution

Entries in the table represent area under the
curve between $t = 0$ and a positive value of t.
Because of the symmetry of the curve, area under
the curve between $t = 0$ and a negative value of
t would be found in a like manner.

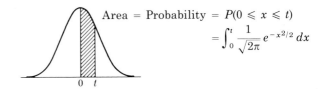

Area = Probability = $P(0 \leqslant x \leqslant t)$
$$= \int_0^t \frac{1}{\sqrt{2\pi}} e^{-x^2/2} \, dx$$

t	0.00	0.01	0.02	0.03	0.04	0.05	0.06	0.07	0.08	0.09
0.0	.0000	.0040	.0080	.0120	.0160	.0199	.0239	.0279	.0319	.0359
0.1	.0398	.0438	.0478	.0517	.0557	.0596	.0636	.0675	.0714	.0753
0.2	.0793	.0832	.0871	.0910	.0948	.0987	.1026	.1064	.1103	.1141
0.3	.1179	.1217	.1255	.1293	.1331	.1368	.1406	.1443	.1480	.1517
0.4	.1554	.1591	.1628	.1664	.1700	.1736	.1772	.1808	.1844	.1879
0.5	.1915	.1950	.1985	.2019	.2054	.2088	.2123	.2157	.2190	.2224
0.6	.2257	.2291	.2324	.2357	.2389	.2422	.2454	.2486	.2517	.2549
0.7	.2580	.2611	.2642	.2673	.2704	.2734	.2764	.2794	.2823	.2852
0.8	.2881	.2910	.2939	.2967	.2995	.3023	.3051	.3078	.3106	.3133
0.9	.3159	.3186	.3212	.3238	.3264	.3289	.3315	.3340	.3365	.3389
1.0	.3413	.3438	.3461	.3485	.3508	.3531	.3554	.3577	.3599	.3621
1.1	.3643	.3665	.3686	.3708	.3729	.3749	.3770	.3790	.3810	.3830
1.2	.3849	.3869	.3888	.3907	.3925	.3944	.3962	.3980	.3997	.4015
1.3	.4032	.4049	.4066	.4082	.4099	.4115	.4131	.4147	.4162	.4177
1.4	.4192	.4207	.4222	.4236	.4251	.4265	.4279	.4292	.4306	.4319
1.5	.4332	.4345	.4357	.4370	.4382	.4394	.4406	.4418	.4429	.4441
1.6	.4452	.4463	.4474	.4484	.4495	.4505	.4515	.4525	.4535	.4545
1.7	.4554	.4564	.4573	.4582	.4591	.4599	.4608	.4616	.4625	.4633
1.8	.4641	.4649	.4656	.4664	.4671	.4678	.4686	.4693	.4699	.4706
1.9	.4713	.4719	.4726	.4732	.4738	.4744	.4750	.4756	.4761	.4767
2.0	.4772	.4778	.4783	.4788	.4793	.4798	.4803	.4808	.4812	.4817
2.1	.4821	.4826	.4830	.4834	.4838	.4842	.4846	.4850	.4854	.4857
2.2	.4861	.4864	.4868	.4871	.4875	.4878	.4881	.4884	.4887	.4890
2.3	.4893	.4896	.4898	.4901	.4904	.4906	.4909	.4911	.4913	.4916
2.4	.4918	.4920	.4922	.4925	.4927	.4929	.4931	.4932	.4934	.4936
2.5	.4938	.4940	.4941	.4943	.4945	.4946	.4948	.4949	.4951	.4952
2.6	.4953	.4955	.4956	.4957	.4959	.4960	.4961	.4962	.4963	.4964
2.7	.4965	.4966	.4967	.4968	.4969	.4970	.4971	.4972	.4973	.4974
2.8	.4974	.4975	.4976	.4977	.4977	.4978	.4979	.4979	.4980	.4981
2.9	.4981	.4982	.4982	.4983	.4984	.4984	.4985	.4985	.4986	.4986
3.0	.4987	.4987	.4987	.4988	.4988	.4989	.4989	.4989	.4990	.4990

Appendix C
MULTIPLE
INTEGRATION

You should be able to evaluate multiple integrals.

1. Evaluate

$$\int_1^2 \int_{-2}^3 9x^2y \; dx \; dy.$$

2. Evaluate

$$\int_{-2}^3 \int_1^2 9x^2y \; dy \; dx.$$

Compare your answer to that of Margin Exercise 1.

MULTIPLE INTEGRATION

A *double integral* is like the following:

$$\int_3^6 \int_{-1}^2 10xy^2 \; dx \; dy, \quad \text{or} \quad \int_3^6 \left(\int_{-1}^2 10xy^2 \; dx \right) dy.$$

We evaluate this integral in a manner similar to partial differentiation. We first evaluate the inside x integral, treating y as a constant:

$$\int_{-1}^2 10xy^2 \; dx = [5x^2y^2]_{-1}^2 = 5y^2(2^2 - (-1)^2) = 15y^2.$$

Then we evaluate the outside y integral:

$$\int_3^6 15y^2 \; dy = [5y^3]_3^6 = 5(6^3 - 3^3) = 945.$$

More precisely the above is called a *double iterated integral*. The word "iterate" means "to do again".

Do Exercise 1.

If the dx and dy and the limits of integration are interchanged, as follows:

$$\int_{-1}^2 \int_3^6 10xy^2 \; dy \; dx,$$

we would first evaluate the inside y integral, treating x as a constant:

$$\int_3^6 10xy^2 \; dy = \left[\frac{10}{3} xy^3 \right]_3^6 = \frac{10}{3} x(6^3 - 3^3) = 630x.$$

Then we evaluate the outside x integral.

$$\int_{-1}^2 630x \; dx = [315x^2]_{-1}^2 = 315(2^2 - (1)^2) = 945.$$

Note that we get the same result. This is not always true, but will be for the types of functions we consider.

Do Exercise 2.

Sometimes variables occur as limits of integration.

Example 1   Evaluate:

$$\int_0^1 \int_{x^2}^x xy^2 \, dy \, dx.$$

Solution   We first evaluate the y integral, treating x as a constant:

$$\int_{x^2}^x xy^2 \, dy = \left[\frac{1}{3} xy^3 \right]_{x^2}^x = \frac{1}{3} x(x^3 - (x^2)^3) = \frac{1}{3}(x^4 - x^7).$$

Then we evaluate the outside integral:

$$\frac{1}{3}\int_0^1 (x^4 - x^7) \, dx = \frac{1}{3}\left[\frac{x^5}{5} - \frac{x^8}{8} \right]_0^1 = \frac{1}{3}\left[\left(\frac{1^5}{5} - \frac{1^8}{8}\right) - \left(\frac{0^5}{5} - \frac{0^8}{8}\right) \right] = \frac{1}{40}.$$

Thus,

$$\int_0^1 \int_{x^2}^x xy^2 \, dy \, dx = \frac{1}{40}.$$

Do Exercise 3.

GEOMETRIC INTERPRETATION OF MULTIPLE INTEGRALS

Suppose the region G in the xy-plane is bounded by the graphs of continuous functions g and h, and lies between the x-values $x = a$ and $x = b$, as in either figure below:

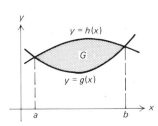 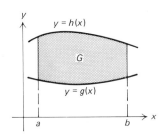

We consider the volume of the solid based on G and capped above by the piece of the surface $z = f(x, y)$ lying over G, where f is a positive (continuous) function of two variables.

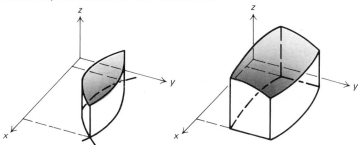

3. Evaluate

$$\int_0^1 \int_{x^2}^x 6x^2y \, dy \, dx.$$

The cross section of this solid in the plane $x = x_0$ is the plane region under the graph of $z = f(x_0, y)$, from $y_1 = g(x_0)$ to $y_2 = h(x_0)$. Its area is:

$$A(x_0) = \int_{y_1}^{y_2} f(x_0, y)\, dy = \int_{g(x_0)}^{h(x_0)} f(x_0, y)\, dy.$$

As we vary the slicing plane, the cross section changes continuously.

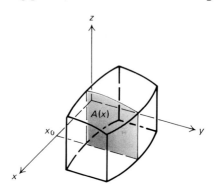

It can then be proved that the volume in question is given by

$$V = \int_a^b A(x)\, dx,$$

or

$$V = \int_a^b \int_{g(x)}^{h(x)} f(x, y)\, dy\, dx.$$

In Example 1, the region of integration G is the plane region between the graphs of $y = x^2$ and $y = x$, as shown on the left below:

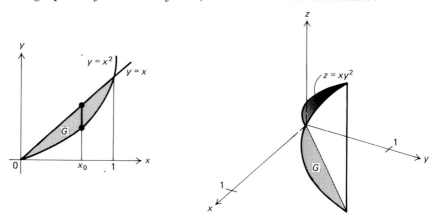

When we evaluated the double integral in Example 1, we found the volume of the solid based on G and capped by the surface $z = xy^2$, as shown above, right.

APPLICATION TO PROBABILITY

Suppose we throw a dart at a region R in the plane. It lands on a point (x, y). We can think of (x, y) as a continuous random variable, which assumes all values in some region R. A function f is said to be a *joint probability density* if

$$f(x, y) \geqslant 0 \quad \text{for all } (x, y) \text{ in } R$$

and

$$\iint_R f(x, y) \, dx \, dy = 1,$$

where $\iint_R$ refers to the double integral evaluated over the region R.

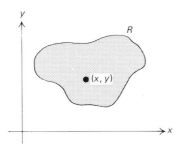

Suppose we wanted to know the probability that a point (x, y) is in a region G, where G is bounded by the set of points where $a \leqslant x \leqslant b$ and $c \leqslant y \leqslant d$. This would be given by

$$\int_c^d \int_a^b f(x, y) \, dx \, dy.$$

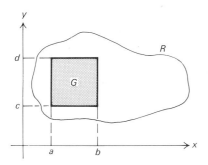

EXERCISE SET, APPENDIX C

Evaluate.

1. $\int_0^1 \int_0^1 2y \, dx \, dy$ **2.** $\int_0^1 \int_0^1 2x \, dx \, dy$ **3.** $\int_{-1}^1 \int_x^1 xy \, dy \, dx$ **4.** $\int_{-1}^1 \int_x^2 (x + y) \, dy \, dx$

5. $\int_0^1 \int_{-1}^3 (x + y) \, dy \, dx$ **6.** $\int_0^1 \int_{-1}^1 (x + y) \, dy \, dx$ **7.** $\int_0^1 \int_{x^2}^x (x + y) \, dy \, dx$

8. $\int_0^1 \int_{-1}^x (x^2 + y^2) \, dy \, dx$ **9.** $\int_0^2 \int_0^x (x + y^2) \, dy \, dx$ **10.** $\int_1^3 \int_0^x 2e^{x^2} \, dy \, dx$

11. Find the volume of the solid capped by the surface $z = 1 - y - x^2$ over the region bounded above and below by $y = 0$ and $y = 1 - x^2$, and left and right by $x = 0$ and $y = 1$, by evaluating the integral:

$$\int_0^1 \int_0^{1-x^2} (1 - y - x^2) \, dy \, dx.$$

12. Find the volume of the solid capped by the surface $z = x + y$ over the region bounded above and below by $y = 0$ and $y = 1 - x$, and left and right by $x = 0$ and $x = 1$, by evaluating the integral:

$$\int_0^1 \int_0^{1-x} (x + y) \, dy \, dx.$$

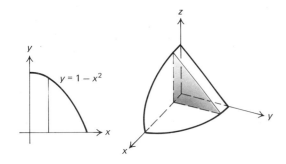

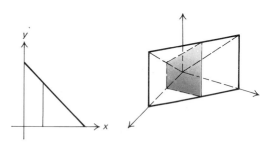

Suppose a continuous random variable has a joint probability density function given by

$$f(x, y) = x^2 + \tfrac{1}{3}xy, \qquad 0 \leqslant x \leqslant 1, \qquad 0 \leqslant y \leqslant 2.$$

13. Find $\int_0^2 \int_0^1 f(x, y) \, dx \, dy$.

14. Find the probability that a point (x, y) is in the region bounded by $0 \leqslant x \leqslant \frac{1}{2}$, $1 \leqslant y \leqslant 2$, by evaluating the integral:

$$\int_1^2 \int_0^{1/2} f(x, y) \, dx \, dy.$$

A *triple iterated integral* such as

$$\int_r^s \int_c^d \int_a^b f(x, y, z) \, dx \, dy \, dz$$

is evaluated in much the same way as a double iterated integral. We first evaluate the inside x integral, treating

y and z as constants. Then we evaluate the middle y integral, treating z as a constant. Finally, we evaluate the outside z integral.

Evaluate these triple integrals.

15. $\displaystyle\int_0^1 \int_1^3 \int_{-1}^2 (2x + 3y - z)\, dx\, dy\, dz$

16. $\displaystyle\int_0^2 \int_1^4 \int_{-1}^2 (8x - 2y + z)\, dx\, dy\, dz$

Appendix D
TRIGONOMETRIC FUNCTIONS

ANGLES AND ROTATIONS

Our goal here is to introduce the trigonometric functions together with their derivatives and integrals.

We shall consider a rotating ray, with its endpoint at the origin of an xy-plane. The ray starts in position along the positive half of the x-axis. A counterclockwise rotation will be called *positive*. Clockwise rotations will be called *negative*.

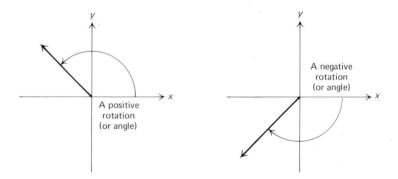

Note that the rotating ray and the positive half of the x-axis form an angle. Thus we often speak of "rotations" and "angles" interchangeably. The rotating ray is often called the *terminal side* of the angle, and the positive half of the x-axis is called the *initial side*.

Measures of Rotations or Angles

The size, or *measure*, of an angle, or rotation, may be given in degrees. Thus a complete revolution has a measure of $360°$, half a revolution has a measure of $180°$, and so on. We can also speak of an *angle* of $90°$, or $720°$, or $-240°$.

An angle between $0°$ and $90°$ has its terminal side in the first quadrant.

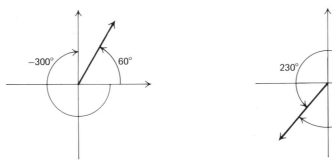

1. In which quadrant does the terminal side of each angle lie?
a) 47°   b) 212°
c) −43°   d) −135°
e) 365°   f) −365°
g) 740°

An angle between 90° and 180° has its terminal side in the second quadrant. An angle between 180° and 270° has its terminal side in the third quadrant.

An angle between 0° and −90° has its terminal side in the fourth quadrant.

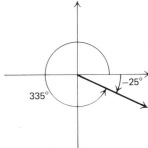

Note that angles with measure 0°, 360°, and 720° have the same terminal side, as do 270° and −90°.

Do Exercise 1.

Radian Measure

A unit of angle or rotation measure other than the degree is very useful for many purposes. This unit is called the *radian*. It is defined as follows:

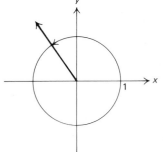

2. Convert to radian measure. Leave answers in terms of π.

a) $135°$ b) $315°$

c) $-90°$ d) $720°$

e) $-225°$ f) $-315°$

g) $405°$ h) $480°$

Consider a circle with radius of length 1, centered at the origin. The distance around this circle, from the initial side to the terminal side, is the measure of the angle, or rotation, in *radians*. Since the circumference of the circle is $2\pi \cdot 1$, or 2π, a complete revolution (360°) has a measure of 2π radians. Half of this (180°) is π radians, and a fourth of this (90°) is $\pi/2$ radians. In general, we can convert from one measure to the other using this proportion:

$$\frac{\text{radian measure}}{\pi} = \frac{\text{degree measure}}{180}.$$

Example 1   Convert 270° to radians.

Solution

$$\frac{\text{radian measure}}{\pi} = \frac{270}{180};$$

$$radian\ measure = \frac{270}{180} \cdot \pi, \quad \text{or} \quad \frac{3}{2}\pi.$$

3. Convert these radian measures to degrees.

a) $\dfrac{\pi}{3}$ b) $\dfrac{3}{4}\pi$

c) $\dfrac{5}{2}\pi$ d) 10π

e) $-\dfrac{7\pi}{6}$ f) 300π

g) -270π h) $\dfrac{25\pi}{4}$

When no unit is specified for an angle measure, it is understood to be radians.

Example 2   Convert $\dfrac{\pi}{4}$ radians to degrees.

Solution

$$\frac{\pi/4}{\pi} = \frac{\text{degree measure}}{180};$$

$$degree\ measure = 180 \cdot \frac{\pi/4}{\pi}, \text{or } 45°.$$

Do Exercises 2 and 3.

TRIGONOMETRIC FUNCTIONS

The concept of rotation or angle is important to functions called *trigonometric*, or *circular* functions.

Consider an angle t, measured in radians, shown as follows on a circle with radius 1.

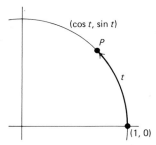

The terminal side of the angle intersects this circle at point P. The distance *around the circle* from $(1, 0)$ to P is t. We define cos t (cosine t) and sin t (sine t) as the first and second coordinates of P.

$$\cos t = \text{first coordinate of } P;$$
$$\sin t = \text{second coordinate of } P.$$

Certain values of these functions are easy to determine. When $t = \pi$, for example, the terminal side of the angle is on the horizontal axis, and P is one unit to the left; hence the first coordinate is -1 and the second coordinate is 0. Thus,

$$\cos \pi = -1 \quad \text{and} \quad \sin \pi = 0.$$

Similarly, when $t = \pi/2$, the point P is one unit up on the vertical axis; hence the first coordinate is 0 and the second coordinate is 1. Thus,

$$\cos \frac{\pi}{2} = 0 \quad \text{and} \quad \sin \frac{\pi}{2} = 1.$$

When $t = 0$, the terminal side is on the horizontal axis and P is one unit to the right; hence the first coordinate is 1 and the second coordinate is 1. Thus

$$\cos 0 = 1 \quad \text{and} \quad \sin 0 = 0.$$

Using properties of right triangles, we can develop these other values.

For $t = \dfrac{\pi}{4}$ (45°), we have

$$\cos \frac{\pi}{4} = \frac{\sqrt{2}}{2} \approx 0.707 \quad \text{and} \quad \sin \frac{\pi}{4} = \frac{\sqrt{2}}{2} \approx 0.707.$$

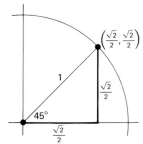

For $t = \dfrac{\pi}{3}$ (60°), we have

$$\cos \frac{\pi}{3} = \frac{1}{2} = 0.5 \qquad \text{and} \qquad \sin \frac{\pi}{3} = \frac{\sqrt{3}}{2} \approx 0.866.$$

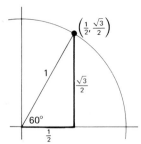

For $t = \dfrac{\pi}{6}$ (30°), we have

$$\cos \frac{\pi}{6} = \frac{\sqrt{3}}{2} \approx 0.866 \qquad \text{and} \qquad \sin \frac{\pi}{6} = \frac{1}{2} = 0.5.$$

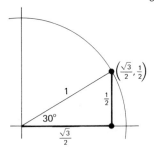

Other function values follow from certain symmetries on the unit circle. Some are exemplified below:

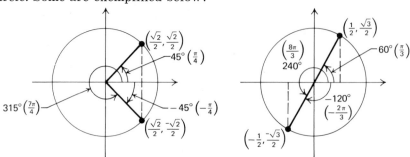

From (A) we get

$$\cos\left(-\frac{\pi}{4}\right) = \frac{\sqrt{2}}{2} \approx 0.707$$

$$\sin\left(-\frac{\pi}{4}\right) = -\frac{\sqrt{2}}{2} \approx -0.707,$$

and

$$\cos\left(\frac{7\pi}{4}\right) = \frac{\sqrt{2}}{2} \approx 0.707$$

$$\sin\left(\frac{7\pi}{4}\right) = -\frac{\sqrt{2}}{2} \approx -0.707.$$

From (B) we get

$$\cos\left(-\frac{2\pi}{3}\right) = -\frac{1}{2} = -0.5$$

$$\sin\left(-\frac{2\pi}{3}\right) = -\frac{\sqrt{3}}{2} = -0.866,$$

and

$$\cos\left(\frac{8\pi}{3}\right) = -\frac{1}{2} = -0.5$$

$$\sin\left(\frac{8\pi}{3}\right) = -\frac{\sqrt{3}}{2} \approx -0.866.$$

Do Exercise 4.

Note that $\cos t$ and $\sin t$ are functions of t defined for all real numbers t. For $|t|$ very large we may "wrap around" the circle several times before coming to the terminal point P. Nevertheless, P still has one first coordinate, $\cos t$, and one second coordinate, $\sin t$. For example,

$$\cos 3\pi = \cos \pi = -1 \quad \text{and} \quad \sin 3\pi = \sin \pi = 0.$$

Also,

$$\cos\left(\frac{15\pi}{4}\right) = \cos\left(\frac{7\pi}{4}\right) = \frac{\sqrt{2}}{2} \quad \text{and} \quad \sin\left(\frac{15\pi}{4}\right) = \sin\left(\frac{7\pi}{4}\right) = -\frac{\sqrt{2}}{2}.$$

Plotting points previously obtained, we get the graphs of the cosine and sine functions as follows:

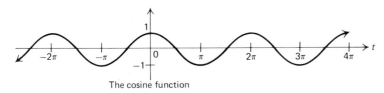

The cosine function

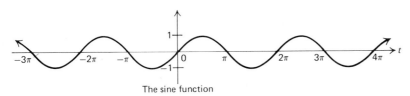

The sine function

At the origin, t is of course 0. Hence the point P is on the horizontal axis, so $\cos 0 = 1$ and $\sin 0 = 0$. Moving to the right on the graphs

4. Using the following:

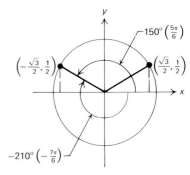

find:

a) $\cos\left(\frac{5\pi}{6}\right)$

b) $\sin\left(\frac{5\pi}{6}\right)$

c) $\cos\left(-\frac{7\pi}{6}\right)$

d) $\sin\left(-\frac{7\pi}{6}\right)$

corresponds to having the terminal side of the angle rotate counter-clockwise. Moving to the left corresponds to having the terminal side move clockwise. Note that each graph repeats itself, as the terminal side makes successive revolutions. From 0 to 2π is one complete revolution, or *cycle*. The cycle repeats itself from there on. We say that the *period* of each function is 2π. Algebraically, this means that, for any t,

$$\cos(t + 2\pi) = \cos t \quad \text{and} \quad \sin(t + 2\pi) = \sin t.$$

A function f is *periodic* if there exists a positive number p such that

$$f(x + p) = f(x).$$

This means that adding p to an input does not change the output. The smallest such number p is called the *period*.

The printout from an electrocardiogram forms a periodic function:

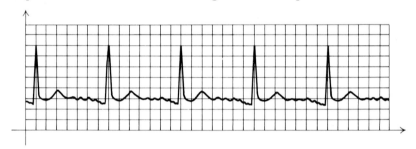

OTHER TRIGONOMETRIC FUNCTIONS

The functions $\sin x$ and $\cos x$ are the basic trigonometric functions, but there are four others, the tangent, cotangent, secant, and cosecant functions, defined as follows.

$$\tan x = \frac{\sin x}{\cos x} \qquad \cot x = \frac{\cos x}{\sin x} = \frac{1}{\tan x}$$

$$\sec x = \frac{1}{\cos x} \qquad \csc x = \frac{1}{\sin x}$$

Let us find some values of the tangent function.

Example 3 Find $\tan \dfrac{\pi}{6}$ and $\tan \dfrac{\pi}{2}$.

Solution

$$\tan \frac{\pi}{6} = \frac{\sin(\pi/6)}{\cos(\pi/6)} = \frac{1/2}{\sqrt{3}/2} = \frac{1}{\sqrt{3}} = \frac{1}{\sqrt{3}} \cdot \frac{\sqrt{3}}{\sqrt{3}} = \frac{\sqrt{3}}{3} \approx 0.578;$$

$$\tan \frac{\pi}{2} = \frac{\sin(\pi/2)}{\cos(\pi/2)} = \frac{1}{0} = \text{undefined}.$$

Do Exercises 5 and 6.

The graph of tan x is as follows.

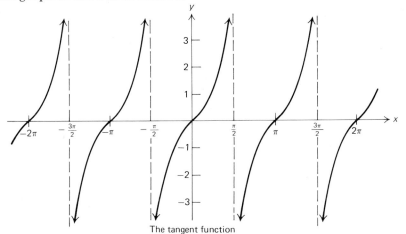

The tangent function

Identities

The properties

$$\cos(x + 2\pi) = \cos x \qquad \text{and} \qquad \sin(x + 2\pi) = \sin x$$

hold for all real numbers x. They are examples of *trigonometric identities*. Another identity which holds for all real numbers is

$$\sin^2 t + \cos^2 t = 1, \tag{1}$$

where $\sin^2 t$ means $(\sin t)^2$ and $\cos^2 t$ means $(\cos t)^2$.

To see why this holds, note the right triangle inside the unit circle in the accompanying figure.

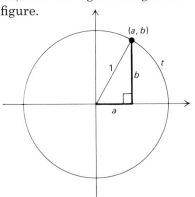

5. Find

a) $\tan \dfrac{\pi}{4}$ b) $\tan \dfrac{\pi}{3}$

c) $\tan 0$ d) $\sec \dfrac{\pi}{4}$

e) $\sec \dfrac{\pi}{3}$ f) $\sec 0$

6. Find

a) $\cot \dfrac{\pi}{6}$ b) $\cot 0$

c) $\cot \dfrac{\pi}{3}$ d) $\csc \dfrac{\pi}{6}$

e) $\csc 0$ f) $\csc \dfrac{\pi}{4}$

7. Multiply identity (1) by $\dfrac{1}{\sin^2 t}$ to develop another identity.

Since the length of the radius is 1, we know from the Pythagorean Theorem that

$$a^2 + b^2 = 1^2, \quad \text{or} \quad a^2 + b^2 = 1;$$

and, since for any point (a, b) on the unit circle, $\cos t = a$ and $\sin t = b$, the identity follows.

If we multiply identity (1) by $1/(\cos^2 t)$, we get another identity:

$$\frac{\sin^2 t}{\cos^2 t} + \frac{\cos^2 t}{\cos^2 t} = \frac{1}{\cos^2 t}$$

$$\mathbf{\tan^2 t + 1 = \sec^2 t.} \tag{2}$$

Do Exercise 7.

8. Use identity (6) to find $\sin 15°$.

The following are *sum and difference* identities:

$$\cos(u + v) = \cos u \cos v - \sin u \sin v; \tag{3}$$
$$\cos(u - v) = \cos u \cos v + \sin u \sin v; \tag{4}$$
$$\sin(u + v) = \sin u \cos v + \cos u \sin v; \tag{5}$$
$$\sin(u - v) = \sin u \cos v - \cos u \sin v. \tag{6}$$

9. Use identity (5) to find

$$\sin\left(\frac{\pi}{4} + \frac{\pi}{3}\right).$$

Example 4   Use identity (4) to find $\cos 15°$.

Solution   We think of $15°$ as $45° - 30°$. Then

$$\cos 15° = \cos(45° - 30°)$$
$$= \cos 45° \cos 30° + \sin 45° \cos 30°$$
$$= \frac{\sqrt{2}}{2} \cdot \frac{\sqrt{3}}{2} + \frac{\sqrt{2}}{2} \cdot \frac{1}{2}$$
$$= \frac{\sqrt{6} + \sqrt{2}}{4}.$$

Do Exercises 8 and 9.

10. Let $u = v$ in identity (5) to find an identity for $\sin 2u$.

If we let $u = v$ in identity (3), we obtain a so-called *double angle* identity:

$$\cos 2u = \cos(u + u)$$
$$= \cos u \cos u - \sin u \sin u;$$
$$\mathbf{\cos 2u = \cos^2 u - \sin^2 u.}$$

Do Exercise 10.

DERIVATIVES OF THE TRIGONOMETRIC FUNCTIONS

The development of the derivatives of $\sin x$ and $\cos x$ is comparable to the development of the derivative of e^x. We first find the value of the derivative at 0, and then extend this to the general formula. The derivatives at 0 are given by the following limits:

$$\sin'(0) = \lim_{h \to 0} \frac{\sin(0 + h) - \sin 0}{h} = \lim_{h \to 0} \frac{\sin h}{h};$$

$$\cos'(0) = \lim_{h \to 0} \frac{\cos(0 + h) - \cos 0}{h} = \lim_{h \to 0} \frac{\cos h - 1}{h}.$$

We find the limits on the right using input–output tables.

h (in radians) with decimal approximation	$\sin h$	$\cos h$	$\dfrac{\sin h}{h}$	$\dfrac{\cos h - 1}{h}$
$\dfrac{\pi}{2}$ (1.5708)	1	0	0.6366	-0.6366
$\dfrac{\pi}{3}$ (1.0472)	$\dfrac{\sqrt{3}}{2}$ (0.8660)	$\dfrac{1}{2}$ (0.5000)	0.8270	-0.4775
$\dfrac{\pi}{4}$ (0.7854)	$\dfrac{\sqrt{2}}{2}$ (0.7071)	$\dfrac{\sqrt{2}}{2}$ (0.7071)	0.9003	-0.3729
$\dfrac{\pi}{6}$ (0.5234)	$\dfrac{1}{2}$ (0.5000)	$\dfrac{\sqrt{3}}{2}$ (0.8660)	0.9553	-0.2560
$\dfrac{\pi}{20}$ (0.1571)	0.1564	0.9877	0.9955	-0.0783
$\dfrac{\pi}{50}$ (0.0628)	0.0628	0.9980	1.0000	-0.0314
$\dfrac{\pi}{400}$ (0.0008)	0.0008	0.99997	1.0000	-0.0038

Values from the table above could also be checked. It follows that

$$\lim_{h \to 0} \frac{\sin h}{h} = 1 \quad \text{and} \quad \lim_{h \to 0} \frac{\cos h - 1}{h} = 0.$$

Now let us consider the general derivatives.

$$\frac{d}{dx} \sin x = \lim_{h \to 0} \frac{\sin(x + h) - \sin x}{h}.$$

11. Prove that

$$\frac{d}{dx} \cot x = -\csc^2 x.$$

Using identity (5), we get

$$\frac{\sin(x+h) - \sin x}{h} = \frac{\sin x \cos h + \cos x \sin h - \sin x}{h}$$

$$= \frac{\sin x \cos h - \sin x}{h} + \frac{\cos x \sin h}{h}$$

$$= \sin x \left(\frac{\cos h - 1}{h} \right) + \cos x \left(\frac{\sin h}{h} \right).$$

Then using the limits just developed

$$\frac{d}{dx} \sin x = \lim_{h \to 0} \frac{\sin(x+h) - \sin x}{h}$$

$$= (\sin x) \cdot 0 + (\cos x) \cdot 1$$

$$= \cos x.$$

A development for the derivative of $\cos x$ is similar but uses identity (3). The result is $-\sin x$.

In summary,

$$\frac{d}{dx} \sin x = \cos x \qquad \text{and} \qquad \frac{d}{dx} \cos x = -\sin x.$$

The derivatives of the remaining trigonometric functions are computed from their definitions in terms of $\sin x$ and $\cos x$ together with the Quotient Rule and/or the Extended Power Rule. The remaining formulas are:

$$\frac{d}{dx} \tan x = \sec^2 x, \qquad \frac{d}{dx} \cot x = -\csc^2 x,$$

$$\frac{d}{dx} \sec x = \tan x \sec x, \qquad \frac{d}{dx} \csc x = -\cot x \csc x.$$

Example 5   Prove that $\dfrac{d}{dx} \tan x = \sec^2 x$.

Solution   By definition

$$\tan x = \frac{\sin x}{\cos x}.$$

We can therefore find its derivative using the Quotient Rule:

$$\frac{d}{dx} \tan x = \frac{\cos x(\cos x) - \sin x(-\sin x)}{\cos^2 x}$$

$$= \frac{\cos^2 x + \sin^2 x}{\cos^2 x} = \frac{1}{\cos^2 x} = \sec^2 x.$$

Do Exercise 11.

Example 6   Find the derivative of $\sec^3 x$.

Solution   We use the Extended Power Rule:

$$\frac{d}{dx} \sec^3 x = 3 \sec^2 x \cdot \left(\frac{d}{dx} \sec x\right) = 3 \sec^2 x \cdot \tan x \cdot \sec x.$$

Replacing the factors by the definitions in terms of $\sin x$ and $\cos x$, we can simplify this as follows:

$$3 \sec^2 x \cdot \tan x \cdot \sec x = 3 \cdot \frac{1}{\cos^2 x} \cdot \frac{\sin x}{\cos x} \cdot \frac{1}{\cos x}$$

$$= \frac{3 \sin x}{\cos^4 x}.$$

Do Exercise 12.

Using the Chain Rule (see p. 133):

$$\frac{d}{dx} f(\square) = f'(\square) \frac{d}{dx} \square,$$ **(Derivative of the outside function times the derivative of the inside function)**

we can find other derivatives.

Example 7   Differentiate $\sin(x^3 - 5x)$.

$$\frac{d}{dx} \sin(x^3 - 5x) = \cos(x^3 - 5x) \cdot (3x^2 - 5)$$

$$= (3x^2 - 5)\sin(x^3 - 5x).$$

Example 8   Differentiate $\cos(e^{4x})$.

$$\frac{d}{dx} \cos(e^{4x}) = -\sin(e^{4x}) \cdot 4e^{4x}$$

$$= -4e^{4x} \sin(e^{4x}).$$

Do Exercises 13 and 14.

INTEGRATION OF THE TRIGONOMETRIC FUNCTIONS

Each of the previously developed differentiation formulas yields an integration formula. For example,

$$\int \sin x \, dx = -\cos x + C, \qquad \int \cos x = \sin x + C,$$

$$\int \sec^2 x \, dx = \tan x + C, \qquad \int \csc^2 x \, dx = -\cot x + C.$$

12. Differentiate

$$\tan^3 x.$$

Differentiate.

13. $\sin(x^4 + 3x^2)$

14. $\cos(e^{x^2})$

15. Find the area under the graph of $y = \sin x$ on the interval $[0, \pi]$.

Example 9 Find the area under $y = \cos x$ on the interval $\left[0, \dfrac{\pi}{2}\right]$.

Solution

$$\int_0^{\pi/2} \cos x \, dx = \Big[\sin x \Big]_0^{\pi/2} = \left(\sin \frac{\pi}{2} \right) - (\sin 0) = 1.$$

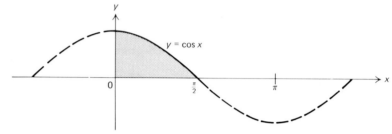

Do Exercise 15.

We use substitution in the following examples.

16. Integrate.

$$\int (\sin x)^3 \cos x \, dx$$

Example 10

$$\int (\sin x)^2 \cos x \, dx = \int u^2 \, du \quad \underline{\text{Substitution}} \quad \boxed{\begin{array}{l} u = \sin x \\ du = \cos x \, dx \end{array}}$$

$$= \frac{u^3}{3} + C$$

$$= \frac{(\sin x)^3}{3} + C.$$

Do Exercise 16.

17. Integrate.

$$\int \cos 4x \, dx$$

Example 11

$$\int \sin 3x \, dx = \frac{1}{3} \int \sin u \, du \quad \underline{\text{Substitution}} \quad \boxed{\begin{array}{l} u = 3x \\ du = 3 \, dx \end{array}}$$

$$= -\frac{1}{3} \cos u + C$$

$$= -\frac{1}{3} \cos 3x + C.$$

Do Exercise 17.

We use integration by parts in the following example.

Example 12   Integrate $\int x \cos x \, dx$.

Let

$$u = x \quad \text{and} \quad dv = \cos x \, dx.$$

Then

$$du = dx \quad \text{and} \quad v = \sin x.$$

Using the integration-by-parts formula, we get:

$$\int \overset{u}{(x)}\overset{dv}{(\cos x \, dx)} = \overset{u}{(x)}\overset{v}{(\sin x)} - \int \overset{v}{(\sin x)}\overset{du}{(dx)}$$

$$= x \sin x - (-\cos x) + C$$

$$= x \sin x + \cos x + C.$$

Do Exercise 18.

Applications

Equations of the type

$$y = A \sin(Bx - C) + D$$

have many applications. The equation can also be expressed as

$$y = A \sin\left[B\left(x - \frac{C}{B}\right)\right] + D.$$

The numbers A, B, and C play an important role in graphing such an equation. The number A corresponds to a vertical stretching or shrinking of the graph of $y = \sin x$. The number B corresponds to a horizontal stretching or shrinking. The number C/B corresponds to a shift to the left or right of the entire graph. These names are attached to the numbers.

The *amplitude* $= |A|$.

The *period* $= \dfrac{2\pi}{B}$.

The *phase shift* $= \dfrac{C}{B}$.

18. Integrate.

$$\int x \sin x \, dx$$

Example 13   A weight is attached to the end of a spring. When the weight is disturbed, it bobs up and down with a definite frequency. If the motion were to occur in a perfect vacuum, and if the spring were perfectly elastic, then the oscillatory motion would continue undiminished forever. Suppose a spring is oscillating in such a way that its vertical position at time t, from its position at rest, is given by

$$y = 3 \sin \left(2t + \frac{\pi}{2} \right) = 3 \sin \left[2 \left(t - \left(-\frac{\pi}{4} \right) \right) \right].$$

a) Find the amplitude, period, and phase shift.

b) Graph the equation.

c) Find $\dfrac{dy}{dt}$.

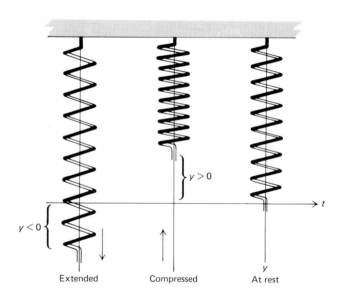

Extended   Compressed   At rest

Solution

a) Amplitude $= |3| = 3$.

   Period $= \dfrac{2\pi}{2} = \pi$.

   Phase shift $= -\dfrac{\pi}{4}$.

b) We graph the various equations needed to get the final graph.

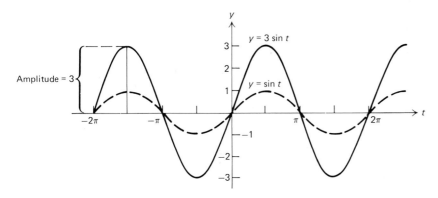

The graph of $y = 3 \sin t$ is a vertical stretching by a factor of 3 of the graph of $y = \sin t$. The period of $y = 3 \sin t$ is still 2π. The graph of $y = 3 \sin 2t$ is a horizontal shrinking by a factor of $\frac{1}{2}$ of the graph of $y = 3 \sin t$. The period of $y = 3 \sin 2t$ is π.

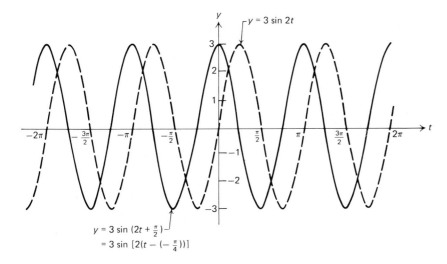

The graph of $y = 3 \sin\left[2\left(t - \left(-\dfrac{\pi}{4}\right)\right)\right]$ is shifted $\dfrac{\pi}{4}$ units to the left of the graph of $y = 3 \sin 2t$. If the phase shift were positive, the shift would be to the right.

c) $\dfrac{dy}{dt} = 3 \cos\left(2t + \dfrac{\pi}{2}\right) \cdot 2 = 6 \cos\left(2t + \dfrac{\pi}{2}\right).$

19. Suppose a spring is oscillating in such a way that its vertical position at time t, from its position at rest, is given by

$$y = 4 \sin\left(2t - \frac{\pi}{2}\right).$$

a) Find the amplitude, period, and phase shift.
b) Graph the equation.
c) Find $\dfrac{dy}{dt}$.

Do Exercise 19.

The motion of the spring in the preceding example is called *simple harmonic motion*. Other types of simple harmonic motion are sound waves and light waves. For sound waves the amplitude is the loudness. For light waves the amplitude is the brightness. The *frequency*, which is the reciprocal of the phase shift, is the tone of a sound wave and the color of a light wave.

Do Exercises 20 and 21.

20. A sound wave is given by

$$y = 0.03 \sin 1.198\pi x.$$

Find $\dfrac{dy}{dx}$.

Example 14   A corridor of width a meets a corridor of width b at right angles. Workmen wish to push a heavy beam of length c on dollies around the corner, but, before starting, they want to be sure it will be able to make the turn. How long a beam will go around the corner (neglecting the width of the beam)?

Solution   This is essentially the problem of maximizing the length l of the segment cut off by the corridor on a varying line through the corner point P. The beam will go around the corner if its length c is less than the maximum of l.

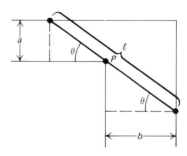

21. A light wave is given by

$$L = A \sin\left(2\pi f T - \frac{d}{\omega}\right).$$

Find $\dfrac{dL}{dT}$.

In terms of the angle θ shown in the figure, the length l can be shown to be given by

$$l = \frac{a}{\sin \theta} + \frac{b}{\cos \theta}.$$

The domain of θ is $(0, \ \pi/2)$, and l approaches $+\infty$ as θ approaches 0 or

$\pi/2$. The maximum of l will therefore occur at a point where $\dfrac{dl}{d\theta} = 0$. We see that

$$\frac{dl}{d\theta} = -\frac{a \cos \theta}{\sin^2 \theta} + \frac{b \sin \theta}{\cos^2 \theta}$$

$$= \frac{b \sin^3 \theta - a \cos^3 \theta}{\sin^2 \theta \cos^2 \theta},$$

so $\dfrac{dl}{d\theta} = 0$ if and only if

$$b \sin^3 \theta - a \cos^3 \theta = 0 \quad \text{or} \quad \tan \theta = \left(\frac{a}{b}\right)^{1/3}.$$

The corresponding value of l then works out to be

$$l = (a^{2/3} + b^{2/3})^{3/2}.$$

This is a good exercise in algebra. Anyway, the beam will go around the corner if its length is not greater than this value of l.

Do Exercise 22.

INVERSE TRIGONOMETRIC FUNCTIONS (Optional)

Look back at the graph of $\sin x$. Note that outputs ranged from -1 to 1. Suppose we wanted to work backwards from an output to an input. More specifically, suppose x is some number such that $-1 \leqslant x \leqslant 1$ and we wanted to find a number y such that $-\dfrac{\pi}{2} \leqslant y \leqslant \dfrac{\pi}{2}$ and

$$\sin y = x.$$

This determines a function, called the inverse sine function, given by

$$y = \text{Sin}^{-1} x, \quad \text{or} \quad \text{Arcsin } x.$$

Such a function is an *inverse trigonometric function*.

Example 15   Find $\text{Sin}^{-1}\left(\dfrac{\sqrt{3}}{2}\right)$.

Solution   *Think:* The number from $-\dfrac{\pi}{2}$ to $\dfrac{\pi}{2}$ whose sine is $\dfrac{\sqrt{3}}{2}$ is $\dfrac{\pi}{3}$.

22. In reference to Example 14, how long a beam will go around the corner when $a = 8$ and $b = 5\sqrt{5}$?

Find:

23. $\text{Sin}^{-1}(\tfrac{1}{2})$

24. $\text{Sin}^{-1}(0)$

25. $\text{Sin}^{-1}\left(-\dfrac{\sqrt{3}}{2}\right)$

Find:

26. $\text{Tan}^{-1}(\sqrt{3})$

27. $\text{Cos}^{-1}\left(\dfrac{\sqrt{3}}{2}\right)$

28. $\text{Cos}^{-1}(-\tfrac{1}{2})$

Thus,

$$\text{Sin}^{-1}\left(\frac{\sqrt{3}}{2}\right) = \frac{\pi}{3}$$

Do Exercises 23 through 25.

The inverse cosine function is defined

$$y = \text{Cos}^{-1} x,$$

where $x = \cos y$ and $0 \leqslant y \leqslant \pi$.

The inverse tangent function is defined as

$$y = \text{Tan}^{-1} x,$$

where $x = \tan y$ and $\dfrac{\pi}{2} \leqslant y \leqslant \dfrac{\pi}{2}$.

Do Exercises 26 through 28.

The graphs of these functions are as follows:

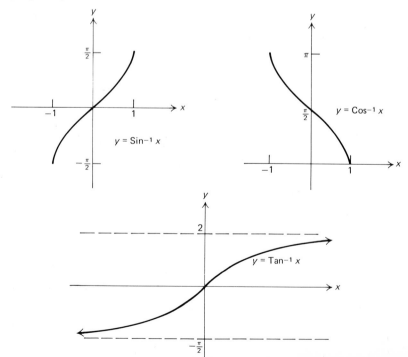

Inverse trigonometric functions are integrals of certain functions. You will often see them in tables of integrals.

Example 16   Prove that $\int \dfrac{1}{1 + x^2}\, dx = \operatorname{Tan}^{-1} x + C.$

We use substitution.

$$\int \frac{1}{1 + x^2}\, dx = \int \frac{1}{1 + \tan^2 u}\, \sec^2 u\, du \qquad \text{Substitution} \quad \begin{array}{l} u = \operatorname{Tan}^{-1} x \\ x = \tan u \\ dx = \sec^2 u\, du \end{array}$$

$$= \int \frac{1}{\sec^2 u}\, \sec^2 u\, du, \qquad \text{by Identity (2)}$$

$$= \int du$$

$$= u + C$$

$$= \operatorname{Tan}^{-1} x + C.$$

Do Exercise 29.

Example 17   Prove that $\int - \dfrac{1}{\sqrt{1 - x^2}}\, dx = \operatorname{Cos}^{-1} x + C.$

$$\int - \frac{1}{\sqrt{1 - x^2}}\, dx$$

$$= \int \frac{1}{\sqrt{1 - \cos^2 u}}\, \sin u\, du. \qquad \text{Substitution} \quad \begin{array}{l} u = \operatorname{Cos}^{-1} x \\ x = \cos u \\ dx = -\sin x\, dx \end{array}$$

By identity (1), $\sin^2 u + \cos^2 u = 1$, so

$$1 - \cos^2 u = \sin^2 u.$$

Then, since u is such that $0 \leqslant u \leqslant \pi$, $\cos u \geqslant 0$, so $\sqrt{\operatorname{Sin}^2 u} = \sin u$ and the integral becomes:

$$\int \frac{1}{\sqrt{\sin^2 u}} \cdot \sin u\, du \qquad \text{by Identity (1)}$$

$$= \int \frac{1}{\sin u} \cdot \sin u\, du$$

$$= \int du = u + C$$

$$= \operatorname{Cos}^{-1} x + C$$

Do Exercise 30.

29. Find $\displaystyle\int \frac{1}{1 + 25x^2}\, dx$ by using the substitution $u = 5x$ in the integral

$$\int \frac{1}{1 + x^2}\, dx = \operatorname{Tan}^{-1} x + C.$$

30. Find $\displaystyle\int - \frac{1}{\sqrt{1 - 4x^2}}\, dx$ by using the substitution $u = 2x$ in the integral

$$\int - \frac{1}{\sqrt{1 - x^2}}\, dx = \operatorname{Cos}^{-1} x + C.$$

EXERCISE SET, APPENDIX D

Prove the following derivative formulas.

1. $\dfrac{d}{dx}\sec x = \tan x \sec x$

2. $\dfrac{d}{dx}\csc x = -\cot x \csc x$

Differentiate:

3. $x \sin x$

4. $x \cos x$

5. $e^x \sin x$

6. $e^x \cos x$

7. $\dfrac{\sin x}{x}$

8. $\dfrac{\cos x}{x}$

9. $\sin^2 x$

10. $\cos^2 x$

11. $\sin x \cos x$

12. $\cos^2 x + \sin^2 x$

13. $\dfrac{\sin x}{1 + \cos x}$

14. $\dfrac{1 - \cos x}{\sin x}$

15. $\tan^2 x$

16. $\sec^2 x$

17. $\sqrt{1 + \cos x}$

18. $\sqrt{1 - \sin x}$

19. $x^2 \cos x - 2x \sin x - 2 \cos x$

20. $x^2 \sin x - 2x \cos x + 2 \sin x$

21. $e^{\sin x}$ **22.** $e^{\cos x}$

23. Find $\dfrac{d^2 y}{dx^2}$ if $y = \sin x$

24. Find $\dfrac{d^2 y}{dx^2}$ if $y = \cos x$

25. $\sin(x^2 + x^3)$

26. $\sin(x^5 - x^4)$

27. $\cos(x^5 - x^4)$

28. $\cos(x^2 + x^3)$

29. $\cos \sqrt{x}$

30. $\sin \sqrt{x}$

31. $\sin(\cos x)$

32. $\cos(\sin x)$

33. Find the area under $y = \sin x$ on the interval $[0, \pi/3]$.

34. Find the area under $y = \cos x$ on the interval $[0, \pi/3]$.

Integrate, using substitution.

35. $\int (\sin x)^4 \cos x \, dx$

36. $\int (\sin x)^5 \cos x \, dx$

37. $\int - (\cos x)^2 \sin x \, dx$

38. $\int (\cos x)^3 (- \sin x) dx$

39. $\int \cos(x + 3) dx$

40. $\int \sin(x + 4) dx$

41. $\int \sin 2x \, dx$

42. $\int \cos 3x \, dx$

43. $\int x \cos x^2 \, dx$

44. $\int x \sin x^2 \, dx$

45. $\int e^x \sin(e^x) dx$

46. $\int e^x \cos(e^x) dx$

47. $\int \tan x \, dx$

  Hint: $\tan x = \dfrac{\sin x}{\cos x}$

48. $\int \cot x \, dx$

  Hint: $\cot x = \dfrac{\cos x}{\sin x}$

Integrate by parts.

49. $\int x \cos 4x \, dx$

50. $\int x \sin 3x \, dx$

51. $\int 3x \cos x \, dx$

52. $\int 2x \sin x \, dx$

53. $\int x^2 \sin x \, dx$

Hint: Let $u = x$ and $dv = x \sin x \, dx$ and use the result of Margin Exercise 18.

54. $\int x^2 \cos x \, dx$

Hint: Let $u = x$ and $dv = x \cos x \, dx$ and use the result of Example 12.

55. $\int \tan^2 x \, dx$

56. $\int \cot^2 x \, dx$

57. $\int e^x \cos x \, dx$

58. $\int e^x \sin x \, dx$

59. A spring is oscillating in such a way that its vertical position at time t, from its position at rest, is given by

$$y = 5 \sin(4t + \pi).$$

a) Find the amplitude, period, and phase shift.

b) Find $\dfrac{dy}{dt}$.

60. The current i at time t of a wire passing through a magnetic field is given by

$$i = I \sin(\omega t + a).$$

a) Find the amplitude, period, and phase shift.

b) Find $\dfrac{di}{dt}$.

61. A pendulum oscillates in such a way that its horizontal position at time t, from its position at rest, is given by:

$$y = 2 \sin(2t - \pi).$$

a) Find the amplitude, period, and phase shift.

b) Find $\dfrac{dy}{dt}$.

62. A water wave has height h at time t from its position at still water given by:

$$h = 5 \sin\left(\frac{\pi}{4} t + c\right).$$

a) Find the amplitude, period, and phase shift.

b) Find $\dfrac{dh}{dt}$.

63. A company determines that profit during the t'th month is given by

$$P(t) = 40{,}000(\sin t + \cos t).$$

The profit is seasonal and fluctuates. Find $P'(t)$.

64. A piston, connected to a crankshaft, moves up and down in such a way that its second coordinate after time t is given by:

$$y(t) = \sin t + \sqrt{25 - \cos^2 t}.$$

Find the rate of change $y'(t)$.

65. In reference to Example 14, how long a beam will go around the corner when $a = 8$ and $b = 8$?

66. In reference to Example 14, how long a beam will go around the corner when $a = 3\sqrt{3}$ and $b = 5\sqrt{5}$?

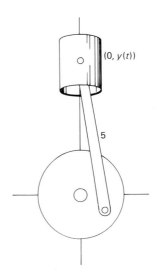

67. Two towers 40 ft apart are 30 and 20 ft high, respectively. A wire fastened to the top of each tower is guyed to the ground at a point between the towers, and is tightened so there is no sag. How far from the tallest tower will the wire touch the ground if the length of the wire is a minimum?

68. The illumination from a light source is inversely proportional to the square of the distance from the light and directly proportional to the sine of the angle of incidence. How high should a light be placed on a pole in order to maximize the illumination on the ground along the circumference of a circle of radius 25 feet?

These problems involve inverse trigonometric functions.

Integrate.

69. $\displaystyle \int \frac{e^t}{1 + e^{2t}}\, dt$

70. $\displaystyle \int -\frac{1}{\sqrt{1 - 25x^2}}\, dx$

71. Show that:

$$\int \frac{1}{\sqrt{1 - x^2}}\, dx = \operatorname{Sin}^{-1} x + C.$$

ANSWERS

CHAPTER 1

MARGIN EXERCISES

1. $3 \cdot 3 \cdot 3 \cdot 3$, or 81   **2.** $(-3)(-3)$, or 9   **3.** $1.02 \times 1.02 \times 1.02$, or 1.061208   **4.** $\frac{1}{4} \cdot \frac{1}{4}$, or $\frac{1}{16}$ **5.** 1

6. $5t$ **7.** 1   **8.** m **9.** $\frac{1}{4}$ **10.** 1   **11.** $\frac{1}{2 \cdot 2 \cdot 2 \cdot 2}$, or $\frac{1}{16}$ **12.** $\frac{1}{10 \cdot 10}$, or $\frac{1}{100}$, or 0.01   **13.** 64

14. $\frac{1}{t^7}$ **15.** $\frac{1}{e^t}$ **16.** $\frac{1}{M}$ **17.** $\frac{1}{(x+1)^2}$ **18.** t^9 **19.** t^{-3} **20.** $50e^{-13}$ **21.** t^{-6} **22.** $24b^3$

23. x^4 **24.** x^{-4} **25.** 1   **26.** e^{2-k} **27.** e^{12} **28.** e^2 **29.** x^{-12} **30.** e^4 **31.** e^{3x}

32. t^{4k} **33.** $25x^6y^{10}$ **34.** $2x + 14$ **35.** $P - Pi$ **36.** $x^2 + 3x - 28$ **37.** $a^2 - 2ab + b^2$

38. $a^2 - b^2$ **39.** $x^2 - 2xh + h^2$ **40.** $9x^2 + 6xt + t^2$ **41.** $25t^2 - m^2$ **42.** $P(1 - i)$ **43.** $(x + 5y)^2$

44. $(x + 5)(x + 2)$ **45.** $(5c - d)(5c + d)$ **46.** $h(3x^2 + 3xh + h^2)$ **47.** 1.01   **48.** \$1144.90

49. \$1081.60   **50.** $\frac{56}{9}$ **51.** \$725   **52.** $0, -2, \frac{3}{2}$ **53.** $-4, 3$ **54.** $0, -1, 1$ **55.** $x < \frac{11}{5}$ **56.** $\frac{20}{17} \leqslant x$

57. More than 19,975 suits   **58.** a) $(-1, 3)$ b) $(1, 4)$ **59.** a) $(-1, 4)$ b) $(-\frac{1}{4}, \frac{1}{4})$

60. a) $[-1, 4]$ b) $(-1, 4]$ c) $[-1, 4)$ d) $(-1, 4)$

61. a) $(-\sqrt{2}, \sqrt{2})$ b) $[0, 1)$ c) $(-6.7, -4.2]$ d) $[3, 7\frac{1}{2}]$

62. a) $(-\infty, 5]$ b) $(4, \infty)$ c) $(-\infty, 4.8)$ d) $(-\infty, 5]$

63. a) $[8, \infty)$ b) $(-\infty, -7)$ c) $(10, \infty)$ d) $(-\infty, -0.78]$

64.

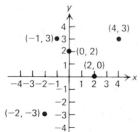

65. a) Yes   b) No

66.

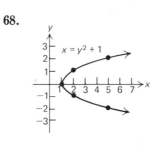

67.

68.

69.

Inputs	Outputs
5	$\frac{1}{5}$
$-\frac{2}{3}$	$-\frac{3}{2}$
$\frac{1}{4}$	4
$\frac{1}{a}$	a
k	$\frac{1}{k}$
$1 + t$	$\dfrac{1}{1 + t}$

70. $f(5) = \frac{1}{5}, f(-2) = -\frac{1}{2}, f(\frac{1}{4}) = 4, f(\frac{1}{a}) = a, f(k) = \frac{1}{k}, f(1 + t) = \dfrac{1}{1 + t}, f(x + h) = \dfrac{1}{x + h}$

71. $t(5) = 30, t(-5) = 20, t(x + h) = x + h + x^2 + 2xh + h^2$

72. a) All real numbers except 3 because an input of 3 would result in division by 0.   b) $f(5) = \frac{1}{2}, f(4) = 1, f(2.5) = -2$

73. Same as margin exercise 66, only labeled $f(x) = -2x + 1$

74. Same as margin exercise 67, only labeled $g(x) = x^2 - 3$

75. c, d **76.** a) f b) g, h c) i **77.** a) $[1, 3]$ b) $[-1, 1]$

78. a) Horizontal line through $(0, 3)$ b) Yes

79. a) Vertical line through $(1, 0)$ b) No

80. a) See Exercise Set 1.3, Ex. 10   b) Yes c) -2 **81.** a) A
b) B c) C d) E e) A f) E

82. a) $T = \frac{1}{36}h$ b) 4.5 **83.** a)

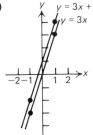

b) By moving it upward 1 unit

84. $m = -\frac{2}{3}$, y-intercept: $(0, 2)$

85. $y = -4x + 1$

86. $y + 7 = -4(x - 2)$, or $y = -4x + 1$ **87.** 2 **88.** $\frac{1}{8}$

89. $-\frac{17}{2}$ **90.** 0 **91.** 0 **92.** No slope   **93.** a) Decreasing b) Increasing c) Neither

94. a)

b) $C(100) = \$18,000, C(400) = \$27,000$

c) $C(400) - C(100) = \$9000$

95. a) b)   c) Break even is 250

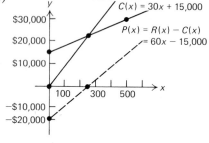

96.

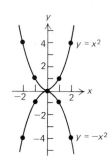

97. a)

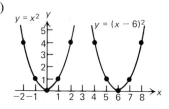

b) By moving it to the right
6 units

98.

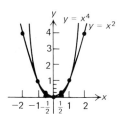

99. a) All real numbers except
-4

b) All real numbers except
$-5, 1$

c) All real numbers except
5

100.

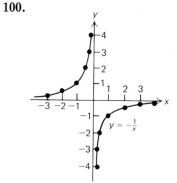

101.

102.

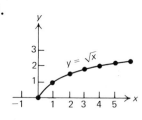

103. a) $t^{3/4}$ b) $y^{1/5}$ c) $x^{-2/5}$ d) $t^{-1/3}$ e) x^3 f) $x^{7/2}$ **104.** a) $\sqrt[7]{y}$ b) $\sqrt{x^3}$ c) $\dfrac{1}{\sqrt{t^3}}$ d) $\dfrac{1}{\sqrt{b}}$ **105.** (2, \$9)

106. a) $S = 8500t + 1500$ b) $44,000; $2000 less than (b) of Example 1

107. a) $A = \frac{131}{300}x^2 - 39\frac{7}{10}x + 1039\frac{1}{3}$, or $A = 0.437x^2 - 39.7x + 1039.333$ b) 516

EXERCISE SET 1.1, p. 8

1. $5 \cdot 5 \cdot 5$, or 125   **3.** $(-7)(-7)$, or 49   **5.** 1.0201   **7.** $\frac{1}{4}$ **9.** 1   **11.** t **13.** 1   **15.** $\frac{1}{3^2}$, or $\frac{1}{9}$

17. 8   **19.** 0.1   **21.** $\frac{1}{e^b}$ **23.** $\frac{1}{b}$ **25.** x^5 **27.** x^{-6} **29.** $35x^5$ **31.** x^4 **33.** 1   **35.** x^3

37. x^{-3} **39.** 1   **41.** e^{t-4} **43.** t^{14} **45.** t^2 **47.** t^{-6} **49.** e^{4x} **51.** t^{4x} **53.** $8x^6y^{12}$

55. $5x - 35$ **57.** $x - xt$ **59.** $x^2 - 7x + 10$ **61.** $x^2 + 3x - 10$ **63.** $2x^2 + 3x - 5$ **65.** $a^2 - 4$

67. $25x^2 - 4$ **69.** $a^2 - 2ah + h^2$ **71.** $25x^2 + 10xt + t^2$ **73.** $x(1 - t)$ **75.** $(x + 3y)^2$

77. $(x - 5)(x + 3)$ **79.** $(x - 5)(x + 4)$ **81.** $(7x - t)(7x + t)$ **83.** $4(3t - 2m)(3t + 2m)$

85. a) 0.81 b) 0.0801 c) 0.008001   **87.** a) 1.261 b) 0.120601 c) 0.012006001

89. a) $1080 b) $1081.60 c) $1082.43 d) $1083.28 assuming 365 days in a year

EXERCISE SET 1.2, p. 16

1. $\frac{7}{4}$ **3.** -8 **5.** 120   **7.** 200   **9.** 480 lb   **11.** $650

13. 810,000   **15.** $0, -3, \frac{4}{5}$ **17.** 0, 2   **19.** 0, 3   **21.** 0, 7

23. $0, \frac{1}{3}, -\frac{1}{3}$ **25.** 1   **27.** $-\frac{4}{5} \leq x$ **29.** $x > -\frac{1}{12}$ **31.** $x > -\frac{4}{7}$

33. More than 7000 units   **35.** $60\% \leq x < 100\%$ **37.** $(0, 5)$

39. $[-9, -4)$ **41.** $[x, x + h]$ **43.** (p, ∞) **45.** $[-3, 3]$

47. $[-14, -11)$ **49.** $(-\infty, -4]$

EXERCISE SET 1.3, p. 29

1. a)

Inputs	Outputs
4.1	11.2
4.01	11.02
4.001	11.002
4	11

b) $f(5) = 13, f(-1) = 1, f(k) = 2k + 3,$
$f(1 + t) = 2t + 5,$
$f(x + h) = 2x + 2h + 3$

3. $g(-1) = -2, g(0) = -3, g(1) = -2, g(5) = 22, g(u) = u^2 - 3,$
$g(a + h) = a^2 + 2ah + h^2 - 3, g(1 - h) = h^2 - 2h - 2$

5. a) $f(4) = 1, f(-2) = 25, f(0) = 9, f(a) = a^2 - 6a + 9,$
$f(t + 1) = t^2 - 4t + 4, f(t + 3) = t^2,$
$f(x + h) = x^2 + 2xh + h^2 - 6x - 6h + 9$

b) Take an input, square it, subtract 6 times the input, add 9

7.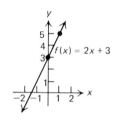

9.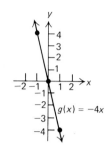

11.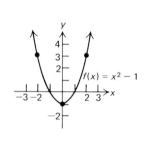

13.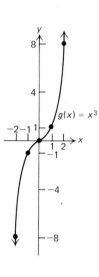

15. Yes   **17.** Yes   **19.** No   **21.** No   **23.** a)   b) No

25. $f(x + h) = x^2 + 2xh + h^2 - 3x - 3h$

27. $R(10) = \$70$, $R(100) = \$250$ **29.** Increasing   **31.** Decreasing

33. Neither   **35.** Increasing on $[-3, -1]$; decreasing on $[-1, 1]$

EXERCISE SET 1.4, p. 44

1. Horizontal line through $(0, -4)$ **3.** Vertical line through $(4.5, 0)$

5.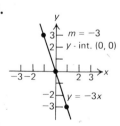

7.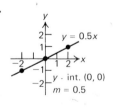

9.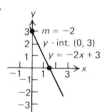

11.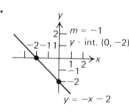

13. $m = -2$, y-int.: $(0, 2)$ **15.** $m = -1$, y-int.: $(0, -\frac{5}{2})$ **17.** $y + 5 = -5(x - 1)$, or $y = -5x$

19. $y - 3 = -2(x - 2)$, or $y = -2x + 7$ **21.** $y = \frac{1}{2}x - 6$ **23.** $y = 3$ **25.** $\frac{3}{2}$ **27.** $\frac{1}{2}$ **29.** No slope

31. 0   **33.** 3   **35.** 2   **37.** $y - 1 = \frac{3}{2}(x + 2)$, or $y + 2 = \frac{3}{2}(x + 4)$, or $y = \frac{3}{2}x + 4$

39. $y + 4 = \frac{1}{2}(x - 2)$, or $y = \frac{1}{2}x - 5$ **41.** $x = 3$ **43.** $y = 3$ **45.** $y = 3x$ **47.** $y = 2x + 3$

49. Neither   **51.** Decreasing   **53.** Increasing   **55.** a) $R = 4.17T$ b) $R = 25.02$

57. a) $B = 0.025W$ b) $B = 2.5\% W$. The weight of the brain is 2.5% of the body weight.   c) 3 lb.

59. a) $A = P + 8\% P = P + 0.08P = 1.08P$ b) \$108   c) \$240

61. a) $D(0°) = 115$ ft, $D(-20°) = 75$ ft, $D(10°) = 135$ ft, $D(32°) = 179$ ft

b)

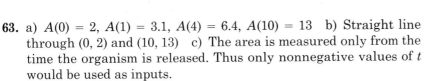

c) Temperatures below $-57.5°$ would yield a negative stopping distance which has no meaning here. For temperatures above $32°$ there would be no ice.

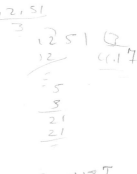

63. a) $A(0) = 2$, $A(1) = 3.1$, $A(4) = 6.4$, $A(10) = 13$ b) Straight line through (0, 2) and (10, 13)   c) The area is measured only from the time the organism is released. Thus only nonnegative values of t would be used as inputs.

65. a) $C(x) = 20x + 100,000$ b) $R(x) = 45x$ c) $P(x) = R(x) - C(x) = 25x - 100,000$
d) \$3,650,000, a profit   e) 4000

EXERCISE SET 1.5, p. 58

1.

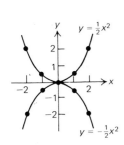

3. See margin exercise 96 for the graph of $y = x^2$. Move it to the right 1 unit to get the graph of $y = (x - 1)^2$.

5. See margin exercise 96 for $y = x^2$. Move it to the left 1 unit to get $y = (x + 1)^2$.

7.

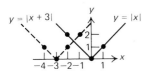

9. See Exercise Set 1.3, Ex. 13 for $y = x^3$. Move it up 1 unit for $y = x^3 + 1$.

11. See margin exercise 102 for $y = \sqrt{x}$. Move it to the left 1 unit for $y = \sqrt{x + 1}$

13.

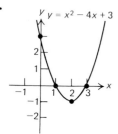

15.

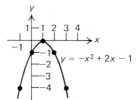

17.

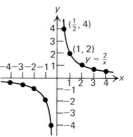

19.

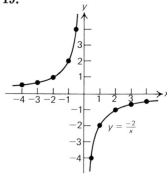

21.

x	-2	-1	$-\frac{1}{2}$	$\frac{1}{2}$	1	2
y	$\frac{1}{4}$	1	4	4	1	$\frac{1}{4}$

23.

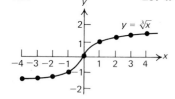

25. $x^{3/2}$ **27.** $a^{3/5}$ **29.** $t^{1/7}$ **31.** $t^{-4/3}$ **33.** $t^{-1/2}$ **35.** $(x^2 + 7)^{-1/2}$ **37.** $\sqrt[5]{x}$

39. $\sqrt[3]{y^2}$ **41.** $\dfrac{1}{\sqrt[5]{t^2}}$ **43.** $\dfrac{1}{\sqrt[3]{b}}$ **45.** $\dfrac{1}{\sqrt[6]{e^{17}}}$ **47.** $\dfrac{1}{\sqrt{x^2 - 3}}$

49. All real numbers except 5

51. All real numbers except 2, 3

53. (2, \$4)   **55.** (1, \$4)   **57.** (2, \$4)

59.

W	0	10	20	30	40	50	100	150
T	0	20	51	86	126	168	417	709

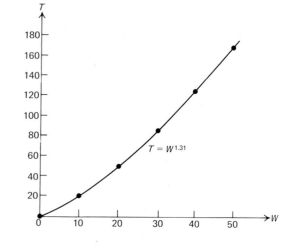

EXERCISE SET 1.6, p. 66

1. b) Linear   c) $y = 32x + 9998$ d) \$10,126; \$10,318   e) $C = 29.5x + 10,000$ f) \$10,118; \$10,295

3. b) quadratic   c) $D = 0.9875x^2 - 121.5x + 3756.25$ d) 21.25

5. b) Constant, linear   c) $S = -20x + 100,330$
   d) Let $S = b$, where b is the average of the sales totals: \$100,296.25.

CHAPTER 1, TEST, p. 68

1. $\dfrac{1}{e^k}$ **2.** e^{-13} **3.** $x^2 + 2xh + h^2$ **4.** $(5x - t)(5x + t)$ **5.** \$920   **6.** $x > -4$

7. a) $f(-3) = 5$ b) $x^2 + 2xh + h^2 - 4$ **8.** $m = -3$; y-int.: $(0, 2)$ **9.** $y + 5 = \frac{1}{4}(x - 8)$, or $y = \frac{1}{4}x - 7$

10. $m = 6$ **11.** $F = \frac{2}{3}W$

12. a) $C(x) = 0.5x + 10,000$ b) $R(x) = 1.3x$ c) $P(x) = R(x) - C(x) = 0.8x - 10,000$ d) $12,500$

13. Decreasing   **14.** $(3, \$16)$

15.

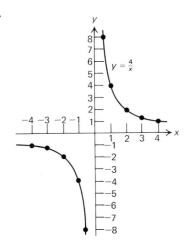

16. $t^{-1/2}$ **17.** $\dfrac{1}{\sqrt[5]{t^3}}$

18. All real numbers except $2, -7$

19. $y = 4x - 1$

20. $y = -4.5x^2 + 17.5x - 8$

21. $[c, d)$

CHAPTER 2

MARGIN EXERCISES

1. a) 0.61 b) 0.0601 c) 0.006001 d) Yes   **2.** a, b **3.** a) No, Yes   b) Yes, No

4. $\sqrt[3]{x}$ is continuous by II; 7 is continuous by I, and x^2 is continuous by II, so $7x^2$ is continuous by III. Then $\sqrt[3]{x} - 7x^2$ is continuous by III. Now x is continuous by II, and 2 is continuous by I, so $x - 2$ is continuous by III. Thus the quotient $\dfrac{\sqrt[3]{x^2 - 7x}}{x - 2}$ is continuous by IV.

5. a) $20, 19.7, 18.2, 17.3, 17.03, 17.003; 14, 16.1, 16.4, 16.7, 16.97, 16.997$ b) 17 c) 17

6. a) $7, 6.6, 6.2, 6.1, 6.01, 6.001; 4, 5, 5.4, 5.9, 5.99, 5.999$ b) 6

7. $-0.2679, -0.2583, -0.2516, -0.2502, -0.250016$

8. a) $1, 1.667, 5, 10, 100, 1000; -0.5, -1, -1.667, -10, -100, -1000$ b) Does not exist

9. a) $-0.3333, -0.2778, -0.2632, -0.2564, -0.251, -0.2501; -0.2, -0.2222, -0.2273, -0.2439, -0.2494, -0.2499$ b) -0.25, or $-\frac{1}{4}$

10. a) $2x + 1, 2x + 0.7, 2x + 0.4, 2x + 0.1, 2x + 0.01, 2x + 0.001$ b) $\mathbf{2x}$

11. a) 3.25, 2.25, 2.0625, 2.025, 2.005, 2.0005   b) 2

12. a) $20 \dfrac{\text{suits}}{\text{hr}}$, $35 \dfrac{\text{suits}}{\text{hr}}$, $9 \dfrac{\text{suits}}{\text{hr}}$, $36 \dfrac{\text{suits}}{\text{hr}}$ b) 11 A.M. to 12 P.M.   c) Workers were anticipating the lunch break; answers may vary   d) 10 A.M. to 11 A.M.   e) Workers were fatigued or took longer breaks than they should have; answers may vary   f) $25 \dfrac{\text{suits}}{\text{hr}}$

13. a) 21 b) 7 c) 28 d) 21   **14.** a) $\frac{1}{2}$ b) $\frac{1}{2}$ c) $\frac{1}{2}$

15.

x	h	$x + h$	$f(x)$	$f(x + h)$	$f(x + h) - f(x)$	$\dfrac{f(x + h) - f(x)}{h}$
3	2	5	36	100	64	32
3	1	4	36	64	28	28
3	0.1	3.1	36	38.44	2.44	24.4
3	0.01	3.01	36	36.2404	0.2404	24.04
3	0.001	3.001	36	36.024004	0.024004	24.004

16. a) $f(x + h) = 4x^2 + 8xh + 4h^2$ b) $f(x + h) - f(x) = 8xh + 4h^2$ c) $\dfrac{f(x + h) - f(x)}{h} = 4(2x + h)$

  d) 36, 40, 44, 47.6, 47.96, 47.996

17. a) $4(3x^2 + 3xh + h^2)$ b) 28, 45.64, 47.7604, 47.976004

18. a) $\dfrac{-1}{x(x + h)}$ b) $-0.1, -0.1667, -0.2381, -0.2488, -0.2499$

19. L_2, L_3, L_4, L_6 **20.**

21. a) Answers may vary; $-4, -3, -2, -1, 0, 1, 2, 3, 4$
  b) Line through $(0, 0)$ and $(1, 2)$

22. $f'(5) = 10$ **23.** $f'(x) = 8x, f'(5) = 40 = $ the slope of the tangent line at $(5, f(5))$, or $(5, 100)$

24. $f'(x) = 12x^2, f'(-5) = 300, f'(0) = 0$

25. $f'(x) = \dfrac{-1}{x^2}, f'(-10) = -\frac{1}{100} = -0.01, f'(-2) = -\frac{1}{4} = -0.25$

26. x_2, x_4, x_5, x_6 **27.** $3x^2$ **28.** 48   **29.** $\dfrac{dy}{dx} = 6x^5$ **30.** $\dfrac{dy}{dx} = -7x^{-8}$ **31.** $\dfrac{dy}{dx} = \frac{1}{3}x^{-2/3}$, or $\dfrac{1}{3\sqrt[3]{x^2}}$

32. $\dfrac{dy}{dx} = -\frac{1}{4}x^{-5/4}$, or $\dfrac{-1}{4\sqrt[4]{x^5}}$ **33.** $f'(x) = 0$ **34.** $g'(x) = 0$ **35.** $\dfrac{dy}{dx} = 100x^{19}$ **36.** $\dfrac{dy}{dx} = \dfrac{3}{x^2}$

37. $\dfrac{dy}{dx} = -4x^{-1/2}$, or $\dfrac{-4}{\sqrt{x}}$ **38.** $\dfrac{dy}{dx} = x^{5.25}$ **39.** $\dfrac{dy}{dx} = -\frac{1}{4}$ **40.** $\dfrac{dy}{dx} = 28x^3 + 12x$

41. $\dfrac{dy}{dx} = 30x - \dfrac{4}{x^2} + \dfrac{1}{2\sqrt{x}}$ **42.** $(-3, 27), (1, -5)$ **43.** $(2, 8), (-2, -8)$ **44.** a) $70\,\dfrac{\text{mi}}{\text{hr}}$ b) $100\,\dfrac{\text{mi}}{\text{hr}}$

45. a) $v(t) = 32t$ b) 64 ft/sec   c) $v(10) = 320$ ft/sec   **46.** $a(t) = 32$ ft/sec^2

47. a) $V'(s) = 3s^2$ b) $V'(10) = 300$ ft^2

48. a) $P'(t) = 9700 + 20{,}000t$ b) $308{,}500; 109{,}700\,\dfrac{\text{bacteria}}{\text{hr}}$ c) $428{,}200; 129{,}700\,\dfrac{\text{bacteria}}{\text{hr}}$

49. a) $P(x) = 40x - 0.5x^2 - 3$

b) $R(40) = \$1200, C(40) = \$403, R(40) = \$797$
c) $R'(x) = 50 - x, C'(x) = 10, P'(x) = 40 - x$
d) $R'(40) = \$10$ per unit, $C'(40) = \$10$ per unit, $P'(40) = \$0$ per unit

e) No   **50.** $f'(x) = 54x^{17}$

51. $f'(x) = (9x^3 + 4x^2 + 10)(-14x + 4x^3) + (27x^2 + 8x)(-7x^2 + x^4)$

52. $f'(x) = 4x^3$ **53.** $\dfrac{3x^2 - 5}{x^6}$ **54.** $\dfrac{-x^4 + 3x^2 + 2x}{(x^3 + 1)^2}$

55. a) $R(x) = x(200 - x) = 200x - x^2$ b) $R'(x) = 200 - 2x$

56. $20x(1 + x^2)^9$ **57.** $\dfrac{-x}{\sqrt{1 - x^2}}$ **58.** $-2x(1 + x^2)(1 + 3x^2)$

59. $2(x - 4)^4(6 - x)^2(21 - 4x)$ **60.** $\left(\dfrac{x + 5}{x - 4}\right)^{-2/3} \cdot \dfrac{-3}{(x - 4)^2}$

EXERCISE SET 2.1, p. 82

1. No   **3.** Yes   **5.** a) yes   b) no   **7.** a) Yes   b) Yes

9. a) $1, -0.75, -1.56, -1.79, -1.9799, -1.997999$ b) -2

11. -10 **13.** Does not exist.   **15.** $-\frac{3}{2}$ **17.** 12   **19.** $\frac{2}{3}$ **21.** $\frac{1}{2}$

23. a) $\dfrac{-1}{x(x + 1)}, \dfrac{-1}{x(x + 0.9)}, \dfrac{-1}{x(x + 0.6)}, \dfrac{-1}{x(x + 0.1)}, \dfrac{-1}{x(x + 0.01)}, \dfrac{-1}{x(x + 0.001)}$ b) $\dfrac{-1}{x^2}$

25. a) $0.3, 0.3867, 0.392, 0.398, 0.399867$ (rounded), 0.39996 b) 0.4, or $\frac{2}{5}$ **27.** 0   **29.** 2

31. a) $\$800, \$736, \$677.12, \$622.95, \$573.11$ b) $\$5656.12$ c) $\$10{,}000$

EXERCISE SET 2.2, p. 91

1. a) $70, 39, 29, 23$ pleasure units/unit of product
   b) The more you get, the less pleasure you get from each additional unit.

3. a) $1.25\ \dfrac{\text{words}}{\text{min}}$, $1.25\ \dfrac{\text{words}}{\text{min}}$, $0.625\ \dfrac{\text{words}}{\text{min}}$, $0\ \dfrac{\text{words}}{\text{min}}$, $0\ \dfrac{\text{words}}{\text{min}}$
   b) You have reached a saturation point, you cannot memorize any more.

5. a) $125\ \dfrac{\text{million people}}{\text{yr}}$ for each   **b)** No   **c)** A: $290\ \dfrac{\text{million people}}{\text{yr}}$, $-40\ \dfrac{\text{million people}}{\text{yr}}$, $-50\ \dfrac{\text{million people}}{\text{yr}}$, $300\ \dfrac{\text{million people}}{\text{yr}}$; B: $125\ \dfrac{\text{million people}}{\text{yr}}$ in all intervals   **d)** A

7. a) $\$93.99$ **b)** $\$100$ **c)** $-\$6.01$ **d)** $-\$6.01$ **9. a)** 144 ft   **b)** 256 ft   **c)** $128\ \dfrac{\text{ft}}{\text{sec}}$ **11.** $57, 143\ \dfrac{\text{marriages}}{\text{yr}}$

13. $0.069\ \dfrac{\text{gal}}{\text{mi}}$ **15. a)** $7(2x + h)$ **b)** $70, 63, 56.7, 56.07$ **17. a)** $-7(2x + h)$ **b)** $-70, -63, -56.7, -56.07$

19. a) $7(3x^2 + 3xh + h^2)$ **b)** $532, 427, 344.47, 336.8407$

21. a) $\dfrac{-5}{x(x + h)}$ **b)** $-0.2083, -0.25, -0.3049, -0.3117$ **23. a)** -2 **b)** All -2

25. a) $2x + h - 1$ **b)** $9, 8, 7.1, 7.01$

EXERCISE SET 2.3, p. 101

1.
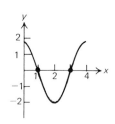

3.
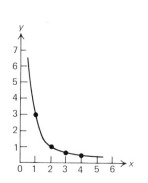

5.
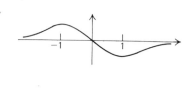

7. $y = x$ **9.** $y = 2x$ **11.** $y = 2x + 1$ **13.** $y = 3$ **15.** $y = 0$ **17.** $y = 3x^2$

EXERCISE SET 2.4, p. 109

1. $f'(x) = 10x$, $f'(-2) = -20$, $f'(-1) = -10$, $f'(0) = 0$, $f'(1) = 10$, $f'(2) = 20$
3. $f'(x) = -10x$, $f'(-2) = 20$, $f'(-1) = 10$, $f'(0) = 0$, $f'(1) = -10$, $f'(2) = -20$
5. $f'(x) = 15x^2$, $f'(-2) = 60$, $f'(-1) = 15$, $f'(0) = 0$, $f'(1) = 15$, $f'(2) = 60$ **7.** $f'(x) = 2$, all 2

9. $f'(x) = -4$, all -4 **11.** $f'(x) = 2x + 1, f'(-2) = -3, f'(-1) = -1, f'(0) = 1, f'(1) = 3, f'(2) = 5$

13. $f'(x) = \dfrac{-4}{x^2}, f'(-2) = -1, f'(-1) = -4, f'(0)$ does not exist, $f'(1) = -4, f'(2) = -1$

15. $f'(x) = m$, all m **17.** x_3, x_4, x_6, x_{12}

EXERCISE SET 2.5, p. 117

1. $7x^6$ **3.** 0 **5.** $600x^{149}$ **7.** $3x^2 + 6x$ **9.** $\dfrac{4}{\sqrt{x}}$ **11.** $0.07x^{-0.93}$ **13.** $\frac{14}{9}$ **15.** $\dfrac{-3}{x^4}$ **17.** $6x - 8$

19. $\dfrac{1}{4\sqrt[4]{x^3}} + \dfrac{1}{x^2}$ **21.** $1.6x^{1.5}$ **23.** $\dfrac{-5}{x^2} - 1$ **25.** 4 **27.** 4 **29.** x^3 **31.** $-0.02x - 0.5$ **33.** $2ax + b$

35. $(0, 0)$ **37.** $(0, 0)$ **39.** $(\frac{5}{6}, \frac{23}{12})$ **41.** $(-25, 76.25)$ **43.** There are none.

45. Tangent is horizontal at all points on graph.   **47.** $(\frac{5}{3}, \frac{148}{27}), (-1, -4)$ **49.** $(\frac{19}{2}, \frac{399}{4})$ **51.** $(60, 150)$

EXERCISE SET 2.6, p. 124

1. a) $v(t) = 3t^2 + 1$ b) $a(t) = 6t$ c) $v(4) = 49$ ft/sec, $a(4) = 24$ ft/sec^2

3. a) $v(t) = 3$ b) $a(t) = 0$ c) $v(2) = 3$ mile/hr, $a(2) = 0$ mile/hr^2

5. $P'(t) = 1.25$ **7.** $\dfrac{dC}{dr} = 2\pi$ **9.** a) $T'(t) = -0.2t + 1.2$ b) $100.175°$ c) 0.9 degrees/day

11. $\dfrac{dB}{dx} = 0.1x - 0.9x^2$ **13.** $\dfrac{dT}{dW} = 1.31W^{0.31}$

15. a) $P(x) = -0.001x^2 + 3.8x - 60$ b) $R(100) = \$500, C(100) = \$190, P(100) = \$310$ c) $R'(x) = 5$,
$C'(x) = 0.002x + 1.2, P'(x) = -0.002x + 3.8$ d) $R'(100) = \$5$ per unit, $C'(100) = \$1.4$ per unit, $P'(100)$
$= \$3.6$ per unit

EXERCISE SET 2.7, p. 130

1. $11x^{10}$ **3.** $\dfrac{1}{x^2}$ **5.** $3x^2$ **7.** $(8x^5 - 3x^2 + 20)(32x^3 - \dfrac{3}{2\sqrt{x}}) + (40x^4 - 6x)(8x^4 - 3\sqrt{x})$ **9.** $300 - 2x$

11. $\dfrac{300}{(300 - x)^2}$ **13.** $\dfrac{17}{(2x + 5)^2}$ **15.** $\dfrac{-x^4 - 3x^2 - 2x}{(x^3 - 1)^2}$ **17.** $\dfrac{1}{(1 - x)^2}$ **19.** $\dfrac{2}{(x + 1)^2}$ **21.** $\dfrac{-1}{(x - 3)^2}$

23. $\dfrac{-2x^2 + 6x + 2}{(x^2 + 1)^2}$ **25.** $\dfrac{-18x + 35}{x^8}$ **27.** a) $R(x) = x(400 - x) = 400x - x^2$ b) $R'(x) = 400 - 2x$

29. a) $R(x) = 4000 + 3x$ b) $R'(x) = 3$ **31.** $A'(x) = \dfrac{xC'(x) - C(x)}{x^2}$

EXERCISE SET 2.8, p. 133

1. $-55(1 - x)^{54}$ **3.** $\dfrac{1}{2\sqrt{1 + x}}$ **5.** $\dfrac{3x}{\sqrt{3x^2 - 4}}$ **7.** $-240x(3x^2 - 6)^{-41}$ **9.** $\sqrt{2x + 3} + \dfrac{x}{\sqrt{2x + 3}}$

11. $2x\sqrt{x - 1} + \dfrac{x^2}{2\sqrt{x - 1}}$ **13.** $\dfrac{-3}{(x + 8)^4}$ **15.** $(1 + x^3)^2(-3x^2 - 12x^5)$, or $-3x^2(1 + x^3)^2(1 + 4x^3)$

17. $4x - 400$ **19.** $2(x + 6)^9(x - 5)^3(7x - 13)$ **21.** $4(x - 4)^7(3 - x)^3(10 - 3x)$ **23.** $4(2x - 3)^2(3 - 8x)$

25. $\left(\dfrac{x - 1}{x + 1}\right)^{-1/2} \cdot \dfrac{1}{(x + 1)^2}$ **27.** a) $\dfrac{2x - 3x^2}{(1 + x)^6}$ b) $\dfrac{2x - 3x^2}{(1 + x)^6}$ c) Same   **29.** $C'(x) = \dfrac{500}{\sqrt{x + 2}}$

CHAPTER 2, TEST, p. 135

1. Yes   **2.** No   **3.** a) 19, 15.25, 12.61, 12.0601, 12.006001   b) 12   **4.** $3(2x + h)$

5. a) 3.4, 3.9625, 3.985, 3.9997   b) 4   **6.** $(0, 0), (2, -4)$ **7.** $84x^{83}$ **8.** $\dfrac{5}{\sqrt{x}}$ **9.** $\dfrac{10}{x^2}$ **10.** $\frac{5}{4}x^{1/4}$, or $\frac{5}{4} \cdot \sqrt[4]{x}$

11. $-x + 0.61$ **12.** $x^2 - 2x + 2$ **13.** $\dfrac{-6x + 20}{x^5}$ **14.** $\dfrac{5}{(5 - x)^2}$ **15.** $(x + 3)^3(7 - x)^4(-9x + 13)$

16. $-5(x^5 - 4x^3 + x)^{-6}(5x^4 - 12x^3 + 1)$ **17.** $\sqrt{x^2 + 5} + \dfrac{x^2}{\sqrt{x^2 + 5}}$, or $\dfrac{2x^2 + 5}{\sqrt{x^2 + 5}}$

18. a) $P(x) = -0.001x^2 + 48.8x - 60$ b) $R(10) = \$500$, $C(10) = \$72.10$, $P(10) = \$427.90$

     c) $R'(x) = 50$, $C'(x) = 0.002x + 1.2$, $P'(x) = -0.002x + 48.8$

     d) $R'(10) = \$50$ per unit, $C'(10) = \$1.22$ per unit, $P'(10) = \$48.78$

19. a) $\dfrac{dM}{dt} = -0.003t^2 + 0.2t$ b) 9   c) 1.7 words/min

CHAPTER 3

MARGIN EXERCISES

1. $f'(x) = 12x^5 - 5x^4$, $f''(x) = 60x^4 - 20x^3$, $f'''(x) = 240x^3 - 60x^2$,

     $f^{(4)}(x) = 720x^2 - 120x$, $f^{(5)}(x) = 1440x - 120$, $f^{(6)}(x) = 1440$

2. a) $\dfrac{dy}{dx} = 7x^6 - 3x^2$ b) $\dfrac{d^2y}{dx^2} = 42x^5 - 6x$ c) $\dfrac{d^3y}{dx^3} = 210x^4 - 6$ d) $\dfrac{d^4y}{dx^4} = 840x^3$ **3.** $\dfrac{d^2y}{dx^2} = \dfrac{4}{x^3}$

4. $a(t) = 12t^2$ **5.** a) $[a, b], [c, d]$ b) $[a, b), (c, d)$ c) $[b, c], [d, e]$ d) $(b, c), (d, e)$

6. a) $[b, c]$ $[d, e]$ b) $[a, b]$, $[c, d]$ **7.** a) $[0, b]$ b) $[a, 0]$ **8.** R, T, V

9. a) At $x = 3$ the function is increasing and the graph is concave up.

b) At $x = 1$, the function has a horizontal tangent and is concave up.

10. a) $x_1, x_3, x_5, x_6, x_8, x_{10}$ b) x_4, x_7, x_9 c) $x_1, x_3, x_4, x_5, x_6, x_7, x_8, x_9, x_{10}$

11. Answers will vary on the graph, but it must have at least one critical point.

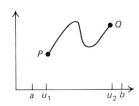

12. It is not possible.

13. a) Maximum at c_2, minimum at b b) Maximum at c_1, minimum at c_2 **14.** Maximum $= 4$ at $x = 2$, minimum $= 1$ at $x = 1$ and $x = -1$ **15.** Maximum $= 176$ at $x = 6$, minimum $= 97$ at $x = 5$

16. Minimum $= -4$ at $x = 2$. There is no maximum   **17.** Minimum $= -4$ at $x = 2$, maximum $= 0$ at $x = 0$ and $x = 4$ **18.** a) Maximum $= 8$ at $x = 2$, minimum $= -8$ at $x = -2$ b) There are none.

19. Minimum $= 400$ at $x = 20$. There is no maximum.

20. a) y: 20, 16, 13.5, 12, 10, 8, 6.8, 0 A: 0, 64, 87.75, 96, 100, 96, 89.76, 0

b)

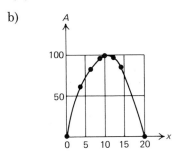

c) Yes   d) Max. $= 100$ ft^2 at $x = 10$ ft

21. 25 ft by 25 ft; 625 ft^2

22. a) $R(x) = x(200 - x) = 200x - x^2$ b) $P(x) = -x^2 + 192x - 5000$ c) 96   d) \$4216

e) $200 - 96$, or \$104 per unit

23. a) h: 4, 3.5, 3, 2.5, 2, 1.7, 1.5, 1, 0.6, 0.5, 0; V: 0, 3.5, 12, 22.5, 32, 35.972, 37.5, 36, 27.744, 24.5, 0

b)

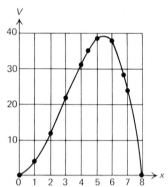

c) About 38; between 5 and 6, maybe 5.2

24. Max. volume $= 74\frac{2}{27}$ in.; dimensions $6\frac{2}{3}$ in. by $6\frac{2}{3}$ in. by $1\frac{2}{3}$ in.

25. Min. area $= 300$ sq. cm.; dimensions 10 cm by 10 cm by 5 cm

26. 40¢

27.

x	$\dfrac{2500}{x}$	$\dfrac{x}{2}$	$10 \cdot \dfrac{x}{2}$	$20 + 9x$	$(20 + 9x)\dfrac{2500}{x}$	$10 \cdot \dfrac{x}{2} + (20 + 9x)\dfrac{2500}{x}$
2500	1	1250	$12,500	$22,520	$22,520	$35,020
1250	2	625	$ 6250	$11,270	$22,540	$28,790
500	5	250	$ 2500	$ 4520	$22,600	$25,100
250	10	125	$ 1250	$ 2270	$22,700	$23,950
167	15	84	$ 840	$ 1523	$22,845	$23,685
125	20	63	$ 630	$ 1145	$22,900	$23,530
100	25	50	$ 500	$ 920	$23,000	$23,500
90	28	45	$ 450	$ 830	$23,240	$23,690
50	50	25	$ 250	$ 470	$23,500	$23,750

28. 15 times per year at lot size 40

29. a)

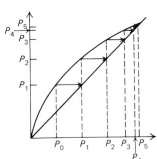

b)

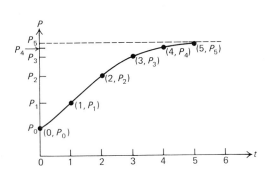

30. a)

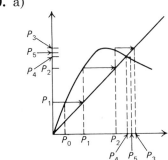

b) oscillating

31. 3.6, 3.67, 3.74, 3.81, 3.89, 3.97, 4.05, 4.13, 4.21, 4.29, 4.38; these were rounded each time to the nearest hundredth of a billion.   **32.** $f(P) = 1.0825P$ **33.** $f(P) = 1.01P$

34. 3500, Maximum sustainable harvest $= 12,250$ **35.** $\Delta y = -0.59$ **36.** $\Delta y = 19$

37. 8.1875; 8.185 in Table 1   **38.** a) $\Delta C = \$4.11$, $C'(5) = \$4.10$ b) $\Delta C = \$6.01$, $C'(100) = \$6$

EXERCISE SET 3.1, p. 139

1. 0   **3.** $-\dfrac{2}{x^3}$ **5.** $-\frac{3}{16}x^{-7/4}$ **7.** $12x^2 + \dfrac{8}{x^3}$ **9.** $\dfrac{12}{x^5}$ **11.** $n(n-1)x^{n-2}$ **13.** $12x^2 - 2$

15. $-\frac{1}{4}(x-1)^{-3/2}$, or $\dfrac{-1}{4\sqrt{(x-1)^3}}$ **17.** $2a$ **19.** 24   **21.** $720x$

23. $n(n-1)(n-2)(n-3)(n-4)(n-5)x^{n-6}$ **25.** $a(t) = 6t + 2$ **27.** $P''(t) = 200,000$

EXERCISE SET 3.2, p. 155

1. a) 41 mph   b) 80 mph   c) 13.5 mpg   d) 16.5 mph   e) about 22%
3. Max. $= 5\frac{1}{4}$ at $x = \frac{1}{2}$; min. $= 3$ at $x = 2$ 5. Max. $= 4$ at $x = 2$, min. $= 1$ at $x = 1$
7. Max. $= \frac{59}{27}$ at $x = -\frac{1}{3}$, min. $= 1$ at $x = -1$ 9. Max. $= 1$ at $x = 1$, min. $= -5$ at $x = -1$ 11. None
13. Max. $= 1225$ at $x = 35$ 15. Min. $= 200$ at $x = 10$ 17. Max. $= \frac{1}{3}$ at $x = \frac{1}{2}$
19. Max. $= \frac{289}{4}$ at $x = \frac{17}{2}$ 21. Max. $= 797$ at $x = 40$ 23. Max. $= 5700$ at $x = 2400$
25. Min. $= -55\frac{1}{3}$ at $x = 1$ 27. Max. $= 2000$ at $x = 20$, min. $= 0$ at $x = 0$ and $x = 30$
29. Min. $= 24$ at $x = 6$ 31. Min. $= 108$ at $x = 6$ 33. Max. $= 3$ at $x = -1$, min. $= -\frac{3}{8}$ at $x = \frac{1}{2}$
35. Max. $= 3\sqrt{6}$ at $x = 3$, min. $= -2$ at $x = -2$ 37. Max. $= 1$ at $x = -1$ and $x = 1$, min. $= 0$ at $x = 0$
39. 22506; $150,000   41. a) 179 ft at 32°   b) 0 ft at $-57.5°$ 43. 61.25 mph

EXERCISE SET 3.3, p. 166

1. 25 and 25. Max. prod. $= 625$ 3. No. $Q = x(50 - x)$ has no minimum.   5. 2 and -2. Min. prod. $= -4$
7. $x = \frac{1}{2}, y = \sqrt{\frac{1}{2}}$; Max. $= \frac{1}{4}$ 9. $x = 10, y = 10$; min. $= 200$ 11. $x = 2, y = \frac{32}{3}$; max. $= \frac{64}{3}$
13. $x = 30$ yd, $y = 60$ yd; max area $= 1800$ yd^2 15. 13.5 ft by 13.5 ft; 182.25 ft^2
17. 46 units; max. profit $= \$1048$ 19. 70 units; max. profit $= \$19$
21. Approx. 1667 units; max. profit $\approx \$5500$
23. a) $R(x) = 150x - 0.5x^2$ b) $P(x) = -0.75x^2 + 150x - 4000$ c) 100   d) $3500   e) $100
25. 20 in. by 20 in. by 5 in.; max. $= 2000$ in^3 27. 5 in. by 5 in. by 2.5 in.; min. $= 75$ in^2
29. $5.75, 72,500 (Will the stadium hold that many?)   31. 25   33. 14 in. by 14 in. by 28 in.

35. $x = \dfrac{24\pi}{\pi + 4} \approx 10.55, 24 - x = \dfrac{96}{\pi + 4} \approx 13.45$ 37. 4 ft by 4 ft by 20 ft

39. $x = \dfrac{24}{4 + \pi}, y = 12\left[1 - \left(\dfrac{2 + \pi}{4 + \pi}\right)\right]$

41. The only thing that is the same is the perimeter of 40 ft. Using calculus we know that the maximum area (that is, the largest sign) is obtained when the dimensions are 10 ft by 10 ft.

43. a) $A'(x) = \dfrac{xC'(x) - C(x)}{x^2}$

b) Assuming $A'(x)$ exists for all $x \neq 0$, $A'(x) = 0$, when $xC'(x) - C(x) = 0$, or $xC'(x) = C(x)$, or $C'(x) = \dfrac{C(x)}{x}$.

But $\dfrac{C(x)}{x} = A(x)$. Thus when average cost and marginal cost are the same, the product is being

produced at the least average cost.

EXERCISE SET 3.4, p. 173

1. Reorder 5 times per year; lot size = 20.   **3.** Reorder 12 times per year; lot size = 30.

EXERCISE SET 3.5, p. 179

1. 9500; max. sus. yield = 90,250   **3.** 60,000; max. sus. yield = 90,000   **5.** There is none.

EXERCISE SET 3.6, p. 184

1. $\Delta y = 0.0401$; $f'(x)\,\Delta x = 0.04$ **3.** 0.2816, 0.28   **5.** $-0.556, -1$ **7.** 6, 6   **9.** $\Delta C = \$2.01$, $C'(70) = \$2$
11. $\Delta R = \$2$, $R'(70) = \$2$ **13.** a) $P(x) = -0.01x^2 + 1.4x - 30$ b) $\Delta P = \$-0.01$, $P'(70) = 0$ **15.** 4.375
17. 10.1   **19.** 2.167   **21.** 2.512 cm^3

CHAPTER 3, TEST, p. 186

1. $\dfrac{d^3 y}{dx^3} = 24x$ **2.** Max. = 9 at $x = 3$ **3.** Max. = 2 at $x = -1$, min. = -1 at $x = -2$
4. Max. = 28.49 at $x = 4.3$ **5.** Max. = 7 at $x = -1$, min. = 3 at $x = 1$ **6.** None
7. Min. = $-\frac{13}{12}$ at $x = \frac{1}{6}$ **8.** Min. = 48 at $x = 4$ **9.** 4 and -4 **10.** $x = 5, y = -5$; min. = 50
11. Max. profit = \$24,980; 500 units   **12.** 40 in. by 40 in. by 10 in.; max. volume = 16,000 in^3
13. 50 times at lot size 25   **14.** 49,500; max. sus. harvest = 2,450,250   **15.** $\Delta y = 1.01$, $f'(x)\Delta x = 1$ **16.** 10.2

CHAPTER 4

MARGIN EXERCISES

1. a)

x	0	$\frac{1}{2}$	1	2	-1	-2
3^x	1	1.7	3	9	$\frac{1}{3}$	$\frac{1}{9}$

b)

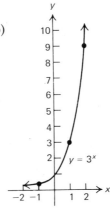

$y = 3^x$

2. a)

x	0	$\frac{1}{2}$	1	2	-1	-2
3^x	1	0.6	$\frac{1}{3}$	$\frac{1}{9}$	3	9

b)

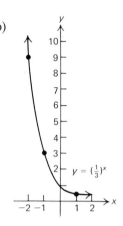

$y = \left(\frac{1}{3}\right)^x$

3. a) $b^T = P$ **b)** $9^{1/2} = 3$ **c)** $10^3 = 1000$ **d)** $10^{-1} = 0.1$

4. a) $\log_e T = k$ **b)** $\log_{16} 2 = \frac{1}{4}$ **c)** $\log_{10} 10{,}000 = 4$ **d)** $\log_{10} 0.001 = -3$

5.   **6.** 1   **7.** -0.398 **8.** 0.398   **9.** -0.699 **10.** $\frac{3}{2}$ **11.** 1.699

$y = \log_3 x$

12. 1.204   **13. a)** 4   **b)** -4 **14.** 0.8954   **15.** 0.5051   **16.** 0.9996   **17.** 0.0000   **18.** 0.4771

19. a) 4.7193   **b)** $-4 + 0.7193$, or -3.2807

20. a) $3 + 0.8954$, or 3.8954

b) $2 + 0.8954$, or 2.8954

c) $1 + 0.8954$, or 1.8954

d) 0.8954

e) $-1 + 0.8954$, or -0.1046

f) $-2 + 0.8954$, or -1.1046

g) $-3 + 0.8954$, or -2.1046

21. a) 1.8831   **b)** 3.3674   **c)** $-3 + 0.9395$, or -2.0605 **22.** $\log y = \log 5 + t \cdot \log 2$

23. $\log Q = \log Q_0 + kt \cdot \log e$ **24.** $t \approx 4.4$ **25.** $t \approx 44.3$ **26.** 23 decibels   **27.** 90 decibels

28. 8, 8.57, 8.81, 8.82, 8.82; $8.82 \approx 2^\pi$

29. a) 1.4142, 1.1892, 1.0905, 1.0443, 1.0219; 0.8284, 0.7568, 0.7241, 0.7083, 0.7008   b) 0.7

30. a) 1.732, 1.3161, 1.1472, 1.071, 1.0349; 1.4641, 1.2642, 1.1372, 1.1168, 1.1177   b) 1.1

31. a)

x	-3	-2	-1	0	1	2	3
2^x	0.125	0.25	0.5	1	2	4	8
$(0.7)2^x$	0.09	0.18	0.35	0.7	1.4	2.8	5.6

b) See later text figure.

32. a)

x	-2	-1	0	1	2
3^x	0.11	0.33	1	3	9
$(1.1)3^x$	0.12	0.36	1.1	3.3	9.9

b) See later text figure.

33. \$2, \$2.25, \$2.37, \$2.44, \$2.48, \$2.70, \$2.71, \$2.716, \$2.717   **34.** $6e^x$ **35.** $e^x(x^3 + 3x^2)$, or $x^2e^x(x + 3)$

36. $\dfrac{e^x(x - 2)}{x^3}$ **37.** $-4e^{-4x}$ **38.** $(3x^2 + 8)e^{x^3 + 8x}$ **39.** $\dfrac{xe^{\sqrt{x^2+5}}}{\sqrt{x^2 + 5}}$ **40.**

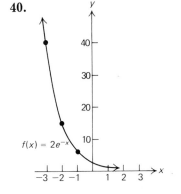

$f(x) = 2e^{-x}$

41. a)

x	0	$\frac{1}{2}$	1	2	3	4
$f(x)$	0	0.39	0.63	0.86	0.95	0.98

b)

42. 87.5 days   **43.** a) $\ln 7$ b) $\ln 10$ c) $\ln M$ d) $\ln P$

44. a)

x	0.5	1	2	3	4
$\ln x$	-0.7	0	0.7	1.1	1.4

b) Same as text figure

45. 2.3025   **46.** -0.9163 **47.** 0.9163   **48.** 2.7724   **49.** 2.6094   **50.** $\frac{1}{2}$ **51.** -1.6094

52. a) Answers will vary

x	$\frac{1}{2}$	1	2	3	4	5
$f'(x)$	2	1	0.5	0.3	0.25	0.2

b) $f'(x) = \dfrac{1}{x}$

53. $\dfrac{5}{x}$ **54.** $x^2(1 + 3\ln x) + 4$ **55.** $\dfrac{1 - 2\ln x}{x^3}$ **56.** $\dfrac{1}{x}$ **57.** $\dfrac{6x}{3x^2 + 4}$ **58.** $\dfrac{1}{x\ln 5x}$ **59.** $\dfrac{4x^5 + 2}{x(x^5 - 2)}$

60. a) 500   b) $N'(a) = \dfrac{200}{a}$ c) Min. $= 500$ at $a = 1$ **61.** a) $\dfrac{dy}{dx} = 20e^{4x}$ b) $\dfrac{dy}{dx} = 4y$

62. a) $N(t) = ce^{kt}$ b) $f(t) = ce^{kt}$

63. a) Should be about $\frac{1}{8}$ in. or 0.125 in.   b) 0.032, 0.064, 0.128   c) About 2 mi

64. a) $P(t) = P_0 e^{0.08t}$ b) \$1083.30   c) 8.7 yr

65. 2%, 34.7; 6.9%, 10; 4%, 17.3; 4.6%, 15; 1%, 69.3

66. a) $P(t) = 210e^{0.05t}$ b) 230 million   c) 46.2 yr (2020)

67. a) $E(t) = 800e^{kt}$ b) $k = 0.08$ c) $E(t) = 800e^{0.08t}$ d) 8818.4 billion kW-hr

68. See Exercises 27 and 31 of Exercise Set 4.2

69. a) $N(t) = N_0 e^{-0.14t}$ b) 246.6 gr   c) 5 days   **70.** 30 yr   **71.** 5.3%   **72.** 13,412 yr

73. a) $a = 130°$ b) $k = 0.01$ c) $188°$ d) 256 min

74. Answers will vary, "Theoretically" it is never possible for the temperature of the water to be the same as the room temperature.

75. 10:00 A.M.   **76.** $e^{6.9315}$ **77.** $e^{0.6931x}$ **78.** $(\ln 5)5^x$ **79.** $(\ln 4)4^x$ **80.** $(\ln 4.3)(4.3)^x$ **81.** $\dfrac{1}{\ln 2} \cdot \dfrac{1}{x}$

82. $-\dfrac{7}{x\ln 10}$ **83.** $x^5\left(\dfrac{1}{\ln 10} + 6\log x\right)$

EXERCISE SET 4.1, p. 196

1.

3.

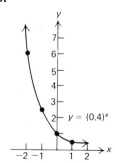

5.

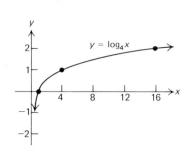

7. $2^3 = 8$ **9.** $8^{1/3} = 2$ **11.** $a^J = K$ **13.** $b^v = T$ **15.** $\log_e b = M$ **17.** $\log_{10} 100 = 2$
19. $\log_{10} 0.1 = -1$ **21.** $\log_M V = p$ **23.** 2.708   **25.** 0.51   **27.** -1.609 **29.** $\frac{3}{2}$
31. 2.609   **33.** 3.218
35. a) 3.3284   b) 2.3284   c) 1.3284   d) 0.3284   e) $-1 + 0.3284$, or -0.6716
 f) $-2 + 0.3284$, or -1.6716 g) $-3 + 0.3284$, or -2.6716
37. 2.9571   **39.** $-2 + 0.0414$, or -1.9586 **41.** 3.6532   **43.** 4.8927   **45.** $\log y = \log 3 + x$
47. $\log y = \log a + t \cdot \log b$ **49.** $t \approx 4.6$ **51.** $t \approx 4.1$ **53.** $t = 2.3$ **55.** $t \approx 140.7$
57. 64 decibels   **59.** 120 decibels   **61.** 8.25   **63.** 7.8

EXERCISE SET 4.2, p. 208

1. $3e^{3x}$ **3.** $-10e^{-2x}$ **5.** e^{-x} **7.** $-7e^x$ **9.** e^{2x} **11.** $x^3 e^x (x + 4)$ **13.** $\dfrac{e^x(x - 4)}{x^5}$

15. $(-2x + 7)e^{-x^2 + 7x}$ **17.** $-xe^{-x^2/2}$ **19.** $\dfrac{e^{\sqrt{x-7}}}{2\sqrt{x - 7}}$ **21.** $\dfrac{e^x}{2\sqrt{e^x - 1}}$ **23.** $(1 - 2x)e^{-2x} - e^{-x} + 3x^2$

25. e^{-x} **27.** ke^{-kx}
29.

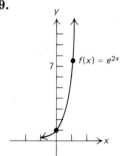

31.

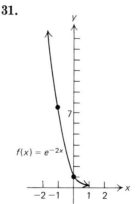

33.

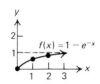

35. 57.5 days   **37.** a) $C'(t) = 50e^{-t}$ b) \$50 million   c) \$.915 million

EXERCISE SET 4.3, p. 216

1. 2.9957   **3.** 0.2231   **5.** -1.3863 **7.** 2.3863   **9.** 4   **11.** 2.7726   **13.** $-\dfrac{6}{x}$ **15.** $x^3(1 + 4\ln x) - x$

17. $\dfrac{1 - 4\ln x}{x^5}$ **19.** $\dfrac{1}{x}$ **21.** $\dfrac{10x}{5x^2 - 7}$ **23.** $\dfrac{1}{x \ln 4x}$ **25.** $\dfrac{x^2 + 7}{x(x^2 - 7)}$ **27.** $e^x\left(\dfrac{1}{x} + \ln x\right)$ **29.** $\dfrac{e^x}{e^x + 1}$

31. $\dfrac{2 \ln x}{x}$ **33.** a) 68% b) 36% c) 3.6% d) 5% e) $-\dfrac{20}{t + 1}$ f) Max. = 68% at $t = 0$

35. a) 1000 b) $N'(a) = \dfrac{200}{a}$, $N'(10) = 20$ c) Min. = 1000 at $a = 1$

EXERCISE SET 4.4, p. 227

1. $Q(t) = Q_0 e^{kt}$ **3.** a) $P(t) = P_0 e^{0.09t}$ b) \$1094.20, \$1197.20 c) 7.7 yr
5. 19.8 yr   **7.** 6.9%   **9.** a) $P(t) = 209 e^{0.01t}$ b) 312 million c) 69.3 yr   **11.** .20%
13. a) $N(t) = 50 e^{0.1t}$ b) 369 c) 6.9 yr   **15.** 6.9 yr (1983)   **17.** a) $k = .08$ b) 124 thousand   **19.** 6.18%
21. 9%   **23.** $T_3 = \dfrac{\ln 3}{k}$ **25.** Answers depend on particular data.

EXERCISE SET 4.5, p. 237

1. 7.2 days   **3.** 23% per min   **5.** 10.1 g   **7.** 19,188 yr   **9.** 7636 yr   **11.** a) $A = A_0 e^{-kt}$ b) 9 hr
13. a) 0.8% b) 79% W_0 **15.** a) 11 watts b) 173 days c) 402 days d) 50 watts   **17.** a) \$40,000 b) \$5412
19. a) 25% I_0, 6% I_0, 1.5% I_0 b) 0.00008%   **21.** a) $a = 25°$ b) $k = 0.05$ c) 84.2° d) 32 min.   **23.** 3 P.M.

EXERCISE SET 4.6, p. 242

1. $e^{6.4376}$ **3.** $e^{12.238}$ **5.** $e^{k \cdot \ln 4}$ **7.** $e^{kT \cdot \ln 8}$ **9.** $\ln 6 \cdot 6^x$ **11.** $\ln 10 \cdot 10^x$ **13.** $(6.2)^x[x \ln 6.2 + 1]$
15. $10^x x^2[x \ln 10 + 3]$
17. a) $I = 10^7 \cdot I_0$ b) $I = 10^8 \cdot I_0$ **19.** $\dfrac{1}{\ln 4} \cdot \dfrac{1}{x}$ **21.** $\dfrac{2}{\ln 10} \cdot \dfrac{1}{x}$
    c) The intensity in (b) is 10 times greater than (a)
    d) $\dfrac{dI}{dR} = (I_0 \cdot \ln 10) \cdot 10^R$

23. $\dfrac{1}{\ln 10} \cdot \dfrac{3}{x}$ **25.** $x^2\left[\dfrac{1}{\ln 8} + 3 \log_8 x\right]$ **27.** $\dfrac{dR}{dI} = \dfrac{1}{\ln 10} \cdot \dfrac{1}{I}$ **29.** $\dfrac{dy}{dx} = \dfrac{m}{\ln 10} \cdot \dfrac{1}{x}$

CHAPTER 4, TEST, p. 244

1. e^x **2.** $\dfrac{1}{x}$ **3.** $-2xe^{-x^2}$ **4.** $\dfrac{1}{x}$ **5.** $e^x - 15x^2$ **6.** $3e^x\left(\dfrac{1}{x} + \ln x\right)$ **7.** $\dfrac{e^x - 3x^2}{e^x - x^3}$

8. $\dfrac{\frac{1}{x} - \ln x}{e^x}$, or $\dfrac{1 - x \ln x}{xe^x}$ **9.** 2.639   **10.** -1.2528 **11.** 2.9459   **12.** $M(t) = M_0 e^{kt}$

13. 17.3% per hr   **14.** 10 yr   **15.** a) $F(t) = 3e^{0.12t}$ b) 33 billion gal   c) 5.8 yr (1966)

16. 0.000069% per yr   **17.** 63 days   **18.** a) $A(t) = 5e^{-0.1t}$ b) 1.8 cc   c) 6.9 hr

19. $\ln 20 \cdot 20^x$ **20.** $\dfrac{1}{\ln 20} \cdot \dfrac{1}{x}$

CHAPTER 5

MARGIN EXERCISES

1. $y = 7x, y = 7x - \frac{1}{2}, y = 7x + C$, answers can vary

2. $y = -2x, y = -2x + 27, y = -2x + C$, answers can vary

3. $\dfrac{x^2}{2} + C$ **4.** $\dfrac{x^4}{4} + C$ **5.** $e^x + C$ **6.** $\ln x + C$ **7.** $\dfrac{x^4}{4} + C$ **8.** $\dfrac{x^2}{2} + C$ **9.** $\ln x + C$

10. $\frac{7}{5}x^5 + x^2 + C$ **11.** $e^x - \frac{5}{7}x^{7/5} + C$ **12.** $5 \ln x - 7x - \frac{1}{5}x^{-5} + C$

13.
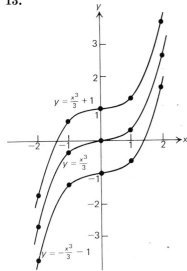

14. $f(x) = \dfrac{x^3}{3} + \dfrac{23}{3}$ **15.** $g(x) = x^2 - 4x + 13$

16. $C(x) = \frac{1}{3}x^3 + \frac{5}{2}x^2 + 35$ **17.** $s(t) = t^4 + 13$ **18.** $s(t) = 2t^4 - 6t^2 + 7t + 8$

19. a) $A(x) = 3x$ b) $A(1) = 3, A(2) = 6, A(5) = 15$ c)   d) $A(x)$ is an antiderivative of $f(x)$

20. a) $C(x) = 50x$

b) $A(x) = 50x$

c) As x increases, the area over $[0, x]$ increases

21. a) $5000 + 4000 + 3000 + 2000$, or $\$14{,}000$ b) $14{,}000$, same

22. a) $A(x) = \frac{3}{2}x^2$ b) $A(1) = \frac{3}{2}$ c) $A(2) = 6$ d) $A(3.5) = 18.375$ e)

    f) $A(x)$ is an antiderivative of $f(x)$.

23. a) $C(x) = -0.05x^2 + 50x$ b) $A(x) = -0.05x^2 + 50x$

    c) $\$12{,}000$; less than in margin exercise 21   **24.** $5\frac{1}{3}$ **25.** $13\frac{1}{2}$

26. a) Yes   b) $\$4100$ **27.** $\displaystyle\int_a^b 2x\,dx = b^2 - a^2$

28. $\displaystyle\int_a^b e^x\,dx = e^b - e^a$ **29.** 8 **30.** $1 - \dfrac{1}{e^2}$ **31.** $\frac{2}{3}$ **32.** $e + e^3 - 3$ **33.** $5\frac{1}{3}$ **34.** $13\frac{1}{2}$ **35.** $\ln 7$

36. $-\frac{1}{3}b^{-3} + \frac{1}{3}$ **37.** 75 **38.** $17\frac{1}{3}$ **39.** a) $\$596{,}000$ b) $k = 7.3$, so it is the 8th day   c) $\$3{,}809{,}000$

40. 4 **41.** 4 **42.** a) $-\frac{1}{6}$ b) $\frac{5}{6}$ c) $\frac{4}{6}$ **43.** a) -4 b) 4 c) 0 **44.** a) 0 b) $A - A$, or 0

45. a) Negative   b) $A - 2A$, or $-A$ **46.** a) Positive   b) $3A - A$, or $2A$ **47.** a) Negative   b) $-3A$

48. $\frac{1}{6}$ **49.** a) $P(k) = 5k^2 + 10k$ b) $P(5) = 175$ **50.** $dy = (12x + 1)\,dx$ **51.** $du = dx$ **52.** $e^{x^3} + C$

53. $\ln(5 + x^2) + C$ **54.** $-\dfrac{1}{3 + x^2} + C$ **55.** $\dfrac{(\ln x)^2}{2} + C$ **56.** $\frac{1}{3}e^{x^3} + C$ **57.** $\frac{1}{5}e^{5x} + C$

58. $\dfrac{1}{0.02}e^{0.02x} + C$, or $50e^{0.02x} + C$ **59.** $-e^{-x} + C$ **60.** $\frac{1}{80}(x^4 + 5)^{20} + C$

61. $\displaystyle\int \dfrac{\ln x\,dx}{x} = \dfrac{(\ln x)^2}{2} + C$, so $\displaystyle\int_1^e \dfrac{\ln x\,dx}{x} = \left[\dfrac{(\ln x)^2}{2}\right]_1^e = \dfrac{(\ln e)^2}{2} - \dfrac{(\ln 1)^2}{2} = \frac{1}{2} - 0 = \frac{1}{2}$

62. $xe^{3x} - \frac{1}{3}e^{3x} + C$ **63.** $\dfrac{x^2}{2}\ln x - \dfrac{x^2}{4} + C$; let $u = \ln x$, $dv = x\,dx$

64. $\frac{2}{3}x(x + 3)^{3/2} - \frac{4}{15}(x + 3)^{5/2} + C$ **65.** $2\ln 2 - \frac{3}{4}$ **66.** $\frac{1}{10}\ln\left(\dfrac{x - 5}{x + 5}\right) + C$ **67.** $\displaystyle\sum_{i=1}^{6} i^2$ **68.** $\displaystyle\sum_{i=1}^{4} e^i$

69. $\displaystyle\sum_{i=1}^{38} P(x_i)\,\Delta x$ **70.** $4^1 + 4^2 + 4^3$, or 84 **71.** $e^1 + 2e^2 + 3e^3 + 4e^4 + 5e^5$

72. $t(x_1)\,\Delta x + t(x_2)\,\Delta x + \cdots + t(x_{20})\,\Delta x$ **73.** $\$11{,}250$

74. a) 3.0667 b) 2.4501 c) $\displaystyle\int_1^7 \dfrac{1}{x}\,dx = \ln 7 \approx 1.9459$ **75.** 2 **76.** $\$257$

EXERCISE SET 5.1, p. 254

1. $\dfrac{x^7}{7} + C$ **3.** $2x + C$ **5.** $\frac{4}{5}x^{5/4} + C$ **7.** $\dfrac{x^3}{3} + \dfrac{x^2}{2} - x + C$ **9.** $\dfrac{t^3}{3} - t^2 + 3t + C$ **11.** $5e^x + C$

13. $\dfrac{x^4}{4} - \dfrac{7}{15}x^{15/7} + C$ **15.** $1000 \ln x + C$ **17.** $-x^{-1} + C$ **19.** $f(x) = \dfrac{x^2}{2} - 3x + 13$

21. $f(x) = \dfrac{x^3}{3} - 4x + 7$ **23.** $C(x) = \dfrac{x^4}{4} - x^2 + 100$

25. a) $R(x) = \dfrac{x^3}{3} - 3x$ b) If you sell no products you make no money

27. $s(t) = t^3 + 4$ **29.** $v(t) = 2t^2 + 20$

31. $s(t) = -\frac{1}{3}t^3 + 3t^2 + 6t + 10$ **33.** $s(t) = -16t^2 + v_0 t + s_0$

35. a) $E(t) = 30t - 5t^2 + 32$ b) $E(3) = 77\%$, $E(5) = 57\%$

EXERCISE SET 5.2, p. 267

1. 8   **3.** 8   **5.** $41\frac{1}{3}$ **7.** $\frac{1}{4}$ **9.** $10\frac{2}{3}$ **11.** $e^3 - 1 \approx 19.086$ **13.** $\ln 3 \approx 1.0986$ **15.** 51

17. An antiderivative, velocity

19. An antiderivative, energy used in time t

21. An antiderivative, total revenue

23. An antiderivative, amount of drug in blood

25. a) $s(t) = t^3 + t^2$ b) 150

27. a) $C(x) = 100x - 0.1x^2$ b) $R(x) = 100x + 0.1x^2$ c) $P(x) = 0.2x^2$ d) $P(1000) = \$200{,}000$

29. $77\frac{1}{2}$ thousand

EXERCISE SET 5.3, p. 277

1. $\frac{1}{6}$ **3.** $\frac{4}{15}$ **5.** $e^b - e^a$ **7.** $b^3 - a^3$ **9.** $\dfrac{e^2}{2} + \frac{1}{2}$ **11.** $\frac{2}{3}$ **13.** $\frac{5}{34}$ **15.** 4   **17.** $9\frac{5}{6}$ **19.** 12

21. $e^5 - \dfrac{1}{e}$ **23.** $7\frac{1}{3}$ **25.** $17\frac{1}{3}$ **27.** a) \$2948.20 b) \$2820.42 c) $k = 6.9$, so it will be on the 7th day

29. 88   **31.** \$3,600   **33.** 9

EXERCISE SET 5.4, p. 285

1. $\frac{1}{4}$ **3.** $\frac{9}{2}$ **5.** $\frac{125}{6}$ **7.** $\frac{9}{2}$ **9.** $\frac{1}{6}$ **11.** $\frac{125}{3}$ **13.** $\frac{32}{3}$ **15.** 3   **17.** a) B b) 2

EXERCISE SET 5.5, p. 291

1. $\ln(7 + x^2) + C$ **3.** $\frac{1}{4}e^{4x} + C$ **5.** $2e^{x/2} + C$ **7.** $\frac{1}{4}e^{x^4} + C$ **9.** $-\frac{1}{3}e^{-t^3} + C$ **11.** $\dfrac{(\ln 4x)^2}{2} + C$

13. $\ln(1 + x) + C$ **15.** $-\ln(4 - x) + C$ **17.** $\frac{1}{24}(t^3 - 1)^8 + C$

19. $\frac{1}{8}(x^4 + x^3 + x^2)^8 + C$ **21.** $\ln(4 + e^x) + C$ **23.** $\frac{1}{4}(\ln x^2)^2 + C$ **25.** $\ln(\ln x) + C$

27. $\dfrac{2}{3a}(ax + b)^{3/2} + C$ **29.** $\dfrac{b}{a}e^{ax} + C$ **31.** $e - 1$ **33.** $\frac{21}{4}$ **35.** $\ln 4 - \ln 2 = \ln \frac{4}{2} = \ln 2$ **37.** $\ln 19$

39. $1 - \dfrac{1}{e^b}$ **41.** $1 - \dfrac{1}{e^{mb}}$ **43.** $\frac{117}{3}$

45. a) $\dfrac{100,000}{0.025}(e^{1.9} - 1) \approx 22{,}743{,}600$ **b)** $\dfrac{100,000}{0.025}(e^{1.9} - e^{1.8}) \approx 2{,}545{,}200$

EXERCISE SET 5.6, p. 296

1. $xe^{5x} - \frac{1}{5}e^{5x} + C$ **3.** $\frac{1}{2}x^6 + C$ **5.** $\dfrac{x}{2}e^{2x} - \frac{1}{4}e^{2x} + C$ **7.** $-\dfrac{x}{2}e^{-2x} - \frac{1}{4}e^{-2x} + C$ **9.** $\dfrac{x^3}{3}\ln x - \dfrac{x^3}{9} + C$

11. $\dfrac{x^2}{2}\ln x^2 - \dfrac{x^2}{2} + C$

13. $(x + 3)\ln(x + 3) - x + C$. Let $u = \ln(x + 3)$, $dv = dx$, and choose $v = x + 3$ for an antiderivative of v

15. $\left(\dfrac{x^2}{2} + 2x\right)\ln x - \dfrac{x^2}{4} - 2x + C$

17. $\left(\dfrac{x^2}{2} - x\right)\ln x - \dfrac{x^2}{4} + x + C$

19. $\frac{2}{3}x(x + 2)^{3/2} - \frac{4}{15}(x + 2)^{5/2} + C$ **21.** $\dfrac{x^4}{4}\ln 2x - \dfrac{x^4}{16} + C$ **23.** $x^2e^x - 2xe^x + 2e^x + C$

25. a) Let $u = x^n$ and $dv = e^x\,dx$. Then $du = nx^{n-1}\,dx$ and $v = e^x$. Then use integration by parts

   b) $x^3e^x - 3\int x^2e^x\,dx = x^3e^x - 3[x^2e^x - 2\int xe^x\,dx]$
   $$= x^3e^x - 3x^2e^x + 6[xe^x - \int x^0e^x\,dx]$$
   $$= x^3e^x - 3x^2e^x + 6xe^x - 6e^x + C$$

27. $\frac{8}{3}\ln 2 - \frac{7}{9}$ **29.** $9\ln 9 - 5\ln 5 - 4$ **31.** 1 **33.** $\frac{1}{9}e^{-3x}(-3x - 1) + C$ **35.** $\dfrac{5^x}{\ln 5} + C$

37. $\frac{1}{8}\ln\left(\dfrac{4 + x}{4 - x}\right) + C$ **39.** $5 - x - 5\ln(5 - x) + C$ **41.** $\dfrac{1}{5(5 - x)} + \dfrac{1}{25}\ln\left(\dfrac{x}{5 - x}\right) + C$

43. a) $\int_0^T 10te^{-t}\,dt = 10[e^{-t}(-t-1)]_0^T = 10[e^{-T}(-T-1) - e^{-0}(-0-1)] = 10[e^{-T}(-T-1) + 1]$

b) $\int_0^4 10te^{-t}\,dt = 10[e^{-4}(-4-1) + 1] \approx 9.085$

EXERCISE SET 5.7, p. 303

1. a) 1.4914 b) 0.8571   **3.** 0   **5.** $e - 1$ **7.** $\frac{4}{3}$ **9.** 13   **11.** $\dfrac{1}{n+1}$ **13.** a) 100 after 10 hr b) $33\frac{1}{3}$

CHAPTER 5, TEST, p. 305

1. $x + C$ **2.** $200x^5 + C$ **3.** $e^x + \ln x + \frac{8}{11}x^{11/8} + C$ **4.** $\frac{1}{6}$ **5.** $4 \ln 3$

6. An antiderivative, total number of words typed in t minutes

7. 12   **8.** $-\dfrac{1}{2}\left(\dfrac{1}{e^2} - 1\right)$ **9.** $\ln b - \ln a$ **10.** 0

11. negative   **12.** positive   **13.** $\ln(x + 8) + C$

14. $-2e^{-0.5x} + C$ **15.** $\frac{1}{40}(t^4 + 1)^{10} + C$ **16.** $\dfrac{x}{5}e^{5x} - \dfrac{e^{5x}}{25} + C$

17. $\dfrac{x^4}{4}\ln x^4 - \dfrac{x^4}{4} + C$ **18.** $\dfrac{2^x}{\ln 2} + C$ **19.** $\frac{1}{7}\ln\left(\dfrac{x}{7-x}\right) + C$

20. 6   **21.** $\frac{5}{12}$ **22.** 95   **23.** $49,000   **24.** 94 words

CHAPTER 6

MARGIN EXERCISES

1. $400(e^{0.25h} - 1)$ **2.** $1161.80   **3.** $2157.33   **4.** $29,786.67   **5.** $215.41   **6.** 348,814.9 million barrels
7. By 1987   **8.** $2231   **9.** $24,260   **10.** $15,564.60   **11.** $\frac{2}{3}, \frac{9}{10}, \frac{99}{100}, \frac{199}{200}$ **12.** $\frac{1}{2}$ **13.** ∞
14. Convergent, 1   **15.** Divergent   **16.** $20,000   **17.** a) $\frac{7}{20}$ b) $\frac{6}{20}$, or $\frac{3}{10}$ c) $\frac{4}{20}$, or $\frac{1}{5}$ d) 0
18. a) $\frac{1}{2}$ b) $\frac{1}{8}$ c) $\frac{1}{4}$ d) $\frac{1}{8}$ **19.** a) $[15, 25]$ b) $[0, \infty)$ **20.** $\frac{2}{3}$

21. $\int_1^2 \dfrac{2}{3}x\,dx = \left[\dfrac{2}{3}\cdot\dfrac{1}{2}x^2\right]_1^2 = \dfrac{1}{3}(2^2 - 1) = 1$

22. a) $\int_3^6 \dfrac{24}{t^3}\,dt = \left[24\left(-\dfrac{t^{-2}}{2}\right)\right]_3^6 = -12\left(\dfrac{1}{6^2} - \dfrac{1}{3^2}\right) = 1$ b) $\frac{64}{75}$ c) $\frac{5}{12}$

23. $\frac{3}{26}$ **24.** 4   **25.** $\frac{1}{4}$ **26.** $\frac{1}{4}$ **27.** 0.3297   **28.** $E(x) = \frac{2}{3}, E(x^2) = \frac{1}{2}$

29. $\mu = \frac{2}{3}, \sigma^2 = \frac{1}{18}, \sigma = \sqrt{\frac{1}{18}} = \frac{1}{3}\sqrt{\frac{1}{2}}$

30. a) 0.4850 b) 0.4608 c) 0.9559 d) 0.2720 e) 0.1102 f) 0.0307

31. 0.1210   **32.** a) (2, $16) b) $18.67   **33.** $\dfrac{\pi}{3}$ **34.** $\dfrac{\pi}{2}(e^2 - e^{-4})$

EXERCISE SET 6.1, p. 314

1. \$131 **3.** \$344.44 **5.** \$5610.67 **7.** \$259.37 **9.** 1, 343, 724, 583 tons **11.** By 2001

EXERCISE SET 6.2, p. 318

1. \$826.50 **3.** \$40,218 **5.** \$17,802 **7.** \$511,481.25

EXERCISE SET 6.3, p. 322

1. $\frac{1}{3}$ **3.** Divergent **5.** 1 **7.** $\frac{1}{2}$ **9.** Divergent **11.** 5 **13.** Divergent **15.** Divergent

17. Divergent **19.** 1 **21.** $\dfrac{B}{k}$ **23.** \$30,000

EXERCISE SET 6.4, p. 333

1. $\displaystyle\int_0^1 2x\,dx = [x^2]_0^1 = 1^2 - 0^2 = 1$ **3.** $\displaystyle\int_4^7 \frac{1}{3}\,dx = \left[\frac{1}{3}x\right]_4^7 = \frac{1}{3}(7-4) = 1$

5. $\displaystyle\int_1^3 \frac{3}{26}x^2\,dx = \left[\frac{3}{26}\cdot\frac{x^3}{3}\right]_1^3 = \frac{1}{26}(3^3 - 1^3) = 1$

7. $\displaystyle\int_1^e \frac{1}{x}\,dx = [\ln x]_1^e = \ln e - \ln 1 = 1 - 0 = 1$

9. $\displaystyle\int_{-1}^1 \frac{3}{2}x^2\,dx = \left[\frac{3}{2}\cdot\frac{1}{3}x^3\right]_{-1}^1 = \frac{1}{2}(1^3 - (-1)^3) = \frac{1}{2}(1+1) = 1$

11. $\displaystyle\int_0^\infty 3e^{-3x}\,dx = \lim_{b\to\infty}\int_0^b 3e^{-3x}\,dx = \lim_{b\to\infty}\left[\frac{3}{-3}e^{-3x}\right]_0^b = \lim_{b\to\infty}[-e^{-3x}]_0^b$

$\qquad = \lim_{b\to\infty}[-e^{-3b} - (-e^{-3\cdot 0})] = \lim_{b\to\infty}\left(1 - \frac{1}{3^b}\right) = 1$

13. $k = \frac{1}{4}$ **15.** $k = \frac{3}{2}$ **17.** $k = \frac{1}{5}$ **19.** $k = \frac{1}{2}$ **21.** $k = \dfrac{1}{\ln 3}$ **23.** $k = \dfrac{1}{e^3 - 1}$ **25.** $\frac{8}{25}$ **27.** $\frac{1}{2}$

29. 0.3297 **31.** 0.99995 **33.** 0.9502 **35.** 0.3935 **37.** $b = \sqrt[4]{4}$, or $\sqrt{2}$

EXERCISE SET 6.5, p. 343

1. $\mu = E(x) = \frac{7}{2}$, $E(x^2) = \frac{117}{9}$, $\sigma^2 = \frac{3}{4}$, $\sigma = \frac{1}{2}\sqrt{3}$

3. $\mu = E(x) = 2$, $E(x^2) = \frac{9}{2}$, $\sigma^2 = \frac{1}{2}$, $\sigma = \sqrt{\frac{1}{2}}$

5. $\mu = E(x) = \frac{14}{9}$, $E(x^2) = \frac{5}{2}$, $\sigma^2 = \frac{13}{162}$, $\sigma = \sqrt{\frac{13}{162}}$

7. $\mu = E(x) = \frac{17}{12}$, $E(x^2) = \frac{11}{5}$, $\sigma^2 = \frac{139}{720}$, $\sigma = \sqrt{\frac{139}{720}} = \frac{1}{12}\sqrt{\frac{139}{5}}$

9. $\mu = E(x) = \dfrac{2}{\ln 3}$, $E(x^2) = \dfrac{4}{\ln 3}$, $\sigma^2 = \dfrac{4\ln 3 - 4}{(\ln 3)^2}$, $\sigma = \dfrac{2}{\ln 3}\sqrt{\ln 3 - 1}$

11. $\mu = E(x) = \dfrac{a+b}{2}$, $E(x^2) = \dfrac{b^3 - a^3}{3(b-a)}$, or $\dfrac{b^2 + ba + a^2}{3}$, $\sigma^2 = \dfrac{(b-a)^2}{12}$, $\sigma = \dfrac{b-a}{2\sqrt{3}}$ **13.** 0.4964

15. 0.3665   **17.** 0.6442   **19.** 0.0078   **21.** 0.1716   **23.** 0.0013   **25.** a) 0.6826 b) 68.26%

27. 0.2898   **29.** 0.4514   **31.** a) 0.2088 b) 0.3830 c) 0.2420   **33.** 0.62%

EXERCISE SET 6.6, p. 348

1. a) (6, $5) b) $15   **3.** a) (1, $9) b) $3.33   **5.** a) (3, $9) b) $36

EXERCISE SET 6.7, p. 350

1. $\dfrac{9\pi}{2}$ **3.** $\dfrac{7\pi}{3}$ **5.** $\dfrac{\pi}{2}(e^{10} - e^{-4})$ **7.** $\dfrac{2\pi}{3}$ **9.** $\pi \ln 3$ **11.** 32π

13. $\dfrac{32\pi}{5}$ **15.** 9π **17.** 56π **19.** 6π **21.** $\dfrac{32\pi}{3}$ **23.** $\frac{4}{3}\pi r^3$

CHAPTER 6, TEST, p. 351

1. $29,192   **2.** $344.66   **3.** 11,098,350 thousand tons   **4.** By 2010   **5.** $2466   **6.** $11,971.50
7. $15,000   **8.** Convergent, $\frac{1}{4}$ **9.** Divergent   **10.** $k = \frac{1}{4}$ **11.** 0.8647   **12.** $E(x) = \frac{3}{4}$ **13.** $E(x^2) = \frac{3}{5}$
14. $\mu = \frac{3}{4}$ **15.** $\sigma^2 = \frac{3}{80}$ **16.** $\sigma = \frac{1}{4}\sqrt{\frac{3}{5}}$ **17.** 0.4332   **18.** 0.4420   **19.** 0.9071   **20.** 0.4207

21. (3, $16)   **22.** $45   **23.** $\pi \ln 5$ **24.** $\dfrac{5\pi}{2}$

CHAPTER 7

MARGIN EXERCISES

1. $y = x^3 + C$ **2.** a) $y = x^3 + C$ b) $y = x^3 - 7$, $y = x^3 + \frac{1}{2}$, $y = x^3$, answers may vary
3. $y = x^2 + 6$ **4.** $f(x) = \ln x - x^2 + \frac{2}{3}x^{3/2} + \frac{13}{3}$
5. $y' = 2e^x - 21e^{3x}$, $y'' = 2e^x - 63e^{3x}$. Then

$$y'' - 4y' + 3y = 0$$

$$\begin{array}{c|c} 2e^x - 63e^{3x} - 4(2e^x - 21e^{3x}) + 3(2e^x - 7e^{3x}) & 0 \\ 2e^x - 63e^{3x} - 8e^x + 84e^{3x} + 6e^x - 21e^{3x} & \\ 0 & \end{array}$$

6. $\dfrac{dy}{dx} = 2xe^{2x} + e^{2x}$. Then

$$\dfrac{dy}{dx} - 2y = e^{2x}$$

$$\begin{array}{c|c} (2xe^{2x} + e^{2x}) - 2(xe^{2x}) & e^{2x} \\ \hline e^{2x} & \end{array}$$

7. $y = C_1 e^{x^3}$, where $C_1 = e^C$.   **8.** $y = \sqrt[3]{x^2 + C}$

9. $y = \sqrt{10x + C_1}$, $y = -\sqrt{10x + C_1}$, where $C_1 = 2C$

10. $y = -2 + C_1 e^{x^2/2}$, where $C_1 = e^C$

11. $R = C_1 \cdot S^k$, where $C_1 = e^C$

12. a)

t	-3	-2	-1	0	1	2	3
$P(t)$	0.05	0.12	0.27	0.5	0.73	0.88	0.95

b)

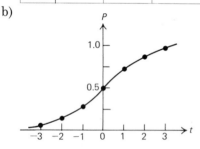

13. a) $P = \dfrac{\dfrac{P_0}{L - P_0} \cdot Le^{Lkt}}{1 + \dfrac{P_0}{L - P_0} e^{Lkt}} = \dfrac{P_0 Le^{Lkt}}{(L - P_0) + P_0 e^{Lkt}}$

b) $\dfrac{P_0 Le^{Lkt}}{(L - P_0) + P_0 e^{Lkt}} \cdot \dfrac{e^{-Lkt}}{e^{-Lkt}} = \dfrac{P_0 L}{P_0 + e^{-Lkt}(L - P_0)}$ (add exponents)

14. 3312   **15. a)** $P(t) = \dfrac{80,000}{20 + 3980e^{-2t}}$ **b)**   **c)** $t = 1.95$

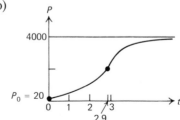

16. $Q(y) = \dfrac{Q_0 M}{Q_0 + e^{-Mry}(M - Q_0)}$

17. a) Undefined, 5%, 2.5%, 1.2%, 0.7%, 0.3%   **b)**

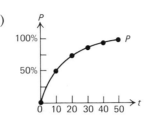

c)

d) No **e)** No **f)** 100% **g)** Decreasing

18. a)

t	0	1	2	3	4	5
$P(t)$	0	1.9	2.6	2.85	2.95	2.98

b)

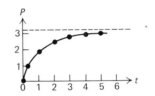

19. a) $k = 0.05$ **b)** $P(t) = 1 - e^{-0.05t}$ **c)** $P(60) = 0.9502$, or 95.02%   **d)** $t \approx 92$

EXERCISE SET 7.1, p. 357

1. $y = x^4 + C; y = x^4 + 3, y = x^4, y = x^4 - 796$, answers may vary

3. $y = \frac{1}{2}e^{2x} + \frac{1}{2}x^2 + C; y = \frac{1}{2}e^{2x} + \frac{1}{2}x^2 - 5, y = \frac{1}{2}e^{2x} + \frac{1}{2}x^2 + 7; y = \frac{1}{2}e^{2x} + \frac{1}{2}x^2$, answers may vary

5. $y = 3 \ln x - \frac{1}{3}x^3 + \frac{1}{6}x^6 + C; y = 3 \ln x - \frac{1}{3}x^3 + \frac{1}{6}x^6 - 15,$
$y = 3 \ln x - \frac{1}{3}x^3 + \frac{1}{6}x^6 - 7, y = 3 \ln x - \frac{1}{3}x^3 + \frac{1}{6}x^6$, answers may vary

7. $y = \frac{1}{3}x^3 + x^2 - 3x + 4$ **9.** $y = \frac{3}{5}x^{5/3} - \frac{1}{2}x^2 - \frac{61}{10}$ **11.** $y'' = \frac{1}{x}$, Then $y'' - \frac{1}{x} = 0$

$\frac{1}{x} - \frac{1}{x}$	0

13. $y' = 4e^x + 3xe^x, y'' = 7e^x + 3xe^x.$
Then

$$y'' - 2y' + y = 0$$

$(7e^x + 3xe^x) - 2(4e^x + 3xe^x) + (e^x + 3xe^x)$	0
$7e^x + 3xe^x - 8e^x - 6xe^x + e^x + 3xe^x$	
0	

15. $C(x) = 2.6x - 0.01x^2 + 120, A(x) = 2.6 - 0.01x + \dfrac{120}{x}$

EXERCISE SET 7.2, p. 362

1. $y = C_1 e^{x^4}$, where $C_1 = e^C$ **3.** $y = \sqrt[3]{\frac{5}{2}x^2 + C}$ **5.** $y = \sqrt{2x^2 + C_1}$, $y = -\sqrt{2x^2 + C_1}$, where $C_1 = 2C$
7. $y = \sqrt{6x + C_1}$, $y = -\sqrt{6x + C_1}$, where $C_1 = 2C$
9. $y = -3 + C_1 e^{x^2/2}$, where $C_1 = e^C$ **11.** $y = \sqrt[3]{15x + C_1}$, where $C_1 = 3C$ **13.** $y = C_1 e^{3x}$, where $C_1 = e^C$
15. $P = C_1 e^{2t}$, where $C_1 = e^C$ **17.** a) $P = C_1 e^{kt}$, where $C_1 = e^C$ b) $P = P_0 e^{kt}$
19. a) $R = k \cdot \ln(S + 1) + C$ b) $R = k \cdot \ln(S + 1)$ c) No units, no pleasure from them

EXERCISE SET 7.3, p. 371

1. 900   **3.** a) $P(t) = \dfrac{7000}{10 + 690e^{-0.56t}}$ b)   c) $t = 9.197$

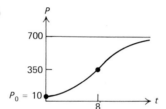

5. a) $N(t) = \dfrac{4800}{6 + 794e^{-800kt}}$ b) $k = 0.0005$ c) $t = 17.08$

7. a) $P(w) = \dfrac{.04}{.04 + .96e^{-kw}}$ b) $k = 1.06$ c) $P(w) = \dfrac{.04}{.04 + .96e^{-1.06w}}$ d) $w = 4.3$ (about 106 g)

EXERCISE SET 7.4, p. 379

1. 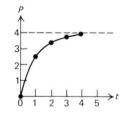   **3.**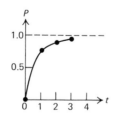

5. a) $P(t) = 0.5(1 - e^{-kt})$ b) $k = 0.07$ c) $P(t) = 0.5(1 - e^{-0.07t})$ d) $P(30) = 0.439$, or 43.9%   e) $t = 56$
7. a) $P(t) = 1 - e^{-kt}$ b) $k = 0.18$ c) $P(t) = 1 - e^{-0.18t}$ d) $P(10) = .8347$ e) 13
9. $M(t) = \dfrac{P}{k}(1 - e^{-kt})$

CHAPTER 7, TEST, p. 382

1. $y = \frac{1}{3}x^3 + \frac{3}{2}x^2 - 5x + 7$ **2.** $y = C_1 e^{x^8}$, where $C_1 = e^C$

3. $y = \sqrt{18x + C_1}$, $y = -\sqrt{18x + C_1}$, where $C_1 = e^C$

4. $y = C_1 e^{6t}$, where $C_1 = e^C$ **5.** 1360

6. a) $P(t) = \dfrac{16{,}000}{20 + 780e^{-0.72t}}$ b)

c) $t = 5.798$

7.

8. a) $S(t) = 20(1 - e^{-kt})$ b) $k = 0.11$ c) $S(t) = 20(1 - e^{-0.11t})$
d) \$13.342 million e) $t = 12.6$ yr, or the 13th year

CHAPTER 8

MARGIN EXERCISES

1. a) 128, the profit from selling 14 items of the first product and 12 of the second is \$128. b) 48, the profit from selling none of the first product and 8 items of the second is \$48.

2. 140   **3.** 2000   **4.** a) 302 b) -7 **5.** \$1173.50   **6.** a) 4 b) 4

7. a) $f(x, 4) = -x^2 - 15$ b) $-2x$ **8.** $\dfrac{\partial f}{\partial x} = -2x$ **9.** a) $\dfrac{\partial z}{\partial x} = 6xy + 15x^2$ b) $\dfrac{\partial z}{\partial y} = 3x^2$

10. a) $\dfrac{\partial t}{\partial x} = y + z + 2x$ b) $\dfrac{\partial t}{\partial y} = x + 3y^2$ c) $\dfrac{\partial t}{\partial x} = x$

11. a) $f_x = 9x^2y + 2y$ b) $f_x(-4, 1) = 146$ c) $f_y = 3x^3 + 2x$ d) $f_y(2, 6) = 28$

12. a)

13. a) $\dfrac{\partial z}{\partial y} = 6xy + 2x$ b) $\dfrac{\partial}{\partial x}\left(\dfrac{\partial z}{\partial y}\right) = 6y + 2$ c) $\dfrac{\partial}{\partial y}\left(\dfrac{\partial z}{\partial y}\right) = 6x$

14. a) $f_y = 6xy + 2x$ b) $f_{yx} = 6y + 2$ c) $f_{yy} = 6x$ **15.** $\dfrac{\partial^2 f}{\partial x^2} = 2$, $\dfrac{\partial^2 f}{\partial y\,\partial x} = 6y + 2$, $\dfrac{\partial^2 f}{\partial x\,\partial y} = 6y + 2$, $\dfrac{\partial^2 f}{\partial x^2} = 6x$

16. Min. $= -9$ at $(-3, 3)$ **17.** Max. $= \frac{1}{108}$ at $(\frac{1}{6}, \frac{1}{6})$

18. a) 75.7 yr, answers will vary. b) 75 yr, answers will vary. c) 0.7 yr difference, answers will vary.

19. a) $y = 1.5x + 63.7$ b) 69.7 yr   **20.** $y = 1.5x + 63.7$

21. a) $A(x, y) = xy$, subject to $x + y = 50$ b) Max. $= 625$ at $(25, 25)$

22. Max. $= 125$ at $(2.5, 10)$

23. $r \approx 1.8$ in., $h \approx 3.6$ in. Surface area is about 61.04 in².

24. $h = 184$ ft, $k = 75$ ft; dimensions are 74 ft by 74 ft by 194 ft.

EXERCISE SET 8.1, p. 394

1. $f(0, -2) = 0, f(2, 3) = -8, f(10, -5) = 200$

3. $f(0, -2) = 1, f(-2, 1) = -13\frac{8}{9}, f(2, 1) = 23$

5. $f(e, 2) = \ln e + 2^3 = 1 + 8 = 9, f(e^2, 4) = 66, f(e^3, 5) = 128$

7. $f(-1, 2, 3) = 6, f(2, -1, 3) = 12,$

9. $\dfrac{\partial z}{\partial x} = 2 - 3y, \ \dfrac{\partial z}{\partial y} = -3x, \ \dfrac{\partial z}{\partial x}\bigg|_{(-2\ -3)} = 11, \ \dfrac{\partial z}{\partial y}\bigg|_{(0\ -5)} = 0$

11. $\dfrac{\partial z}{\partial x} = 6x - 2y, \ \dfrac{\partial z}{\partial y} = -2x + 1, \ \dfrac{\partial z}{\partial x}\bigg|_{(-2\ -3)} = -6, \ \dfrac{\partial z}{\partial y}\bigg|_{(0,\ -5)} = 1$

13. $f_x = 2, f_y = -3, f_x(-2, 4) = 2, f_y(4, -3) = -3$

15. $f_x = \dfrac{x}{\sqrt{x^2 + y^2}}, f_y = \dfrac{y}{\sqrt{x^2 + y^2}}, f_x(-2, 1) = \dfrac{-2}{\sqrt{5}}, f_y(-3, -2) = \dfrac{-2}{\sqrt{13}}$

17. $f_x = 2e^{2x+3y}, f_y = 3e^{2x+3y}$ **19.** $f_x = ye^{xy}, f_y = xe^{xy}$

21. $f_x = \dfrac{y}{x+y}, f_y = \dfrac{y}{x+y} + \ln(x+y)$ **23.** $f_x = 1 + \ln xy, f_y = \dfrac{x}{y}$

25. $f_x = \dfrac{1}{y} + \dfrac{y}{x^2}, f_y = -\dfrac{x}{y^2} - \dfrac{1}{x}$

27. $f_x = 12(2x + y - 5), f_y = 6(2x + y - 5)$

29. $f_x = 3y - 2\lambda, f_y = 3x - \lambda, f_\lambda = -(2x + y - 8)$

31. $f_x = 2x - 10\lambda, f_y = 2y - 2\lambda, f_\lambda = -(10x + 2y - 4)$

33. $\dfrac{\partial f}{\partial b} = 12m + 6b - 30, \dfrac{\partial f}{\partial m} = 28m + 12b - 64$

EXERCISE SET 8.2, p. 398

1. $\dfrac{\partial^2 f}{\partial x^2} = 6, \dfrac{\partial^2 f}{\partial y\, \partial x} = \dfrac{\partial^2 f}{\partial x\, \partial y} = -1, \dfrac{\partial^2 f}{\partial y^2} = 0$

3. $\dfrac{\partial^2 f}{\partial x^2} = 0, \dfrac{\partial^2 f}{\partial y\, \partial x} = \dfrac{\partial^2 f}{\partial x\, \partial y} = 3, \dfrac{\partial^2 f}{\partial y^2} = 0$

5. $\dfrac{\partial^2 f}{\partial x^2} = 20x^3y^4 + 6xy^2, \dfrac{\partial^2 f}{\partial y\, \partial x} = \dfrac{\partial^2 f}{\partial x\, \partial y} = 20x^4y^3 + 6x^2y, \dfrac{\partial^2 f}{\partial y^2} = 12x^5y^2 + 2x^3$

7. $f_{xx} = 0, f_{yx} = 0, f_{xy} = 0, f_{yy} = 0$

9. $f_{xx} = 4y^2e^{2xy}, f_{yx} = f_{xy} = 4xye^{2xy} + 2e^{2xy}, f_{yy} = 4x^2e^{2xy}$

11. $f_{xx} = 0, f_{yx} = f_{xy} = 0, f_{yy} = e^y$

13. $f_{xx} = -\dfrac{y}{x^2}, f_{yx} = f_{xy} = \dfrac{1}{x}, f_{yy} = 0$

15. $\dfrac{\partial^2 f}{\partial x^2} = \dfrac{2y^2 - 2x^2}{(x^2 + y^2)^2}, \dfrac{\partial^2 f}{\partial y^2} = \dfrac{2x^2 - 2y^2}{(x^2 + y^2)^2}$, so the sum is 0.

EXERCISE SET 8.3, p. 406

1. Min. $= -\frac{1}{3}$ at $\left(-\frac{1}{3}, \frac{2}{3}\right)$ **3.** Max. $= \frac{4}{27}$ at $\left(\frac{2}{3}, \frac{2}{3}\right)$ **5.** Min. $= -1$ at $(1, 1)$

7. Min. $= -7$ at $(1, -2)$ **9.** Min. $= -5$ at $(-1, 2)$ **11.** None

13. Max. of $P = 35$ (million dollars) when $a = 10$ (million dollars) and $p = \$3$

15. a) $R(p_1, p_2) = 78p_1 - 6p_1^2 - 6p_1p_2 + 66p_2 - 6p_2^2$

b) $p_1 = 5\ (\$50), p_2 = 3\ (\$30)$

c) $q_1 = 78 - 6 \cdot 5 - 3 \cdot 3 = 39$ (hundreds), $q = 33$ (hundreds)

d) $R = 50 \cdot 3900 + 30 \cdot 3300 = \$294{,}000$

EXERCISE SET 8.4, p. 412

1. 79.3 yr   **3.** a) $y = 1.5x + 17.7$ b) 23.7 c) 26.7   **5.** a) $y = \frac{1}{4}x + 40$ b) $61°$

EXERCISE SET 8.5, p. 419

1. Max. $= 8$ at $(2, 4)$ **3.** Max. $= -16$ at $(2, 4)$ **5.** Min. $= 20$ at $(4, 2)$ **7.** Min. $= -96$ at $(8, -12)$
9. Min. $= \frac{3}{2}$ at $(1, \frac{1}{2}, -\frac{1}{2})$ **11.** 35 and 35   **13.** 3 and -3 **15.** $9\frac{3}{4}$ in., $9\frac{3}{4}$ in.; $95\frac{1}{16}$ in^2
17. $r = \sqrt[3]{\dfrac{27}{2\pi}} \approx 1.6$ ft. $h = 2 \cdot r \approx 3.2$ ft, min. surface area ≈ 48.3 ft^2
19. Max. of $S = 800$ at $L = 20$, $M = 60$
21. a) $C(x, y, z) = 7xy + 6yz + 6xz$
    b) $x = 60$ ft, $y = 60$ ft, $z = 70$ ft; \$75,600
23. $\lambda = \dfrac{p_x}{c_1} = \dfrac{p_y}{c_2}$

EXERCISE SET 8.6, p. 426

1. $h = \sqrt[3]{10{,}240{,}000} \approx 217$ ft, $k \approx 54$ ft; dimensions are 54 ft by 54 ft by 225 ft.
3. $h = \sqrt[3]{\dfrac{Aca^2}{b^2}}$, $k = \sqrt[3]{\dfrac{Abc}{a}}$; dimensions are k by k by $h + c$.

CHAPTER 8, TEST, p. 427

1. $\dfrac{\partial f}{\partial x} = e^x + 6x^2y$ **2.** $\dfrac{\partial f}{\partial y} = 2x^3 + 1$ **3.** $\dfrac{\partial^2 f}{\partial x^2} = e^x + 12xy$ **4.** $\dfrac{\partial^2 f}{\partial x\,\partial y} = 6x^2$ **5.** $\dfrac{\partial^2 f}{\partial y\,\partial x} = 6x^2$

6. $\dfrac{\partial^2 f}{\partial y^2} = 0$ **7.** Min. $= -\frac{7}{16}$ at $(\frac{3}{4}, \frac{1}{2})$ **8.** None   **9.** a) $y = \frac{9}{2}x + \frac{17}{3}$ b) \$23.7   **10.** Max. $= -19$ at $(4, 5)$

FINAL EXAMINATION, p. 429

1. $y = -4x - 27$ **2.** $x^2 + 2xh + h^2 - 5$ **3.** -8 **4.** -9 **5.** $2x - 7$ **6.** $\frac{1}{4}x^{-3/4}$ **7.** $-6x^{-7}$
8. $(x - 3)5(x + 1)^4 + (x + 1)^5$, or $2(x + 1)^4(3x - 7)$ **9.** $\dfrac{5 - 2x^3}{x^6}$ **10.** Min. $= -7$ at $x = 1$ **11.** None
12. Max. $= 6\frac{2}{3}$ at $x = -1$, Min. $= 4\frac{1}{3}$ at $x = -2$ **13.** 15   **14.** 30 times; lot size 15

15. $P = 199,500$; max. sus. harv. $= 39,800,250$ **16.** $\Delta y = 3.03$, $f'(x) \Delta x = 3$ **17.** $\dfrac{e^x(1-x)}{e^{2x}}$, or $\dfrac{1-x}{e^x}$

18. $\dfrac{2x}{x^2 + 5}$ **19.** $e^{\ln x} \cdot \dfrac{1}{x}$, or 1   **20.** $3e^{3x} + 2x$ **21.** a) $A(t) = 20,300e^{0.1t}$ b) 40,880.14 million barrels

22. $\frac{1}{2}x^6 + C$ **23.** $3 - \dfrac{2}{e}$ **24.** $\frac{232}{3}$ **25.** $\frac{1}{4}e^{x^4} + C$ **26.** $\left(\dfrac{x^2}{2} + 3x\right) \ln x - \dfrac{x^2}{4} - 3x + C$

27. $\dfrac{7}{9(7 - 3x)} + \dfrac{1}{9} \ln(7 - 3x) + C$ **28.** \$525.22   **29.** \$49,445   **30.** Convergent, $\frac{1}{4374}$ **31.** $\frac{3}{2} \ln 3$

32. 0.6826   **33.** (7, \$169); \$751.33   **34.** $-\dfrac{\pi}{2}\left(\dfrac{1}{e^{10}} - 1\right)$ **35.** $y = C_1 e^{x^2/2}$

36. a) $P(t) = 1 - e^{-kt}$ b) $k = 0.12$ c) $P(t) = 1 - e^{-0.12t}$ d) $P(20) = 0.9093$, or 90.93%

37. $8xy^3 + 3$ **38.** $e^y + 24x^2 y$ **39.** None   **40.** Max. $= 4$ at $(3, 3)$

APPENDIX B

MARGIN EXERCISES

1.

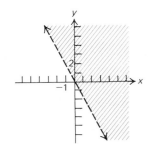

2.

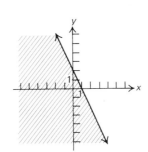

3.

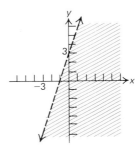

4.

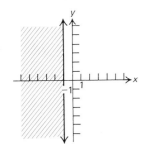

5.

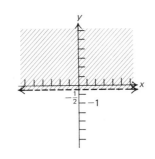

6.

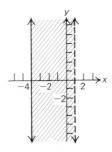

7.

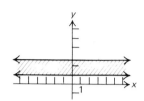

8. Vertex: $(-\frac{1}{2}, \frac{3}{2})$

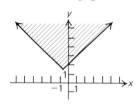

9. Vertices: $(0, 0)$, $(4, 0)$, $(4, \frac{5}{3})$, $(0, 3)$, $(\frac{12}{5}, 3)$

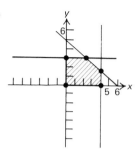

10. Max. = 120, when $x = 3$, $y = 3$; min. = 34, when $x = 1$, $y = 0$

11. Max. = 45, when $x = 6$, $y = 0$; min. = 12, when $x = 0$, $y = 3$

12. Maximum profit = \$23.70 occurs by selling 50 hot dogs and 40 hamburgers.

EXERCISE SET, APPENDIX B, A13

1. Max. = 168, when $x = 0$, $y = 6$; min. = 0, when $x = 0$, $y = 0$

3. Max. = 152, when $x = 7$, $y = 0$; min. = 32, when $x = 0$, $y = 4$

5. Max. score: 102 points 8 of type A, 10 of type B

6. Max. score: 425 points, doing 5 of type A, 15 of type B

7. \$7000 in Bank X, \$15,000 in Bank Y which will yield maximum income of \$1395

8. \$18,000 in municipal bonds; \$22,000 in corporate bonds which will yield maximum income of \$3110

9. Maximum profit \$192 by making 2 knit suits and 4 worsted suits

10. $83\frac{1}{3}$ batches of *Smello*, 250 batches of *Roppo*. Max. profit is \$2480.

APPENDIX C

MARGIN EXERCISES

1. $\dfrac{315}{2}$ **2.** $\dfrac{315}{2}$ **3.** $\dfrac{6}{35}$

EXERCISE SET, APPENDIX C

1. 1   **3.** 0   **5.** 6   **7.** $\frac{3}{20}$ **9.** 4   **11.** $\frac{4}{15}$ **13.** 1   **15.** 39

APPENDIX D

MARGIN EXERCISES

1. a) I b) III c) IV d) III e) I f) IV g) I

2. a) $\dfrac{3}{4}\pi$ b) $\dfrac{7}{4}\pi$ c) $-\dfrac{\pi}{2}$ d) 4π e) $-\dfrac{5\pi}{4}$ f) $-\dfrac{7\pi}{4}$ g) $\dfrac{9\pi}{4}$ h) $\dfrac{8\pi}{3}$

3. a) $60°$ b) $135°$ c) $450°$ d) $1800°$ e) $-210°$ f) $54{,}000°$ g) $-48{,}600°$ h) $1125°$

4. a) $-\dfrac{\sqrt{3}}{2}$ b) $\dfrac{1}{2}$ c) $-\dfrac{\sqrt{3}}{2}$ d) $\dfrac{1}{2}$ **5.** a) 1 b) $\sqrt{3}$ c) 0 d) $\sqrt{2}$ e) 2 f) 1

6. a) $\sqrt{3}$ b) undefined c) $\dfrac{\sqrt{3}}{3}$ d) 2 e) undefined f) $\sqrt{2}$ **7.** $1 + \cot^2 t = \csc^2 t$ **8.** $\dfrac{\sqrt{6} - \sqrt{2}}{4}$

9. $\dfrac{\sqrt{2} + \sqrt{6}}{4}$ **10.** $2 \sin u \cos u$

11. $\cot x = \dfrac{\cos x}{\sin x}$, so $\dfrac{d}{dx} \cot x = [\sin x(-\sin x) - \cos x(\cos x)] \div \sin^2 x = \dfrac{-(\sin^2 x + \cos^2 x)}{\sin^2 x} = -\dfrac{1}{\sin^2 x} = -\csc^2 x$

12. $\dfrac{3 \sin^2 x}{\cos^4 x}$ **13.** $(4x^3 + 6x)\cos(x^4 + 3x^2)$ **14.** $-2xe^{x^2} \sin(e^{x^2})$ **15.** 2 **16.** $\dfrac{(\sin x)^4}{4} + C$

17. $\frac{1}{4} \sin 4x + C$ **18.** $\sin x - x \cos x + C$

19. a) amplitude $= 4$, period $= \pi$, phase shift $= \dfrac{\pi}{4}$

b)

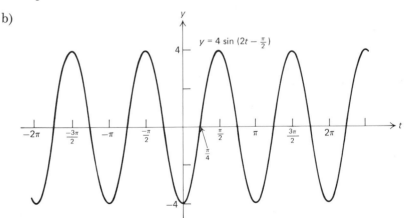

$y = 4 \sin \left(2t - \dfrac{\pi}{2}\right)$

20. $\dfrac{dy}{dx} = 0.03594\pi \cos 1{,}198\pi x$ **21.** $\dfrac{dL}{dt} = 2\pi A f \cos\left(2\pi f T - \dfrac{d}{\omega}\right)$ **22.** 27 **23.** $\dfrac{\pi}{6}$ **24.** 0

25. $-\dfrac{\pi}{3}$ **26.** $\dfrac{\pi}{3}$ **27.** $\dfrac{\pi}{6}$ **28.** $\dfrac{2\pi}{3}$ **29.** $\frac{1}{5} \mathrm{Tan}^{-1}(5x) + C$ **30.** $\frac{1}{2} \mathrm{Cos}^{-1}(2x) + C$

EXERCISE SET, APPENDIX D

1. $\sec x = \dfrac{1}{\cos x}$, so $\dfrac{d}{dx} \sec x = \dfrac{\cos x \cdot 0 - (-\sin x) \cdot 1}{\cos^2 x} = \dfrac{\sin x}{\cos^2 x} = \dfrac{\sin x}{\cos x} \cdot \dfrac{1}{\cos x} = \tan x \sec x$

3. $x \cos x + \sin x$ **5.** $e^x(\cos x + \sin x)$ **7.** $\dfrac{x \cos x - \sin x}{x^2}$ **9.** $2 \sin x \cos x$

11. $\cos^2 x - \sin^2 x$ **13.** $\dfrac{1}{1 + \cos x}$ **15.** $\dfrac{2 \sin x}{\cos^3 x}$ **17.** $\dfrac{-\sin x}{2\sqrt{1 + \cos x}}$ **19.** $-x^2 \sin x$

21. $\cos x \cdot e^{\sin x}$ **23.** $-\sin x$ **25.** $(2x + 3x^2)\sin(x^2 + x^3)$ **27.** $(4x^3 - 5x^4)\sin(x^5 - x^4)$

29. $-\frac{1}{2} x^{-1/2} \cdot \sin \sqrt{x}$ **31.** $-\sin x \cdot \cos(\cos x)$ **33.** $\dfrac{1}{2}$ **35.** $\dfrac{(\sin x)^5}{5} + C$ **37.** $\dfrac{(\cos x)^3}{3} + C$

39. $\sin(x + 3) + C$ **41.** $-\frac{1}{2} \cos 2x + C$ **43.** $\frac{1}{2} \sin x^2 + C$ **45.** $-\cos(e^x) + C$

47. $-\ln(\cos x) + C$, assuming $\cos x > 0$ **49.** $\frac{1}{4} x \sin 4x + \frac{1}{16} \cos 4x + C$ **51.** $3x \sin x + 3 \cos x + C$

53. $2x \sin x - (x^2 - 2)\cos x + C$ **55.** $\tan x - x + C$ **57.** $\dfrac{e^x}{2}(\cos x + \sin x) + C$

59. a) Amp. $= 5$, Period $= \dfrac{\pi}{2}$, Phase shift $= -\dfrac{\pi}{4}$ b) $\dfrac{dy}{dt} = 20 \cos(4t + \pi)$

61. a) $2, \pi, \dfrac{\pi}{2}$ b) $\dfrac{dy}{dt} = 4 \cos(2t - \pi)$ **63.** $P'(t) = 40{,}000(\cos t - \sin t)$ **65.** $8\sqrt{8}$ **67.** 16

69. $\text{Tan}^{-1}(e^t) + C$

71. Use substitution. Let $u = \text{Sin}^{-1} x$. Then $x = \sin u$ and $dx = \cos u \, du$. Then the integral

$$\int \frac{1}{\sqrt{1 - x^2}} \, dx = \int \frac{1}{\sqrt{1 - \sin^2 u}} \cos u \, du = \int \frac{1}{\cos u} \cdot \cos u \, du = \int du = u + C = \text{Sin}^{-1} x + C$$

INDEX

Index

TEST FORM A

CHAPTER 1 TEST FORM A

Name _____ Class _____ Score _____ Grade _____

1. Rename without negative exponents:
   $(\frac{1}{3})^{-2}$

2. Multiply:
   $6y^3 \cdot 4y^{-2}$.

3. Multiply: $(x - h)^2$.

4. Factor: $9y^2 - 4x^2$.

5. Suppose $1500 is invested at 6%. How much is in the account at the end of 1 year if interest is compounded semiannually?

6. Solve:
   $(x - 4)(x + 3) = -6$

7. Write interval notation for the graph:

8. If f is a function such that $f(x) = 2x^2 - 3x + 7$, find:
   a) $f(-1)$ b) $f(2 + h)$

9. What is the y-intercept and slope of the equation $y = 5 - 3x$?

10. Write an equation of the line with slope of $\frac{2}{3}$ and with y-intercept $(0, -6)$.

11. The temperature in a classroom seems to vary directly as the number of students. If the temperature is $70°$ when 25 students are in class, what will the temperature be when 30 students are in the classroom?

12. A camera company has fixed costs of $75,000 for producing a minicamera. Variable costs for producing each camera are estimated to be $28. The cameras will be sold at a price of $55 each.
    a) Formulate a function $R(x)$ for the total revenue from the sale of x cameras.
    b) Formulate a function $C(x)$ for the total cost of producing x cameras.
    c) Formulate a function $P(x)$ for the total profit from the production and sale of x cameras.
    d) What profit or loss will the company realize from expected sales of 12,000 cameras?
    e) How many cameras must the company sell to break even?

ANSWERS

1. _____

2. _____

3. _____

4. _____

5. _____

6. _____

7. _____

8. a) _____

   b) _____

9. $m =$ _____ $y-$int: _____

10. _____

11. _____

12. a) _____

    b) _____

    c) _____

    d) _____

    e) _____

ANSWERS

13. Decide whether the function $g(x) = \frac{3}{2}x - 6$ is increasing, decreasing, or neither.

13. _____

14. Find the equilibrium point if $D(x) = x^2 + 5x + 7$ and $S(x) = x^2 + 22$.

14. _____

15. See graph. _____

15. Sketch the graph of the equation $y = x^2 - 2$.

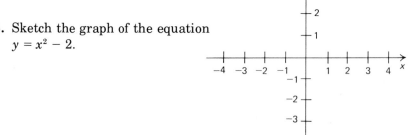

16. _____

17. _____

16. Find the domain of the function $h(x) = \dfrac{1}{x - 4}$.

17. Convert to fractional exponents: $\sqrt[4]{y^6}$

18. _____

18. Convert to radical notation: $x^{3/4}$

19. _____

19. Derive a quadratic function which fits the data points $(1,-4)$, $(2,-6)$, and $(3,-6)$.

20. _____

20. Derive a linear function which fits the data points $(5,-2)$ and $(-1,9)$.

CHAPTER 2 TEST FORM A

Name _____ Class _____ Score _____ Grade _____

Which functions are continuous?

ANSWERS

1.

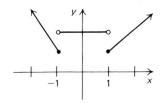

2.

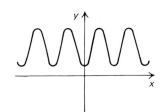

1. _____

2. _____

3. a) Complete.

Inputs x	Outputs $\dfrac{2}{x+2}$
-1	
-1.5	
-1.9	
-1.99	
-1.999	

b) Find:

$$\lim_{x \to -2} \frac{2}{x+2}$$

4. Find a simplified difference quotient for
$$f(x) = \frac{10}{x}.$$

3. a) _____See table._____

b) _____

5. a) Complete.

x	$5 + \dfrac{3}{x}$
4	
80	
500	
60,000	

b) Find:

$$\lim_{x \to \infty} \left(5 + \frac{3}{x}\right)$$

4. _____

5. a) _____See table._____

b) _____

6. Find the points on the graph of $y = 3x^2 - 11x + 7$ at which the tangent line has slope 1.

6. _____

ANSWERS

Find $f'(x)$.

7. _____

7. $f(x) = 4x^7$ 8. $f(x) = \dfrac{3}{x^3}$ 9. $f(x) = 6x^{2/3}$

8. _____

9. _____

10. $f(x) = 6\sqrt{x}$ 11. $f(x) = 8x^6 - 5x^3 + 2x^2 - 11$

10. _____

11. _____

Differentiate.

12. $\frac{2}{3}x^3 + \frac{3}{2}x^2 - 5x + 6$ 13. $\dfrac{x^2 - 2x + 1}{x - 1}$

12. _____

13. _____

14. $\dfrac{2x + 3}{2 - x}$ 15. $(2x + 3)^4 (2 - x)^3$

14. _____

15. _____

16. $(3x + 4)^{15}$ 17. $2x^3 (x^2 + 1)^{\frac{1}{2}}$

16. _____

17. _____

18. Given $R(x) = 40x$ and $C(x) = 8x^2 - 7x - 10$. Find:

18. a) _____
    a) $P(x)$
    b) $R(20), C(20), P(20)$

    b) _____
    c) $R'(x), C'(x), P'(x)$
    d) $R'(20), C'(20), P'(20)$

    c) _____

    d) _____

19. The temperature T of a person during an illness is given by
    $T(t) = -0.2t^2 + 2.2t + 98.6$, where T is the temperature (°F) at time t, meas-
    ured in days.

19. a) _____
    a) Find the rate of change of temperature with respect to time.

    b) _____
    b) Find the temperature at $t = 3$ days.

    c) _____
    c) Find the rate of change of the temperature at $t = 3$ days.

CHAPTER 3 TEST FORM A

Name _____ Class _____ Score _____ Grade _____

1. If $y = x^6 + 3x^2$, find $\dfrac{d^5y}{dx^5}$.

Find the maximum and minimum values, if they exist, over the indicated interval. If no interval is specified, use the real line.

2. $f(x) = \frac{1}{3}x^3 + 2x^2 + 4x + 5$

3. $f(x) = x^2 - 6x + 7 \,; [-1,4]$

4. $f(x) = 2x^3 + 3x^2 - 12x + 8 \,; [-3,2]$

5. $f(x) = x^4 - 2x^3 - 2x^2 + 2 \,; [-2,3]$

6. $f(x) = 3x - 4 \,; [-2,2]$

7. $f(x) = 3x - 4$

8. $f(x) = x^2 - \dfrac{2}{x} \,; (-\infty, 0)$

9. Of all numbers whose sum is 80, find the two which have the maximum product.

10. Find the minimum value of $S = 8x^2 + 3y^2$, where $2x - y = 5$.

ANSWERS

1. _____

2. _____

3. _____

4. _____

5. _____

6. _____

7. _____

8. _____

9. _____

10. _____

ANSWERS

11. If $R(x) = 2x^2 + 140x + 70$ and $C(x) = 2.1x^2 + 20x + 90$, find the maximum profit and the number of units which must be produced and sold to yield this maximum profit.

11. _____

12. A rectangular box with a square base and a cover is to contain 2500 cu ft. If the cost per sq ft for the bottom is $2, for the top $3 per sq ft, and for the sides $1 per sq ft, what should be the dimensions for minimum cost? What is the minimum cost?

12. _____

13. A store in Alaska sells 400 snowmobiles per year. It costs $20 to store one snowmobile for one year. To reorder snowmobiles there is a fixed cost of $10 plus $2 for each snowmobile. How many times per year should the store owner order snowmobiles, and in what lot size, to minimize inventory costs?

13. _____

14. A certain population has a reproduction curve given by $f(P) = P(25 - P)$, where P is measured in thousands. Find the population at which the maximum sustainable harvest occurs and find the maximum sustainable harvest.

14. _____

15. _____

15. If $y = f(x) = x^3 - x^2$, $x = 5$ and $\Delta x = -0.1$, find Δy and $f'(x)\Delta x$.

16. _____

16. Approximate $\sqrt{67}$ using $\Delta y \approx f'(x)\Delta x$.

Name _____ Class _____ Score _____ Grade _____

Differentiate.

1. e^x **2.** $\ln x$ **3.** e^{-x^2} **4.** $\ln \dfrac{x}{5}$

5. $\ln(e^x)$ **6.** $e^x \ln(x^2)$ **7.** $x^2 - 2(\ln x)$ **8.** $\dfrac{\ln 2x}{e^{2x}}$

Given $\log_a 3 = 2.0986$ and $\log_a 5 = 2.6094$, find:

9. $\log_a 15$ **10.** $\log_a \frac{3}{5}$ **11.** $\log_a 45$

12. State the solution of $\dfrac{dB}{dt} = kB$, in terms of B_0.

13. If the number of bacteria in a certain culture doubles in 6 days, what is its growth rate?

14. If $3000 is deposited in a bank where the interest rate of 6% is compounded continuously, how long will it take for the $3000 to double itself?

15. The demand for coal in the United States is increasing at the rate of 4% per year, that is

$\dfrac{dA}{dt} = 0.04\,A$, where A = the amount of coal used and t = time in years.

  a) 500 million tons of coal were used in 1970. Find the solution of the equation assuming $A_0 = 500$ and $k = 0.04$.

  b) How much coal will be needed in 1975?

  c) When will the demand be double that of 1970?

ANSWERS

1. _____

2. _____

3. _____

4. _____

5. _____

6. _____

7. _____

8. _____

9. _____

10. _____

11. _____

12. _____

13. _____

14. _____

15. a) _____

    b) _____

    c) _____

ANSWERS

16. _____

17. _____

18. a) _____

    b) _____

    c) _____

19. _____

20. _____

16. If the half-life of a radioactive isotope of carbon is 20 minutes, what is its decay rate?

17. What is the half-life of Iodine-131 if its decay rate is 9% per day?

18. The formula $\dfrac{dA}{dt} = -kA$ applies to the radioactive decay of a certain element, where A = the amount present at time t and t = time in years.
   a) If 80 grams of this substance is reduced through radioactive decay after 12 years to 60 grams, what is the decay rate? Round to the nearest one percent.
   b) Using the decay rate found in (a), find the solution to the equation.
   c) After how many years will exactly 40 grams of this substance remain?

Differentiate.

19. 8^x

20. $\log_{12} x$

CHAPTER 5 TEST FORM A

Name _____ Class _____ Score _____ Grade _____

Integrate.

ANSWERS

1. $\int 5x^3\, dx$

2. $\int \left(4t^3 + 5t + \dfrac{1}{t}\right) dt$

3. $\int (2e^x + 1)\, dx$

4. If $f'(x) = 4x - 5$ and $f(2) = -1$, find f.

Find the area under the curve on the interval indicated.

5. $y = x^2 + 2x + 2$; $[0,3]$

6. $y = 4x^3 - 3x^2$; $[2,3]$

7. Give two interpretations of the shaded region. ▶

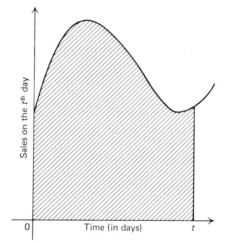

8. A particle starts out from the origin. Its velocity at any time t, $t \geqslant 0$, is given by $v(t) = 3t^2 + 2t$. Find the distance the particle travels during the first 3 hours (from $t = 0$ to $t = 3$).

Integrate.

9. $\int_1^2 (3x^2 - 5x)\, dx$

10. $\int_0^1 (t + e^t)\, dt$

11. $\int_1^3 (\sqrt{x} + x^{-1})\, dx$

12. Decide if $\int_a^b f(x)\, dx$ is positive, negative, or zero.

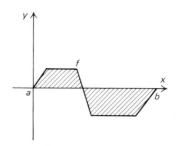

1. _____

2. _____

3. _____

4. _____

5. _____

6. _____

7. _____

8. _____

9. _____

10. _____

11. _____

12. _____

ANSWERS

13. Find the area of the region bounded by $y = x^2$ and $y = 3x + 4$.

13. _____

Integrate. Use substitution. Do not use Table 5.

14. $\int x \sqrt{x^2 + 1}\, dx$ **15.** $\int \dfrac{6t}{3t^2 + 1}\, dt$ **16.** $\int x\, e^{x^2}\, dx$

14. _____

Integrate. Use integration by parts. Do not use Table 5.

15. _____

17. $\int x\, e^{-x}\, dx$ **18.** $\int 2x\, \ln x\, dx$

16. _____

Integrate. Use Table 5.

17. _____

19. $\int (\ln x)^2\, dx$ **20.** $\int \dfrac{1}{x^2 - 9}\, dx$

18. _____

19. _____

21. Approximate $\int_1^4 \dfrac{2}{x}\, dx$ by computing the area of each rectangle to three decimal places and adding.

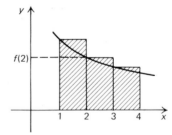

20. _____

21. _____

22. Find the average value of $y = x + \dfrac{1}{x}$ over $[1,3]$.

22. _____

23. Pizza Ltd. estimates that its sales will grow continuously according to the function $S(t) = 3e^{2t}$, where $S(t) = $ sales, in dollars, on the tth day. Find the accumulated sales for the first week.

23. _____

Name _____ Class _____ Score _____ Grade _____

1. Find the amount of an annuity where $2400 per year is being invested at 8%, compounded continuously, for 10 years.

2. What annual payment should be made so the amount of an annuity over 25 years at 8%, compounded continuously, will be $40,000?

3. *The Demand for Potash.* In 1973 ($t = 0$) the world use of potash was 23,000 thousand tons, and the demand for it was growing exponentially at the rate of 1% per year. If the demand continues to grow at this rate, how many tons of potash will the world use from 1973 to 1993?

4. *The Depletion of Potash.* The world reserves of potash are 25,000,000 thousand tons. Assuming the growth rate of Question 3 continues and that no new reserves are discovered, when will the world reserves of potash be exhausted?

5. Find the present value of $100,000, due 50 years later at 8%, compounded continuously.

6. Find the capital value of a rental property over a 20-year period where the annual rent is $3600 and the going interest rate is 9%.

7. Find the capital value of the rental property in Question 6 if the rent is to be paid perpetually.

Determine whether each of the following improper integrals is convergent or divergent, and calculate its value if convergent.

8. $\int_1^\infty \frac{1}{x^3}\, dx$

9. $\int_1^\infty e^{3x}\, dx$

ANSWERS

1. _____

2. _____

3. _____

4. _____

5. _____

6. _____

7. _____

8. _____

9. _____

10. Find k such that $f(x) = \dfrac{k}{k^2}$ is a probability density function over the interval $[1,3]$.

11. A person randomly arrives at a bus stop where the waiting time t for a bus is 0 to 30 minutes. The probability density function for t is $f(t) = \frac{1}{30}$, for $0 \leq t \leq 30$. Find the probability that a person will have to wait no more than 20 minutes for a bus.

Given the probability density function $f(x) = 4x^3$, over $[0,1]$, find:

12. $E(x^2)$ 13. $E(x)$ 14. the mean

15. the variance   16. the standard deviation

Let x be a continuous random variable with standard normal density. Using Table 6, find:

17. $P(0 \leq x \leq 1.83)$ 18. $P(-1.76 \leq x \leq 1.41)$

19. $P(-2.04 \leq x \leq -1.02)$

20. The number of pizzas sold daily at Benito's Pizzeria is normally distributed with mean 500 and standard deviation 80. What is the probability that the number sold during one day is 600 or more?

Given $D(x) = (x - 8)^2$, and $S(x) = x^2 + 2x + 10$, find:

21. the equilibrium point   22. the consumer's surplus

Find the volume generated by revolving about the x-axis the region bounded by each of the following graphs:

23. $y = x^3$, $x = 1$, $x = 2$, x-axis

24. $y = \dfrac{1}{x + 1}$, $x = 0$, $x = 1$, x-axis

Name _____ Class _____ Score _____ Grade _____

1. Solve the differential equation $\dfrac{dy}{dx} = 2x^2 - 4x + 3$, given that

   $y = \frac{2}{3}$ when $x = 1$.

Solve these differential equations.

2. $\dfrac{dy}{dx} = 6x^2y$ 3. $y' = 5x^2 - x^2y$ 4. $\dfrac{dv}{dt} = 2v^{-3}$

5. Graph $P(t) = 1 - e^{-4t}$

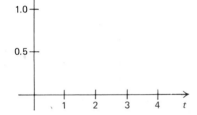

6. A group of 8 students at Loonie University start the rumor "All final exam-
   inations for the year have been cancelled." The rate at which this rumor
   spreads satisfies the equation

   $$\dfrac{dN}{dt} = kN(L - N),$$

where
   N = number of students who have heard this rumor after t minutes.
   $L = 1200$, the total enrollment of the university.
   $N_0 = 8$, the number of students who started the rumor.
   $k = 0.0002$

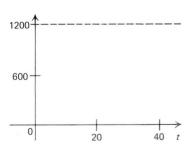

   a) Write the equation
      for $N(t)$.

   b) Sketch a graph of $P(N)$
      given that the point
      of inflection occurs
      at $t = 21$ minutes.

   c) After how many minutes t will 800 students have heard the rumor?

ANSWERS

1. _____

2. _____

3. _____

4. _____

5. ____See graph.____

6. a) _____

   b) ____See graph.____

   c) _____

7. The Hullian Model of Learning is $\dfrac{dP}{dt} = k(L - P)$, where

P = probability of mastery of the process of differentiating quotients after t learning trials.

$L = 1$, the limiting value of mastery of the learning.

k = constant.

7. a) _____

a) Write the solution $P(t)$ in terms of L and k.

b) _____

b) Suppose the probability of mastery of differentiating quotients after 10 trials is 0.80. Use this information to determine k to the nearest hundredth.

c) _____

c) Rewrite $P(t)$ in terms of k.

d) _____

d) Find $P(12)$.

e) _____

e) Using the value of k determined in (b), find the number of trials required so that $P(t) = 0.95$.

Name _____ Class _____ Score _____ Grade _____

Given $f(x,y) = e^x + 3x^2y^2 + 5x$,

find:

  1. f_y

  2. f_x

  3. f_{xx}

  4. f_{yx}

  5 f_{xy}

  6. f_{yy}

Find the maxima or minima.

  7. $f(x,y) = x^3 + y^3 - 12xy + 48$

  8. $f(x,y) = x^2 - xy + y^2 - 2x + 4y$

ANSWERS

1. _____

2. _____

3. _____

4. _____

5. _____

6. _____

7. _____

8. _____

9. Consider this data regarding enrollment in colleges and universities during a recent three-year period.

Year — x	1	2	3
Enrollment — y (in millions)	7.4	8.1	8.3

a) Find the regression line $y = mx + b$.

9. a) _____

b) Use the regression line to predict enrollment in the 4th year.

b) _____

10. Minimize $f(x,y) = x^2 - 2xy + 2y^2 + 10$ subject to the constraint $2x - 6y = 15$.

10. _____

FINAL EXAMINATION FORM A

Name _____ Class _____ Score _____ Grade _____

Chapter 1

1. Find the slope and y-intercept of the line $y = -9x + 7$.

2. For $f(x) = 4x^2 + 7$, find find $f(2 - h)$.

Chapter 2

3. Find $\lim\limits_{x \to \infty} \left(\dfrac{5 + x}{x} \right)$

Differentiate.

4. $4x^3 - x^5$

5. $x^{\frac{1}{2}}$

6. $4x^{-9}$

7. $(5 - 2x)(x + 7)^3$

8. $\dfrac{1 - x^3}{x^4}$

9. $(x^3 - x^4 + 7)^8$

Chapter 3

Find the maximum and minimum values, if they exist, over the indicated interval. If no interval is indicated, use the real line.

10. $f(x) = -3x^2 - 6x + 5$

11. $f(x) = 4x + 10;\ [-2,1]$

12. $f(x) = x^3 - x^2;\ [1,5]$

13. For a certain product the total revenue and total cost functions are given by

$R(x) = -0.0525x^2 + 40x,$

$C(x) = 0.01x^2 + 20x + 400.$

Find the number of units that must be produced and sold to maximize profit.

14. A car dealer sells 1000 cars each year. It costs $40 to store one car for one year. To order cars there is a fixed cost of $200 plus $100 for each car. How many times per year should the dealer reorder cars, and in what lot size, to minimize inventory costs?

ANSWERS

1. _____

2. _____

3. _____

4. _____

5. _____

6. _____

7. _____

8. _____

9. _____

10. _____

11. _____

12. _____

13. _____

14. _____

15. A certain population of fur-bearing animals has the reproduction curve

$$f(P) = P(30 - P),$$

where P is measured in thousands. Find the population at which the maximum sustainable harvest occurs, and find the maximum sustainable harvest.

16. Approximate $\sqrt{66}$ using $\Delta y \approx f'(x)\Delta x$.

Chapter 4

Differentiate.

17. $\dfrac{2x - e^x}{e^x}$

18. $\ln (x^4 - 3x)$

19. e^{4x}

20. $e^{x^2+5x} - 4x^5$

21. The demand for a certain mineral is increasing at the rate of 8% per year; that is,

$$\frac{dA}{dt} = 0.08A,$$

where A = amount used, and
          t = time in years.

a) 200,000,000 tons were used in 1974. Find the solution assuming $A_0 = 200,000,000$ and $k = 0.08$.

b) How much of the mineral will be used in 1984?

Chapter 5

Integrate.

22. $\displaystyle\int_0^1 3e^x\, dx$

23. $\displaystyle\int \left(\frac{1}{x} - 7x^3\right) dx$

24. Find the area under the graph of $y = x^3 + x$ on the interval [0,2].

Name _____ Class _____ Score _____ Grade _____

25. Integrate. Use substitution. Do not use Table 5.

$$\int \frac{6x^5 dx}{1 + x^6}$$

26. Integrate. Use integration by parts. Do not use Table 5.

$$\int \ln 3x \, dx$$

27. Integrate. Use Table 5.

$$\int \frac{1}{\sqrt{x^2 + 49}} dx$$

Chapter 6

28. Find the amount of an annuity where $5000 per year is being invested at 8%, compounded continuously, for 20 years.

29. An annual rent of $4800 is being paid for a property for which there is a permanent lease. The going interest rate is 8%. Find the capital value.

30. Determine whether the following improper integral is convergent or divergent, and calculate its value if convergent.

$$\int_5^\infty \frac{1}{x} \, dx$$

31. Find k such that the following is a probability density function over the given interval.

$$f(x) = kx^3; [0,2]$$

32. Let x be a continuous random variable which is normally distributed with mean $\mu = 10$ and standard deviation $\sigma = 4$. Using Table 6, find

$$P(11 \le x \le 12).$$

33. Given the demand and supply functions

$$D(x) = (x - 10)^2 \text{ and } S(x) = x^2 + 10x + 10,$$

find the equilibrium point and the consumer's surplus.

ANSWERS

25. _____

26. _____

27. _____

28. _____

29. _____

30. _____

31. _____

32. _____

33. _____

34. Find the volume of the solid of revolution generated by rotating the region under the graph of

$$y = 1 + x \text{ from } x = 0 \text{ to } x = 3.$$

34. _____

Chapter 7

35. Solve the differential equation $\dfrac{dy}{dx} = \dfrac{y}{x}$.

35. _____

36. In an experiment it was found that the rate of growth of yeast cells in a laboratory satisfied the inhibited growth model

$$\frac{dP}{dt} = kP(L - P),$$

36. a) _____

where P = the number of cells present after time t (in hours);
   L = 1000, the limiting value;
   k = 0.0005;
   P_0 = 20.

b) _____

a) Write the equation for $P(t)$ in terms of the given constants.

b) At what time t are 800 cells present?

37. _____

Chapter 8

Given $f(x,y) = \ln y + x^4 y^4 - 7x^2$, find:

38. _____

37. f_y **38.** f_{xy}

39. Find the relative maximum and minimum values of

$$f(x,y) = x^3 + y^3 - 3xy.$$

39. _____

40. Minimize

$$f(x,y) = x^2 + y^2 - 4y + 4$$

subject to the constraint $x^2 - y^2 = 1$.

40. _____